373

Elementary
Heat
Power

Elementary
Heat
Power

Second Edition

HARRY L. SOLBERG
Head, School of Mechanical Engineering

ORVILLE C. CROMER
Associate Professor of Mechanical Engineering

ALBERT R. SPALDING
Associate Professor of Mechanical Engineering

Purdue University

John Wiley & Sons, Inc., New York
Chapman & Hall, Limited, London

Library of Congress Catalog Card Number: 52–6210

PRINTED IN THE UNITED STATES OF AMERICA

Preface to the Second Edition

In preparing the second edition, we have made certain major changes without losing sight of the original objectives of the book. These changes were decided on after a careful evaluation of our own experience and that of our colleagues in the use of this book and the teaching of students in subsequent courses in thermodynamics, and after a study of the opinions expressed by teachers who have used the book in other engineering schools.

1. A discussion of the English engineering system of units and dimensions has been included in Chapter 1 to review and clarify the subject and provide a transition from the units used in physics. That part of the subject dealing with the dimensional constant used to convert mass to weight has been set in finer print and may be omitted at the discretion of the instructor.

2. In Chapter 1, the general energy equation for the steady-flow process has been developed and its applications as the first law of thermodynamics to fundamental types of equipment such as prime movers, compressors and pumps, heat exchangers, and nozzles have been discussed in considerable detail. In subsequent chapters, the student is referred to the basic discussion in Chapter 1 of the application of the first law to the particular type of apparatus under consideration so as to review and emphasize fundamental principles and unify the presentation.

3. Entropy has been introduced as a property that is constant during an ideal or frictionless adiabatic expansion. This limited but very important concept of entropy is adequate for the objectives of this text and permits the logical introduction and use of the Mollier diagrams for steam and ammonia.

4. Enthalpy has been introduced in Chapter 1 as a property of the fluid. The discussion of the enthalpy of steam has been completely rewritten. A brief table of the thermodynamic properties of air has been included in the appendix to permit the calculation of enthalpy changes in such apparatus as gas tur-

v

bines where the variable specific heat is important, and to familiarize students with the existence of such tables.

5. A brief discussion of the second law of thermodynamics and the principle of degradation of energy has been included in Chapter 1 to emphasize the limitations on the thermal efficiency of heat-power machinery.

6. A summary of basic concepts and definitions has been added to Chapter 1 for emphasis, review, and ready reference.

7. The material on combustion calculations has been rewritten for the purpose of developing analytical thinking and facility in the use of the pound-mole in such calculations and to eliminate so far as possible the use of equations which too often are neither understood nor remembered by the student.

8. The descriptive material in the book has been revised where necessary to conform to the latest practices and to illustrate the most modern equipment. As in the first edition, an attempt has been made to illustrate basic types of equipment and their principles of operation with minimum attention to details that are peculiar to a particular manufacturer or subject to rapid change.

Throughout this revision, the original objectives of the book have been kept in mind and every effort has been made to produce a balanced book that would familiarize the student with the construction, principles of operation, and simple performance calculations of heat-power equipment (1) as a basis for an intelligent study of a thorough course in thermodynamics, and (2) as a terminal one-semester course in the field of heat power.

H. L. SOLBERG

O. C. CROMER

A. R. SPALDING

March 1952

Preface to the First Edition

During World War II, it became necessary to abandon the civilian engineering curricula at Purdue University and to transfer all civilian engineering students to the curricula of the Navy V-12 program. This situation made it possible to evaluate critically the prewar curriculum in mechanical engineering, to consider extensive changes in the curriculum, and to develop a postwar curriculum without the compromises that must often be considered in making changes to a curriculum that is in operation.

A great deal of attention was given to the heat-power sequence of courses. It was felt that they should be so arranged as to stimulate student interest in the mastery of the basic course in thermodynamics. The student should acquire a clear understanding of the theoretical performance of heat-power equipment and the factors that limit its performance. Such concepts as entropy, the availability of energy, and the second law of thermodynamics should have real meaning to him instead of being a group of hazy ideas.

The members of the staff of the School of Mechanical Engineering had had many years of cumulative experience in the teaching of practically all possible combinations of thermodynamics and heat power, including internal-combustion engines, steam power, refrigeration, heating and ventilating, and air conditioning. It was believed that best results would be achieved by the study first of a course in heat power in which emphasis would be placed upon fuels as sources of energy, the functions of the equipment used for power generation, the construction of such equipment, and its actual performance. With this background, the student could then be given a one- or two-semester course in thermodynamics in which he could *intelligently* study the laws that govern the ideal performance of heat-power equipment.

After a further study of the problem as it affects the non-mechanical-engineering student, this book on Elementary Heat Power has been written to meet the following objectives:

vii

1. To develop an understanding of the functions, principles of construction, and actual performance of heat-power machinery so that the student will appreciate the importance of and may intelligently study and apply the principles of engineering thermodynamics.

2. To provide an adequate and balanced terminal course for those students who do not study engineering thermodynamics.

3. To provide a background for the testing of heat-power equipment in the laboratory.

This book is written for students who have had a course in college chemistry, who have completed at least one semester of college physics including heat and mechanics, and who are studying or have completed the usual course in integral calculus.

Throughout the book emphasis has been placed upon the energy balance and the law of conservation of energy which, as applied to the prime mover, is the first law of thermodynamics. Numerous problems involving material and energy balances have been included as well as many problems on the calculation of the actual performance of heat-power machinery. Use is made of the characteristic equation of the perfect gas which the student has studied in physics and chemistry. Extensive use is made of the steam tables for the determination of enthalpy and specific volume.

Particular care has been exercised in the selection of illustrations and in the preparation of the descriptive material dealing with the construction of heat-power equipment to emphasize the basic *types* of equipment and their *functions* rather than the design details that are characteristic of the equipment of a particular manufacturer. It is believed that this descriptive material has been made sufficiently comprehensive so that much of the descriptive material that is included in the usual specialized heat-power courses that follow thermodynamics may be eliminated, and the time thus saved may be spent on a more analytical and advanced treatment of the subject.

H. L. SOLBERG
O. C. CROMER
A. R. SPALDING

October 1946

Acknowledgment

We gratefully acknowledge the many helpful suggestions that have been received from the members of the staff of the School of Mechanical Engineering. We are particularly indebted to Professors C. L. Brown, W. E. Fontaine, G. A. Hawkins, W. L. Sibbitt, C. R. St. Clair, and O. W. Witzell for their criticism of parts of the manuscript. We also express our thanks to the many teachers of heat power in other engineering schools who have used the first edition of this book and have given us their suggestions and criticisms which have been so valuable in the preparation of the second edition.

We wish to express appreciation to Professors J. T. Agnew, M. H. Bolds, S. B. Elrod, and F. H. Thompson of Purdue University for their assistance in the preparation of illustrations; to Professor Edgar MacNaughton for permission to reproduce Fig. 8·1 from his book on *Elementary Steam Power Engineering*, John Wiley & Sons, publishers; to Professor Edwin F. Church for permission to prepare Table 7·1 and Fig. 7·7 in accordance with similar subject matter in his book on *Steam Turbines*, McGraw-Hill Book Company, publishers; and to P. W. Thompson, Detroit Edison Company, for permission to reproduce Fig. 6·10 from his paper on "Operating Experiences with High-Pressure, High-Temperature Steam Central Stations" presented at the Fourth World Power Conference in London in 1950.

We gratefully acknowledge our indebtedness to the following companies for their courtesy and co-operation in making illustrations available for inclusion in this book:

Allis-Chalmers Mfg. Co.: Figs. 7·31, 9·26, 11·8, 11·9, 12·1, 12·2.
American Arch Co.: Fig. 4·3.
American Blower Corp.: Figs. 10·8, 10·9, 10·10, 10·14, 10·15.
American Bosch Corp.: Figs. 3·39, 3·40.
American Engineering Co.: Figs. 4·20, 4·21.
Ames Iron Works Co.: Fig. 8·18.
Babcock & Wilcox Co.: Figs. 4·7, 4·13, 4·22, 5·13, 5·16, 5·17, 5·20, 5·25, 5·31, 5·32, 5·33.

ix

Bacharach Industrial Instrument Corp.: Figs. 3·10, 3·11.
Bendix Aviation Corp.: Figs. 3·32, 3·33, 3·34, 3·36, 3·37, 3·38.
Buffalo Forge Co.: Figs. 10·4, 10·5, 10·7, 10·12, 10·13.
Chicago Pneumatic Tool Co.: Figs. 10·27, 10·28, 10·29, 10·30, 10·31.
Combustion Engineering-Superheater, Inc.: Figs. 5·6, 5·10, 5·18, 5·19, 5·21,
    5·23, 5·24, 5·26, 5·30, 5·34.
Cooper-Bessemer Corp.: Figs. 3·43, 3·51.
Cummins Engine Co., Inc.: Figs. 3·23, 3·24.
Dean Brothers Pumps, Inc.: Figs. 9·16, 9·17.
DeLaval Steam Turbine Co.: Figs. 7·2, 9·28, 10·20, 10·21, 10·22, 10·23.
M. H. Detrick Co.: Fig. 4·1.
Detroit Stoker Co.: Figs. 4·17, 4·18.
Dynamatic Corp.: Fig. 3·14.
Ex-Cell-O Corp.: Figs. 3·41, 3·42, 3·45.
Fairbanks-Morse & Co.: Fig. 3·27.
Foster Wheeler Corp.: Fig. 5·14.
General Electric Co.: Fig. 7·5.
Hays Corp.: Figs. 2·9, 9·5, 9·6.
Ingersoll-Rand Co.: Figs. 10·18, 10·19, 10·26, 11·11, 11·12.
Laclede-Christy Clay Products Co.: Fig. 4·2.
Le Roi Co.: Fig. 3·48.
Lummus Co.: Fig. 11·3.
National Advisory Committee for Aeronautics: Fig. 12·11.
National Airoil Burner Co., Inc.: Fig. 4·6.
Parr Instrument Co.: Fig. 2·8.
Roots-Connersville Blower Corp.: Figs. 10·16, 10·17.
Skinner Engine Co.: Figs. 8·10, 8·12.
Studebaker Corp.: Fig. 3·21.
C. J. Tagliabue Mfg. Co.: Fig. 3·18.
Terry Steam Turbine Co.: Fig. 7·29B.
Troy Engine & Machine Co.: Fig. 8·8.
Kennedy Van Saun Mfg. & Engrg. Corp.: Fig. 4·23.
Vilter Mfg. Co.: Fig. 13·5.
Henry Vogt Machine Co.: Fig. 5·14.
Westinghouse Electric Corp.: Figs. 4·16, 7·20, 7·26, 7·32, 7·33, 7·36, 7·37,
    7·38, 9·25, 9·27, 11·6, 11·7, 11·10, 12·12.
Willys-Overland Motors, Inc.: Fig. 3·22.
Worthington Pump & Machinery Corp.: Figs. 9·29, 9·32, 9·33, 9·34.

Contents

Abbreviations

brake horsepower	bhp
brake horsepower-hour	bhp-hr
brake mean effective pressure	bmep
brake specific fuel consumption	bsfc
British thermal unit	Btu
cubic feet per minute	cfm
cubic foot	cu ft
degrees centigrade	C
degrees Fahrenheit	F
degrees Kelvin	K
degrees Rankine	R
electromotive force	emf
feet per minute	fpm
feet per second	fps
foot	ft
foot-pound	ft-lb
gallon	gal
gallons per minute	gpm
horsepower	hp
horsepower-hour	hp-hr
hour	hr
inch	in.
indicated horsepower	ihp
indicated horsepower-hour	ihp-hr
kilowatt	kw
kilowatt-hour	kw-hr
mean effective pressure	mep
minute	min
outside diameter	OD
pound	lb
pounds of force	lb_f
pounds of mass	lb_m
pounds per square foot	psf
pounds per square foot absolute	psfa
pounds per square inch	psi
pounds per square inch absolute	psia
pounds per square inch gage	psig
revolutions per minute	rpm
second	sec
square foot	sq ft
square inch	sq in.

Symbols

A	area
a	acceleration
c	specific heat
c_p	specific heat at constant pressure
c_v	specific heat at constant volume
C	constant
d	diameter
D	draft
D_p	piston displacement
F	force
g	local acceleration of gravity
g_c	dimensional constant
h	head
h	enthalpy, per unit mass; $h = u + pv/J$
h_c	enthalpy of compressed liquid
h_f	enthalpy of saturated liquid
h_{fg}	enthalpy of evaporation
h_g	enthalpy of dry saturated vapor
h_x	enthalpy of wet vapor
h_s	enthalpy of superheated vapor
H	height of chimney
J	mechanical equivalent of heat
k	specific heat ratio; $k = c_p/c_v$
L	length
m	mass
M	molecular weight
n	exponent of polytropic expansion
n	number of revolutions per minute
N	number of power impulses per minute
p	pressure, absolute or gage
P_b	brake mean effective pressure
P_i	indicated mean effective pressure
q	rate of heat transfer
Q	quantity of heat
Q_H	higher heating value
Q_L	lower heating value
r	compression ratio
r	radius
R	gas constant in equation $pv = RT$
s	entropy per unit mass

t	temperature in degrees Fahrenheit or centigrade
t	torque
T	absolute temperature in degrees Rankine or Kelvin
u	internal energy per unit mass
U	overall coefficient of heat transfer
v	specific volume; volume per unit mass
V	total volume
V	velocity
w	weight; gravitational force acting on a mass
W	work
x	quality of vapor
y	distance measured from a datum level
γ	specific weight; weight per unit volume
ρ	density; mass per unit volume
η	efficiency
θ	time
ω	angular velocity

1 . Matter and Energy

1·1 Introduction. At the beginning of the 19th century, the stagecoach and the saddle horse were still the principal means of travel on land. Freight was transported on land in wagons drawn by horses or oxen. Barge canals were built where practical, and the barges were drawn by horses. At sea the sailing ship had not reached the zenith of its development, and man was to be dependent upon the wind for another half-century. Although the "overshot" water wheel had been in use for several centuries to drive flour mills and small manufacturing establishments, man was still largely dependent for his livelihood upon his own physical exertions, the efforts of his family including his children, and the work of his domesticated animals. However, during the latter half of the 18th century, the development of an efficient steam engine, the application of this engine to the operation of factories, the introduction of wrought iron, and the development of machine tools and machinery accelerated the industrial revolution and ultimately resulted in our modern industrial civilization which is founded upon the low-cost mass production of goods that can be sold cheaply throughout the world.

The Newcomen steam engine was invented in 1705 to pump water from the English coal mines. It was fairly well developed by 1720 and remained in extensive use for the next 50 years. As illustrated in Fig. 1·1, a piston was hung in a steam cylinder from one end of an overhead oscillating or "walking" beam by a chain and piston rod. The piston of the water cylinder was attached to the other end of the walking beam, also by a chain and piston rod. When the steam valve A was opened with the piston near the bottom of the cylinder, steam from the boiler filled the steam cylinder at atmospheric pressure as the counterweight W caused

the steam piston to rise. When the steam piston reached the top
position in its stroke as shown in Fig. 1·1, the steam valve A was
closed, and cold water was sprayed into the cylinder by the

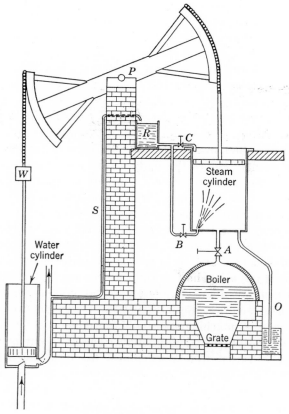

FIG. 1·1   Newcomen's engine

opening of the injection-water valve B. The vacuum created by
the condensation of the steam caused the steam piston to descend,
thus raising the water piston and filling the water cylinder with
water. The water was delivered by the pump on the downward
stroke of the water piston which coincided with the upward
stroke of the steam piston. Part of the water delivered by the
pump was discharged to the reservoir R through the supply line

S. Water from the reservoir was sprayed into the steam cylinder at the proper time by manipulation of valve *B.* Valve *C* was regulated to produce a layer of water on the top side of the piston and thus prevent air leakage into the steam cylinder between the cylinder walls and the poorly fitted piston.

The original engine had hand-operated valves. The story is told that a boy named Humphrey Potter became tired of manipulating the valves on one of these engines and arranged a mechanism for operating them from the walking beam. Mechanically operated valves were soon applied to all Newcomen engines. The boiler, which was little more than a large kettle with a fire under it on a grate *G,* was provided with a safety valve as a protection against excessive pressure. The Newcomen engine was used extensively to pump water from mines, to supply water for cities and for the operation of canals, and to fill reservoirs from which the water could be used in water wheels to drive machinery.

James Watt, an instrument maker at the University of Glasgow, while repairing a model of a Newcomen engine in 1763, noticed the large waste of energy due to alternately heating the steam cylinder with steam and cooling it with injection water. He realized that this loss could be reduced by keeping the cylinder as hot as possible with insulation and by using a separate condenser or water-cooled chamber which could be connected to the steam cylinder at the proper time by a valve. He patented the idea of the separate condenser in 1769. Subsequently, he closed the top of the steam cylinder with a cover or cylinder head, introduced steam alternately on both sides of the piston, and thus made the engine double acting. He invented a governor to regulate the speed of the engine; a slide valve to control the admission, expansion, and exhaust of the steam; a pump to remove the air and condensate from the condenser, and, in fact, brought the steam engine to a fairly high state of development.

In 1774 Wilkinson patented a boring machine with which he was able to machine quite accurately the steam cylinders required by Watt. Without this invention it is doubtful if Watt's engine would have been successful. About 1780 methods were developed for producing "puddled" or wrought iron, a material that soon became available in reasonable quantities for the fabrication of machinery. Improvements in materials and manufacturing processes made it possible to replace wooden shafts, gears, wheels, and other machine parts with parts constructed of cast or wrought iron. These developments not only made the steam engine possible but also created a market for it. As stated by Wood, "Coal could not have been won without the steam engine; the steam engine could not have been worked without coal. Automatic machinery could not have been developed without steam power; the steam engine could not have been constructed without machine tools. Neither engine nor machinery could have been developed without iron, and the iron could not have been wrought without mechanism and power. It was one great cycle of interacting and reacting forces, no one of which could have come to perfection without the aid of the rest." *

By 1790 the use of Watt's engine had spread throughout England and made available an efficient machine for producing power wherever needed in sufficient amounts to operate large factories. Machinery had already been invented for the spinning of thread and the weaving of cloth, and the great textile industry of England developed rapidly under the impetus given to it by the steam engine.

It was natural that efforts should be made to apply the steam engine to the field of transportation. In 1804 Trevithick built a self-propelled steam carriage to run on a horse tramway in Wales. In 1807 Robert Fulton, using engines built to Watt's designs, successfully operated his steamboat, the *Clermont,* on the Hudson River. In 1829 George Stephenson built the famous *Rocket,* a locomotive that traveled at a speed of 30 miles per hr in competitive trials. The application of the steam engine to the ship and to the locomotive ultimately made it possible to move raw materials cheaply and quickly to manufacturing plants and to distribute the finished products throughout the world.

In 1882 Thomas Edison started the Pearl Street Station in New York for the purpose of supplying electricity to the users of the new incandescent lamp, thus laying the foundation for the great central-station industry which now supplies the general public with electric light and power. Parsons patented a reaction turbine in 1884, and in 1889 de Laval was granted patents on an

* Wood, *Industrial Engineering in the Eighteenth Century,* pp. 17–18.

impulse turbine. By 1910 the steam turbine had replaced the reciprocating steam engine in the central-station industry, and units of 220,000 hp driving a single electric generator have now been in successful operation for more than 20 years.

In 1860 Lenoir patented a gas engine which operated without compression, and it is reported that 400 Lenoir engines were operating in Paris in 1865. In 1876 Otto developed a successful four-stroke-cycle gas engine. Daimler in 1887 applied a light-weight high-speed Otto cycle engine to a motor car, and the development of the automobile followed. In 1892 Dr. Rudolph Diesel patented the Diesel cycle engine for burning nonvolatile oil in an internal-combustion engine at high efficiency. In 1902 the Wright brothers made the first successful flight of a heavier-than-air plane powered by a gasoline engine; thus began the development of the aircraft industry. At the present time, much attention is being given to the gas turbine, and the results obtained to date indicate that this type of prime mover is particularly applicable to high-speed airplanes and probably is well suited to several other fields of power generation.

Today airplanes, automobiles, buses, railroads, and steam- and Diesel-powered ships provide quick and cheap transportation. Electric power is available at low rates and in ample quantities in all sections of the United States. The productive capacity of American industry in World War II was a decisive factor in determining the outcome of the war. This accomplishment was made possible by the high degree of mechanization of industry based upon an ample supply of cheap power. In the years to come, the gas turbine, the internal-combustion engine, and the steam power plant will continue to turn the wheels of industry; light our homes, offices, stores, and factories; provide transportation on land, sea, and in the air; contribute to greater comfort in the home and factory; increase the productivity of the worker; and help to maintain the highest standard of living that any people has ever enjoyed.

This book, *Elementary Heat Power*, is concerned with the principles of operation, details of construction, and actual performance of the major types of equipment that are used for the generation of power from fuel. The subject matter includes fuels and their combustion, internal-combustion engines, equipment for burning fuels for steam generation and industrial applications, steam generation, steam engines and turbines, fans, pumps and compressors, heat exchangers, gas turbines, and mechanical refrigeration. The student who wishes to pursue the subject further should follow a study of this book by a thorough course in *thermodynamics*, a subject that is concerned with the laws governing the transformation of energy from one form to another. Engineering thermodynamics deals with the properties of the fluids used in heat-power machinery, the energy relationships and the behavior of these fluids when subjected to changes under specified conditions, the theoretical performance of heat-power machinery, and the factors that affect and limit this performance. Further study in the field of heat power is possible in such specialized areas as internal-combustion engines, steam power plants, steam and gas turbines, compressors and pumps, combustion of fuels, steam generation, refrigeration and air conditioning.

1·2   The steam power plant. The function of a steam power plant is to convert the raw energy in coal, oil, or gas into mechanical or electric energy through the expansion of steam from a high pressure to a low pressure in a suitable *prime mover* such as a turbine or engine. Where the output of the plant is electric energy distributed for general sale to all customers who wish to purchase it, the plant is called a *central station*. If the plant is operated by a manufacturing company which takes the output of the plant for its own use, it is called an *industrial plant*. A *noncondensing* plant discharges the steam from the prime mover at an exhaust pressure equal to or greater than atmospheric pressure. A *condensing* plant exhausts from the prime mover into a *condenser* at a pressure *less than* atmospheric pressure. In general, central-station plants are condensing plants since their sole output is electric energy and a reduction in the exhaust pressure at the prime mover decreases the amount of steam required to produce a given quantity of electric energy. Industrial plants are frequently noncondensing plants because large quantities of low-pressure steam are required for manufacturing operations. The power required for operation of a manufacturing plant may often be obtained as a by-product by generating steam at high pressure and expanding this steam in a prime mover to the back pressure at which the steam is needed for manufacturing processes.

Figure 1·2 illustrates diagrammatically the major pieces of equipment that are installed in a condensing steam power plant fired by pulverized coal. The *steam-generating unit* consists of a *furnace* in which the fuel is burned, a *boiler, superheater,* and *economizer,* in which high-pressure steam is generated, and an *air heater* in which the loss of the energy due to combustion of the fuel is reduced to a minimum. The *boiler* is composed of a drum, in which a water level is maintained at about the mid-point so as to permit separation of the steam from the water, and a bank of inclined tubes, connected to the drum in such a manner as to permit water to circulate from the drum through the tubes and back to the drum. The hot products of combustion from the furnace flow across the boiler tubes and evaporate part of the water in the tubes. The furnace walls are composed of tubes which are also connected to the boiler drum to form very effective steam-generating surfaces. The steam which is separated from the water in the boiler drum then flows through a *superheater* which is in effect a coil of tubing surrounded by the hot products of combustion. The temperature of the steam is increased in the superheater to perhaps 800 to 1000 F at which temperature the high-pressure superheated steam flows through suitable piping to the turbine.

Since the gaseous products of combustion leaving the boiler tube bank are at a relatively high temperature and their discharge to the chimney would result in a large loss in energy, an *economizer* may be used to recover part of the energy in these gases. The economizer is a bank of tubes through which the boiler feedwater is pumped on its way to the boiler drum. Inasmuch as this feedwater will be at a temperature considerably below that of the water in the boiler tubes, the temperature of the products of combustion may be reduced in the economizer to less than the boiler exit-gas temperature. A further reduction in gas temperature may be made by passing the products of combustion through an *air heater* which is a heat exchanger cooled by the air required for combustion. This air is supplied to the air heater at normal room temperature and may leave the air heater at 400 to 600 F, thus returning to the furnace energy that would otherwise be wasted up the chimney. The products of combustion are usually cooled in an air heater to an exit tem-

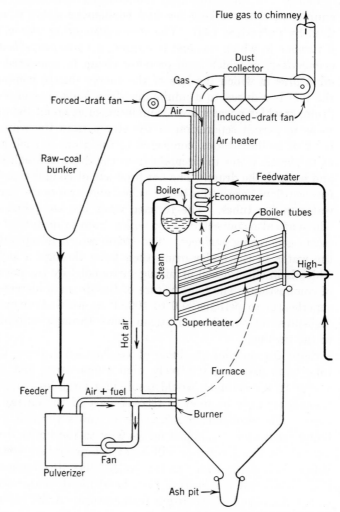

FIG. 1·2 Diagrammatic arrangement

perature of 275 to 400 F, after which they may be passed through a *dust collector* which will remove objectionable dust and thence through an *induced-draft fan* to the chimney. The function of the induced-draft fan is to pull the gases through the heat-transfer surfaces of the boiler, superheater, economizer, and air heater and to maintain a pressure in the furnace that is slightly less than atmospheric pressure. A *forced-draft fan* forces the combustion air to flow through the air heater, duct work, and *burner* into the furnace.

Coal is delivered to the plant in railroad cars or barges which are unloaded by machinery. The coal may be placed in storage or may be crushed and elevated to the overhead raw-coal bunker in the boiler room. As shown in Fig. 1·2, the coal flows by gravity from the overhead bunker to the *pulverizer* or *mill* through a *feeder* which automatically maintains the correct amount of coal in the mill. In the mill the coal is ground to a fine dust. Some of the hot air from the air heater is forced through the mill to dry the coal and to pick up the finely pulverized particles and carry them in suspension to the burner

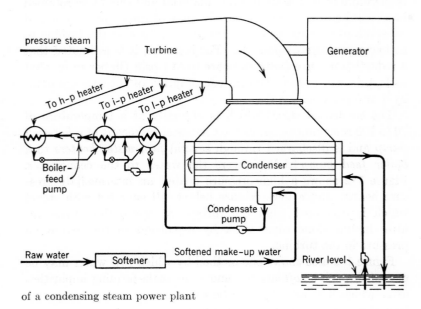

of a condensing steam power plant

where they are mixed with the air required for their combustion and discharged into the furnace at high velocity to promote good combustion.

The high-pressure high-temperature steam is expanded in a *steam turbine* which is generally connected to an electric generator. From 3 to 5 per cent of the output of the generator is needed to light the plant and to operate the many motors required for fans, pumps, etc., in the plant. The rest of the generator output is available for distribution outside of the plant.

In a central-station plant, the exhaust steam from the turbine is delivered to a *condenser*, the function of which is to convert this steam into condensate (water) at the lowest possible pressure. The condenser is a large gas-tight chamber filled with tubes through which cold water is pumped. Under average conditions, about 800 tons of cooling water are required in the condenser for each ton of coal burned. Consequently, large power plants must be located on lakes, rivers, or the seacoast where plenty of cool water is available for use in the condenser. The exhaust steam is condensed for two reasons: (1) It was distilled in the boiler and is therefore free of scale-forming material and should be retained in a closed system, and (2) the efficiency of the plant is increased substantially by reducing the exhaust pressure at the turbine to as low a pressure as possible. For instance, it is estimated that a reduction in the exhaust pressure from 1 psia (lb per sq in. abs) to $\frac{1}{2}$ psia will reduce the coal consumption of the average plant by 4 or 5 per cent.

The condensed steam which is normally at a temperature of 70 to 100 F is pumped out of the condenser by means of a *hot-well pump* and is discharged through several *feed-water heaters* to a *boiler feed pump* that delivers the water to the economizer. Figure 1·2 shows a high-pressure heater, an intermediate-pressure heater, and a low-pressure heater, all supplied with steam which is extracted from the turbine at appropriate pressures after having done some work by expansion to the extraction pressure in the turbine.

Figure 1·2 also shows one method by which raw water may be passed through a *softener* to remove the scale-forming impurities, after which it is admitted to the condenser at such a rate as to keep the system full of scale-free water.

Most of the steam power plants of large size are now being built for operation at steam pressures of 900 to 2000 psi, and in some cases pressures up to 2400 psi are being used. Steam temperatures of 900 to 1050 F are in general use. Turbine-generator capacities of 100,000 kw (1 kilowatt = 1.34 horsepower) are common, and units of 165,000 kw in one generator and 208,000 kw in three generators have been in operation for a number of years. Steam-generating units capable of delivering 1,400,000 lb of steam per hr are now in operation. Overall efficiency of the plant from raw coal supplied to electric energy delivered to the transmission line depends upon size, steam pressure, temperature, and other factors, and 37 per cent is now being realized on the basis of a full year of operation. Figure 1·3 shows the decrease

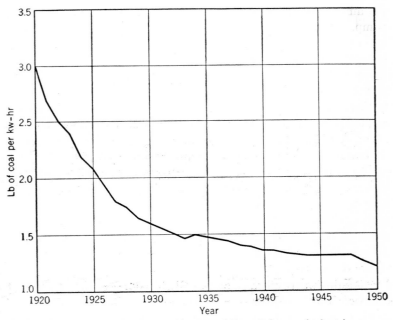

Fig. 1·3 Average coal consumption per kilowatt-hour of electric energy generated in the United States

in coal required to turn out a kilowatt-hour (kw-hr), the unit of electric energy, over the past 30 years. Since the best of the modern power plants will generate 1 kw-hr on 0.75 lb of coal, the downward trend in fuel consumption may be expected to continue as the older and less efficient power plants are replaced by new plants.

1·3   The internal-combustion-engine power plant.   The internal-combustion-engine power plant including essential auxiliaries is shown diagrammatically in Fig. 1·4.   The fuel is burned directly in the cylinder of the *engine* or *prime mover,* and the high pressure thus generated drives the *piston* downward and rotates a *crankshaft.*

Air is supplied to the engine through a *silencer* and *cleaner,* the function of which is to reduce noise and remove dust which would accelerate cylinder and piston wear if allowed to enter the cylinder.   Figure 1·4 shows a *supercharger* installed in the air-intake system.   The function of the supercharger is to increase the amount of air supplied to the cylinder by acting as an air pump.   This in turn permits burning more fuel and obtaining more power from a given size of cylinder.   An *intake manifold* is used to distribute the air equally from the supercharger to the various cylinders of a multicylinder engine.

The exhaust system consists of an *exhaust manifold* for collecting the discharge gases from each of the cylinders into a common exhaust line, an exhaust silencer or *muffler* for reducing noise, and the *exhaust stack* for disposing of the exhaust gases to the atmosphere without creating a public nuisance.

The cooling system includes a *pump* for circulating water through the cylinder jackets and heads of each cylinder and a *heat exchanger* to remove the heat absorbed in the engine by the cooling water.   The heat exchanger may be air-cooled as in the automobile radiator, or it may be water-cooled as shown in Fig. 1·4.   Seldom is raw water fit to circulate directly through the jackets of an internal-combustion engine.

The lubricating oil may be passed through a *cooler, filter,* and *reservoir* and is supplied to the engine under pressure by means of an *oil-pump,* usually to a hollow crankshaft.   The oil serves as a lubricant for the rubbing surfaces of the engine and also as a coolant to remove heat from those surfaces.

The fuel system consists of a storage tank from which the fuel may be supplied to a small day tank or reservoir.   The oil is filtered and pumped as needed to the fuel-injection system which is an integral part of the engine.

Since the fuel is burned directly in the cylinder of the prime mover, the internal-combustion-engine power plant is simpler and

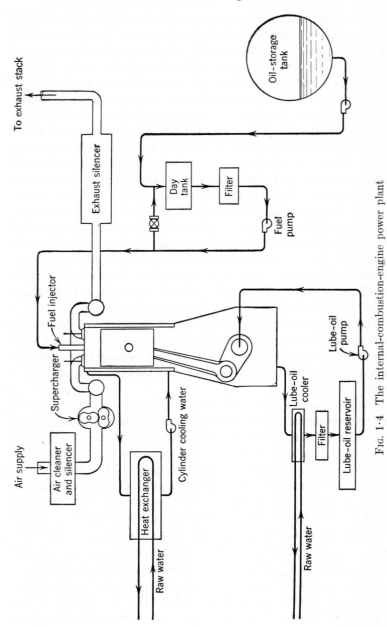

FIG. 1·4 The internal-combustion-engine power plant

more compact than the steam power plant. It is seldom built in engine sizes of more than 4000 hp whereas a 150,000-hp steam turbine is common. It is more efficient than a steam power plant of comparable size but not so efficient as large steam central-station plants which moreover can burn a cheaper grade of fuel. Consequently, the internal-combustion engine is used primarily in the transportation field for driving automobiles, buses, trucks, tractors, locomotives, ships, and airplanes where a compact, light-weight, efficient power plant of relatively small size is necessary. About 1 per cent of the electric energy generated in the United States is produced by internal-combustion engines, 70 per cent is produced by steam, and the rest is generated by water power.

1·4   Dimensions and units. A physical quantity is some-thing that can be measured. A dimension is a property or quality of the quantity or entity that characterizes or describes that quantity. Thus, distance has the characteristic property or di-mension of length. Area is a function of length and breadth or, dimensionally, $[A] = [L^2]$. Also, volume is a function of length $\times$ breadth $\times$ height or, dimensionally, $[V] = [L^3]$.

The dimension of length may be expressed in various *units,* such as inches, feet, yards, miles, centimeters, meters, and kilo-meters. Any physical quantity is exactly specified by a dimen-sion and by a multiple or fraction of a defined unit, such as a length of 14 ft.

A dimensional system that will completely describe an event can be constructed from a relatively small number of fundamental dimensions. One of these fundamental dimensions usually is *time,* $[\theta]$. The unit of time is the *second,* which is defined as $1/86,400$ part of a mean solar day. Length, $[L]$, is usually con-sidered to be another of the fundamental dimensions. In the system of units that is used in most engineering calculations in the United States, the unit of length is the *foot* which is defined as $1200/3937$ of the distance between two lines, measured at 32 F, on a particular bar of platinum-iridium that is kept at the Inter-national Bureau of Weights and Measures at Sèvres, France.

Matter is that which occupies space and has inertia or re-sistance to change of motion. Mass may be defined as the quantity of matter. If a mass, m, is acted upon by an unbalanced force, F (a force being a push or pull), then, according to Newton's second law of motion,

$$F \propto ma$$

or $$F = kma \qquad (1 \cdot 1)$$

where a represents the acceleration imparted to the mass and k is a constant of proportionality. Acceleration may be expressed dimensionally as follows:

$$\text{Velocity, } [V] = \frac{[L]}{[\theta]}$$

$$\text{Acceleration} = \frac{[V]}{[\theta]} = \frac{[L]}{[\theta^2]} = [L\theta^{-2}]$$

Therefore Equation $1 \cdot 1$ may be written dimensionally as follows:

$$[F] = [M][L\theta^{-2}] = [ML\theta^{-2}] \qquad (1 \cdot 2)$$

If three of the dimensions in Equation $1 \cdot 2$ are defined, the fourth dimension may be expressed in terms of the known three. The dimensions of length and time have already been defined. The system can be fully specified by defining *either* mass or force as the third dimension.

Mass as the third dimension. The standard pound of mass (lb_m) is *defined* as 0.4535924+ of the mass of a particular block of platinum-iridium located at Sèvres, France. The unit of force is defined in such a manner that the factor of proportionality, k, in Equation $1 \cdot 1$ is equal to unity, or an unbalanced force of one unit will impart to a mass of one standard pound an acceleration of 1 ft per sec². Such a force is called a *poundal,* or

$$1 \text{ poundal} = 1 \text{ lb}_m \times 1 \text{ ft per sec}^2 \qquad (1 \cdot 3)$$

It may be seen by inspection of Equation $1 \cdot 3$ that the poundal has the dimensions of $ML\theta^{-2}$, or Equation $1 \cdot 3$ can be expressed dimensionally as

$$[F] = [ML\theta^{-2}]$$

The equation is dimensionally homogeneous because the terms on each side of the equality sign have the same dimensions in accordance with Equation $1 \cdot 2$. The dimensional system based upon the pound of mass, the foot, and the second, is known as the English absolute or dynamical system of units or the $ML\theta$ system.

In the metric system, a force of one dyne will accelerate a mass of one gram at the rate of 1 centimeter per sec².

Force as the third dimension. If a block of material at sea level and at 45 degrees latitude is allowed to fall freely in a vacuum, it will be accelerated by the gravitational field of the earth at a rate of 32.174 ft per sec². By *definition* 1 lb of force (lb_f) is that force which will accelerate the standard pound of mass at the rate of 32.174 ft per sec². Using this unit of force, the unit of mass is then defined in such a manner that the factor of proportionality, k, in Equation 1·1 is equal to unity, or an unbalanced force equal to one standard pound of force (lb_f) will impart to the unit of mass an acceleration of 1 ft per sec². Such a unit of mass is called the *slug*, or

$$1 \; lb_f = 1 \; slug \times 1 \; ft \; per \; sec^2 \qquad (1·4)$$

It may be noted from Equation 1·4 that the slug has the dimensions of $FL^{-1}\theta^2$, or Equation 1·4 may be expressed dimensionally as

$$[F] = [FL^{-1}\theta^2][L\theta^{-2}] = [F]$$

This equation is therefore dimensionally homogeneous.

The dimensional system based upon the standard pound of force, the second, and the foot is called the English gravitational system or the $FL\theta$ system. In this system, since the factor of proportionality, k, of Equation 1·1 is unity, then

$$F = m_s a \qquad (1·5)$$

where m_s is the mass expressed in *slugs*.

Weight is *defined* as the gravitational *force* or pull acting on a given mass in any gravitational field. In accordance with Newton's second law, the acceleration of a body is directly proportional to the unbalanced force acting on the body. If an unbalanced force F acting on a given mass m produces an acceleration a, a different force F' acting on the same mass would produce a different acceleration a' such that

$$\frac{F}{a} = \frac{F'}{a'}$$

If the body were allowed to fall freely in a vacuum, the unbalanced force acting on it would be its weight w, and the acceleration would be the *local* acceleration due to gravity, g, or

$$\frac{F}{a} = \frac{w}{g}$$

Then
$$F = \frac{w}{g} a \qquad (1\cdot6)$$

or, dimensionally, $\quad [F] = \dfrac{[F]}{[L\theta^{-2}]} [L\theta^{-2}] = [F]$

A comparison of Equations 1·5 and 1·6 shows that w/g is the mass of the body in slugs.

The local acceleration of gravity varies with latitude and elevation and for some specific locations is as follows:

At sea level at the Equator	32.088 ft per sec²
At sea level at 45° of latitude	32.174 ft per sec²
40,000 ft above sea level at 45° of latitude	32.050 ft per sec²
At sea level at the North Pole	32.258 ft per sec²

The weight or gravitational force acting on a given mass varies with location in accordance with the value of the local acceleration of gravity. However, this variation is generally less than the inaccuracies introduced into engineering calculations through the use of the slide rule, uncertainties in physical properties of substances, and the errors in engineering instrumentation in measuring such quantities as pressure, temperature, rate of flow, and speed. Consequently, in the solution of problems in this book, the acceleration of gravity on the surface of the earth may be assumed to have a constant value of 32.174 ft per sec², or, for slide-rule calculations, 32.2 ft per sec² may be used.

Example 1. Compute the unbalanced force required to accelerate a body weighing 500 lb at the rate of 10 ft per sec², if the local acceleration of gravity is 32.2 ft per sec².

Solution:
$$F = \frac{w}{g} a = \frac{500 \text{ lb}_f}{32.2 \frac{\text{ft}}{\text{sec}^2}} \times 10 \frac{\text{ft}}{\text{sec}^2} = 155.4 \text{ lb}_f$$

Alternate Solution: The problem may also be solved by first finding the mass of the body in slugs.

$$\text{The mass of the body in slugs} = \frac{w}{g} = \frac{500 \text{ lb}_f}{32.2 \frac{\text{ft}}{\text{sec}^2}} = 15.54 \text{ slugs}$$

$$F = m_s a = 15.54 \text{ slug} \times 10 \frac{\text{ft}}{\text{sec}^2} = 155.4 \frac{\text{slug-ft}}{\text{sec}^2} = 155.4 \text{ lb}_f$$

The units here follow from Equation 1·4.

Notice that in Example 1 it was necessary to specify the local acceleration of gravity only in order for the mass to be determined from the weight. For a given body, the force required for a particular acceleration does not depend on the strength of the gravitational field. Compare the result of Example 1 with that of Example 2 below.

Example 2. Compute the force required to accelerate the body of Example 1 at a rate of 10 ft per sec^2 when located where the local acceleration of gravity is 32.0 ft per sec^2.

Solution: The mass of the body is the same in all locations. In Example 1 it was stated that the body weighed 500 lb$_f$ where the local acceleration of gravity was 32.2 ft per sec^2. At the new location, this body falling in a vacuum would accelerate at only 32.0 ft per sec^2; therefore, the force of gravity on the body (its weight) must be less than 500 lb$_f$ to cause the lower acceleration of the same mass.

To find the new weight of the body,

$$\frac{F}{a} = \frac{F'}{a'}$$

where the primes refer to the conditions where $g = 32.0$ ft per sec^2. If F and F' are values of weight, then a and a' are values of g and g', since the force of gravity (weight) acting alone causes a body to undergo the particular acceleration g.

$$\text{New weight of body} = F' = F\frac{a'}{a} = 500 \text{ lb}_f \times \frac{32.0\,\dfrac{\text{ft}}{\text{sec}^2}}{32.2\,\dfrac{\text{ft}}{\text{sec}^2}} = 496.9 \text{ lb}_f$$

Then, as in Example 1,

$$F = \frac{w}{g}a = \frac{496.9 \text{ lb}_f}{32.0\,\dfrac{\text{ft}}{\text{sec}^2}} \times 10\,\frac{\text{ft}}{\text{sec}^2} = 155.4 \text{ lb}_f$$

Alternate Solution: The mass of the body is the same in all locations. Using the value of mass obtained in Example 1,

$$F = m_s a = 15.54 \text{ slug} \times 10\,\frac{\text{ft}}{\text{sec}^2} = 155.4 \text{ lb}_f$$

The common or engineering English system of units, often called the $FML\theta$ system, uses the standard pound of force (lb$_f$) and the standard pound of mass (lb$_m$) as already defined. Since one standard pound of force by definition will accelerate one standard pound of mass at the rate of 32.174 ft per sec^2, therefore, from Equation 1·1, Newton's second law may be expressed as

$$1 \text{ lb}_f = k \times 1 \text{ lb}_m \times 32.174 \text{ ft per sec}^2 \qquad (1 \cdot 7)$$

It is unfortunate that the word pound is used as the unit of mass which is a scalar quantity since it has magnitude only, and also as the unit of force which is a vector quantity since it has both direction and magnitude. Where confusion might result in this book, the pound of mass will be designated as lb_m and the pound of force as lb_f.

The following paragraphs which are set in smaller print discuss the dimensional relationship between the pound of mass and the pound of force and show that, within the limits of slide-rule accuracy and for bodies on the surface of this earth, 1 lb of mass weighs 1 lb of force.

The factor of proportionality in Equation 1·1, $F = kma$, is equal to unity in the $ML\theta$ system (Equation 1·3) and is also equal to unity in the $FL\theta$ system (Equation 1·4). In the $FML\theta$ system, the factor of proportionality may be evaluated by writing Equation 1·1 for two different conditions as follows:

$$\frac{F}{F'} = \frac{ma}{m'a'}$$

Since, by definition, $1 \text{ lb}_f = k \times 1 \text{ lb}_m \times 32.174 \text{ ft per sec}^2$, then,

$$\frac{F}{1 \text{ lb}_f} = \frac{ma}{\text{lb}_m \, 32.174 \, \dfrac{\text{ft}}{\text{sec}^2}}$$

or

$$F = \frac{ma}{32.174 \, \dfrac{\text{lb}_m \, \text{ft}}{\text{lb}_f \, \text{sec}^2}} = \frac{1}{g_c} ma \qquad (1 \cdot 8)$$

where $\dfrac{1}{g_c} = \dfrac{1}{32.174 \, \dfrac{\text{lb}_m \, \text{ft}}{\text{lb}_f \, \text{sec}^2}}$ is a dimensional constant. Equation 1·8 is dimen-

sionally homogeneous since it may be written as follows:

$$[F] = \frac{[M] \, \dfrac{[L]}{[\theta^2]}}{\dfrac{[M] \, [L]}{[F] \quad \theta^2}} = [F] \, .$$

It should be noted that in Equation 1·6, $F = (w/g)a$, g is the *local* acceleration of gravity in ft per sec^2, and w/g is the mass in *slugs*. In Equation 1·8, $1/g_c$ is a dimensional constant numerically equal to the *standard* acceleration of gravity at sea level and 45 degrees of latitude in a vacuum. *It differs from* g *in dimensions and in being a constant.* This results from the difference in the dimensions of force or weight and mass, and the fact that the weight of a given mass varies with the local acceleration of gravity whereas the force pound is *defined* as the force that will accelerate one mass pound at the rate of 32.174 ft per sec^2.

Example 3. Determine the force required to accelerate a mass of 500 lb$_m$ at the rate of 10 ft per sec^2.

Solution:

$$F = \frac{1}{g_c} ma$$

$$F = \frac{1}{32.174 \frac{lb_m}{lb_f} \frac{ft}{sec^2}} \times 500 \ lb_m \times 10 \frac{ft}{sec^2}$$

$$= \frac{500 \times 10}{32.174} lb_f = 155.5 \ lb_f$$

Weight has been defined as the gravitational force or pull acting on a given mass. If a body is allowed to fall freely in a vacuum in any gravitational field, it will be accelerated at a rate of g ft per sec^2 where g is the local acceleration of gravity in that field. Let w be the weight or gravitational force acting on a body having a mass of m lb$_m$.

Since

$$F = \frac{1}{g_c} ma$$

then,

$$w = \frac{1}{g_c} mg = \frac{g}{g_c} m \qquad (1\cdot9)$$

If the local acceleration of gravity is numerically equal to the proportionality constant, g_c, or 32.174 ft per sec^2, then *one pound of mass weighs one pound of force.* Within the limits of accuracy of the slide rule and for problems dealing with masses on the surface of the earth, it may be concluded that weight expressed in pounds of force (lb$_f$) and mass expressed in pounds of mass (lb$_m$) are *numerically* equal but *differ* in dimensions.

Example 4. What will be the weight of a mass of 100 lb$_m$ when the local acceleration of gravity is (a) 32.174 ft per sec^2, and (b) 30 ft per sec^2?

Solution:

$$w = \frac{g}{g_c} m$$

(a)

$$w = \frac{32.174 \frac{ft}{sec^2}}{32.174 \frac{lb_m}{lb_f} \frac{ft}{sec^2}} \times 100 \ lb_m = 100 \ lb_f$$

(b)

$$w = \frac{30 \frac{ft}{sec^2}}{32.174 \frac{lb_m}{lb_f} \frac{ft}{sec^2}} \times 100 \ lb_m = 93.4 \ lb_f$$

The weight of a body is normally measured by means of a platform scale or beam balance in which an unknown mass is suspended on one side of a knife-edge support and known masses are suspended on the other side of this support. Since the local acceleration of gravity acts upon both the known and unknown masses, it is mass rather than weight or gravitational pull in standard force pounds that is measured by the beam balance or platform scale. Although it is usually illegal, the weighing can be done on a spring scale in which the gravitational force acting on the unknown mass stretches a calibrated spring by an amount that is proportional to the force acting (the weight of the body). However, the spring scale must be checked or calibrated from time to time to insure accurate readings, and this calibration is done by hanging standard "weights" or masses of material on the spring. Thus, even the spring scale, through the process of calibration, becomes a device for comparing masses rather than measuring gravitational pull or weight in standard force pounds. Consequently, when either a beam balance or a calibrated spring is used to "weigh" a body, mass rather than gravitational force or weight in standard force pounds is measured.

It may be concluded that the word "weight" as commonly used in engineering literature has the following different meanings: (1) gravitational *force* acting on a body (the preferred meaning), and (2) quantity of matter or *mass* as determined by a beam balance or platform scale. The confusion that results from this double meaning can be resolved by using the word *weight* only when meaning gravitational force acting on a mass and using the term *mass* when meaning the quantity of matter.

Example 5. A piece of metal is "weighed" at sea level and 45 degrees of latitude where $g = 32.174$ ft per sec^2 by means of a platform scale and also by means of a calibrated spring scale and is found by each method to "weigh" 50 lb. The piece of metal together with the spring scale and the platform scale and associated standard "weights" are transported to the moon where the acceleration of gravity is 5.47 ft per sec^2. What will be the "weight" of the block of matter at the moon as determined by (a) the platform scale, and (b) the spring scale?

Solution: (a) Platform scale. The block of metal will be placed on the platform on the left side of the knife-edge support, and the standard weights which belong to the scale and were used for performing the weighing operation on the earth will be placed on the beam or support on the right side of the knife-edge. Since the same local acceleration of gravity acts on the standard scale weights and on the mass to be weighed, masses are being compared, and the platform scale will give the same reading of 50 lb as was obtained at the surface of the earth.

(b) Spring scale. In accordance with Equation 1·6, $F/a = w_e/g_e = w_m/g_m$ where the subscripts e and m refer to the earth and moon, respectively. Then,

$$w_m = w_e \times \frac{g_m}{g_e} = 50 \times \frac{5.47}{32.174} = 8.5 \text{ lb}_f$$

However, if the standard "weights" (masses) which were used to calibrate the spring scale on the surface of the earth are used on the moon to obtain a new calibration for the spring, it will be found that the piece of metal will cause the spring to deflect the same amount as the deflection caused by hanging 50 lb of mass on the spring.

A unit of mass that is in common use, particularly in connection with chemical reactions, is the *pound-mole*, normally called the *mole*. The mole is that quantity of matter which has a mass in pounds numerically equal to the molecular weight of the element or compound. Thus, since the molecular weights of oxygen, hydrogen, and carbon dioxide are 32, 2, and 44, respectively, the mass of 1 mole of each of these substances is 32, 2, and 44 lb_m, respectively. Also, 1 *pound-mole* of any substance consists of 2.7319×10^{26} molecules. It will be shown in a subsequent article that the volume of 1 mole of every perfect gas is the same at a given pressure and temperature.

Summary:

One *second* is $\frac{1}{86,400}$ part of a mean solar day.

One *foot* is 1200/3937 of the distance between two marks on a standard bar of platinum-iridium held at a temperature of 32 F at the International Bureau of Weights and Measures at Sèvres, France.

One *pound of mass* (lb_m) is 0.4535924 of the mass of a particular block of platinum-iridium at Sèvres, France.

One *pound of force* (lb_f) is the unbalanced force required to accelerate one standard pound of mass at the rate of 32.174 ft per sec².

32.174 ft per sec² is the standard acceleration of gravity. This is the local value of g at sea level and 45 degrees of latitude.

One *slug* is the mass that will be accelerated at a rate of 1 ft per sec² when acted upon by an unbalanced force of one standard force pound and is equal to w/g, or weight divided by local acceleration of gravity. Also, 1 slug = 32.174 lb_m.

One *poundal* is the unbalanced force that will accelerate one standard mass pound at the rate of 1 ft per sec².

The *weight* of a body is the force acting on the mass of the body by the gravitational field of the earth. If the variation in the local acceleration of gravity is neglected, then 1 lb_m weighs 1 lb_f.

In the *FLθ* system, force in lb_f = mass in slugs × acceleration in ft per sec², or

$$F = m_s a = \frac{w}{g} a \qquad (1 \cdot 5)$$

In the *FMLθ* system, force in lb_f = $\dfrac{1}{g_c}$ × mass in lb_m × acceleration in ft per sec² or

$$F = \frac{1}{g_c} ma \qquad (1 \cdot 8)$$

where $1/g_c$ is a dimensional conversion factor equal to

$$\frac{1}{32.174 \dfrac{lb_m}{lb_f} \dfrac{ft}{sec^2}}$$

$$w(\text{in } lb_f) = \frac{g}{g_c} m(\text{in } lb_m) \qquad (1 \cdot 9)$$

One *mole* = M lb_m of material where M is the molecular weight.

1·5 Matter. The molecule is the smallest division of matter that has all of the chemical and physical properties of a large quantity of matter. Molecules in turn are composed of atoms, of which there are 92 different kinds, called elements, found in Nature, in addition to several elements that have been made by Man in his development of the atomic bomb. Each atom consists of a nucleus in which most of the mass is concentrated and around which electrons move in orbits in much the same manner as the planets revolve about our sun.

When chemical reactions occur, the atoms are regrouped to form molecules of different substances. In the combustion process, which is very important to the engineer, this rearrangement of atoms into different molecules is accompanied by the release of large quantities of energy, a part of which may be converted into work in a suitable heat engine. The *law of con-*

servation of matter states that matter is indestructible, that the amount of material is the same before and after the chemical reactions occur, and that, at any given point on the earth, the weight of each of the chemical elements remains unchanged during chemical reactions. Thus, if fuel and air are supplied to the cylinder of an automobile engine, the weight of exhaust gases leaving the cylinder in a given period of time equals the weight of fuel and air supplied; also, the weight of carbon, hydrogen, oxygen, nitrogen, and other elements entering the cylinder is equal to the weight of these same elements leaving the cylinder, although an entirely new set of chemical compounds may result from the combustion of fuel in the cylinder.

Matter ordinarily exists as a solid, liquid, or gas. In the solid phase or condition, the molecules are held in fixed positions by powerful forces. However, the atoms may vibrate about mean positions within the molecule. Solids, therefore, have definite shape and volume, and relatively great external forces are required to deform them. In the liquid phase, the molecules have a motion of translation with frequent collisions from which they rebound as perfectly elastic bodies. They occupy a definite volume at a given temperature but conform to the shape of the confining vessel. In the gaseous phase, the molecules are far apart in comparison to their size, move in straight lines between collisions, and will escape into space unless confined within a closed vessel.

Many substances, such as water, may exist in the solid, liquid, or gaseous phase, depending upon the pressure and temperature. Thus, ice may melt to form water, and water may evaporate to form steam. When a substance is in the gaseous phase but at a temperature and pressure not far from the temperature and pressure at which it can be liquefied, it is often referred to as a *vapor*. A *perfect gas* is at a temperature and pressure far removed from the temperature and pressure at which it can be liquefied.

1·6   Properties of matter. Work is obtained from a heat engine by causing a fluid such as steam or gas to undergo heating, cooling, expansion, and compression processes or changes in a suitable mechanism. It is important that the *state* or molecular condition of the fluid be known while it is being subjected to these changing conditions. Among the easily measured properties that define the state of the fluid are volume, temperature, and pressure. Other properties such as internal energy, enthalpy, and entropy will be considered later. In general, if a proper combination of two of these properties is known, the state or molecular condition of the fluid is defined, and the values of the other properties are fixed. Also, if a fluid initially occupying some known volume at a known pressure and temperature undergoes some process after which the final volume, pressure, and temperature can be determined, then the change in volume, pressure, and temperature may be computed by subtracting the final values of these properties from the initial values without regard to the kind of change that may have occurred between the initial and final states. Such properties are known as point or state functions since a change in their values during any process depends upon the initial and final values of the properties and is independent of the path or kind of changes that take place between the initial and final states.

1·7 Specific volume. The specific volume, v, is defined as the volume occupied by a unit quantity of matter. In the English engineering system of units, it is usually expressed as cubic feet per pound of mass (cu ft per lb_m).

Specific volume is sometimes expressed as cubic feet per pound of weight (cu ft per lb_f). However, in tables of the physical properties of substances, such as the steam tables, the specific volume (as well as the enthalpy, entropy, etc.) is given for 1 lb of *mass* because the weight of 1 mass pound varies with the local acceleration of gravity in accordance with the equation

$$w = \frac{g}{g_c} m \qquad (1·9)$$

If the deviation of the local acceleration of gravity from the standard value of 32.174 ft per sec² is neglected, the numerical value of the specific volume will be the same for 1 lb of mass and a mass weighing 1 lb.

Density, ρ, is the reciprocal of specific volume and may be expressed as pounds of mass per cubic foot or slugs per cubic foot, depending upon whether the $MFL\theta$ or the $FL\theta$ system is used.

Specific weight, γ, is defined as the weight of 1 cu ft of material (lb_f per cu ft).

Since the specific volume depends upon the mass of the individual molecules and the number of molecules per cubic foot, it follows that the specific volume of any particular element or compound is determined by the state of the substance and therefore is a property of the substance.

1·8 Temperature. It is a common experience that bodies feel hot or cold to the sense of touch, depending upon their tem-

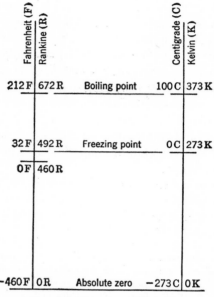

Fig. 1·5 Temperature scales

F = Fahrenheit scale
R = absolute temperature, degrees Rankine
C = centigrade scale
K = absolute temperature, degrees Kelvin

perature. In setting up a scale for the measurement of temperature, it is customary to use for one reference point the temperature of a mixture of cracked ice and water and for a second reference point the temperature of boiling water at standard barometric pressure. On the Fahrenheit (F) scale, the numbers 32 and 212 are assigned to these reference temperatures. The numbers 0 and 100 are assigned to these temperatures on the centigrade (C) scale. Then, as seen by reference to Fig. 1·5, 180 F is equivalent to 100 C, 1 F is equal to ⅝ C, or

$$t_C = \tfrac{5}{9}(t_F - 32) \qquad\qquad (1 \cdot 10)$$

where t_C = temperature, C
$\quad\; t_F$ = temperature, F

Temperatures below zero on both F and C scales are common in nature and in engineering practice. It would be desirable to have a temperature scale with the zero at the lowest conceivable temperature. It has been pointed out that the molecules of a gas are in motion at high velocities. If a gas is confined within a closed vessel at a given temperature, the average velocity of translation of the molecules is a function of the temperature. If the temperature is increased, the mean molecular velocity of translation is increased; if the temperature of the gas is decreased, the mean molecular velocity of translation is decreased. If the gas could be cooled until the molecular motion of translation ceased and the molecules came to rest, the temperature would be the lowest temperature of which man can conceive. This temperature is called the absolute zero of temperature.

On the Fahrenheit scale, absolute zero is −459.6 F (approximately −460 F) as indicated in Fig. 1·5. Absolute temperatures measured in Fahrenheit degrees are called degrees Rankine (R). On the centigrade scale, absolute zero is −273 C, and absolute temperatures measured in degrees centigrade are called degrees Kelvin (K).

Then,

$$T_R = t_F + 460 \text{ (approximately)} \qquad\qquad (1 \cdot 11)$$

$$T_K = t_C + 273 \qquad\qquad (1 \cdot 12)$$

where T_R = absolute temperature, R
$\quad\; T_K$ = absolute temperature, K

Since the absolute temperature is a function of the mean molecular velocity of a gas, the numerical value of the absolute temperature is one of the measurable properties which defines the state or molecular condition of the substance.

1·9 Pressure. Pressure is the push or force exerted on a confining or supporting surface. For fluids, it may be considered as the effect of the impacts of moving molecules upon the walls of the confining vessel. If more air is put into an automobile tire, the pressure is increased because of the greater number of molecular impacts per unit area. If the sun is allowed to shine on the tire, the temperature of the air in the tire is increased, the mean molecular velocity is increased, the molecules hit the

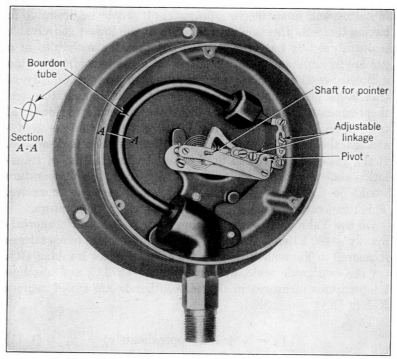

FIG. 1·6 Bourdon-type pressure gage

wall of the tire harder and more frequently, and the pressure is therefore higher.

The Bourdon type of pressure gage (Fig. 1·6) is the commonest type of gage that is used for the measurement of pressures of considerable magnitude. The tube is elliptical in cross section, bent into the arc of a circle, rigidly attached to the case of the gage at one end, and free to move at the other end. When a pressure is applied to the inside of the Bourdon tube, the elliptical cross section tends to become circular, and the free end of the tube moves outward. By means of a suitable link, pivoted gear sector, and pinion, a needle is moved around a graduated scale on the face of the gage to indicate the pressure.

If the pressure within the Bourdon tube is less than the atmospheric pressure on the outside of the tube, the elliptical cross section tends to be flattened, the free end of the tube moves nearer the center, and the pointer is moved in the opposite direction. Thus, the gage is operated by the *difference* between atmospheric pressure on the outside of the Bourdon tube and the pressure within the tube. Pressure readings obtained with the gage are called *gage pressures* and may be expressed in pounds per square inch gage, usually abbreviated to read psig.

Atmospheric pressure is measured by means of a barometer as illustrated in Fig. 1·7. If a glass tube, over 30 in. long and closed at its lower end, is filled with mercury, closed with a stopper, inverted, and mounted with its lower end in a dish of mercury, and the stopper is then removed, the mercury will fall in the tube until the weight of the column of mercury is balanced by the pressure of the atmosphere. The height of the column of mercury is then a measure of the atmospheric or barometric presure. Standard atmospheric pressure may be expressed in any of the following units:

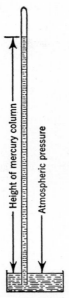

Fig. 1·7
Barometer

$$760 \text{ mm of Hg} = 29.92 \text{ in. of Hg} = 14.696 \text{ psia} \qquad (1·13)$$

The following relationship between pressure in pounds per square inch and inches of mercury may be derived from Equation 1·13 and should be memorized:

$$1 \text{ in. of Hg} = 0.491 \text{ psi} \qquad (1·14)$$

The scale of the Bourdon gage is usually graduated to read pressures above atmospheric pressure in pounds per square inch and pressures below atmospheric pressure in inches of mercury. Since atmospheric pressure varies with altitude above sea level and with constantly changing atmospheric conditions, it is necessary to use *absolute* pressures when dealing with the properties of

substances.   As indicated in Fig. 1·8, the absolute pressure in
pounds per square inch (psia) may be determined for gage pressures above atmospheric pressure by adding to the gage reading
in pounds per square inch the barometric pressure in pounds per
square inch absolute.   For pressures below atmospheric pressures,
the absolute pressure in inches of mercury may be obtained by

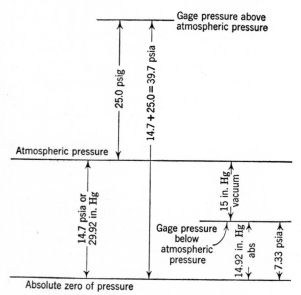

FIG. 1·8   Gage and absolute pressure

subtracting the gage reading in inches of mercury from the
barometric pressure in inches of mercury.   The result which will
be in inches of mercury absolute may be converted to pounds
per square inch absolute by using the conversion factors in
Equation 1·14.

Example 6.   What is the absolute pressure in psia if the gage reads 100.0
psig and the barometer reads 29.0 in. of Hg?
Solution:

Barometric pressure = 29.0 × 0.491 = 14.24 psia

Absolute pressure = 14.24 + 100.0 = 114.24 psia

Example 7.   What is the absolute pressure in in. of Hg and in psia if a
vacuum gage reads 10 in. of Hg and the barometer reads 29.5 in. of Hg?

Solution:

Absolute pressure = 29.5 − 10.0 = 19.5 in. Hg

or 19.5 × 0.491 = 9.57 psia

1·10   Perfect gases. A perfect gas is a substance for which the relationship among the properties of pressure, temperature, and volume may be expressed by the following *characteristic* equation:

$$pv = RT \tag{1·15}$$

where p = absolute pressure, psfa (lb per sq ft abs)
   v = specific volume, cu ft per lb_m
   T = absolute temperature, degrees Rankine, $(t_F + 460)$
   R = gas constant from Table 1·1

TABLE 1·1

GAS CONSTANTS AND SPECIFIC HEATS OF SOME COMMON GASES

Average Values at Room Temperature and Atmospheric Pressure

Gas	R	c_v	c_p
Air	53.3	0.171	0.237
Oxygen (O_2)	48.2	0.156	0.218
Nitrogen (N_2)	55.1	0.175	0.245
Hydrogen (H_2)	767	2.42	3.41
Carbon dioxide (CO_2)	34.9	0.154	0.203
Carbon monoxide (CO)	55.1	0.175	0.246

Each gas has its particular value for the gas constant R; however, for many gases, the gas constant may be approximated as follows:

$$R = \frac{1544}{M} \tag{1·16}$$

where M is the molecular weight, based on 32 as the molecular weight of oxygen (O_2).

The units of R may be determined as follows:

$$R = \frac{pv}{T} = \frac{(lb_f/ft^2)(ft^3/lb_m)}{\text{deg Rankine}} = \frac{ft\text{-}lb_f}{(lb_m)(\text{deg R})}$$

For more than 1 lb, Equation 1·15 may be written as follows:

$$mpv = mRT$$

or

$$pV = mRT \qquad (1 \cdot 17)$$

where m = quantity of substance, lb_m

        V = total volume, mv

1·11 Vapors. When a perfect gas is compressed to high pressures and cooled to low temperatures, the properties of the gas no longer follow the law $pv = RT$. The usefulness of the equation may be extended by introducing a compressibility factor, C, as follows:

$$pv = CRT$$

where C is a correction factor which must be determined experimentally and varies with pressure and temperature.

All perfect gases have been liquefied by the use of high pressures and low temperatures. Near the point of liquefaction, the relationship among p, v, and T becomes too complex to be expressed in simple equations. The substance is then called a vapor, and the properties of the vapor are presented in tabular form or graphically. Steam and the common refrigerants are well-known examples of vapors. The properties of steam and the use of the steam tables and charts will be discussed in Chapter 5.

1·12 Energy. A body is said to possess energy when it is capable of doing work. In more general terms, energy is "capacity for producing an effect." Energy may be classified as *stored energy* or *energy in transition.*

Chemical energy is *stored* in fuels such as coal or gasoline and may be released by the process of combustion. Energy is *stored* in high explosives and may be released very quickly to do useful or destructive work. Sufficient energy may be *stored* in the projectile fired from a gun on a battleship to cause the projectile to penetrate a thickness of armor plate approximately equal to the diameter of the projectile. Energy is *stored* in the water behind a dam and may be converted into work as the water flows through a hydraulic turbine to a lower level.

When the switch in a suitable electric circuit is closed, electric energy may *flow* from a distant power plant to a motor, an electric toaster, or a radio, in which it is converted into work, heat, or sound, respectively. In a ship, energy *flows* through the rotating drive shaft from the engine to the propeller. Energy is being received by our earth from the sun, and life would soon cease if this *flow* of energy were to be interrupted.

A fluid such as steam, water, or air flows through the various pieces of equipment in a power plant. Also, energy in such forms as heat and work may be transferred in the apparatus. In analyzing the flow of mass and energy in some piece of apparatus, it is convenient to define the *system* as a particular space surrounded by imaginary or real surfaces which can be specified. The real or imaginary surfaces which enclose this space constitute the *boundary*, and everything outside of the boundary is called the *surroundings*. Energy and mass may flow from the surroundings across the boundary to the system. Thus, in an internal-combustion engine, the *system* may be considered as the space above the piston within the engine cylinder. The *boundary* may be defined as the inside surfaces of the cylinder walls, cylinder head, and piston, and the inside surfaces of the valves in their closed positions. The metal of which the engine is constructed and everything else outside of the boundary constitutes the *surroundings*. It may then be possible to analyze the processes that occur in the engine in order to determine the quantities of energy that cross the boundaries of the system as work and heat and also to study the changes that occur when a mass of fluid enters or leaves the cylinder across the boundaries that are set up to define the system.

1·13 Mechanical potential and kinetic energy. The stored energy associated with the position or movement of *tangible bodies* is called mechanical potential or kinetic energy, respectively.

If a heavy object such as a building stone is lifted from the ground to the roof of a building, the energy required to lift it is stored in the stone as potential energy or energy of position. This stored energy exists by reason of the attractive force acting between the earth and the stone, called the weight of the stone (w lb$_f$), and the vertical distance that separates the stone from some selected datum plane such as the surface of the earth (y ft), and is equal to wy ft-lb$_f$. It should be noted that this stored potential energy remains unchanged as long as the stone retains its position in the building.

Matter and Energy

If a body weighing w lb$_f$ is moving with a velocity of V ft per sec with respect to the surface of the earth, a quantity of kinetic energy or energy of motion is stored in the body equal to

$$\frac{1}{2}\,mV^2 = \frac{1}{2}\frac{w}{g}\,V^2 = \frac{w}{2g}\,V^2 \text{ ft-lb}_f$$

where g is the local acceleration of gravity. This energy will remain stored in the body as long as it continues in motion at constant velocity. If a projectile is fired from a gun, the kinetic energy of velocity of the projectile may be utilized to punch a hole in a piece of armor plate. If a moving railroad train or automobile strikes a stationary object, a disastrous wreck may result because of the kinetic energy stored in the moving body. The train or automobile may be brought to rest gradually by application of the brakes, in which case the kinetic energy is transformed into heat by friction at the rubbing surfaces of the brakes.

When the quantity of matter is expressed in pounds of mass instead of weight in pounds of force, expressions for potential and kinetic energy per lb$_m$ may be derived as follows:

$$w(\text{in lb}_f) = \frac{g}{g_c}\,m(\text{in lb}_m) \tag{1.9}$$

where g is the local acceleration of gravity and g_c is a dimensional conversion constant as discussed in Article 1·4.

$$\text{Potential energy} = wy = \frac{g}{g_c}\,my$$

or, dimensionally,

$$[FL] = \frac{\left[\dfrac{L}{\theta^2}\right]}{\left[\dfrac{M}{F}\dfrac{L}{\theta^2}\right]}[ML] = [FL]$$

$$\text{Kinetic energy} = \frac{w}{2g}\,V^2 = \frac{\dfrac{g}{g_c}\,m}{2g}\,V^2 = \frac{mV^2}{2g_c}$$

or, dimensionally,

$$\frac{[F]}{\left[\dfrac{L}{\theta^2}\right]}\left[\frac{L^2}{\theta^2}\right] = \frac{M\dfrac{L^2}{\theta^2}}{\dfrac{M}{F}\dfrac{L}{\theta^2}}$$

or

$$[FL] = [FL]$$

It should be noted that the dimensions of energy are [FL] or, in the English system of units, ft-lb$_f$, not ft-lb$_m$.

1·14   Molecular or internal energy.   Molecules, like tangible bodies, possess mass.   In the liquid and gaseous states, they possess motion of translation or movement, and rotation or spin. Also the atoms of which the molecules are composed may be vibrating about a mean position, and the electrons are traveling in orbits around the nuclei of the atoms.   Consequently, owing to their mass and motion, the molecules have large amounts of kinetic energy stored in them.   In general, any change in temperature is accompanied by a change in the stored molecular kinetic energy, because the mean molecular velocity is a function of temperature.   The entire mass of the substance may be at rest, as for instance, a tank of water or gas, and the *mechanical* kinetic energy is therefore zero, but the molecules have motion with respect to each other within the substance and therefore possess *molecular kinetic energy.*

Also, molecules are attracted to each other by forces that are very large in the solid phase but less in the liquid phase and tend to vanish in the perfect-gas phase where the molecules are far apart in comparison to their size.   In the melting of a solid or the vaporization of a liquid, it is necessary that these powerful molecular attractive forces be overcome.   The energy required to bring about this change of phase is stored in the molecules as *molecular potential energy* and will be released when the substance returns to its initial state.

Thus, molecules have stored in them potential energy of position and kinetic energy of motion in much the same manner that tangible bodies possess mechanical potential and kinetic energy. This stored molecular energy is generally referred to as *internal energy* and is designated by the symbol u.   At any given temperature, pressure, and specific volume, the internal or molecular energy has a definite value.   When the fluid undergoes some change such as an expansion and then returns to its initial pressure, temperature, and specific volume, the internal energy will again have the same value.   Internal energy, like pressure, temperature, and specific volume, is therefore a property of the substance.

1·15   Work. Work is a form of energy in *transition* across
the boundaries of a system because of the force acting through
a distance and is equal to the product of a force times the distance through which the force acts.   Referring to Fig. 1·9, let it
be assumed that the cylinder is fitted with a frictionless gas-tight
piston and a piston rod through which work can flow to some

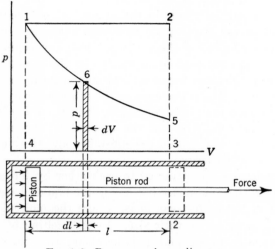

FIG. 1·9   Pressure–volume diagram

external system.   The space between the piston and the cylinder
head is filled with some gas at a pressure p_1 psfa.   On the pV
diagram of Fig. 1·9, the point 1 is so located as to represent to
scale the pressure and volume of the gas behind the piston in its
initial position, 1.   If the piston is allowed to move to some final
position, 2, under such conditions that the pressure of the gas
behind the piston remains constant at its initial value of p_1, the
line 1–2 on the pV diagram is a locus of points representing the
pressure and volume of the gas behind the piston during the
process.

The constant force acting on the piston is

$$F = p_1 A$$

where F = force, lb
p_1 = pressure, psfa
A = area, sq ft

Since work = force × distance, then, for the constant-pressure process 1–2 of Fig. 1·9,

$$W = F \times l = p_1 \times A \times l = p_1(Al)$$
$$= p_1(V_2 - V_1) \tag{1·18}$$

where V_1 and V_2 are the initial and final volumes of the gas behind the piston in cubic feet.

Work is expressed in foot-pound units. Since the foot is the unit of length, volume must be expressed in cubic feet, area in square feet, and pressure in *pounds per square foot absolute* when calculating work done by or on a fluid.

It should be noted on Fig. 1·9 that the product $p_1(V_2 - V_1)$ of Equation 1·18 is equal to the area 1–2–3–4 which therefore represents graphically the work done by the gas during the constant-pressure expansion from 1 to 2.

In the general case, the pressure of the gas varies as the volume changes. A variable-pressure expansion is represented on Fig. 1·9 by the curve 1–5. The equation of the curve 1–5 can often be expressed in the form $pV^n = C$, where C is a constant and n is some exponent between 0 and ∞. When the pressure is changing and the equation showing the relation between p and V is known, it is possible to evaluate the work by considering a small movement of the piston during which the change in pressure is negligible. Assume that the piston is at point 6 on Fig. 1·9. If the piston then moves a small distance dl, the work done may be written as follows:

$$dW = p \times A \times dl = p \times (A\ dl) = p\ dV \tag{1·19a}$$

where $dV = A\ dl$ = increase in the volume of the gas in cubic feet. The elementary cross-hatched area on Fig. 1·9 is $p\ dV$ and represents the work done during the small movement of the piston. By the use of the integral calculus the area under the curve 1–5 can be determined as follows:

$$W = \int_{V_1}^{V_2} p\ dV \tag{1·19b}$$

Equation 1·19b is the general equation for calculating work done by or on a fluid when the algebraic relation between the pressure and volume are known. Equation 1·18 can be derived from Equation 1·19b by making $p_2 = p_1$.

Example 8. A cylinder contains 1 cu ft of gas at a pressure of 100 psia. If the gas expands at *constant pressure* until the volume is doubled, how much work is done?

Solution: Since $p_1 = p_2$,

$$W = \int_{V_1}^{V_2} p \, dV = p \int_{V_1}^{V_2} dV = p(V_2 - V_1)$$

and

$$W = (144 \times 100)(2 - 1) = 14{,}400 \text{ ft-lb}$$

Example 9. A cylinder contains 1 cu ft of gas at an initial pressure of 100 psia. If this gas expands in such a manner that the curve 1–5 of Fig. 1·9 is a straight line, the final pressure is 50 psia, and the final volume is 3 cu ft, how much work is done?

Solution: If the curve 1–5 is a straight line, the average pressure is $\dfrac{100 + 50}{2}$ = 75 psia. Then the work done = $(144 \times 75)(3 - 1) = 21{,}600$ ft-lb.

In the actual engine, the curve representing the relation between p and V must be obtained experimentally by means of an instrument called an *indicator,* as explained in Chapter 3. Let Fig. 1·10 represent a simple engine in which the piston is connected by means of a connecting rod and crank to a rotating shaft on which is mounted a flywheel. As the piston moves to the right on the expansion or power stroke, a plot of the pressure of the gas in the cylinder against the volume of the gas gives the curve 1–2–3–4. The work done *by the gas on the piston* as it moves to the right is represented by the area under this curve on the pV diagram, that is, the cross-hatched area 1–2–3–4–a–b. Part of this work is used to turn the shaft and drive a generator or some other machine, and part of the work is stored in the flywheel by reason of acceleration of its angular velocity. On the return or compression stroke of the piston, while it is traveling toward the left, the energy stored in the flywheel is used to return the piston to the starting point against the pressure of the gas in the cylinder. The curve 4–5–6–1 represents the relation between p and V during the compression stroke, and the cross-hatched area under this curve, or 4–5–6–b–a, represents the work *done on the gas* in returning the piston to the starting point. The net work done by the gas during one revolution of the engine is the difference between the two areas, or the area 1–2–3–4–5–6. It is apparent that work is done because a higher average pressure is maintained in the cylinder during the expansion or power stroke than during the compression or return stroke of the piston. The methods used to measure the net area within the pV diagram and to compute the work done are discussed in Chapter 3.

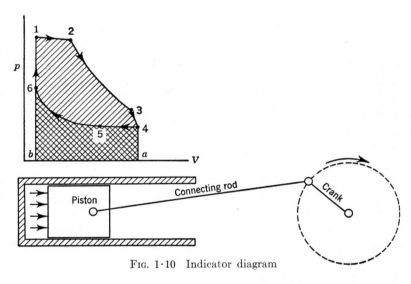

Fig. 1·10 Indicator diagram

Power is the rate of doing work. The horsepower (hp) and the kilowatt (kw) are the units of power used by the engineer and may be defined as follows:

1 hp = 33,000 ft-lb of work per min

1 hp = 0.746 kw

One horsepower-hour (hp-hr) is defined as the *quantity* of work done in 1 hr if work is performed continuously at the *rate* of 33,000 ft-lb per min for a period of 1 hr. Therefore 1 hp-hr = 33,000 × 60 = 1,980,000 ft-lb.

Example 10. During the expansion stroke, the average pressure of the gas on the piston of an engine is 100 psia, whereas, on the return or compression stroke, the average pressure is 25 psia. Compute the work done per revolution of the engine if the volume displaced by the piston in traveling from one end of its stroke to the other end is 2 cu ft.

Solution:

Net work = work of expansion minus work of compression

$$= (144 \times 100 \times 2) - (144 \times 25 \times 2)$$

$$= 21,600 \text{ ft-lb}$$

Example 11.   If the engine of Problem 10 makes 100 rpm, what hp is developed?

Solution:

$$\text{Hp} = \frac{21,600 \times 100}{33,000} = 65.8 \text{ hp}$$

1·16   Heat. Heat is energy in *transition* across the boundaries of a system *because of a temperature difference.* When two bodies at different temperatures are brought into intimate contact, the warmer body will be cooled and the colder body will be warmed. The colder body may be considered as the system and the warmer body as the surroundings. Heat is said to *flow* from the hot body across the system boundary to the cold body by *conduction.* The molecules of the hot body, being at a higher temperature, have a higher level of kinetic energy than the molecules of the cold body, and energy is transferred through the molecular system from the hot body to the cold body. The energy thus being transferred is called heat while it is flowing from the hot body to the cold body. The energy received by the cold body increases its temperature and may be stored in its molecules as an increase in molecular or internal energy.

Heat may also be transferred from one body to another through an intervening space by means of *radiation.* Heat is received from the sun by any body that is exposed to the rays of the sun. The molecules of any substance, particularly at high temperatures, emit waves of energy which travel through the ether with the speed of light and differ from light waves only in their wave lengths. This radiant energy may be absorbed, reflected, or partially absorbed and partially reflected by a body upon which it impinges. Upon absorption, the radiant energy is stored as molecular energy in the receiving body, and a rise in temperature or a change in phase, such as the melting of a solid, occurs.

Heat may be transferred from one body to another body some distance removed from the first one through the mechanism of *convection.* In this case, a fluid is heated or cooled by conduction through contact with one body, after which the fluid flows to another location where heat is transferred between the moving fluid and the second body. For instance, heat is transferred by conduction from the hot metal surface of a domestic warm-air furnace to a stream of moving air, the temperature of which is thereby increased. The heated air is then transported through a duct to a room in which the moving warm air transfers heat by conduction to the objects with which it comes into contact in the room. Heat transfer by convection therefore involves a fluid which conveys the energy from one body to another through movement of the fluid.

The unit of heat is the British thermal unit (Btu) which is defined as $\frac{1}{180}$ of the quantity of heat required to change the temperature of 1 lb_m of water from 32 to 212 F, a temperature increase of 180 F.

1·17 Specific heat. In engineering literature, specific heat (c) is defined as the quantity of heat required to change the temperature of a unit mass of a substance 1 degree. In the English system of units, it is the number of Btu required to change the temperature of 1 lb_m of a substance 1 F. Thus, if it is found experimentally that the temperature of 1 lb of a substance is increased 10 F by the addition of 5 Btu, the specific heat = $\frac{5}{10}$ or 0.5 (Btu per lb_m per F). Although the specific heat of most substances varies somewhat with temperature, especially at high temperatures, it will be sufficiently accurate in this text to use mean or average values of the specific heat.

It should be noted that the term specific heat as used by the engineer is identical with the term thermal capacity as used by the physicist.

In accordance with the definition of the term specific heat, the quantity of heat supplied to a substance to produce a temperature change may be computed as follows:

$$Q = mc(t_2 - t_1) \tag{1·20}$$

where Q = heat supplied, Btu

m = mass of substance being heated, lb

c = mean value of specific heat, Btu per lb per F

t_1 = initial temperature, F

t_2 = final temperature, F

As pointed out in Article 1·4, if the variation in the local acceleration of gravity with position on the surface of the earth is neglected, 1 lb of mass weighs 1 lb of force. Where this variation cannot be neglected, then a conversion from weight to mass can be made by the following relation:

$$w(\text{in lb}_f) = \frac{g}{g_c} m(\text{in lb}_m) \tag{1·9}$$

where g is the local acceleration of gravity and g_c is the dimensional constant in Newton's second law as explained in Article 1·4.

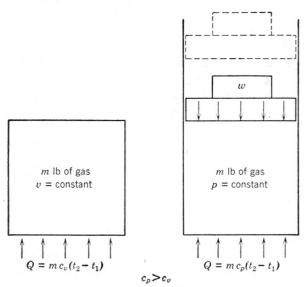

$$Q = m c_v(t_2 - t_1)$$

$$c_p > c_v$$

$$Q = m c_p(t_2 - t_1)$$

Fig. 1·11   Constant-volume and constant-pressure heating of a compressible fluid

If heat is added to a compressible fluid such as a gas, the volume is either constant or changing during the process. If the volume is constant, all of the heat that is supplied is used to increase the temperature of the fluid. The heat required to change the temperature of one pound of a compressible fluid one degree at constant volume is known as the constant volume specific heat and is given the symbol c_v.

A fluid may expand at a constant pressure during the heating process as would be the case if a gas were heated in a vertical cylinder closed by a gas-tight frictionless piston as illustrated in Fig. 1·11. Then work would be done by the expansion of the gas and the work so done would be stored as an increase in the mechanical potential energy of the piston and weight in a final position shown by the dotted line in Fig. 1·11. Sufficient heat must be added to increase the temperature of the gas and also to perform the work of expansion. The heat required to raise the temperature of 1 lb of fluid 1 degree at constant pressure is known as the constant-pressure specific heat and is given the

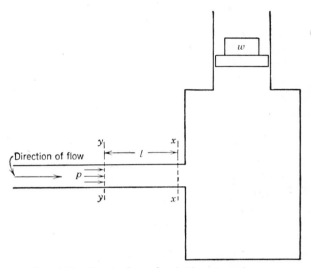

FIG. 1·12 Steady flow of a fluid past section *x–x*

symbol c_p. It is obvious that c_p is greater than c_v, because no work is done during constant-volume heating, but work is done during constant-pressure heating. c_p and c_v are determined experimentally, and their mean values are given in Table 1·1 for a number of common gases. .

1·18   Flow energy. Many engineering problems are concerned not only with the transformation of energy from one form into another but also with the transfer of mass. Let Fig. 1·12 represent a tank into which a fluid is flowing from an inlet pipe. The head of the tank is attached to a cylinder which contains a frictionless gas-tight piston loaded by a weight *w*. The piston is free to move vertically as the volume of the fluid in the tank changes so as to maintain a constant pressure in the tank. Let it be assumed that the tank is well insulated so that no heat transfer occurs between the fluid in the tank and the surroundings.

The fluid in the inlet pipe is at a pressure of p_1 psfa and has a specific volume of v_1 cu ft per lb. The fluid is flowing past the entrance section x because it is being pushed from behind by the fluid further upstream in the pipe; otherwise the fluid would not be flowing. Consider an imaginary plane at section y so located with respect to section x that 1 lb of fluid is contained within the cylinder bounded by these planes. If A represents the internal cross-sectional area of the pipe in square feet, then the volume of this cylinder is $Al = v_1$ cu ft. Assume that the pipe contains an imaginary piston the face of which is located at the plane y. The force exerted by the imaginary piston on the fluid at section y is $p_1 \times A$ lb. The work done in pushing 1 lb of fluid past section x may be computed as follows:

$$W = \text{force} \times \text{distance} = (p_1 A) \times l$$

$$W = p_1(Al) = p_1 v_1 \text{ ft-lb}_f \text{ per lb}_m \text{ of fluid} \qquad (1 \cdot 21)$$

Thus, when a fluid is flowing past a given plane or section, it is flowing because of work being done on it by the fluid behind it to push it past the section, and the amount of this work is $p_1 v_1$ ft-lb per lb of fluid. Since this form of energy is always associated with the pushing of a fluid past a given section, it is called *flow energy* or flow work.

It should be noted that the fluid which is pushed into the tank as the result of $p_1 v_1$ ft-lb of work being done on it has in turn caused the weighted piston to move upward to make room for the gas and has therefore done an equal amount of work on the piston in increasing the potential mechanical energy stored in the piston and weight.

1·19 The law of conservation of energy. The power engineer is concerned with the generation of shaft work from the stored chemical energy in fuels or the stored mechanical potential energy in a body of water behind a dam. The electrical engineer is interested in the conversion of shaft work into electric energy in a generator and the transmission of the electric energy over transmission lines to convenient locations where it can be transformed into work, heat, light, or sound. The refrigerating engineer deals with the removal of heat from an insulated low-temperature space and the discharge of this heat to the atmosphere or to cooling water. The metallurgical engineer requires large quantities of heat at high temperature for the smelting and refining of metals. The chemical engineer requires large amounts of energy in the form of heat and work for manufacturing processes.

The complete or partial transformation of energy from one of the many forms in which it may exist into other forms of energy always takes place in accordance with the *law of conservation of energy*. This law states that energy can be neither created nor destroyed; therefore, when energy is transformed either completely or partially from one form to another, the total amount of energy remains unchanged.

The science of thermodynamics deals with the laws governing the conversion of energy from one form into another. Since energy conversions always occur in strict accordance with the law of conservation of energy, this law is also the *first law of thermodynamics*. The first law of thermodynamics may therefore be stated as follows:

When heat is converted into work or work is converted into heat, the total amount of energy remains unchanged.

The application of the first law of thermodynamics to the various types of equipment used in the field of heat power will be considered in subsequent articles in this chapter. Much space is devoted to a discussion of the actual performance of heat-power equipment throughout this book. These discussions are based directly on the first law of thermodynamics; the principle of conservation of energy. It is expected that the student will learn to recognize the first law of thermodynamics as one of the most important, widely applicable, and generally useful laws in the entire field of the natural sciences.

Since energy is convertible from one form to another without change in the total amount of energy, there is a definite numerical relationship between the various units of energy. The following important conversion factors should be memorized:

$$1 \text{ Btu} = 778 \text{ ft-lb} = J \text{ ft-lb} \qquad (1 \cdot 22)$$

$$1 \text{ hp-hr} = \frac{33{,}000 \times 60}{778} \text{ Btu} = 2545 \text{ Btu} \qquad (1 \cdot 23)$$

$$1 \text{ kw-hr} = 2545 \text{ Btu} \div 0.746 = 3413 \text{ Btu} \qquad (1 \cdot 24)$$

The *efficiency* (η) of a machine is defined as $\dfrac{\text{output}}{\text{input}}$.

Thermal efficiency (η_t) is the ratio of the work output of an engine to the energy input to the engine in a given interval of time, both expressed in consistent units, or

$$\eta_t = \frac{\dfrac{W}{J}}{Q_{\text{in}}} \qquad (1 \cdot 25)$$

where η_t = thermal efficiency
 W = work done per unit of time, ft-lb
 J = 778 ft-lb per Btu = conversion factor for changing ft-lb to Btu
 Q_{in} = energy supplied to the machine per unit of time, Btu

If the unit of time is taken as 1 hr, the Btu equivalent of a given horsepower is equal to $2545 \times$ hp from Equation $1 \cdot 23$, and

$$\eta_t = \frac{\text{hp} \times 2545}{Q_{\text{in}}} \qquad (1 \cdot 26)$$

where Q_{in} is expressed in Btu per hour and is computed in accordance with methods that are specified in the standard test codes pertaining to the particular type of machine under test.

Example 12. An automobile engine is found by test to deliver 50 hp continuously for 1 hr with an hourly fuel consumption of 30 lb of gasoline having a heating value or energy content of 19,000 Btu per lb. What is the thermal efficiency of the engine?

Solution: From equation $1 \cdot 26$,

$$\eta_t = \frac{50 \times 2545}{30 \times 19{,}000} = 0.223 \text{ or } 22.3\%$$

In this case, 22.3 per cent of the energy in the fuel is converted into work. The remaining 77.7 per cent of the energy in the fuel is discharged to the atmosphere in the hot exhaust gases, in the cooling water, or as heat radiated or conducted directly to the atmosphere from the engine.

1·20   Application of the first law of thermodynamics to the steady-flow process. In subsequent chapters in this book, attention will be directed to the construction and principles of operation of such apparatus as turbines, engines, boilers, super-heaters, condensers, heaters, compressors, pumps, and fans. In each case, a fluid will be flowing through the apparatus, and

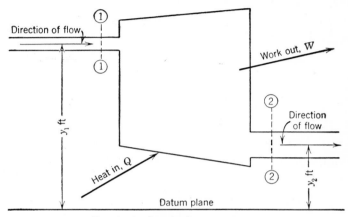

Fig. 1·13   Steady-flow apparatus

energy transformations will be taking place simultaneously. A *steady-flow* process implies that the pressure, temperature, specific volume, and velocity of flow are constant with respect to time at the entrance to the apparatus and also at the exit from the apparatus, and that, for every pound of fluid entering the apparatus, an equal amount of fluid is leaving the apparatus. In some equipment having pulsating flow at the inlet and outlet connections, as in reciprocating engines, the inlet and exit sections often can be selected far enough from the apparatus so that such pulsations are damped out and steady-flow conditions are realized.

In accordance with the first law of thermodynamics, the energy entering a system or region under *steady-flow conditions* must be equal to the energy leaving the system or region in the same interval of time.

Let Fig. 1·13 represent some apparatus through which a fluid is flowing under *steady-flow conditions*. Then

Matter in = matter out

Energy in = energy out

It is convenient to write the energy equation for a flow of one pound (weight) of fluid and to assume that one pound of mass weighs one pound. At the entrance section 1, which is located y_1 ft above some datum plane such as the floor, the fluid has a velocity of V_1 fps, a temperature T_1, a specific volume v_1, an internal energy u_1, and a pressure p_1. The various kinds of energy associated with *one pound* of fluid as it flows past section 1 may be written as follows:

Mechanical potential energy of position	y_1 ft-lb
Mechanical kinetic energy of motion	$\dfrac{V_1^2}{2g}$ ft-lb
Internal or molecular energy	u_1 Btu
Flow energy	$p_1 v_1$ ft-lb

Similarly, at section 2, the energy associated with *one pound* of fluid as it leaves the apparatus is:

Mechanical potential energy of position	y_2 ft-lb
Mechanical kinetic energy	$\dfrac{V_2^2}{2g}$ ft-lb
Internal or molecular energy	u_2 Btu
Flow energy	$p_2 v_2$ ft-lb

Between sections 1 and 2, energy may be added or removed as heat and as work. The basic equation, energy in = energy out, may be written for Fig. 1·13 for *one pound* of fluid with each energy term expressed in Btu units as follows:

$$\frac{y_1}{J} + \frac{V_1^2}{2gJ} + u_1 + \frac{p_1 v_1}{J} + Q = \frac{y_2}{J} + \frac{V_2^2}{2gJ} + u_2 + \frac{p_2 v_2}{J} + \frac{W}{J} \quad (1 \cdot 27)$$

It should be noted that in Fig. 1·13 heat is being put into the system and the Q term is therefore written on the left side of the equality sign. If heat had been removed from the system, it would be indicated on Fig. 1·13 by reversing the direction of the arrow, and the Q term would appear on the right side of the equality sign as Q out. Similarly, in Fig. 1·13, the arrow indicates that energy is leaving the system as work and the work term appears on the right or "energy out" side of the equation. If the apparatus were a compressor, work would be supplied to the apparatus, and the work term would appear on the left or "energy in" side of the equation.

Care must be exercised in the use of consistent units in Equation 1·27. Velocity is expressed in feet per second, pressure in pounds per square foot absolute, specific volume in cubic feet per pound. All energy terms must be expressed in British thermal units as in Equation 1·27 or in foot-pound units.

Equation 1·27 is often used as a mathematical statement of the first law of thermodynamics; also it is frequently called the general-energy equation for the steady-flow process.

Equation 1·27 has been developed for a flow of 1 lb by weight on the assumption that 1 mass pound weighs 1 lb. However, the weight of 1 lb of mass varies with the local acceleration of gravity, and the equation can be written for a flow of 1 lb of mass to make it as general as possible. Tables of fluid properties such as internal energy, enthalpy, and specific volume are tabulated for 1 lb of mass.

In Article 1·4, it was shown that $w = \dfrac{g}{g_c} m$ where g is the local acceleration of gravity, and g_c is the dimensional constant in Equation 1·1, or

$$g_c = \frac{1}{32.174 \, \dfrac{\text{lb}_m}{\text{lb}_f} \dfrac{\text{ft}}{\text{sec}^2}}.$$

In Article 1·13, it was pointed out that the potential and kinetic energies of 1 lb of *mass* are as follows:

$$\text{Potential energy} = \frac{g}{g_c} y$$

$$\text{Kinetic energy} = \frac{V^2}{2g_c}$$

Then Equation 1·27 may be written for a flow of 1 lb of *mass* for *any* local acceleration of gravity, g, as

$$\frac{g}{g_c}\frac{y_1}{J} + \frac{V_1^2}{2g_cJ} + u_1 + \frac{p_1v_1}{J} + Q = \frac{g}{g_c}\frac{y_2}{J} + \frac{V_2^2}{2g_cJ} + u_2 + \frac{p_2v_2}{J} + \frac{W}{J} \quad (1\cdot27a)$$

In subsequent articles in this chapter involving the use of Equation 1·27, it will be assumed that, for slide-rule calculations of engineering data, the difference between the local and standard acceleration of gravity may be neglected so that 1 lb of mass weighs 1 lb of force.

1·21 Enthalpy. In Article 1·14 it was pointed out that the internal energy of a unit mass of substance u is a property of the substance and is therefore a definite quantity for any given pressure, temperature, and specific volume. It is convenient in many engineering problems to combine the pressure, specific-volume, and internal-energy terms into a single new term which in turn will be a property of the substance. This term is called *enthalpy*, h, and, *by definition*,

$$h = u + \frac{pv}{J} \text{ Btu per lb of substance} \qquad (1·28)$$

It should be noted that the pv product in Equation 1·28 is the product of two properties of a substance and only represents flow energy when flow occurs. Tables giving enthalpy values for steam appear in the back of this book and will be used extensively in the solution of problems concerned with the generation and utilization of steam.

Reference to the textbooks on thermodynamics will show that, for 1 lb of a perfect gas having a constant specific heat, the change in enthalpy between an initial and a final state, $h_1 - h_2 = c_p(T_1 - T_2)$.

By substituting enthalpy h for the internal-energy and flow-energy terms of Equation 1·27, the general-energy equation for the steady-flow process reduces to the following form:

$$\frac{y_1}{J} + \frac{V_1{}^2}{2gJ} + h_1 + Q = \frac{y_2}{J} + \frac{V_2{}^2}{2gJ} + h_2 + \frac{W}{J} \qquad (1·29)$$

The first law of thermodynamics will now be applied to the following equipment or processes, all of which will be discussed in subsequent chapters in this book:

1. Heat exchangers such as boilers, superheaters, economizers, air heaters, condensers, and feed-water heaters.
2. Prime movers such as steam and gas turbines and steam and internal-combustion engines.
3. Pumps.
4. Compressors and fans.
5. Nozzles.
6. The throttling process, governors, and calorimeters.

1·22   Application of the first law of thermodynamics to heat exchangers.   Heat exchangers are a class of equipment in which steam or some other vapor is generated or condensed, or a liquid or gas such as oil or air is heated or cooled.   A simple boiler in which water is being converted into steam is shown diagrammatically in Fig. 1·14.

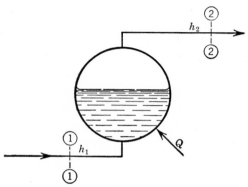

FIG. 1·14   Heat exchanger

$$Q_{in} = h_2 - h_1$$

For a *steady-flow* process in a *heat exchanger* the following assumptions may be made:

1. One pound of fluid leaves the apparatus for each pound of fluid entering the apparatus.

2. No work is done between the entrance and exit sections since no shaft is being rotated.

3. The velocities at the entrance and exit sections are low and of the same order of magnitude in order to keep the pressure drop in the piping system to a reasonably low value.

4. The change in mechanical potential energy of the fluid, $(y_1 - y_2)/J$, is in the order of a small fraction of 1 Btu and may be neglected.   It may be noted that a difference in elevation of 77.8 ft between the entrance and exit sections will amount to only 0.1 Btu.

The general-energy equation may be written again for convenience with the negligible terms canceled as follows:

$$\frac{y_1}{J} + \frac{V_1^2}{2gJ} + u_1 + \frac{p_1v_1}{J} + Q = \frac{y_2}{J} + \frac{V_2^2}{2gJ} + u_2 + \frac{p_2v_2}{J} + \frac{W}{J} \quad (1\cdot27)$$

Then, $\qquad\qquad\qquad h_1 + Q = h_2$

or $\qquad\qquad\qquad\qquad Q = h_2 - h_1 \qquad\qquad\qquad (1\cdot30)$

where h_1 and h_2 are the enthalpies per pound of fluid at entrance and exit, and Q is the heat added or removed per pound of fluid. A discussion of the determination of enthalpy values for water and steam is given in Chapter 5.

1·23   Application of the first law of thermodynamics to prime movers. The function of a prime mover is to perform work. Let Fig. 1·15 represent diagrammatically a prime mover such as a steam turbine through which a fluid is flowing under steady-state conditions. The following assumptions may be made:

1. One pound of fluid leaves the apparatus for each pound of fluid entering the apparatus.

2. The velocities at the entrance and exit sections are low and of the same order of magnitude in order to keep the pressure drop in the piping system to a reasonably low value.

3. The change in mechanical potential energy of the fluid between entrance and exit, $(y_1 - y_2)/J$, may be neglected.

The general-energy equation for the steady-flow process may be written again for convenience with the negligible terms canceled as follows:

$$\frac{y_1}{J} + \frac{V_2^2}{2gJ} + u_1 + \frac{p_1v_1}{J} = Q + \frac{y_2}{J} + \frac{V_2^2}{2gJ} + u_2 + \frac{p_2v_2}{J} + \frac{W}{J} \quad (1\cdot27)$$

Then, $\qquad\qquad\qquad h_1 = Q + h_2 + \dfrac{W}{J}$

or $\qquad\qquad\qquad\qquad \dfrac{W}{J} = (h_1 - h_2) - Q \qquad\qquad (1\cdot31)$

where h_1 and h_2 are the enthalpies per pound of fluid at entrance and exit, W is the work done per pound of fluid, and Q is the heat removed per pound of fluid.

It is apparent by examination of Fig. 1·15 and Equation 1·31 that any energy removed from the system as heat cannot be converted into work, and thereby the efficiency of the machine is reduced. The ideal expansion in a prime mover should therefore be one in which there is *no heat transfer to the cooler surround-*

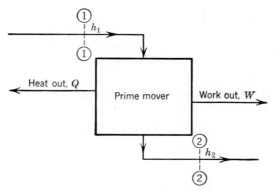

Fig. 1·15 Prime mover

$$\frac{W}{J} = (h_1 - h_2) - Q_{out}$$

ings. The heat-transfer term Q in Equation 1·31 would then be zero, and the equation would reduce to the form

$$\frac{W}{J} = h_1 - h_2 \qquad (1·32)$$

Such an expansion or compression which takes place under conditions of thermal isolation, that is, with no heat transfer between the working fluid and its surroundings, is called an *adiabatic process.*

As the working fluid flows through the prime mover shown in Fig. 1·15, the amount of work produced may be less than the work obtainable under ideal conditions because of mechanical friction in the mechanism or fluid friction due to high velocities in crooked passages in the machine. Such frictional effects reduce the work done and increase the enthalpy of the fluid at the point of exit from the apparatus in accordance with the law of conservation of energy. Consequently, the ideal expansion in a prime mover is a *frictionless adiabatic* expansion, that is, an expansion without friction and without heat transfer to the cooler surroundings. During a frictionless adiabatic expansion, a property of the substance called *entropy* is constant, and such a process is frequently called an *isentropic* (meaning constant-entropy) process. A discussion of the determination and use of entropy will be presented in Chapter 5. A full understanding of the significance of entropy requires a thorough study of the science of thermodynamics and is beyond the scope of this book. However, the student should understand that the *ideal* expansion in a prime mover is a *frictionless adiabatic* or *constant entropy* (*isentropic*) process.

1·24 Application of the first law of thermodynamics to pumps. A pump is a device for transferring a *liquid* from one place to another, usually against an external pressure, and is illus-

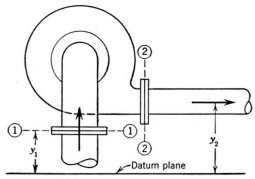

FIG. 1·16 Diagrammatic arrangement of a pump

trated diagrammatically in Fig. 1·16. The following assumptions may be made concerning the flow of a liquid through the pump:

1. One pound of fluid leaves the apparatus for each pound of fluid entering the apparatus.

2. The liquid is at room temperature or the apparatus is well insulated so that there will be no significant change in temperature of the liquid between the entrance and exit sections.

3. The liquid is assumed to be incompressible.

4. There will be no appreciable change in internal energy inasmuch as the temperature and specific volume of the liquid remain constant.

The general-energy equation may be written again for convenience with some of the terms canceled in accordance with the above assumptions:

$$\frac{y_1^2}{J} + \frac{V_1^2}{2gJ} + \cancel{u_1} + \frac{p_1 v_1}{J} + \frac{W}{J} = \frac{y_2}{J} + \frac{V_2^2}{2gJ} + \cancel{u_2} + \frac{p_2 v_2}{J} + \cancel{Q} \quad (1 \cdot 27)$$

This equation may be written in foot-pound units, and the reciprocal of the specific weight, γ, may be substituted for the specific volume, v, on the assumption that 1 lb of mass weighs 1 force pound, to give the following equation:

$$y_1 + \frac{V_1^2}{2g} + \frac{p_1}{\gamma_1} + W = y_2 + \frac{V_2^2}{2g} + \frac{p_2}{\gamma_2} \quad (1 \cdot 33)$$

Since the liquid is practically incompressible, $\gamma_1 = \gamma_2$, and

$$W = (y_2 - y_1) + \frac{V_2^2 - V_1^2}{2g} + \frac{p_2 - p_1}{\gamma} \quad (1 \cdot 34)$$

The application of this equation to the pumping of liquids will be discussed in Chapter 9.

1·25   Application of the first law of thermodynamics to gas compressors and fans. Gas compressors and fans are used to move or compress air and many industrial gases at pressures that vary from a fraction of 1 psi to more than 15,000 psi. The operating conditions vary over such wide limits that the analysis should start with the general-energy equation 1·27. Depending on the particular conditions of operation, some of the terms in this equation may be canceled to produce a simpler equation applicable to the particular equipment under consideration.

1·26   Application of the first law of thermodynamics to the nozzle. A nozzle is a flow channel that is so proportioned as to permit a fluid to expand from its initial pressure to a lower pressure with a conversion of as much as possible of the energy stored in the fluid in other forms at the entrance section into the kinetic energy of a high-velocity jet. Let Fig. 1·17 represent a nozzle in which a fluid at the entrance section 1 expands to a lower pressure at the exit section 2. The following assumptions may be made:

1. One pound of fluid leaves the apparatus for each pound of fluid entering the apparatus.

2. The change in mechanical potential energy of the fluid between the entrance and exit sections may be neglected.

3. No work is done between the entrance and exit sections since no shaft is being rotated.

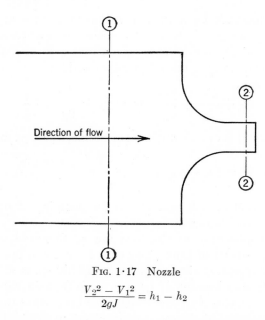

FIG. 1·17　Nozzle

$$\frac{V_2{}^2 - V_1{}^2}{2gJ} = h_1 - h_2$$

4. Because of the high final velocity and the short distance between entrance and exit sections, the heat transferred to the surroundings per pound of fluid may be neglected.

The general-energy equation may be written as follows with certain terms canceled because of the above-mentioned assumptions:

$$\cancel{\frac{z_1}{J}} + \frac{V_1{}^2}{2gJ} + u_1 + \frac{p_1v_1}{J} + \cancel{Q} = \cancel{\frac{z_2}{J}} + \frac{V_2{}^2}{2gJ} + u_2 + \frac{p_2v_2}{J} + \cancel{\frac{W}{J}} \quad (1\cdot27)$$

Then,
$$\frac{V_1{}^2}{2gJ} + h_1 = \frac{V_2{}^2}{2gJ} + h_2$$

or
$$\frac{V_2{}^2 - V_1{}^2}{2gJ} = h_1 - h_2 \quad (1\cdot35)$$

Equation 1·35 shows that the increase in kinetic energy as a fluid flows through a nozzle is equal to the decrease in enthalpy. The use of the equation in designing steam-turbine nozzles will be discussed in Chapter 7.

1·27 Application of the first law of thermodynamics to the throttling process. The high-velocity jet produced in the nozzle as discussed in the preceding article could be directed against suitably shaped blades mounted on the periphery of a

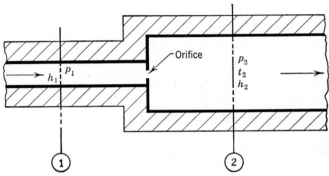

FIG. 1·18 The throttling process
$$h_1 = h_2$$

rotating disk, and the kinetic energy of the jet could then be used to do work in rotating a shaft. This is the principle upon which the turbine operates. On the other hand, the high velocity may be dissipated in internal whirls and eddies with the resultant conversion of the kinetic energy into internal energy of the fluid. Such a process is called a throttling process and may take place in the apparatus shown in Fig. 1·18.

The following assumptions are made in developing the energy equation for the throttling process:

1. One pound of fluid leaves the apparatus at section 2 for each pound of fluid that enters the apparatus at section 1.

2. The apparatus is well insulated, and the heat transfer to the cooler surroundings may be neglected.

3. No work is done between the entrance and exit sections; no shaft is being rotated.

4. The areas at the entrance and exit sections are such that the kinetic energy of the fluid is negligible or of the same order

of magnitude so that the change in kinetic energy in the apparatus may be neglected.

5. The change in mechanical potential energy due to a difference in elevation between the entrance and exit sections may be neglected.

On the basis of the above assumptions, the general energy equation may be written as follows with the negligible terms canceled:

$$\frac{\cancel{V_1}}{J} + \frac{\cancel{V_1}^2}{2g\cancel{J}} + u_1 + \frac{p_1 v_1}{J} + \cancel{Q} = \frac{\cancel{V_2}}{J} + \frac{\cancel{V_2}^2}{2g\cancel{J}} + u_2 + \frac{p_2 v_2}{J} + \frac{\cancel{W}}{\cancel{J}} \qquad (1\cdot27)$$

Then, $h_1 = h_2$ $(1\cdot36)$

The throttling calorimeter which is used for the determination of the quality of wet steam is discussed in Chapter 5. The steam-turbine governor uses the throttling process to control the amount of steam admitted to the turbine and is considered in Chapter 7.

1·28   The second law of thermodynamics.   The first law of thermodynamics states that for a closed cycle the work done is equal to the heat that disappears. However, this law does not say anything about *how completely* a given quantity of energy in the form of heat can be converted into work.

In 1824, Sadi Carnot, a young French scientist, published an essay entitled "Reflections on the Motive Power of Heat," in which he pointed out that a temperature difference is necessary for the conversion of heat energy into work. He stated that, when a source of heat exists at a temperature T_S which is above the temperature T_R of a sink or receiver into which the energy can be dumped that cannot be converted into work, maximum efficiency of conversion of heat into work occurs when the following conditions are fulfilled:

1. Heat is transferred from the source to a working fluid in a suitable mechanism at the highest temperature at which the transfer of heat can take place which is the temperature of the source, T_S.

2. The heat that cannot be converted into work is rejected to the sink or receiver at the lowest possible temperature at which it can be rejected which is the temperature of the receiver, T_R.

3. The other expansion and compression processes which constitute the cycle of operations are frictionless adiabatic processes in which there is no heat transfer to the cooler surroundings and no losses due to friction.

If these conditions are fulfilled, then the thermal efficiency or ratio of heat converted into work to heat supplied is given by the equation

$$\eta = 1 - \frac{T_R}{T_S} \tag{1.37}$$

and it is impossible to realize a higher thermal efficiency for the given temperatures.

The second law of thermodynamics may be stated as follows:

Given a source of heat at an absolute temperature T_S and an environment or sink at a lower absolute temperature T_R to which the heat engine may reject the energy that it cannot convert into work, the maximum conceivable thermal efficiency is given by the equation

$$\eta_{max} = 1 - \frac{T_R}{T_S} \tag{1.37}$$

Complete conversion of heat into work requires that the sink or receiver temperature T_R be equal to absolute zero. Since the temperature of the atmosphere or a large body of water is normally the lowest temperature at which heat can be rejected in nature, it is apparent that no machine can ever be built with a thermal efficiency approaching 100 per cent. Maximum efficiency requires the highest possible initial temperature, and much of the effort to improve the efficiency of heat-power machinery has been devoted to the utilization of higher initial temperatures. The maximum temperature is limited by the strength, corrosion resistance, and stability of metals at high temperature, and, as better materials become available for operation at higher temperature, efficiencies will continue to increase.

In all natural processes, there is a universal tendency for heat to flow by radiation, conduction, and convection to regions of lower temperature, with the result that less of the energy can be converted into work. Also, there is a universal tendency for work to be converted into heat energy at low temperature through friction, and little or none of this energy can be converted back into work. Work may be considered as high-grade energy because it can be completely transformed into other forms of energy and is useful to mankind in performing his chores. On the other hand, heat energy is low-grade energy which can be converted into work only partially and with difficulty and is always tending to flow into a region of lower temperature from which less or perhaps none of it can be converted into work. This is known as the principle of *degradation of energy*. It may be concluded that heat is a low-grade form of energy which can be converted into work with an efficiency not greater than that specified in the second law of thermodynamics and that in all natural processes, its temperature level tends to decrease with a corresponding decrease in the proportion that can be converted into work.

1·29   Review of basic concepts and definitions. Experience has shown that there are certain ideas and terms that must be thoroughly understood as a foundation for the study of heat power and thermodynamics. The student has been introduced to some of these concepts and definitions in courses in chemistry and physics, and they have been reviewed in this chapter. Others have been presented to him for the first time in this chapter. They are summarized in the following paragraphs for convenience and emphasis.

Matter: that which occupies space and has inertia; the substance of which physical objects are composed.

Mass: a quantity of matter. The unit of mass in general engineering use in the United States is called the pound mass (lb_m) which is 0.4535924+ of the mass of a particular block of platinum-iridium known as the international kilogram mass. This international unit of mass is located at Sèvres, France, and replicas of it are preserved at the U. S. National Bureau of Standards.

Force: a push or pull. The standard unit of force in general engineering use in the United States is called the pound force (lb_f) which is defined as the unbalanced force that will accelerate 1 lb of mass at the rate of 32.174 ft per sec² where 32.174 ft per sec² is the standard acceleration of gravity at mean sea level and 45 degrees of latitude.

Slug: a unit of mass which is accelerated at the rate of 1 ft per sec² by an unbalanced force equal to one standard force pound. One slug equals 32.174 lb mass.

— *Mole or pound-mole:* that quantity of matter which has a mass in pounds numerically equal to the molecular weight of the element or compound. One pound-mole of any substance consists of 2.7319×10^{26} molecules.

Weight: the force of gravity acting on the mass of a body in any gravitational field. On the surface of the earth at mean sea level and 45 degrees of latitude, 1 lb of mass weighs 1 lb of force. When a body is "weighed" on a beam balance or platform scale, the mass of the body is measured by comparison with standard masses.

System: a definite region or space enclosed within specified *boundaries* or surfaces which may be real or imaginary, fixed or movable. A system is sometimes defined as the mass within a specified region.

Surroundings: the space outside of the boundaries of the system; normally the space in the immediate vicinity of the system which is measurably affected by energy or mass transfer to or from the system.

State: the chemical and physical condition of the system.

Property: a property of a system is any observable characteristic of a system. Common properties are pressure, temperature, specific volume, internal energy, enthalpy, and entropy. In general, the state of a system of given composition may be determined by measuring two properly selected properties.

—*Specific volume:* the volume of a unit mass of material. In the English engineering system of units, specific volume is generally expressed as cubic feet per pound of mass.

Specific weight: the *weight* of a unit volume of material. In the English engineering system of units, specific weight is generally expressed as weight (lb$_f$) per cubic foot.

—*Density:* the *mass* of a unit volume of material. In the English engineering system of units, density is generally expressed either as pounds mass per cubic foot or slugs per cubic foot.

Process: a physical or chemical occurrence during which an effect is produced by the exchange, transformation, or redistribution of energy or mass.

Energy: the capacity to produce a change or effect.

Internal energy: energy that is *stored* within a mass of molecules by reason of their random motion and configuration.

Heat: energy that is being transferred across the boundaries of a system because of a temperature difference between the system and surroundings.

Specific heat: specific heat, often called thermal capacity by the chemist and physicist, is the quantity of energy that must be supplied to a system to change the temperature of a unit mass of substance 1 degree. In the English engineering system of units, the specific heat is usually expressed in Btu required to change the temperature of 1 lb of mass 1 F.

Work: energy which is being transferred across the boundaries of a system by reason of a force acting through a distance in the direction of motion.

Power: the rate of doing work; work done per unit of time. In the English engineering system of units, power is generally expressed in foot-pounds of work done per minute, horsepower (one hp = 33,000 ft-lb per min) or kilowatts (1 kw = 1.34 hp).

Flow energy (sometimes called "flow work" or "displacement energy"): energy transferred across the boundaries of a system by virtue of the work done upon a flowing fluid in pushing it across the system boundaries.

Enthalpy: a property of a substance that is obtained by arbitrarily adding the values of the internal energy and the product of the pressure and volume, all expressed in consistent units. In the English engineering system of units, enthalpy (or specific enthalpy) is normally expressed in Btu per pound of mass, or $h = u + pv/J$.

Adiabatic process: a process that occurs without heat transfer between the system and its surroundings.

Entropy: for the limited purpose of this book, entropy may be defined as a property that is constant when an expansion or compression occurs without friction and without heat transfer across the boundaries of the system. Such a process is often called a frictionless adiabatic or isentropic process.

Efficiency: in general, the various efficiencies, such as thermal efficiency, mechanical efficiency, volumetric efficiency, express useful output over input. In each case, the methods of measuring output and input are established by more or less arbitrary definitions. The word efficiency has no engineering significance unless preceded by a limiting or qualifying adjective which indicates precisely the quantities that are being compared and is meaningless when used without strict adherence to the established definition for each application.

Thermal efficiency: as applied to a prime mover, thermal efficiency is the ratio of useful work output of a system to the heat supplied to the system where both work done and heat supplied are determined in accordance with procedures specified in standard test codes.

Law of conservation of matter: excluding nuclear transformations, matter is indestructible; during chemical reactions, the chemical composition may change, but the mass of each element involved in the reaction remains constant.

Law of conservation of energy: excluding nuclear reactions, during any process involving energy transformation or transfer, the total amount of energy remains constant.

First law of thermodynamics: the law of conservation of energy is the first law of thermodynamics. When heat is converted into work or work is converted into heat, the total amount of energy remains unchanged.

Second law of thermodynamics: for the limited purposes of this book, the second law of thermodynamics may be stated as follows: No engine operating in a cycle can continuously convert into work all of the heat supplied to it. Given a source of heat at a constant absolute temperature T_1 and a sink or receiver into which the waste heat from the engine may be rejected at a lower constant absolute temperature T_2, the maximum thermal efficiency of a heat engine operating between these temperatures is given by the equation

$$\eta_{max} = \frac{T_1 - T_2}{T_1}$$

PROBLEMS

1. During a test of a domestic heating plant, 25 lb of coal were fired, 2 lb of dry refuse were collected from the ash pit, and 314 lb of gaseous products of combustion were discharged up the chimney. How much air was supplied?

2. A total of 60 lb of gasoline and 840 lb of dry air were supplied to an internal-combustion engine, and 792 lb of dry gaseous products of combustion were discharged from the exhaust pipe. How much water vapor was discharged in the exhaust gases?

3. Convert the following temperatures from Fahrenheit to Rankine: 300 F, −20 F.

4. Convert the following temperatures from centigrade to Kelvin: 240 C, −100 C.

5. Convert the following Fahrenheit temperatures to centigrade: 100 F, −20 F.

6. Convert the following centigrade temperatures to Fahrenheit: −60 C, 150 C.

7. Convert the following pressures in in. of Hg to psi and psf: 40, 27, 3.

8. Convert the following pressures from psi to in. of Hg: 4, 14.7, 25.

9. A pressure gage reads 150 psi, and the barometric pressure is 29.8 in. of Hg. What is the absolute pressure in psi and psf?

10. A pressure gage reads 10 in. of Hg vac. If the barometric pressure is 29.5 in. of Hg, determine the absolute pressure in in. of Hg, psi, and psf.

11. Compute the specific volume of air at 100 psia and 100 F.

12. Compute the specific volume of nitrogen at 50 psia and 70 F.

13. How many lb of air are contained in a room 20 ft wide, 40 ft long, and 12 ft high if the room temperature is 70 F and the barometric pressure is 29.7 in. of Hg?

14. Oxygen in a tank having a volume of 8 cu ft is at a pressure of 8.3 in. of Hg gage and a temperature of 40 C. Barometric pressure is 29.7 in. of Hg. Calculate the amount of oxygen in the tank.

15. A 100-cu-ft steel tank contained compressed air at 150 psig and 100 F. Some of the air escaped through a leak, and the final pressure and temperature were found to be 40 psig and 80 F. Barometric pressure is 29.9 in. of Hg. (*a*) How much air escaped from the tank? (*b*) What was the volume occupied by the air that escaped if the room temperature was 70 F?

16. A balloon contained 10 lb of helium (molecular weight = 4). At a given elevation, the atmospheric pressure was 22 in. of Hg abs, and the temperature was 30 F. Calculate the total volume of the balloon in cu ft under these conditions.

17. A tank having an internal volume of 100 cu ft contains methane (CH_4) at a pressure of 80 psig and a temperature of 70 F. Barometric pressure is 29.9 in. of Hg. Assuming that methane is a perfect gas, how many lb of methane are contained in the tank?

18. An automobile weighing 3500 lb is traveling on a level road at a speed of 60 miles per hr. What is the kinetic energy of the automobile in ft-lb? How much energy expressed in Btu would be dissipated in the brakes in bringing the car to rest as quickly as possible?

19. If the driver of the car in Problem 18 applied the brakes at the foot of a hill 25 ft high in such a manner as to bring the car to rest at the top of the hill, how much energy expressed in Btu would be dissipated in the brakes?

20. How much mechanical potential energy is stored in a 1000-lb bomb that has been carried by an airplane to a distance of 30,000 ft above the surface of the earth?

21. If the bomb in Problem 20 could be dropped in a frictionless atmosphere so that all of the potential energy could be converted into kinetic energy, what would be the terminal velocity of the bomb at the instant of impact with the surface of the earth?

22. If $W = \int p\, dV$, prove that, for a constant-pressure process, $W = p(V_2 - V_1)$.

23. If a gas expands from p_1 and V_1 to p_2 and V_2 according to the law $pV = C$, prove that $W = p_1 V_1 \ln V_2/V_1$.

24. One pound of air at 100 psia and 100 F expands at constant pressure until the volume is doubled. Compute the work done.

25. Two pounds of air at 70 psig and 60 F expand at constant pressure until the final volume is three times the initial volume. Barometric pressure is 29.9 in. of Hg. Compute the work done.

26. Five pounds of CO_2 at 150 psig and 100 F are heated at constant volume until the pressure is doubled. Compute the work done.

27. The piston of a single-cylinder engine has a diameter of 10 in. and travels 20 in. in moving from one end of the cylinder to the other. If the average gas pressure on the piston during the expansion or working stroke is 120 psia and the average pressure on the piston during the return or compression stroke is 30 psia, compute (a) the work done by the gas during the expansion stroke, (b) the work done on the gas during the compression stroke, (c) the net work done during one revolution of the engine, and (d) the hp developed if the engine runs at 200 rpm.

28. Five pounds of air at 70 F and 14.7 psia are heated at constant volume to a temperature of 300 F. How much heat must be transferred to the air?

29. Five pounds of air at 70 F and 14.7 psia are heated at constant pressure to a temperature of 300 F. (a) How much heat must be transferred to the air? (b) Why is the answer greater than the answer to Problem 28?

30. The specific heat of a substance is 0.5 Btu per lb per F. Compute the quantity of heat in Btu necessary to change the temperature of 10 lb of the substance from 100 to 200 C.

31. A tank contains 40 cu ft of nitrogen at 100 F and 200 psia. How much heat is removed from the nitrogen to cool it to 70 F?

32. How much heat is supplied to the air during the expansion process in Problem 24?

33. How many ft-lb of energy are equivalent to 2000 Btu?

34. If 30 kw-hr of electric energy are supplied to a heater, how many Btu are released?

35. Compute the Btu equivalent of 25 kw-hr; of 50 hp-hr.

36. The internal energy in 1 lb of gas at 100 psia and a specific volume of 3 cu ft is 600 Btu. Compute the enthalpy of 1 lb of the gas.

37. For a perfect gas, $h_2 - h_1 = c_p(T_2 - T_1)$. Assuming that all of the gases listed in Table 1·1 behave as perfect gases, compute the change in enthalpy when 1 lb of each of the following gases is heated from 100 to 400 F: air, nitrogen, hydrogen.

38. How many Btu are required to heat 1000 lb of oil per hr from 70 to 150 F if the specific heat of the oil is 0.52?

39. Air enters a compressor with a velocity of 10 fps and an enthalpy of 120 Btu per lb and leaves with a velocity of 15 fps and an enthalpy of 216 Btu per lb. Assuming no heat transfer to the surroundings, how many ft-lb of work are required per lb of air compressed?

40. Air at 1500 F and 15 psia has an enthalpy of 493.6 Btu per lb. Compute the internal energy per lb of air.

41. A total of 50,000 lb of steam per hr enters a turbine at a velocity of 100 fps and an enthalpy of 1300 Btu per lb. The steam leaves with an enthalpy of 980 Btu per lb and a velocity of 400 fps. The heat transferred to the surroundings is 2 Btu per lb of steam flowing through the turbine. Calculate the power produced by the steam in kw.

42. Air is expanded in a nozzle without heat transfer from an initial temperature of 500 F to a final temperature of 200 F. If the initial kinetic energy of the air is negligible, compute (*a*) the final kinetic energy, and (*b*) the final velocity in fps.

43. An air compressor is supplied with air at 14.7 psia and a specific volume of 13.5 cu ft per lb. The air is discharged at 100 psia and a specific volume of 2.7 cu ft per lb. The initial and final internal energies of the air are 15 Btu per lb and 50 Btu per lb. The jacket cooling water removes 2 Btu per lb of air compressed. The changes in kinetic and potential energy may be neglected. Compute (*a*) the work required to compress 1 lb of air, and (*b*) the hp required to compress 50 lb of air per min.

44. A gasoline engine burns 10 lb of gasoline in 15 min when doing work at the rate of 75 hp. If the heating value or energy content of the fuel is 20,000 Btu per lb, what is the thermal efficiency of the engine?

45. A power plant has an average monthly output of 720,000 kw-hr. (*a*) If the average plant thermal efficiency is 20 per cent when burning coal having a heating value of 12,000 Btu per lb, what is the average monthly coal consumption in tons? (*b*) If the coal costs $8.20 per ton, what is the fuel cost in cents per kw-hr?

46. A Diesel engine consumes 12 lb of fuel oil in 10 min when carrying a steady load of 170 hp. The heating value of the fuel is 19,000 Btu per lb. Calculate (*a*) the thermal efficiency of the engine; and (*b*) the total amount of energy lost in the exhaust gases, cooling water, oil, surrounding air, etc., during the 10-min test.

47. Natural gas having a heating value of 1000 Btu per cu ft is used in a power plant which has an overall thermal efficiency of 25 per cent. What is the gas consumption in cu ft per kw-hr? What is the fuel cost in cents per kw-hr if the gas costs 20 cents per 1000 cu ft?

48. Determine the weight of 100 lb_m where the acceleration of gravity is 25 ft per sec^2.

49. According to the steam tables, the enthalpy of steam at 1000 psia and 900 F is 1448.2 Btu per lb_m. What is the enthalpy of a quantity of steam at this pressure and temperature which weighs 1 lb_f where the local acceleration of gravity is 30 ft per sec^2.

50. According to the steam tables, the specific volume of steam at 1000 psia and 900 F is 0.7604 cu ft per lb_m. (*a*) What is the specific weight of steam at 1000 psia and 900 F where the local acceleration of gravity is 30 ft per sec^2? (*b*) What is the density of the steam under this condition in (1) slugs per cu ft, and (2) lb_m per cu ft?

51. A body having a mass of 1000 lb_m is moving at a velocity of 100 ft per sec^2 at a point where the acceleration of gravity is 20 ft per sec^2. Calculate the kinetic energy of the body.

52. If the body in Problem 51 weighs 1000 lb_f and all other conditions are the same, what is the kinetic energy?

53. The specific heat of a substance is 0.4 Btu per lb_m per F. If a quantity of this substance weighs 100 lb_f on the surface of the moon where the local acceleration gravity is 5.47 ft per sec^2, how much heat, expressed in Btu, would be required to raise the temperature of the material 50 F?

54. The specific volume of water at 70 F is 0.01606 lb_m per cu ft. If this water is at a location where the local acceleration of gravity is 30 ft per sec^2, determine, (*a*) specific weight, (*b*) density in slugs per cu ft, and (*c*) density in lb_m per cu ft.

55. If the specific heat of water for the conditions given in Problem 54 is 1.00 Btu per lb_m per F, how much heat is required to raise the temperature of a quantity of water weighing 100 lb_f from 50 to 150 F?

2 • Fuels and Combustion

2·1 Introduction. Approximately 96 per cent of the energy used in the United States is obtained from fuels; waterpower accounts for most of the remaining 4 per cent. Fuels are therefore the principal source of energy for power generation, for the heating of buildings, and for industrial uses such as the manufacture of iron and steel or other materials.

Intensive research work is currently being conducted on the problems of power generation by atomic energy. It is possible that atomic energy may be used to generate steam for utilization in steam power plants of conventional design or to heat compressed air for the operation of gas turbines. Many very difficult problems must be solved before power can be generated on a commercial scale. One of the most important of these problems is cost. Widespread commercial utilization of atomic energy will not occur until the cost of such energy compares favorably with the cost of energy from conventional sources such as coal, oil, or gas. However, there are many applications in the field of national defense, such as the possible operation of submarines and aircraft carriers over long distances and periods of time without refueling, which make power generated from atomic energy very attractive, even at much higher cost than that of power generated by conventional equipment.

This chapter is concerned with the classification of fuels, the physical and chemical properties that determine the relative economic importance of various fuels, the elementary principles of combustion of fuels, and the losses that occur when fuels are burned. Since the cost of fuel is the largest item in the operating costs of power generation and is often a major item of manufacturing cost in industrial processes, the selection of the most economical fuel and the efficient utilization of that fuel are of vital importance. Moreover, the type of fuel-burning equipment to be installed in a new plant is dependent upon the characteristics of the fuel to be burned. In many industrial processes, fuels must be selected to avoid contamination of the product by impurities in the fuel, or fuels must be burned that permit control of energy distribution or regulation of furnace atmosphere. Since the best types of fuels are limited in quantity and high in price, it is important that they be utilized wisely and efficiently.

2·2 Classification of fuels. Fuels may be classified as shown in Table 2·1 into solid, liquid, and gaseous fuels. Each of these types of fuels may in turn be classified as natural fuels,

TABLE 2·1

CLASSIFICATION OF FUELS

Type of Fuel	Natural Fuels	Manufactured Fuels
Solid	Coal	Coke
	Lignite	Briquets
	Peat	Charcoal
	Wood	Waste fuels:
		Bagasse
		Sawdust
		Tanbark
Liquid	Petroleum	Gasoline
		Kerosene
		Fuel oil
		Alcohol
		Benzol
		Shale oil
Gaseous	Natural gas	Producer gas
		Blast furnace gas
		Carbureted water gas
		Coal gas
		Acetylene

that is, fuels found in nature, or manufactured fuels. Most of the manufactured fuels are made from natural fuels, sometimes as a by-product, but usually because they are better suited to a particular application than the natural fuel. Gasoline, which is refined from petroleum, is an example of a manufactured fuel that is produced specifically to meet the requirements of a fuel for automobile or aircraft engines.

Table 2·2 shows the sources of energy utilized in the United States, the average amount of energy of each kind used in the decade of 1940–49 in per cent of the total, the fuel resources in per cent of the total, and the estimated life of the various kinds of fuel at the present rate of consumption. Coal comprises the bulk of the fuel resources of the United States and is widely distributed geographically. The proved supplies of oil and natural gas are very limited in comparison to the coal reserves and are

TABLE 2·2

SOURCES OF ENERGY AND FUEL RESERVES OF THE UNITED STATES

Source of Energy	Average Energy Utilization, 1940–49, in Per Cent of Total	Fuel Reserves in Per Cent of Total	Life of Fuel Reserves in Years at Present Rate of Utilization
Coal	48.9	95.4	1824
Petroleum	30.8	0.5	14
Natural gas	12.6	0.5	30
Oil from shale	....	3.6	....
Waterpower	4.0	...	....
Wood	3.7	...	....
Total	100.0	100.0	....

being used rapidly. Substantial amounts of petroleum are currently being imported from foreign countries. Fortunately, during the past 25 years, new petroleum reserves have been discovered as fast as the known reserves have been depleted, but there is no assurance that this situation will continue. The manufacture of gasoline and oil from coal was carried out on a large scale in Germany during World War II. Since that time, intensive research work has been conducted by the United States Bureau of Mines on the development of commercial methods of producing oil from coal, and pilot plants are now operating experimentally on improved processes. The depletion of the petroleum reserves may ultimately result in an increase in the cost of refined petroleum products to the point where liquid fuels can be made economically from coal in the United States.

Large deposits of shale occur in southern Indiana and Kentucky and in the Green River region of Colorado, Wyoming, and Utah.

From one to two barrels of oil can be obtained per ton of shale by roasting it in a suitable retort or chamber in the absence of air and collecting and condensing the gases that are produced. The United States Bureau of Mines and some of the major oil companies are now operating pilot plants for the manufacture of oil from shale, and substantial progress has been made in overcoming the technical difficulties in operating such a process.

To summarize, coal is the basic fuel resource of the United States. The known reserves of petroleum and natural gas are limited and are being depleted rapidly. Fortunately, substitutes for the refined products of petroleum may be made from coal and from shale deposits when the price of petroleum increases because of depletion of the reserves. The development of cheap and controllable atomic energy may at some future time completely alter the fuel situation. Until then, coal will probably continue to be the major source of energy for heating and power generation.

2·3 The proximate analysis of coal. Although coal has been the subject of much study, there is no single set of tests based upon physical or chemical properties which will accurately predict the value of a particular coal for a given use. The *proximate analysis* is readily made, gives much valuable information, and is widely used. The proximate analysis includes the per cent by weight of the moisture, ash, volatile matter, and fixed carbon in the fuel. The heating value of the fuel in Btu per pound is normally reported with the proximate analysis. Although it is not part of the proximate analysis, the amount of sulphur is frequently reported with the proximate analysis because of the difficulties that are encountered in burning fuel that is high in sulphur.

Moisture * is defined as the loss in weight of a 1-gram sample when dried for 1 hr at 105 C in a constant-temperature oven through which dry preheated air is passed, and is expressed as a percentage of the weight of the sample tested. The analysis should report the moisture in the coal "as received," that is, the moisture in the coal at the point of sampling. The moisture content of coal will vary from 2 to 25 per cent or more by weight,

---

* Detailed methods of collecting coal samples and making analyses are given in the publications of the U. S. Bureau of Mines and the ASTM Standards on Coal and Coke, 1949.

depending upon the rank or quality of the coal. Moisture is objectionable because it dilutes the combustible material in the coal and therefore reduces the heating value per pound of fuel. It must be transported from the mine to the point of use at considerable expense. When the coal is burned, the moisture must be evaporated before the coal can be ignited, thus causing a direct loss in energy and reducing the fuel-burning capacity of the equipment.

Ash is the incombustible residue that remains when the sample of the fuel is held at a temperature of 700 to 750 C in the presence of air until the combustible matter has been burned and a constant weight is attained. The ash constitutes from 4 to over 20 per cent by weight of the coal.

The ash in coal comes from three sources: (1) the vegetable matter from which the coal was formed, (2) foreign material washed into the coal beds during their formation and often deposited in seams or veins, and (3) material from the roof and floor of the mine. The ash due to items 2 and 3 can be partially removed by hand picking and mechanical cleaning of the coal at the mine, and many mines are equipped with machinery for reducing the ash content and grading the coal by size. Without mechanical cleaning, the ash content of the fine sizes of coal is normally higher than the ash content of lump coal.

Ash, like moisture, dilutes the combustible substance of the coal, thus reducing the heating value per pound, and not only must be shipped from the mine to the point of use at considerable expense but also will have to be removed after the coal is burned and disposed of, usually at added expense.

The principal constituents of ash are silica (SiO_2), alumina (Al_2O_3), iron oxide (Fe_2O_3), and calcium oxide (CaO). Depending upon the proportions of these compounds and others which are present in smaller amounts, the ash may melt at the temperatures that exist in the fuel bed and furnace. *Clinker* is ash that has fused or melted. The temperature at which the ash fuses is one of the most important characteristics of coal and is determined by mixing finely ground ash with a suitable binder to form a cone that is mounted in a furnace and heated in a mildly reducing atmosphere. The *softening temperature* is the temperature at which the cone fuses to a spherical lump. In general, coals whose ash softens at temperatures above 2600 F give little trouble from clinkers, whereas coals with ash-fusing temperatures below 2200 F will cause serious clinker troubles unless carefully handled. Melted ash which flows readily may choke off the air supply in the fuel bed, is destructive to furnace brick work, and, if carried into boiler surfaces by the moving gas stream, may bridge across the tube bank and block the flow of gas, thus forcing a shutdown of the unit. The ash-fusing temperature has more influence on the design of high-capacity furnaces than any other property or characteristic of coal.

The volatile matter in coal is determined by heating a 1-gram sample of fine coal for 7 min at 950 C in a platinum crucible that has a close-fitting cover to exclude air. The loss in weight is volatile matter plus moisture. The volatile matter is that part of the coal which can be gasified under the conditions of the test. If the volatile matter could be collected and cooled to room temperature, it would be found to consist mainly of tars, oils, and gaseous hydrocarbon compounds. The volatile matter in coal varies from almost nothing to about 50 per cent by weight and is the smoke-producing constituent of coal. In general, coals high in volatile matter produce large quantities of combustible gases upon heating and require large combustion chambers or furnaces and careful firing for their complete and smokeless combustion.

Fixed carbon is determined by subtracting from 100 the sum of the moisture, ash, and volatile matter expressed as per cent by weight. From 25 to 90 per cent of the coal is fixed carbon, the content of fixed carbon increasing with the rank of the coal.

The *heating value* of the coal is normally reported with the proximate analysis and is the energy, expressed in Btu, which is released by the complete combustion of 1 lb of fuel. The method of measuring the heating value is discussed in Article 2·11.

Table 2·3 gives the proximate analysis of representative samples of coal on an "as-received" basis. Since moisture and ash are in a sense extraneous material while the fixed carbon and volatile matter are the useful coal substance, analyses that are used to compare coals are often reported on a "moisture-free" or "moisture-and-ash-free" basis. The method of converting the

TABLE 2·3

ANALYSES OF REPRESENTATIVE COALS IN THE UNITED STATES COMPILED FROM BULLETINS OF THE U. S. BUREAU OF MINES ANALYSIS OF MINE SAMPLES ON THE "AS-RECEIVED" BASIS

Rank	Subgroup	State	County	Proximate Analysis				Ultimate Analysis					Heating Value in Btu per Lb	Mineral-Matter-Free Basis	
				Moisture	Volatile Matter	Fixed Carbon	Ash	Sulphur	Hydrogen	Carbon	Nitrogen	Oxygen		Dry Fixed Carbon	Moist Btu
I. Anthracite	1. Meta-anthracite	R. I.	Providence	4.5	3.0	78.7	13.8	0.9	0.5	82.4	0.1	1.8	11,624	98.2	
	2. Normal anthracite	Pa.	Carbon	4.1	3.5	81.7	10.7	0.5	2.2	81.6	0.6	4.4	12,590	97.1	
		Pa.	Luzerne	3.6	4.7	76.1	15.6	1.1	2.7	74.3	0.8	5.5	12,050	96.1	
		Pa.	Schuylkill	4.5	3.9	83.2	8.4	0.5	2.5	82.5	1.2	4.9	12,970	96.5	
	3. Semi-anthracite	Pa.	Northumberland	1.5	10.1	76.5	11.9	0.8	3.7	78.7	1.4	3.5	13,390	89.7	
		Pa.	Sullivan	2.0	9.6	77.8	10.6	0.6	3.7	79.5	0.9	4.7	13,520	90.1	
		Va.	Montgomery	1.3	11.9	62.2	24.6	0.7	3.2	67.1	0.7	3.7	11,310	86.6	
II. Bituminous	1. Low-volatile	W. Va.	McDowell	1.7	18.1	76.0	4.2	0.6	4.7	85.4	1.2	3.9	14,720	81.2	
		Pa.	Cambria	3.5	18.0	71.7	6.8	2.2	4.7	80.1	1.2	5.0	14,140	81.2	

Rank	State	County												
2. Medium volatile	W. Va.	Fayette	1.7	26.7	69.0	2.6	0.8	5.0	85.1	1.6	4.9	14,930	72.5	14,020
	Pa.	Westmoreland	2.3	26.2	63.4	8.1	3.2	4.9	77.4	1.5	4.9	13,850	72.5	14,820
	Va.	Buchanan	3.1	21.8	67.9	7.2	1.0	5.0	80.1	1.5	5.2	14,030	76.4	14,780
3. High volatile A	Ill.	Jackson	5.7	33.2	52.3	8.8	3.5	5.3	70.0	1.3	11.1	12,590		13,140
	W. Va.	Logan	2.8	35.8	56.3	5.1	0.7	5.5	78.8	1.6	8.3	13,980		13,920
	Pa.	Fayette	3.1	35.1	51.3	10.5	3.5	5.1	71.5	1.5	7.9	13,000		13,200
4. High volatile B	Ill.	Franklin	9.2	33.8	48.6	8.4	0.9	5.5	67.3	1.5	16.3	11,930		12,370
	Ky.	Webster	5.4	34.9	50.4	9.3	1.1	5.1	70.4	1.6	12.5	12,501		12,580
	Ill.	Williamson	9.8	27.3	55.4	8.1	0.9	5.1	68.5	1.1	16.3	12,015		12,200
5. High volatile C	Ill.	Logan	12.8	36.5	40.8	9.9	3.0	5.7	61.5	1.1	18.8	10,990		
	Ind.	Sullivan	13.5	32.5	48.4	5.6	1.1	5.9	66.0	1.5	19.9	11,788		
	Iowa	Polk	13.9	37.0	35.2	14.0	6.2	5.5	54.7	0.8	18.8	10,244		
III. Subbituminous														
1. Subbituminous A	Wyo.	Carbon	12.0	36.9	44.9	6.2	0.4	5.7	60.6	1.0	26.1	10,640		11,440
2. Subbituminous B	Oreg.	Coss	16.1	31.1	39.6	13.2	0.8	5.5	51.1	1.2	28.2	9,031		10,550
	Wyo.	Sheridan	23.9	34.3	38.4	3.4	0.4	6.3	54.1	1.1	34.7	9,335		9,700
3. Subbituminous C	Colo.	Jackson	25.0	30.5	39.3	5.2	1.2	6.2	51.2	0.7	35.5	8,880		9,450
	Wyo.	Sweet Water	19.8	35.7	37.8	6.7	0.7	5.1	48.1	1.3	38.1	7,830		8,450
IV. Lignite	Texas	Houston	34.7	32.2	21.9	11.2	0.8	6.9	39.3	0.7	41.4	7,056		8,040
	S. Dak.	Perkins	39.2	24.7	27.8	8.3	2.2	6.6	38.0	0.5	44.4	6,307		6,890
	N. Dak.	Williams	42.1	25.0	24.4	8.5	1.3	7.1	35.2	0.5	47.5	5,994		6,580

analysis from one basis to another can be illustrated by the following example:

Example 1. Convert the analysis of the Sullivan County, Ind., coal of Table 2·3 from an "as-received" basis to a "moisture-free" and to a "moisture-and-ash-free" basis.

Solution:

	A "As Received"	B "Moisture- Free"	C "Moisture- and-Ash-Free"
Volatile matter	32.5	37.5	40.2
Fixed carbon	48.4	56.0	59.8
Ash	5.6	6.5	....
Moisture	13.5	....	....
Total	100.0	100.0	100.0
Btu per lb	11,788	13,628	14,572

Column *A* is obtained from Table 2·3. The items in column *B* are computed by dividing the items of column *A* by (1.00 − 0.135) = 0.865, since 1 lb of fuel contains 0.865 lb of volatile matter, fixed carbon, and ash. Similarly, column *C* is obtained from column *A* by dividing the volatile matter, fixed carbon, and heating value by 1.00 − (0.135 + 0.056) = 0.809, since 1 lb of fuel contains 0.809 lb of volatile matter plus fixed carbon.

2·4   The ultimate analysis of coal. The ultimate analysis of coal is an analysis on a percentage basis of the chemical elements that form the coal substance. Carbon, hydrogen, nitrogen, and sulphur are determined by the methods of organic chemical analysis while the ash is determined as in the proximate analysis. The oxygen is then calculated by difference. Table 2·3 gives the ultimate analyses of typical coals on the "as-received" basis. It should be noted that the column for "ash" in Table 2·3 applies to *both the proximate and ultimate analyses.*

In Table 2·3 the moisture in the coal is reported in the ultimate analysis as its chemical elements: that is, as hydrogen and oxygen. It is often desirable to report the ultimate analysis with the moisture listed as a separate item. Since hydrogen and oxygen combine to form water in the proportions of 1 lb of hydrogen + 8 lb of oxygen = 9 lb of water, then one ninth of the moisture is hydrogen and eight ninths of the moisture is oxygen. The moisture from the proximate analysis may be inserted into the ultimate analysis by deducting from the hydrogen and oxygen of the ultimate analysis the amount of hydrogen and oxygen in the moisture. The resulting analysis may be converted to a "moisture-free" or "moisture-and-ash-free" basis as in Example 1. This procedure may be illustrated by the following example:

Example 2. Convert the ultimate analysis of the Sullivan, Ind., coal of Table 2·3 from the "as-received" basis to the "as-received" basis with the moisture as a separate item in the ultimate analysis. Then convert this analysis to a "moisture-free" and to a "moisture-and-ash-free" basis.
Solution:

As Received

Con-stituent	A From Table 2·3	B With Moisture as Separate Item		C Moisture-Free	D Moisture-and-Ash-Free
Carbon	66.0		66.0	76.3	81.5
Nitrogen	1.5		1.5	1.7	1.9
Sulphur	1.1		1.1	1.3	1.4
Ash	5.6		5.6	6.5	.....
Hydrogen	5.9	$5.9 - \frac{1}{9} \times 13.5 =$	4.4	5.1	5.4
Oxygen	19.9	$19.9 - \frac{8}{9} \times 13.5 =$	7.9	9.1	9.8
Moisture	.....		13.5	.....	.....
Total	100.0		100.0	100.0	100.0

In column A which is copied from Table 2·3 the moisture appears as hydrogen and oxygen. In column B the moisture from the proximate analysis, amounting to 13.5 per cent, is inserted as a separate item. One ninth of this moisture or $\frac{1}{9} \times 13.5$ is hydrogen which is subtracted from the hydrogen in column A to get the hydrogen in column B. Similarly, eight ninths of the moisture or $\frac{8}{9} \times 13.5$ is oxygen which is subtracted from the oxygen in column A to get the oxygen in column B. Columns C and D are obtained from column B as in Example 1 by dividing the items of column B by $(1.00 - 0.135)$ and $1.00 - (0.135 + 0.056)$, respectively.

The *available* or *combustible* hydrogen of the fuel may be computed by assuming that all of the oxygen in the fuel is combined with hydrogen, the remainder of the hydrogen being available to burn by combining with oxygen from the air. Since 8 lb of oxygen combine with 1 lb of hydrogen, the hydrogen which is inert owing to oxygen in the fuel is one eighth of the oxygen, or

$$H_a = H - \frac{O}{8} \qquad (2 \cdot 1)$$

where H_a = the available or combustible hydrogen
H = the hydrogen from the ultimate analysis
O = the oxygen from the ultimate analysis

Example 3. Compute the available hydrogen in the Indiana coal whose analysis is given in Example 2.
Solution: From column A, Example 2,

$$H_a = H - \frac{O}{8} = 5.9 - \frac{19.9}{8} = 5.9 - 2.5 = 3.4\% \text{ by weight}$$

Also, note that from column B, Example 2,

$$H_a = H - \frac{O}{8} = 4.4 - \frac{7.9}{8} = 3.4\% \text{ by weight}$$

2·5 Origin of coal. It is generally agreed that coal is of vegetable origin. In prehistoric times plant material accumulated in great swamps where the land was slowly sinking at a rate that covered the plant and tree growth with sufficient water to prevent normal decay without destroying plant life. Thus the remains of vegetable growth accumulated to considerable depth and was gradually converted to peat through biochemical decay. The peat was subsequently buried, in some cases to depths of several thousand feet, by sinking of the earth's crust and deposition of soil above the peat bed. Under the influence of time, moderate temperature, the weight of the overburden of soil, and thrust pressures created by movements of the earth's crust in regions where mountains were being formed, the peat was compacted and devolatilized. This brought about a transformation from woody material through the various *ranks* of coal such as lignite, subbituminous, and bituminous coal, to anthracite, as shown in Fig. 2·1. In general, the volatile matter and oxygen content were reduced, and the fundamental coal substance was concentrated into the carbon and ash of the anthracite coal. The "older" coals such as anthracite and low-volatile bituminous coals are found in the Appalachian region of the United States and in some localities in the Rocky Mountain region where earth-thrust pressures have been great. The deposits of lignite, sub-bituminous coal, and high-volatile bituminous coal are found in the Mississippi Valley regions where earth-thrust pressures due to mountain formation have been a minimum.

Figure 2·2 shows the changes in the proximate analysis and heating value of ash-free coal during progressive transformation from lignite to anthracite. It should be noted that the heating value of the "oldest" coals such as anthracite is lower than the

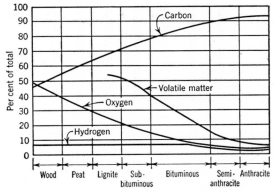

Fig. 2·1   Progressive transformation from wood into coal, based on moisture, ash, and sulphur-free coal

heating value of the high-grade bituminous coals, because the devolatilization of the coal has progressed so far that much of the available hydrogen has been driven out of the coal, and hydrogen has a heating value over four times that of carbon.

2·6   Classification and characteristics of coals by rank. For the purpose of classifying coals, mine samples are taken from freshly exposed faces of the coal seam in the mine. The proximate analyses of such samples of coal which contain the natural bed moisture are reported as being on the "moist" basis. Since moisture and mineral matter are to a certain extent extraneous material, the high-rank coals are classified on the basis of dry mineral-matter-free fixed carbon while the low-rank coals are classified on a moist mineral-matter-free Btu basis. Mineral matter in coal exceeds the ash content as reported in the proximate analysis, owing to changes that occur when the sample

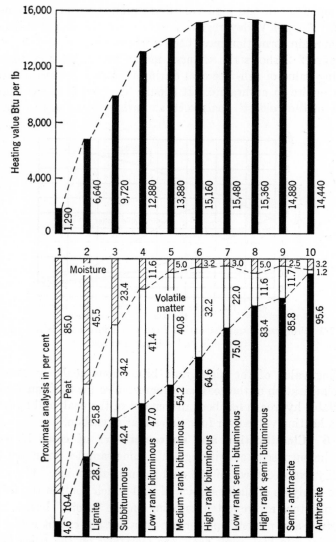

Fɪɢ. 2·2 Proximate analysis and heating value of ash-free coals

is heated during analysis. The following formulas, suggested by Parr, are used for coal classification:

Dry mineral-matter-free fixed carbon

$$= \frac{FC - 0.15S}{100 - (M + 1.08A + 0.55S)} \times 100 \quad (2 \cdot 2)$$

Moist mineral-matter-free Btu

$$= \frac{\text{Btu} - 50S}{100 - (1.08A + 0.55S)} \times 100 \quad (2 \cdot 3)$$

where FC, M, A, and S refer to the percentages of fixed carbon, moisture, ash, and sulphur reported in the analysis of the coal containing its natural bed moisture.

Coals are classified as shown in Table $2 \cdot 4$ into lignite, sub-bituminous, and bituminous coals, and anthracite, with two or

TABLE $2 \cdot 4$

CLASSIFICATION OF COAL BY RANK *

Class	Group	Limits of Dry Mineral-Matter-Free Fixed Carbon, Dry Volatile Matter, and Moist Mineral-Matter-Free Btu
I. Anthracite	1. Meta-anthracite	Fixed carbon 98% or more; dry volatile matter 2% or less
	2. Anthracite	Fixed carbon 92–98%; dry volatile matter 2–8%
	3. Semi-anthracite	Fixed carbon 86–92%; dry volatile matter 8–14%; nonagglomerating
II. Bituminous	1. Low-volatile bituminous coal	Fixed carbon 78–86%; dry volatile matter 14–22%
	2. Medium-volatile bituminous coal	Fixed carbon 69–78%; dry volatile matter 22–31%
	3. High-volatile A bituminous coal	Fixed carbon less than 69%; dry volatile matter over 31%. Moist Btu 14,000 or more
	4. High-volatile B bituminous coal	Moist Btu 13,000 to 14,000
	5. High-volatile C bituminous coal	Moist Btu 11,000–13,000. Either agglomerating or nonweathering
III. Subbituminous	1. Subbituminous A coal	Moist Btu 1 ,000–13,000. Both agglomerating and weathering
	2. Subbituminous B coal	Moist Btu 9500–11,000
	3. Subbituminous C coal	Moist Btu 8000–9500
IV. Lignite	1. Lignite	Moist Btu less than 8300. Consolidated
	2. Brown coal	Moist Btu less than 8300. Unconsolidated

* ASTM Standards on Coal and Coke, 1949.

more groups under each major classification. They are classified by dry volatile matter and dry mineral-matter-free fixed carbon for values of 69 per cent or more fixed carbon, and by moist mineral-matter-free Btu and physical properties for coals having less than 69 per cent dry mineral-matter-free fixed carbon. Weathering coals are those that undergo a certain amount of degradation in size when dried under specified test conditions. Agglomerating coals are those in which the residue from the volatile-matter test is an agglomerate button of coke which will support a 500-gram weight or a button showing swelling or cell structure.

In Table 2·3 the analyses of the coals are grouped in accordance with the classification as given in Table 2·4.

Lignite has a distinct woody or clay-like structure with a moisture content of 30 to 45 per cent when mined. Upon drying, it disintegrates into small flakes. Because of the high moisture content, the heating value as mined is low, varying from 5500 to 8000 Btu per lb, and it is not economical to ship it far from the mine. Extensive lignite deposits exist in such states as Texas, North Dakota, and Montana, and this fuel will undoubtedly become important commercially as the supplies of high-grade coal are depleted and methods are developed for reducing the moisture of the lignite at the mine.

Subbituminous coals are usually glossy black in color, do not have the woody appearance that characterizes much of the lignite, and have a moisture content when mined of 10 to 30 per cent. They "slack" or disintegrate upon exposure to the air and are therefore designated as nonweathering coals. They are classified into groups *A*, *B*, and *C* as shown in Table 2·4, by their heating value on a mineral-matter-free basis. Because of their high moisture content, low heating value, and nonweathering characteristics, they are not mined extensively although large deposits exist in the United States.

Bituminous or "soft" coals are widely distributed throughout the United States and are the principal fuels for steam generation, industrial purposes, and the manufacture of metallurgical coke and coal gas. They vary in composition as shown in Table 2·3 from the high-volatile coals of the Mississippi Valley to the low-volatile coals of the Appalachian region. The high-volatile coals, having a volatile-matter content as mined of 25 to 40 per cent, burn with a long yellow flame. They will produce objectionable quantities of smoke unless properly fired in a furnace of sufficient size to burn the volatile gases.

The low-volatile bituminous coals are relatively smokeless, are low in moisture and ash, have the highest heating value of any coals, and are the premium industrial fuels of the country. They are also sold extensively as high-grade domestic fuels.

Bituminous coals are designated as *free-burning*, or *caking* or *coking* coals. Coking coals soften and swell upon heating and solidify into strong cellular masses of coke or carbon after the volatile matter has been driven off. Free-burning coals do not soften and swell on heating, do not adhere to adjacent pieces, and produce a noncoherent carbon residue after the volatile matter has been expelled.

Semi-anthracite coals occur in small quantities, are smokeless fuels having 8 to 14 per cent volatile matter, and are sold primarily for domestic use.

Anthracite or "hard" coal is a free-burning smokeless fuel having less than 8 per cent of volatile matter and consisting mainly of fixed carbon and ash. It is slow to ignite and burns with a short bluish flame. It commands a premium price as a domestic fuel, and only those sizes too small for domestic consumption are available for steam generation. Most of the anthracite is mined in three counties in eastern Pennsylvania, and the reserves are strictly limited.

Figure 2·3 shows the distribution of coal fields in the United States. These coal fields constitute over 50 per cent of the known coal reserves of the world, and are widely distributed geographically, an important factor in the industrial development of the United States. Nearly one half of these reserves are lignite and subbituminous coal, and the highest grades of coal such as anthracite will be exhausted in 100 years at the present rate of consumption.

2·7 Solid fuels other than coal. *Coke* is the strong porous coherent mass, composed principally of carbon, which is produced when a coking coal is heated to about 2000 F in the absence of air. Coal gas and benzol are by-products of coke manufacture. Coke is the basic fuel of the metallurgical industries and

finds a limited market as a domestic smokeless fuel. The fine
sizes (coke breeze) which are too small for other uses are burned
for steam generation.

Briquets are produced by mixing the fine sizes of high-grade
coal with a suitable binder and pressing the mixture into lumps
about the size of a cake of soap. The briquets have sufficient
strength to resist breakage during shipment. A high-priced

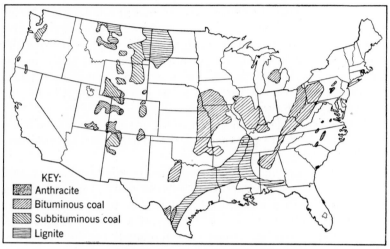

KEY:
Anthracite
Bituminous coal
Subbituminous coal
Lignite

Fig. 2·3 Coal fields of the United States

domestic fuel is thus produced from fine sizes of coal that normally have a low market value.

Sawdust, spent *tanbark*, and *bagasse* (sugar-cane refuse) are
high-moisture waste fuels which like wood are of importance as
industrial fuels in limited areas.

2·8   Petroleum.   Crude petroleum is refined to produce gasoline for internal-combustion engines such as automobile and aircraft engines; kerosene for lighting; Diesel fuel for Diesel engines; lubricating oils; fuel oil for domestic heating, steam
generation, and industrial furnaces; and oil for the manufacture
or enrichment of gas. Petroleum is an intersolution of a mixture
of hydrocarbon compounds of the following families: C_nH_{2n+2},
C_nH_{2n}, C_nH_{2n-2}, C_nH_{2n-4}, C_nH_{2n-6}, $\cdots$, C_nH_{2n-14}. Thus, in
the paraffin series, C_nH_{2n+2}, compounds are found to vary from

gaseous methane (CH_4) to solid paraffin $(C_{30}H_{62})$. The ultimate analysis of crude petroleum falls within the following limits:

Carbon	80–87%
Hydrogen	11–15%
Oxygen, nitrogen, and sulphur	0.1–11%

Crude petroleum is classified into the following three groups, depending upon the type of residue that remains upon distillation: (1) paraffin-base crudes, (2) asphalt-base crudes, and (3) mixed-base crudes, the last having a residue composed of a mixture of paraffin and asphalt.

Although there is no generally accepted theory that explains the origin of petroleum, it is believed to have resulted from the decomposition of marine vegetation or marine animals. Figure

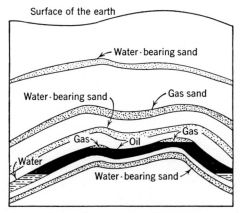

FIG. 2·4 Occurrence of petroleum and natural gas in a typical rock formation

2·4 shows a typical geological formation in which petroleum and natural gas are found. It consists of a porous stratum of rock overlaid with an impervious cover, all so inclined as to produce a pocket into which the oil and gas have collected from adjacent areas. The oil is often found over salt water.

The analyses of typical crude petroleums are given in Table 2·5.

The major oil fields of the United States are shown in Fig. 2·5. The major producing fields are the mid-continent field of Okla-

TABLE 2·5

ANALYSES OF TYPICAL CRUDE OILS

Source of Oil	Degrees API	Carbon, Per Cent	Hydro-gen, Per Cent	Oxygen, Per Cent	Sulphur, Per Cent
California, Kern River	15	86.80	11.57	0.74	0.89
California, Sunset	14	86.73	11.37	0.84	1.06
Pennsylvania crude	39	82.0	14.8	3.20 *	....
West Virginia crude	36	84.3	14.1	1.60 *	....
Ohio crude	28	84.2	13.1	2.7 *	....
Texas crude	22	84.6	10.9	2.87	1.63
Oklahoma crude	25	87.93	11.47	0.19	0.41
Mexican crude	22	85.65	10.2	....	4.15
Russia, Baku	17	86.6	12.3	1.1 *	....

* Oxygen plus nitrogen.

homa and Texas, the Gulf Coast field of Texas and Louisiana, and the California field.

Crude petroleum is refined by distillation into gasoline, kerosene, lubricating oils, distillates, and residual-fuel oils. Because

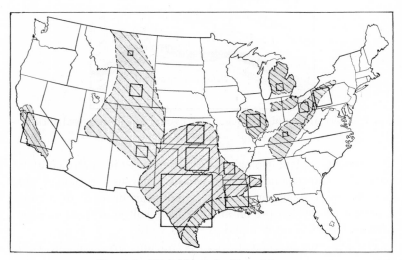

FIG. 2·5 Oil fields of the United States

Production by states is proportional to the areas of the squares in the major oil-producing states

of the demand for gasoline, some of the distillates or residues from the distillation process may be subjected to thermal cracking or partial decomposition to produce gasoline and other lighter fractions. Fuels for internal-combustion engines will be considered in more detail in Chapter 3.

Fuel oils are used for industrial heating, for domestic heating, and for steam generation. They may be distillates obtained by condensation of some of the heavier fractions which are distilled from the crude, residues which remain after the lighter fractions have been removed, or blends of distillates and residues. They may vary from light oils approaching the characteristics of kerosene to fuel oils so heavy that they must be heated to be handled readily.

2·9 Properties of fuel oil. Among the important properties of fuel oil are (1) specific gravity, (2) heating value, (3) flash and burning points, (4) congealing point (pour test), and (5) viscosity.

The specific gravity of fuel oil is determined by placing a hydrometer in a sample of the oil at 60 F. The hydrometer (Fig. 2·6) is a standard weighted glass bulb with a graduated rod indicating the depth to which it sinks in the fluid under test. The hydrometer is graduated in degrees API (American Petroleum Institute), and the gravity of the oil is determined by reading the scale of the hydrometer at the level of the liquid surface. The specific gravity or the ratio of the density of fuel oil at 60 F to the density of water at 60 F may be computed as follows:

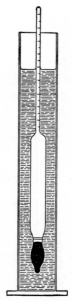

Fig. 2·6
Hydrometer

$$\text{Specific gravity} = \frac{141.5}{131.5 + \text{degrees API}} \qquad (2\cdot4)$$

A gravity of 10 degrees API corresponds to a specific gravity of 1.00. It should be noted that, the higher the API gravity reading, the lower is the specific gravity of the fuel oil.

The heating value of fuel oil, expressed in Btu per pound, may be determined by means of a bomb calorimeter as explained in

Article 2·11.   The American Petroleum Institute has accepted the following formulas for approximating the heating value of fuel oil in Btu per pound:

For uncracked oil,

$$Q_H = 17{,}660 + (69 \times \text{API gravity}) \qquad (2\cdot5)$$

For cracked oil,

$$Q_H = 17{,}780 + (54 \times \text{API gravity}) \qquad (2\cdot6)$$

The heating value per pound increases with the API gravity. However, fuel oil is purchased by the gallon or barrel (42 gal per barrel), and the number of pounds per gallon decreases with increased API gravity.   Consequently, the number of Btu per gallon decreases as the API gravity increases, as shown in Fig. 2·7.

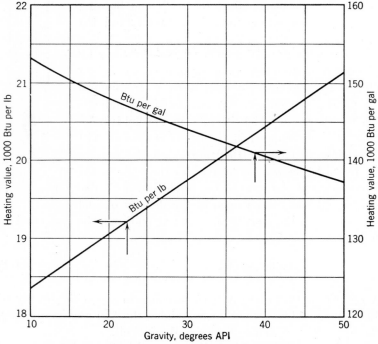

FIG. 2·7   Approximate heating values of uncracked fuel oil
$$Q_H = 17{,}660 + (69 \times \text{API gravity})$$

The *flash point* of an oil is the temperature at which the oil produces vapors in sufficient quantity to form a momentary flash under certain standardized conditions when a flame is brought near the surface of the oil. Since the flash point is the temperature at which combustible vapors are produced, it is an index of the relative safety with which the fuel oil may be handled and stored. A minimum flash point of 150 F is frequently specified. The *burning point* is the temperature at which the oil will produce combustible vapors rapidly enough to burn continuously and is usually about 20 F above the flash point.

The *pour point* is the lowest temperature at which oil will flow and is important in the purchase of oil that must be handled in cold weather.

Viscosity is an index of resistance to flow or a measure of internal friction. The viscosity is usually expressed as the time in seconds required for a specified quantity of oil to flow through an orifice of specified size. Since there are several different orifices in use, it is necessary to specify not only the time but also the temperature and the name of the standard test apparatus. Oils of high viscosity require heating if they are to be pumped or burned readily.

2·10   Natural and manufactured gaseous fuels.   Gaseous fuels are ideal fuels from the standpoint of ease of handling, ease of control, and cleanliness, and are used extensively in many industrial applications where the product must not be contaminated, the furnace atmosphere must be regulated closely, or uniform heating is required.

Natural gas is found in the petroleum fields and may also be found in locations where petroleum is absent. A map of the gas fields would be quite similar to Fig. 2·5 which shows the location of the major oil fields. Natural gas is transmitted long distances through high-pressure pipe lines which are provided with compressor stations at intervals to restore the gas to the high pressure which it gradually loses as a result of pipe-line friction. Thus large quantities of natural gas which were formerly wasted in the oil fields are now being burned usefully. The known reserves of natural gas, like the reserves of oil, are quite limited.

Table 2·6 shows the composition of a number of typical natural gases. They are composed principally of methane (CH_4) and ethane (C_2H_6) with a small amount of inert gases and consequently have a high heating value per cubic foot compared to manufactured gases.

Coke-oven gas is obtained from the by-product coke oven and is used in furnaces at the steel mills and for distribution as "city gas." It is obtained by collecting and cleaning the volatile matter that is distilled from coal in the process of making metallurgical coke.

TABLE 2·6

ANALYSES OF TYPICAL GASEOUS FUELS

Gas	Composition by Volume in Per Cent								Higher Heating Value, Btu per Cu Ft at 60 F and 30 In. Hg
	H_2	CH_4	C_2H_4	C_2H_6	CO	CO_2	O_2	N_2	
Natural gas:									
California		77.5		16.0		6.5			1123
Ohio		83.5		12.5		0.2		3.8	1047
Pennsylvania		88.0		11.2				0.8	1146
Louisiana		94.7				0.4		4.9	1066
Coke-oven gas	57.4	28.5	2.9		5.1	1.4	0.5	4.2	536
Carbureted water gas	35.2	14.8	12.8		33.9	1.5		1.8	578
Producer gas	10.5	2.6	0.4		22.0	5.7		58.8	136
Blast-furnace gas	3.2				26.2	13.0		57.6	93

Carbureted water gas is manufactured for city distribution by alternately blowing air through a deep bed of coke to heat the coke mass and then blowing steam through the hot coke to produce carbon monoxide and hydrogen which is collected and enriched by an oil gas made by spraying oil onto hot brick.

Producer gas is a lean gas too low in heating value for economical distribution through city gas mains. It is made for use in industrial furnaces by passing air plus a small amount of steam through a thick fuel bed in which the fuel is burned incompletely. The resulting gases are high in hydrogen, nitrogen, and carbon monoxide.

Blast-furnace gas is obtained as a by-product from the blast furnace, which is in effect a large gas producer, and is an important fuel in steel manufacture.

2·11   Determination of the heating value of fuels. The heating value or calorific value of a fuel is the amount of energy that is released by the complete combustion of a unit quantity of the fuel. For solid and liquid fuels, the heating value is expressed as Btu per pound of fuel in the English system of units. For gaseous fuels, the heating value is expressed in Btu per cubic foot at some specified temperature and pressure.

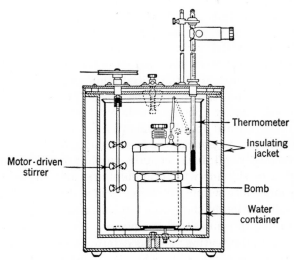

FIG. 2·8   Cross section of Parr oxygen-bomb calorimeter

The heating value of *solid* and *liquid fuels* is determined by means of a *bomb calorimeter*. The cross section of a bomb calorimeter is shown in Fig. 2·8. The bomb consists of a cup-shaped receptacle with a cover that can be screwed down to a gas-tight joint. A carefully weighed sample of fuel, about 1 gram of coal or 0.8 gram of a liquid fuel, is placed in the fuel pan. An electric fuse wire is installed between binding posts so that it dips into the fuel, and the bomb is then assembled and filled with oxygen at a pressure of about 300 psi. The bomb is immersed in a well-insulated container supplied with about 2000 grams of water at approximately room temperature. The water is kept in motion and at a uniform temperature by a motor-driven stirrer. The temperature of the water is measured by a high-grade thermometer equipped with a magnifying glass that permits the measurement of temperature to 0.005 F. The charge is fired electrically. The heating value is calculated from the amount of fuel present and the temperature rise of the jacket water after suitable corrections for radiation, heat supplied by the electric-fuse wire, and so on. The calorimeter may be calibrated by burning carefully weighed samples of standardized materials whose heating values in Btu per pound are known.

The heating value determined by the bomb calorimeter is called the *gross* or *higher heating value*, Q_H. When hydrogen is burned, 9 lb of water vapor are formed from 1 lb of hydrogen. In the bomb calorimeter, the products of combustion are cooled to within a few degrees of the initial temperature, and the water vapor formed from the combustion of the hydrogen in the fuel is condensed, thereby giving up its latent heat to the calorimeter. When fuel is burned for the generation of heat or power, care must be exercised to prevent the condensation of this water vapor since practically all fuels contain sulphur. The products of combustion of sulphur will form sulphuric acid in the presence of water and cause serious corrosion. Since the latent heat given up by condensation of the water formed from the hydrogen cannot be utilized in commercial equipment, this latent heat may be deducted from the heating value as determined by the calorimeter in order to obtain a *net* or *lower heating value*, Q_L. In the United States the higher or gross heating value is normally used.

The higher heating value of gaseous fuels can be measured in a gas calorimeter. The volume of the gaseous fuel to be burned is accurately measured in a calibrated meter, and its pressure and temperature are noted. The gas is then burned in the calorimeter which is a specially constructed water heater in which the energy released by combustion may be computed from the quantity of water circulated through the calorimeter per cubic foot of fuel burned and the temperature rise of the water.

The higher heating value of the better grades of coal can be approximated from *Dulong's formula* which is usually written as follows:

$$Q_H = 14{,}600(C) + 62{,}000\left(H - \frac{O}{8}\right) + 4050(S) \qquad (2 \cdot 7)$$

where Q_H is the higher heating value in Btu per pound of coal and C, H, O, and S are, respectively, the carbon, hydrogen, oxygen and sulphur in 1 lb of fuel as reported in the ultimate analysis but expressed as decimal parts instead of per cent by weight.

Example 4. Compute the heating value of the Sullivan, Ind., coal of Table 2·3 and Example 2.

Solution:

$$Q_H = 14,600(0.66) + 62,000 \left(0.059 - \frac{0.199}{8} \right) + 4050(0.011)$$

Q_H = 11,795 as compared to 11,788 Btu per lb as determined
by the bomb calorimeter and reported in Table 2·3

Note that the same result is obtained by using the analysis of column *B* of Example 2 in which the moisture is reported as a separate item.

$$Q_H = 14,600(0.66) + 62,000 \left(0.044 - \frac{0.079}{8} \right) + 4050(0.011)$$

$$Q_H = 11,795$$

Dulong's formula is based on the following assumptions:

1. All of the oxygen in the fuel is combined with hydrogen.
2. The heating value of the carbon, hydrogen, and sulphur in the fuel is the same as that of an equal amount of pure carbon, hydrogen, and sulphur.

The first assumption is not correct for high-oxygen coals, and the computed results for such fuels do not check the bomb-calorimeter results as well as in Example 4. The formula should not be applied to liquid or gaseous fuels, because they are composed of hydrocarbon compounds in which the heating value of the compound is considerably different from the heating value of the same quantity of uncombined carbon and hydrogen.

COMBUSTION OF FUELS

2·12   Combustion. Combustion is that chemical process in which oxygen combines rapidly with carbon, hydrogen, sulphur, and their compounds in solid, liquid, and gaseous fuels and results in the liberation of energy, the production of high-temperature gases, and the emission of light. The combustion process releases for the use of man some of the energy that had been received upon the surface of the earth from the sun during the millions of years in which the fuel resources of the earth were being formed.

2·13 The mole. The proportions in which the elements enter into the combustion reaction by mass or weight are dependent upon the relative molecular weights, which are approximately as follows:

Element	Symbol	Molecular Weight
Carbon	C	12
Sulphur	S	32
Hydrogen	H_2	2
Oxygen	O_2	32
Nitrogen	N_2	28

The symbols for the gases, hydrogen, oxygen, and nitrogen, are written with the subscript 2 because they occur in nature as diatomic molecules: that is, as molecules composed of two atoms and not as individual atoms. Using these molecular weights, the molecular weights of various compounds can be determined as follows:

CO_2: $12 + 32 = 44$ C_2H_6: $24 + 6 = 30$
CO: $12 + 16 = 28$ SO_2: $32 + 32 = 64$
H_2O: $2 + 16 = 18$ C_3H_8: $36 + 8 = 44$
CH_4: $12 + 4 = 16$ $C_{10}H_{22}$: $120 + 22 = 142$

Avogadro's law states that, at the same pressure and temperature, equal volumes of all perfect gases contain the *same number of molecules*. It follows, therefore, that the masses (or weights at a given location) of equal volumes of all perfect gases at the same pressure and temperature are proportional to the molecular weights of the respective elements or compounds. Thus, at the same pressure and temperature, 2 lb of hydrogen, 28 lb of nitrogen, and 44 lb of carbon dioxide occupy equal volumes.

The pound-mole, hereafter referred to as the mole, is that quantity of matter that has a mass in pounds numerically equal to the molecular weight of the substance. Thus, 1 mole of hydrogen has a mass of 2 lb, 1 mole of nitrogen has a mass of 28 lb, and 1 mole of carbon dioxide has a mass of 44 lb. Also, 1 mole of any substance contains 2.7319×10^{26} molecules.

In accordance with Avogadro's law, 1 mole of each of the various perfect gases occupies the same volume at equal pressures and temperatures. Therefore, for *perfect gases,* the mole is also a unit of volume. The volume of 1 mole of a perfect gas may be calculated as follows:

Let $\qquad$ M = molecular weight

For 1 lb of a perfect gas,

$$pv = RT$$

For M lb of a perfect gas,

$$pMv = MRT$$

Let $\qquad$ V_m = the volume of 1 mole = Mv

Then, $\qquad$ $V_m = MR \dfrac{T}{p}$

Since, for all perfect gases, $R = 1544/M$, then, $MR = 1544$, and

$$V_m = 1544 \frac{T}{p} \tag{2.8}$$

The volume of 1 mole of any perfect gas may be computed at any pressure and temperature by means of Equation 2·8. It is equal to 358 cu ft at 32 F and 14.7 psia. Therefore, at 32 F and 14.7 psia 2 lb of hydrogen, 28 lb of nitrogen, 44 lb of carbon dioxide, and 16 lb of methane (CH_4) each occupy 358 cu ft.

2·14   The conversion of a volumetric analysis of a gas to a gravimetric basis.   As stated in Article 1·4, the weighing of an unkown quantity of matter by means of a beam balance or platform scale is in reality a determination of the mass of the substance through comparison of the unknown mass with standard masses in a common gravitational field. Under these conditions, the terms *weight* and *mass* are commonly used to mean the same thing: that is, quantity of matter. It would be preferable to restrict the term *weight* to mean gravitational force acting on a body instead of also using it synonymously with mass as is common in combustion calculations and many other places in engineering literature. When the term weight is used in the preferred sense as gravitational force, it may be assumed that, for slide-rule calculations involving data obtained on the surface of the earth by ordinary engineering instrumentation, 1 lb of mass weighs one standard force pound.

The ultimate analysis of liquid and solid fuels such as oil and coal is expressed on a gravimetric (mass or weight) basis. Gaseous fuels are analyzed volumetrically. By conversion of this volumetric analysis to a gravimetric ultimate analysis, it is possible to express the analysis of all kinds of fuels by one method and to develop a single method of calculation which will apply to the combustion of all kinds of fuel whether they be solids, liquids, or gases.

The products of combustion of all kinds of fuel are analyzed on a volumetric basis as discussed in Article 2·16. In order to perform combustion calculations, it is necessary to convert this volumetric analysis to a gravimetric basis so as to express the analyses of the fuel and its products of combustion in the same terms.

The conversion of a volumetric analysis of a gas to a gravimetric analysis can be made on the basis that a mole of gas is a unit of volume as well as being a quantity of matter having a mass numerically equal to the molecular weight of the element or compound. Thus, a volumetric analysis of a gas may be expressed as follows:

Constituent	Volumetric Analysis, Per Cent	Cu Ft per 100 Cu Ft of Gas	Moles per 100 Moles of Gas
H_2	30	30	30
CO	30	30	30
CH_4	20	20	20
C_2H_6	10	10	10
O_2	5	5	5
N_2	5	5	5
Total	100	100	100

Taking 100 moles of gas as the basis upon which to make the computations, the mass of 100 moles can be found by multiplying the number of moles of each constituent by the molecular weight of that particular element or compound and adding the results. Thus, in Table 2·7, 10 moles of C_2H_6 (molecular weight = 24 + 6 = 30) have a mass of 10 × 30 = 300 lb. Also, since 1 mole of C_2H_6 contains 24 lb of carbon and 6 lb of hydrogen, the amount of carbon and hydrogen in 10 moles of C_2H_6 is the product of the number of moles of the compound and the molecular weight of each chemical element in the compound. The computations are shown in Table 2·7.

The specific volume, $v = RT/p$, for a gas having an analysis as given in Table 2·7 can be computed at a given pressure and temperature by first determining the value of the gas constant R for this gas. Since 100 moles of this gas have a mass of 1820 lb as shown in column 4 of Table 2·7, the mass of 1 mole is 18.2 lb, or 18.2 is the molecular weight of a hypothetical gaseous compound having the same specific volume as the mixture of elements and compounds that constitute the gas whose analysis is shown in Table 2·7.

Then, since $R = 1544/M$ where M is the molecular weight, $R = 1544/18.2 = 84.8$. At 100 F and 14.7 psia the specific volume of the gas would be $v = \dfrac{RT}{p} = \dfrac{84.8 \times 560}{14.7 \times 144} = 22.4$ cu ft per lb.

2·15 Chemistry of combustion. Except for special applications such as oxyacetylene welding, in which a high-temperature flame is necessary, the oxygen required for combustion is obtained from air. Air is a mechanical mixture of oxygen and nitrogen, plus negligible amounts of other gases, and for engineering purposes may be considered to have the following composition:

$$1 \text{ lb of } O_2 + 3.32 \text{ lb of } N_2 \quad = 4.32 \text{ lb of air}$$

$$1 \text{ cu ft of } O_2 + 3.78 \text{ cu ft of } N_2 = 4.78 \text{ cu ft of air}$$

$$1 \text{ mole of } O_2 + 3.78 \text{ moles of } N_2 = 4.78 \text{ moles of air}$$

When fuel is burned completely, all carbon is burned to carbon dioxide (CO_2), all hydrogen is burned to water vapor (H_2O), and all sulphur is burned to sulphur dioxide (SO_2).

The combustion reactions are written on the basis of the law of conservation of matter which states that the quantity of matter entering into a reaction is equal to the quantity of the matter in the products of the reaction and that, although the chemical composition of the compounds may change, the amount of each element in the reaction remains the same.

TABLE 2·7

CONVERSION OF A VOLUMETRIC ANALYSIS OF A GASEOUS FUEL TO A GRAVIMETRIC ULTIMATE ANALYSIS

(1) Constituent	(2) Volumetric Analysis in Per Cent	(3) Moles per 100 Moles	(4) Total	Lb of Each Constituent per 100 Moles of Gas			
				(5) Carbon	(6) Hydrogen	(7) Oxygen	(8) Nitrogen
H_2	30	30	$30 \times 2 = 60$		$30 \times 2 = 60$		
CO	30	30	$30 \times 28 = 840$	$30 \times 12 = 360$		$30 \times 16 = 480$	
CH_4	20	20	$20 \times 16 = 320$	$20 \times 12 = 240$	$20 \times 4 = 80$		
C_2H_6	10	10	$10 \times 30 = 300$	$10 \times 24 = 240$	$10 \times 6 = 60$		
O_2	5	5	$5 \times 32 = 160$			$5 \times 32 = 160$	
N_2	5	5	$5 \times 28 = 140$				$5 \times 28 = 140$
Total	100	100	1820	840	200	640	140

Ultimate gravimetric analysis:

$$\text{Carbon} = \frac{840}{1820} \times 100 = 46.2\%$$
$$\text{Hydrogen} = \frac{200}{1820} \times 100 = 11.0\%$$
$$\text{Oxygen} = \frac{640}{1820} \times 100 = 35.1\%$$
$$\text{Nitrogen} = \frac{140}{1820} \times 100 = 7.7\%$$

The reaction for the complete combustion of carbon may be written as follows:

$$1C + 1O_2 = 1CO_2 + 14{,}600 \text{ Btu per lb of C} \qquad (2 \cdot 9)$$

The numbers ahead of the symbols for the elements or compounds represent the number of molecules or moles entering into the reaction and are normally omitted if the number is 1. Equation $2 \cdot 9$ may be interpreted as follows:

1 molecule of C + 1 molecule of O_2 = 1 molecule of CO_2

1 mole of C + 1 mole of O_2 = 1 mole of CO_2

or, if the molecular weights are used,

12 lb of C + 32 lb of O_2 = 44 lb of CO_2

1 lb of C + $2\frac{2}{3}$ lb of O_2 = $3\frac{2}{3}$ lb of CO_2

Since oxygen is normally supplied as air, 1 lb of oxygen is accompanied by 3.32 lb of nitrogen.

The reaction for the complete combustion in air of 1 lb of carbon could be written thus:

1 lb of C + 2.67 lb of O_2 + 8.85 lb of N_2

$$= 3.67 \text{ lb of } CO_2 + 8.85 \text{ lb of } N_2$$

or

1 lb of C + 11.52 lb of air = 3.67 lb of CO_2 + 8.85 lb of N_2

Equation $2 \cdot 9$ indicates that the complete combustion of 1 lb of carbon releases 14,600 Btu.

In the absence of sufficient oxygen, the carbon may be burned incompletely in accordance with the following reaction:

$$2C + O_2 = 2CO + 4440 \text{ Btu per lb of C} \qquad (2 \cdot 10)$$

This reaction releases only about 30 per cent of the energy released by complete combustion, and the escape of the CO thus formed is detrimental to efficient utilization of the fuel. In the presence of sufficient oxygen, the combustion of CO to CO_2 may be completed as follows:

$$2CO + O_2 = 2CO_2 + 10{,}160 \text{ Btu per lb of C} \qquad (2 \cdot 11)$$

Thus the total energy released is the same whether 1 lb of carbon is burned directly to CO_2, or is burned to CO and the CO subsequently burned to CO_2.

The complete combustion of hydrogen occurs as follows:

$$2H_2 + O_2 = 2H_2O + 62{,}000 \text{ Btu per lb of } H_2 \qquad (2\cdot12)$$

$$2 \text{ moles of } H_2 + 1 \text{ mole of } O_2 = 2 \text{ moles of } H_2O$$

$$4 \text{ lb of } H_2 + 32 \text{ lb of } O_2 = 36 \text{ lb of } H_2O$$

$$1 \text{ lb of } H_2 + 8 \text{ lb of } O_2 = 9 \text{ lb of } H_2O$$

1 lb of H_2 + 8 lb of O_2 + 26.56 lb of N_2

$$= 9 \text{ lb of } H_2O + 26.56 \text{ lb of } N_2$$

1 lb of H_2 + 34.56 lb of air = 9 lb of H_2O + 26.56 lb of N_2

Sulphur burns as follows:

$$S + O_2 = SO_2 + 4050 \text{ Btu per lb of } S \qquad (2\cdot13)$$

$$1 \text{ mole of } S + 1 \text{ mole of } O_2 = 1 \text{ mole of } SO_2$$

$$32 \text{ lb of } S + 32 \text{ lb of } O_2 = 64 \text{ lb of } SO_2$$

$$1 \text{ lb of } S + 1 \text{ lb of } O_2 = 2 \text{ lb of } SO_2$$

1 lb of S + 1 lb of O_2 + 3.32 lb of N_2

$$= 2 \text{ lb of } SO_2 + 3.32 \text{ lb of } N_2$$

1 lb of S + 4.32 lb of air = 2 lb of SO_2 + 3.32 lb of N_2

Much of the sulphur in fuel is in a chemical form in which it is partially oxidized or completely incombustible. It adds little to the heating value of the fuel and is objectionable because of the corrosive characteristics of the products of combustion.

The hydrocarbons or compounds of carbon and hydrogen, when burned completely, are converted to CO_2 and H_2O as in the following typical reactions:

$$2C_2H_6 + 7O_2 = 4CO_2 + 6H_2O \qquad (2\cdot14)$$

2 moles of C_2H_6 + 7 moles of O_2

$$= 4 \text{ moles of } CO_2 + 6 \text{ moles of } H_2O$$

60 lb of C_2H_6 + 224 lb of O_2 = 176 lb of CO_2 + 108 lb of H_2O

1 lb of C_2H_6 + 3.733 lb of O_2 = 2.933 lb of CO_2 + 1.80 lb of H_2O

$$2C_8H_{18} + 25O_2 = 16CO_2 + 18H_2O \qquad (2 \cdot 15)$$

2 moles of C_8H_{18} + 25 moles of O_2

$$= 16 \text{ moles of } CO_2 + 18 \text{ moles of } H_2O$$

228 lb of C_8H_{18} + 800 lb of O_2 = 704 lb of CO_2 + 324 lb of H_2O

1 lb of C_8H_{18} + 3.509 lb of O_2

$$= 3.088 \text{ lb of } CO_2 + 1.421 \text{ lb of } H_2O$$

Theoretical air is the minimum amount of air that must be supplied to burn 1 lb of fuel completely: that is, to burn all carbon to CO_2, all available hydrogen to H_2O, and all sulphur to SO_2. It has been shown that, for complete combustion, 1 lb of carbon requires 11.52 lb of air, 1 lb of hydrogen requires 34.56 lb of air, and 1 lb of sulphur requires 4.32 lb of air. Therefore, the theoretical air A_t required in pounds per pound of fuel may be computed as follows:

$$A_t = 11.52(C) + 34.56\left(H - \frac{O}{8}\right) + 4.32(S) \qquad (2 \cdot 16)$$

where C, H, O, and S are the amounts of the respective elements present in 1 lb of fuel as determined from the ultimate analysis and expressed as decimals.

Example 5. Compute the theoretical air required to burn 1 lb of the Sullivan, Ind., coal having the ultimate analysis reported in Table 2·3.
Solution:

$$A_t = 11.52(0.66) + 34.56\left(0.059 - \frac{0.199}{8}\right) + 4.32(0.011)$$

A_t = 8.83 lb of air per lb of coal

Excess air is air supplied in excess of the theoretical requirement. If, in Example 5, 25 per cent of excess air were supplied, the actual air supplied would be 1.25 A_t or 1.25 × 8.83 = 11.04 lb of air per lb of fuel.

2·16 Analysis of the dry gaseous products of combustion. If insufficient air is supplied, combustion will be incomplete, and part of the heating value of the fuel will be wasted through the escape of combustible gases such as CO and H_2. If more air is supplied than is necessary for complete combustion, the surplus air is heated from atmospheric temperature to the temperature at which the products of combustion are discharged to waste (usually 350 to 600 F), thus carrying away a considerable amount of energy. Practically, air in excess of that required theoretically to satisfy the chemical requirements of the fuel must be supplied because of inadequate mixing of air and combustible gases, lack

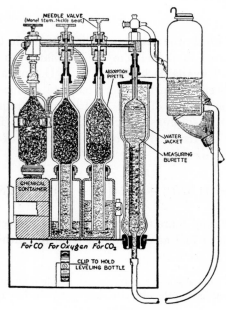

FIG. 2·9 Orsat apparatus

of time to complete combustion, and other factors to be discussed in Chapter 4. At the same time, the quantity of this air must be kept to a minimum consistent with reasonably complete combustion. In order to determine the completeness of combustion and the quantity of excess air being supplied, the dry gaseous products of combustion may be analyzed volumetrically by an *Orsat* apparatus.

The Orsat apparatus is illustrated in Fig. 2·9. The volume of gas may be measured in a burette graduated to read volumes in per cent and water-jacketed to maintain a constant temperature. Three absorption pipettes contain suitable chemicals for the absorption, respectively, of CO_2, O_2, and CO. Each of the absorption pipettes may be connected to the measuring burette by a capillary tube and valve.

The measuring burette is filled at atmospheric pressure with a representative sample of the gas to be analyzed, after which the inlet valve is closed. By manipulation of a leveling bottle containing water, the gas can be transferred to the first pipette for absorption of CO_2. The gas is then drawn back into the measur-

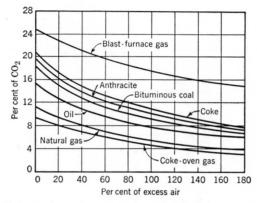

Fig. 2·10   Relation between excess air and CO_2 for representative fuels

ing burette, and the reduction in volume, which is the CO_2 content of the original sample, may be read directly in per cent. The per cent by volume of O_2 and CO in the original sample may be determined successively by passing the sample into the respective absorption pipettes, withdrawing it into the measuring burette, and noting the further reduction in volume of the sample. The remainder of the original gas sample is assumed to be nitrogen. A typical Orsat analysis of the dry products of combustion of coal would be: $CO_2 = 14.2\%$, $O_2 = 5.5\%$, $CO = 0.1\%$, and (by difference) $N_2 = 80.2\%$.

The maximum percentage of CO_2 that is obtainable by the complete combustion without excess air of any given fuel depends upon the ultimate analysis of the fuel and varies from 6 to 25 per cent, as indicated in Fig. 2·10. Excess air dilutes the CO_2 with surplus O_2 and N_2 and thereby reduces the percentage of CO_2 in the gases as shown in Fig. 2·10. Therefore, for any given fuel, the CO_2 content measured in per cent by volume is an indication of the excess air supplied while the CO content is an indication of the incompleteness of combustion.

Carbon dioxide recorders have been on the market for many years for the purpose of continuously recording the CO_2 content

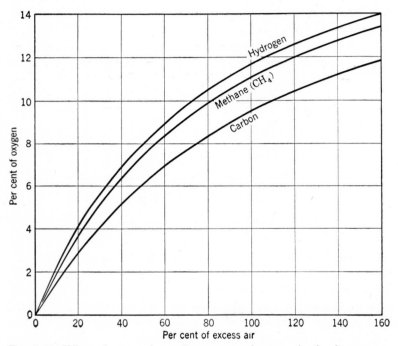

FIG. 2·11   Effect of excess air on the per cent of oxygen in the dry gaseous products of complete combustion

of the products of combustion as an aid to the maintenance of optimum combustion conditions. Oxygen recorders have been developed recently and are being used extensively as a guide to combustion control. Figure 2·11 shows the effect of excess air upon the O_2 content of the products of complete combustion of hydrogen, methane, and carbon. The curve for carbon in Fig. 2·11 corresponds closely to the curve for coke in Fig. 2·10, whereas the curve for methane in Fig. 2·11 corresponds closely to the curve for natural gas in Fig. 2·10. The curve for hydrogen would be a curve of zero per cent of CO_2 in Fig. 2·10. It will be noted that there is much less variation in O_2 content with the various types of fuel at a given per cent of excess air than the variation in CO_2 content for the same fuels. Also, the curve of O_2 content is fairly steep in the region from 10 to 40 per cent of excess air, which is the region of normal operation with good equipment. An inexpensive and reliable device for continuously recording O_2 content would therefore be an excellent instrument for use in regulating the combustion of fuel.

2·17 Dry gaseous products of combustion per pound of fuel. The dry gaseous products of combustion of 1 lb of fuel may be computed from the Orsat analysis of the dry products of combustion, the analysis of the fuel and refuse, and a carbon balance.

The dry products of combustion per *pound of carbon in the dry products of combustion* may be computed from the Orsat analysis by applying the methods outlined in Article 2·14.

Let G_c = weight of dry products of combustion per lb of *carbon* in the dry products of combustion. Then,

$$G_c = \frac{\left\{\begin{array}{l}\text{lb of dry products of combustion per 100 moles of dry} \\ \text{products of combustion}\end{array}\right\}}{\text{lb of C per 100 moles of dry products of combustion}}$$

The numerator and denominator in the above equation can be computed from the Orsat analysis of the dry products of combustion by using 100 moles of the gas as the basis of calculation as follows:

Constituent	Per Cent by Volume	Moles per 100 Moles	Lb per 100 Moles	Lb of Carbon per 100 Moles
CO_2	10	10	$10 \times 44 = 440$	$10 \times 12 = 120$
O_2	9	9	$9 \times 32 = 288$	
CO	1	1	$1 \times 28 = 28$	$1 \times 12 = 12$
N_2	80	80	$80 \times 28 = 2240$	
Total	100	100	2996	132

Then,

$$G_c = \frac{2996 \text{ lb of dry products of combustion per 100 moles of gas}}{132 \text{ lb of C per 100 moles of gas}}$$

$G_c = 22.7$ lb of dry gas per lb of *carbon* in the *gas*

The method of computing the dry gaseous products of combustion per pound of carbon in the dry products of combustion may be expressed mathematically as follows:

Let CO_2, CO, O_2, and N_2 represent the per cent by volume of each of the constituent gases, or in other words, the number of moles per 100 moles of gas

$$\text{Then,} \qquad G_c = \frac{44CO_2 + 32O_2 + 28(CO + N_2)}{12(CO_2 + CO)}$$

Since $\quad CO + N_2 = 100 - (CO_2 + O_2)$

$$\text{then,} \qquad G_c = \frac{44CO_2 + 32O_2 + 28[100 - (CO_2 + O_2)]}{12(CO_2 + CO)}$$

$$\text{or} \qquad G_c = \frac{4CO_2 + O_2 + 700}{3(CO_2 + CO)} \qquad (2 \cdot 17)$$

A *carbon balance* is necessary in order to compute the dry products of combustion per pound of *fuel* from the dry products of combustion per pound of carbon in the dry products of combustion, G_c. From the law of conservation of matter, the carbon balance for operation under steady conditions may be stated as follows:

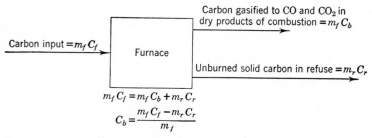

Fig. 2·12   Carbon balance for coal

Carbon input = carbon output

or

Carbon input = carbon in the CO and CO_2 of the dry products of combustion plus unburned solid carbon in the refuse. Figure 2·12 shows diagrammatically a carbon balance for coal in which in a given period of time

m_f = fuel fired, lb
C_f = carbon in 1 lb of fuel, from the ultimate analysis of the fuel, expressed as a decimal
m_r = solid refuse, lb
C_r = carbon in 1 lb of refuse, expressed as a decimal
C_b = carbon in the dry products of combustion per lb of fuel fired

Since $\qquad$ Carbon in = carbon out

$$m_f C_f = m_f C_b + m_r C_r$$

or $$C_b = \frac{m_f C_f - m_r C_r}{m_f} \qquad (2 \cdot 18)$$

The dry gaseous products of combustion per pound of *fuel* may be computed as follows:

$$G_f = \frac{\text{lb of dry products of combustion per 100 moles}}{\text{lb of C in dry products of combustion per 100 moles}}$$

$$\times \frac{\text{lb of C in dry products of combustion}}{\text{lb of fuel}}$$

$$G_f = G_c \times C_b \qquad (2 \cdot 19)$$

where G_f = lb of dry gaseous products of combustion per lb of *fuel*
Combining equations $2 \cdot 17$ and $2 \cdot 19$ gives

$$G_f = C_b \left[\frac{4CO_2 + O_2 + 700}{3(CO_2 + CO)} \right] \qquad (2 \cdot 20)$$

When the fuel is *oil* or *gas*, the ash content is zero or negligible; m_r is zero in the absence of solid refuse, and the carbon in the dry products of combustion, C_b, equals the carbon content of the fuel as reported in the ultimate analysis.

The calculation of the dry products of combustion per pound of fuel may be illustrated by an example.

Example 6. Compute the dry gaseous products of combustion per lb of coal if the Sullivan, Ind., coal the analysis of which is given in Table $2 \cdot 3$ was burned in a test in which the following data were collected:

Coal burned $= 10,000$ lb, (m_f)
Weight of ashpit refuse $= 700$ lb, (m_r)
Carbon in ashpit refuse $= 20\%$, $(C_r = 0.20)$
Orsat analysis in $\%$: $CO_2 = 14.1$, $O_2 = 5.1$, $CO = 0.1$,
    N_2 (by difference) $= 80.7\%$

Solution: From the ultimate analysis of the coal as given in Table 2·3, the carbon content is 66 per cent.

Carbon input $= m_f C_f = 10,000 \times 0.66 = 6600$ lb
Carbon in the ashpit refuse $= m_r C_r = 700 \times 0.20 = 140$ lb
Carbon in the dry products of combustion $= 6600 - 140 = 6460$ lb or 0.646 lb
per lb of fuel $= C_b$

This could have been calculated from formula 2·18, thus:

$$C_b = \frac{(10,000 \times 0.66) - (700 \times 0.20)}{10,000} = 0.646$$

The dry gaseous products of combustion per lb of *carbon*, G_c, may be calculated from the Orsat analysis as follows:

Constituent	Analysis in Per Cent by Volume	Analysis in Moles per 100 Moles	Lb per 100 Moles	Lb of Carbon per 100 Moles
CO_2	14.1	14.1	$14.1 \times 44 = 620.4$	$14.1 \times 12 = 169.2$
O_2	5.1	5.1	$5.1 \times 32 = 163.2$	
CO	0.1	0.1	$0.1 \times 28 = 2.8$	$0.1 \times 12 = 1.2$
N_2 (by difference)	80.7	80.7	$80.7 \times 28 = 2259.6$	
Total	100	100	3046.0	170.4

$$G_c = \frac{3046 \text{ lb of dry gas per 100 moles of dry gas}}{170.4 \text{ lb of C per 100 moles of dry gas}}$$

$$= 17.87 \text{ lb of dry gas per lb of } carbon$$

Then, $G_f = 17.87$ lb of dry gaseous products of combustion per lb of *carbon* in the gas $\times 0.646$ lb of C burned to CO and CO_2 per lb of *fuel* $= 11.57$ lb of dry gaseous products of combustion per lb of *fuel*.

2·18   Carbon burned to CO_2 and CO per pound of fuel.

As shown by Equation 2·10, incomplete combustion of carbon produces CO with the release of only about 30 per cent of the energy released by the complete combustion of carbon. It is important, therefore, to be able to compute the carbon burned incompletely to CO per pound of fuel.

As shown in Article 2·17, the carbon in 100 moles of the dry products of combustion may be determined by multiplying the number of moles of CO_2 and CO in 100 moles of dry products of combustion by the molecular weight of carbon, 12, which is the amount of carbon in 1 mole of CO_2 or CO. In the example in Article 2·17, 100 moles of dry products of combustion contain 12 lb of carbon in the form of CO, 120 lb of carbon in the form of CO_2, and 132 lb of total carbon. Therefore, 12/132 of the carbon burned to CO and CO_2 is in the form of CO.

Let the symbols CO and CO_2 represent the number of moles of carbon monoxide and carbon dioxide, respectively, in 100 moles of the dry gas. Then the carbon in the form of carbon monoxide per lb of carbon in the *dry gaseous products of combustion* =

$$\frac{\text{lb of C in the CO present in 100 moles of gas}}{\text{lb of C in the CO and } CO_2 \text{ present in 100 moles of gas}}$$

$$= \frac{12CO}{12(CO + CO_2)}$$

$$= \frac{CO}{CO + CO_2}$$

Since C_b = lb of carbon burned to CO and CO_2 per lb of fuel, then the carbon burned to CO per lb of *fuel* =

$$C_b \left(\frac{CO}{CO_2 + CO} \right) \tag{2·21}$$

Example 7. For the data in Example 6, compute the carbon burned to CO per lb of fuel.

Solution: From the solution to Example 6, the tabular results show that 100 moles of dry gaseous products of combustion contain 1.2 lb of carbon as CO, and 169.2 lb of carbon as CO_2. Also the carbon burned to CO and CO_2 per lb of fuel, C_b = 0.646 lb. Therefore, the carbon burned to CO per lb of fuel

$$= \frac{1.2 \text{ lb of C in the form of CO per 100 moles of gas}}{(1.2 + 169.2) \text{ lb of C in the form of CO and } CO_2 \text{ per 100 moles of gas}}$$

$$\times 0.646 \text{ lb of C burned to CO and } CO_2 \text{ per lb of fuel}$$

$$= 0.0455 \text{ lb per lb of fuel}$$

or, from Equation 2·21,

$$C_b \left(\frac{CO}{CO + CO_2} \right) = 0.646 \left(\frac{0.1}{0.1 + 14.1} \right) = 0.0455 \text{ lb of carbon per lb of fuel}$$

2·19   Water vapor in the products of combustion per pound of fuel.   If the small amount of moisture in the air supplied for combustion is neglected, the moisture in the products of combustion of 1 lb of fuel comes from two sources: (1) the moisture formed from the combustion of hydrogen, and (2) the moisture in the fuel. Since 1 lb of hydrogen produces 9 lb of moisture when burned, the moisture in the products of combustion of 1 lb of fuel equals $(M + 9H)$ where M and H are the amounts of moisture and hydrogen in the ultimate analysis of the fuel, expressed as decimal parts.

Example 8.   Compute the water vapor present in the products of combustion of 1 lb of Sullivan, Ind., coal having the analysis reported in Table 2·3.

Solution: From column B of the solution to Example 2, the hydrogen and moisture per lb of fuel are found to be 4.4 and 13.5 per cent, respectively. Then the water vapor in the products of combustion of 1 lb of this fuel $= M + 9H = 0.135 + 9 \times 0.044 = 0.531$ lb.

The same result would have been obtained by using the analysis of column A, Example 2, since $9H = 9 \times 0.059 = 0.531$ lb. In column A, the moisture in the coal as given in the proximate analysis is reported as its chemical elements, hydrogen and oxygen, so that a separate item for moisture does not appear in the analysis. Care must be exercised to use the correct moisture and hydrogen values in computing total moisture in the products of combustion.

2·20   Air supplied per pound of fuel.   The air actually supplied per pound of fuel burned can be computed from a material balance as shown in Fig. 2·13.

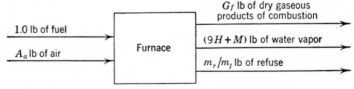

$$1.0 \text{ lb of fuel} + A_a \text{ lb of air} = G_f \text{ lb of dry gas} + (9H + M) \text{ lb of water vapor} + m_r/m_f \text{ lb of refuse}$$

Fig. 2·13   Material balance for steady-state combustion of 1.0 lb of coal

For 1 lb of fuel:

Matter in $= 1$ lb of fuel $+ A_a$ lb of air

Matter out $= G_f$ lb of dry gaseous products of combustion $+ \dfrac{m_r}{m_f}$

lb of solid refuse $+ (9H + M)$ lb of water vapor

Therefore,

Air supplied = matter out − 1 lb of fuel in

or
$$A_a = \left[G_f + (9H + M) + \frac{m_r}{m_f} \right] - 1.0 \qquad (2 \cdot 22)$$

where A_a is the air actually supplied in pounds per pound of fuel. The computation of the air supplied per pound of fuel may be illustrated by Example 9.

Example 9. Using the data from Examples 6 and 8, compute the actual air supplied per lb of fuel.

Solution: From Example 6, $G_f = 11.57$ lb of dry gaseous products of combustion per lb of fuel. From Example 8, the total water vapor in the products of combustion per lb of fuel $= M + 9H = 0.531$ lb. Also, from Example 6, 700 lb of ashpit refuse remain from the combustion of 10,000 lb of coal or

$$\frac{m_r}{m_f} = \frac{700}{10,000} = 0.07 \text{ lb of refuse per lb of fuel}$$

Then, from the material balance or formula $2 \cdot 22$,

$A_a = 11.57$ lb of dry gas $+ 0.53$ lb of water vapor $+ 0.07$ lb of refuse

$- 1.0$ lb of fuel $= 11.17$ lb of air supplied per lb of fuel

The *excess air* supplied for combustion is the actual air A_a minus the theoretical air A_t, as computed from formula $2 \cdot 16$ and illustrated in Example 5. The percentage of excess air is the excess air divided by the theoretical air, expressed in per cent, and may be computed thus:

$$\text{Excess air, } \% = \frac{A_a - A_t}{A_t} \times 100 \qquad (2 \cdot 23)$$

Example 10. Compute the excess air supplied to burn the Sullivan, Ind., coal, from the data and results of Examples 5, 6, and 9.

Solution: From Example 5, the theoretical air required to burn 1 lb of this coal is 8.83 lb. From Example 9, the actual air supplied is 11.17 lb. Then the

$$\text{excess air} = \frac{11.17 - 8.83}{8.83} \times 100 = 26.6\%.$$

2·21   The energy balance. The energy balance is normally based upon 1 lb of fuel and is a tabulation of the amount of energy utilized and the amount of energy lost in various ways. The energy balance for 1 lb of coal may be written as follows:

Item	Btu per Lb	Per Cent of Heating Value
I. Energy utilized	......	......
II. Losses		
1. Loss due to sensible heat in the dry gaseous products of combustion, Q_1	......	......
2. Loss due to CO in the dry gaseous products of combustion, Q_2	......	......
3. Loss due to carbon in the solid refuse, Q_3	......	......
4. Loss due to moisture in the fuel, Q_4	......	......
5. Loss due to water vapor formed from the hydrogen in the fuel, Q_5	......	......
6. Loss due to superheating the water vapor in the air supplied for combustion, loss due to unconsumed hydrogen and hydrocarbons, radiation, and unaccounted-for loss, Q_6	......	......
Total	Heating value of 1 lb of fuel	100

For steam-generating units, the calculation of the energy absorbed or utilized is considered in detail in Article 5·8. This item, expressed as a percentage of the heating value of the fuel, is also the efficiency of the unit. The maximum efficiency with which the energy in fuel may be utilized is limited by the design of the equipment in which it is being used. The attainment of this maximum efficiency in daily operation of the equipment is dependent upon keeping the losses to a minimum. The computation of these losses and the intelligent utilization of the results of these computations are very important if maximum efficiency is to be maintained. The methods of computing the losses are considered in the following paragraphs and are illustrated by Example 11 which is based on the data and results of Example 6 and the following additional data: temperature of air = 70 F = t_a; discharge temperature of gaseous products of combustion = 500 F = t_g.

1. The loss due to sensible heat in the dry gaseous products of combustion results from the discharge to waste of the products of combustion at a temperature above that at which the air for combustion is supplied. This loss may be computed as follows:

$$Q_1 = G_f \times c_p \times (t_g - t_a) = 0.24 G_f (t_g - t_a) \qquad (2 \cdot 24)$$

where Q_1 = sensible heat loss, Btu per lb of fuel
G_f = dry gaseous products of combustion, lb per lb of fuel
c_p = 0.24 = mean specific heat of dry gaseous products of combustion, Btu per lb per F
t_g = temperature at which the gaseous products of combustion are discharged to waste, F
t_a = temperature of air, F

Example 11a. From Example 6,

$$G_f = 11.57 \text{ lb per lb of fuel}$$

$$Q_1 = 0.24 \times 11.57(500 - 70) = 1195 \text{ Btu per lb of fuel}$$

This is the largest loss that occurs in most fuel-burning installations. Inspection of formula $2 \cdot 24$ shows that this loss may be reduced by lowering the exit gas temperature, t_g, or by reducing the dry gaseous products of combustion of 1 lb of fuel, G_f. The minimum value of t_g in an actual installation is generally fixed by the design of the equipment. The quantity of the dry gaseous products of combustion is dependent upon the excess air which cannot be reduced too much without increasing the losses due to incomplete combustion.

2. The loss due to the escape of CO in the dry gaseous products of combustion, Q_2, is the product of the carbon burned to CO per pound of fuel and the heating value of 1 lb of carbon in the form of CO. As pointed out in Article $2 \cdot 15$, 14,600 Btu are released when 1 lb of carbon is burned to CO_2, but only 4440 Btu are released when 1 lb of carbon is burned to CO. The undeveloped energy due to the incomplete combustion of 1 lb of carbon is therefore equal to $14,600 - 4440$ or 10,160 Btu. Therefore,

$$Q_2 = \text{carbon burned to CO per lb of fuel} \times 10,160$$

or, from equation 2·21,

$$Q_2 = \frac{CO}{CO + CO_2} C_b \times 10{,}160 \text{ Btu per lb of fuel} \qquad (2\cdot25)$$

Example 11b.

$$Q_2 = \frac{0.1}{0.1 + 14.1} \times 0.646 \times 10{,}160 = 46 \text{ Btu per lb of fuel}$$

3. The loss due to unburned carbon in the solid refuse, Q_3, may be computed from the heating value of carbon, 14,600 Btu per lb, and the carbon in the refuse per pound of fuel. Then,

$$Q_3 = \frac{m_r C_r}{m_f} \times 14{,}600 \text{ Btu per lb of fuel} \qquad (2\cdot26)$$

Example 11c. $m_f = 10{,}000$ lb of coal burned; $m_r = 700$ lb of refuse; $C_r = 20\%$ carbon in the refuse. Then,

$$Q_3 = \frac{0.2 \times 700}{10{,}000} \times 14{,}600 = 204 \text{ Btu per lb of fuel}$$

4. The loss due to evaporating and superheating the moisture in 1 lb of fuel, Q_4, may be computed from the product of the moisture in 1 lb of fuel as given by the proximate analysis and the heat required to evaporate and superheat 1 lb of moisture. The following empirical equations are given in the ASME test code for steam-generating units:

$$Q_4 = M(1089 + 0.46t_g - t_a) \quad \text{where} \quad t_g < 575 \text{ F} \qquad (2\cdot27)$$

$$Q_4 = M(1066 + 0.50t_g - t_a) \quad \text{where} \quad t_g > 575 \text{ F} \qquad (2\cdot28)$$

where M = moisture in 1 lb of coal as reported in the proximate analysis, expressed as a decimal

Example 11d. Since the proximate analysis of this coal shows 13.5 per cent of moisture, and $t_g = 500$ F,

$$Q_4 = 0.135(1089 + 0.46 \times 500 - 70) = 169 \text{ Btu per lb of fuel}$$

5. The loss due to moisture formed from the combustion of hydrogen, Q_5, results from the fact that this moisture is condensed in the bomb calorimeter, and the heat given up by the condensation of this moisture in the calorimeter is included in the heating value of the fuel, whereas, when the fuel is burned in a commer-

cial installation, the moisture is discharged to waste as a vapor at a temperature t_g. Since 1 lb of H_2 produces by its combustion 9 lb of H_2O, the loss due to the escape of this water vapor at t_g may be computed thus:

$$Q_5 = 9H(1089 + 0.46t_g - t_a) \quad \text{where} \quad t_g < 575 \text{ F} \quad (2 \cdot 29)$$

$$\text{or} \quad Q_5 = 9H(1066 + 0.5t_g - t_a) \quad \text{where} \quad t_g > 575 \text{ F} \quad (2 \cdot 30)$$

In Equations $2 \cdot 29$ and $2 \cdot 30$, the symbol H represents the hydrogen, expressed as a decimal, in the *ultimate analysis in which the moisture is included as a separate item of the ultimate analysis* as in column B of Example 2. If the total hydrogen as reported in Table $2 \cdot 3$ is used in Equation $2 \cdot 29$ or $2 \cdot 30$, the loss thus calculated includes *both* the moisture loss, Q_4, and the loss due to water formed from the hydrogen, Q_5.

Example 11e. Since from column B of Example 2 the hydrogen in 1 lb of fuel is found to be 4.4 per cent, then

$$Q_5 = 9 \times 0.044(1089 + 0.46 \times 500 - 70) = 495 \text{ Btu per lb of fuel}$$

6. Item 6 of the energy balance includes the loss due to superheating the water vapor in the air supplied for combustion, the loss due to unburned hydrogen and hydrocarbons, radiation, and unaccounted for losses. Some of these losses may be computed by methods beyond the scope of this book. Normally these losses are small and vary from 2 to 4 per cent of the heating value of the fuel. Where it is possible to measure the energy utilized, they are obtained by subtracting from the heating value of the fuel the sum of the energy utilized and the losses which may be computed.

An examination of formulas $2 \cdot 27$ to $2 \cdot 30$ shows that a moderate change in the exit temperature t_g of the waste gases will not appreciably affect the numerical values of the moisture and hydrogen losses. Also, the moisture and hydrogen content of the fuel are not under the control of the operator, and he therefore cannot do much to change these losses. However, the losses due to sensible heat in the hot waste gases and incomplete combustion are under control of the operator through regulation of the air supplied to burn the fuel. As indicated in Fig. 2·14, an increase in excess air reduces the losses due to incomplete combustion and increases the loss due to sensible heat in the hot waste gases. There is some air supply at which these losses will be a minimum, which for the particular curves of Fig. 2·14, is 30 per cent of excess air. The

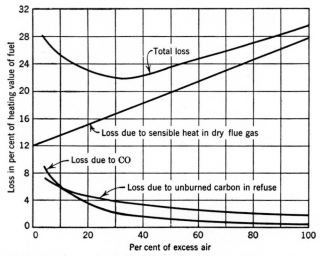

FIG. 2·14   Effect of excess air upon the losses due to CO, carbon in ash and refuse, and sensible heat in the dry flue gas

optimum air supply varies with the kind of fuel and the equipment for burning it and can best be determined by test. Efficient combustion is not attained unless the air supply is closely adjusted to requirements. Automatic CO_2 or O_2 recorders and elaborate systems of automatic-combustion control are often installed to make possible the efficient utilization of the fuel through close control of combustion.

The energy balance for combustion of oil is computed in the same way as the energy balance for combustion of coal, except that there is no solid carbon in the refuse and C_b, the carbon burned to CO and CO_2, is equal to the carbon in the fuel. When the fuel is a gas, the volumetric analysis can be converted to a gravimetric ultimate analysis as outlined in Article 2·14, after which the energy balance is computed as for oil; that is, there will be no solid refuse containing carbon when the fuel is a gas.

PROBLEMS

1. Determine (*a*) the proximate analysis on a moisture-free and a moisture-and-ash-free basis; (*b*) the ultimate analysis on a moisture-free and a moisture-and-ash-free basis; (*c*) the available hydrogen; (*d*) the heating value by Dulong's formula; and (*e*) the theoretical air required per lb of fuel for each of the following coals, the analyses of which are reported in Table 2·3: (1) McDowell Co., W. Va., low-volatile coal; (2) Fayette Co., Pa., high-volatile *A* coal; (3) Logan Co., Ill., high-volatile *C* coal; (4) Sheridan Co., Wyo., subbituminous *B* coal.

2. Compute the theoretical air required for the complete combustion of 1 lb of the following crude oils, the analyses of which are reported in Table 2·5: (1) Texas crude; (2) Oklahoma crude; (3) Sunset, California crude.

3. A coal has the following gravimetric analysis: $C = 78\%$; $H = 5\%$; $O = 7\%$; $N = 1\%$; $S = 2\%$; ash $= 4\%$; free moisture $= 3\%$. If this fuel is burned completely with 100 per cent of excess air, how much air is supplied per lb of fuel?

4. Coal has the following gravimetric analysis: $C = 70\%$; $H = 5\%$; $O = 12\%$; $N = 2\%$; $S = 3\%$; ash $= 8\%$ or a total of 100 per cent. The proximate analysis is as follows: fixed carbon $= 51\%$; volatile matter $= 32\%$; ash $= 8\%$; free moisture $= 9\%$. Compute the air required to burn 1 lb of fuel completely with 50 per cent of excess air.

5. A fuel oil has the following gravimetric analysis: $C = 80\%$; $H = 14\%$; $O = 3\%$; $N = 3\%$. The specific gravity of the oil is 20 degrees API. Calculate the theoretical air required for the complete combustion of 1 gal of this oil.

6. Compute the theoretical air required to burn 1 lb of each of the following fuels: (*a*) CH_4, (*b*) C_3H_8, (*c*) $C_3H_{10}O$, (*d*) $C_5H_{14}O_3$.

7. A fuel gas has the following volumetric analysis: $CH_4 = 60\%$; $CO = 10\%$; $H_2 = 10\%$; $O_2 = 10\%$; $N_2 = 10\%$. Compute the air required to burn 1 lb of this fuel.

8. Determine the heating value per lb and per gal of an uncracked fuel oil having a gravity of 30 degrees API.

9. A cracked fuel oil has a gravity of 34 degrees API and costs 9 cents per gal. At what price per ton will coal with a heating value of 12,000 Btu per lb have the same cost per million Btu?

10. Determine (*a*) the per cent of carbon in 1 lb of fuel gas, (*b*) the gas constant *R*, (*c*) the specific volume at 20 psia and 70 F, and (*d*) the heating value per lb for the following gaseous fuels whose analyses are reported in Table 2·6: (1) Ohio Natural gas, (2) coke-oven gas, (3) producer gas.

11. Dry flue gas has the following volumetric analysis: $CO_2 = 14.1\%$; $O_2 = 5.4\%$; $CO = 0.3\%$; $N_2 = 80.2\%$. Compute (*a*) the per cent of carbon in 1 lb of this gas, (*b*) the per cent of nitrogen in 1 lb of gas, and (*c*) the specific volume of the gas at 500 F and 14.7 psia.

12. Classify in accordance with rank from Table 2·4 the coals having the following ultimate analysis of mine samples:

Item	No. 1	No. 2	No. 3	No. 4
C	77.5	72.8	72.8	49.0
H	5.2	3.9	3.9	3.3
O	6.9	3.3	6.8	15.7
N	1.3	1.1	1.3	0.6
S	1.2	3.2	1.0	0.3
Ash	5.2	13.8	7.3	5.1
Moisture	2.7	1.9	13.5	26.0
Fixed carbon	57.4	64.5	42.9	35.4
Volatile matter	34.7	19.8	36.3	33.5
Btu per lb	14,157	13,043	11,543	8,231

13. The following data were collected from tests of coal-fired steam boilers:

Item		No. 1	No. 2	No. 3
Ultimate analysis of coal as				
fired:	C	65	57	64
	H	6	6	5
	O	14	16	8
	N	2	2	3
	S	3	4	2
	Ash	10	15	8
	Moisture	....	....	10
Proximate analysis of coal				
as fired:				
Fixed carbon		49	44	48
Volatile matter		32	29	34
Ash		10	15	8
Free moisture		9	12	10
Heating value, Btu per lb		12,270	10,960	11,930
Orsat analysis of flue gas:	CO_2	12.0	13.5	14.2
	O_2	7.8	6.2	5.5
	CO	0.2	0.1	0.2
Air temperature, F		70	80	75
Flue-gas temperature, F		500	350	400
Coal burned during test, lb		1,000	5,000	8,000
Dry refuse collected, lb		130	940	850
% of carbon in dry refuse		23	20	25

(*a*) Assuming a radiation and unaccounted for loss of 3 per cent of the heating value of the fuel in each test, calculate a complete energy balance for each test, and express the results in Btu per lb of fuel and in per cent of the heating value of the fuel. (*b*) Compute the air actually supplied per lb of fuel and the per cent of excess air supplied.

14. The following data were collected from tests of oil-fired furnaces:

Item		No. 1	No. 2	No. 3
Ultimate analysis of oil:	C	88.1	85	84.6
	H	10.8	11	10.9
	O	0.3	2	2.6
	N	0.2	1	0.3
	S	0.6	1	1.6
Heating value, Btu per lb		18,600	18,350	18,100
Orsat analysis of flue gas:	CO_2	12.0	11.8	10.6
	O_2	5.8	5.9	7.3
	CO	0.1	0.2	0.1
Air temperature, F		80	60	70
Flue-gas temperature, F		400	350	440

Assume in each test that the radiation and unaccounted for losses are 3 per cent of the heating value of the fuel. (*a*) Calculate a complete energy balance for each test, expressing the results in Btu per lb of fuel and in per cent of the heating value of the fuel. (*b*) Calculate the air supplied per lb of fuel and the per cent of excess air supplied.

15. The following data were obtained from tests of gas-fired furnaces:

Item		No. 1	No. 2	No. 3
Volumetric analysis, %:	H_2		54.5	14
	CO		11.9	27
	CH_4	83.2	24.2	3
	C_2H_6	15.6		
	O_2		0.4	0.6
	N_2	1.2	5.7	50.9
	CO_2		3.3	4.5
Heating value, Btu per cu ft at 60 F and 14.7 psia		1025	530	160
Orsat analysis of products of combustion, %	CO_2	9.5	9.8	10.1
	O_2	2.4	2.2	5.8
	CO	0.1	0.2	0.1
Air temperature, F		75	90	85
Flue-gas temperature F		500	700	450

For each of these tests, calculate (*a*) the loss in Btu per lb due to sensible heat in dry gaseous products of combustion, (*b*) the loss due to the CO in the dry gaseous products of combustion, (*c*) the loss due to moisture formed from the hydrogen, (*d*) the heating value of the fuel in Btu per lb, (*e*) the air actually supplied per lb of fuel, and (*f*) the per cent of excess air supplied.

16. A Diesel engine has a thermal efficiency of 30 per cent when delivering 300 bhp (brake horsepower). The fuel has a heating value of 140,000 Btu per gal and a specific gravity of 32 degrees API. Calculate the fuel consumption in lb per hr.

3 · Internal-Combustion Engines

3·1   Introduction. A heat engine is a machine that converts heat into mechanical energy. In the practical heat engine the energy is derived from the combustion of a fuel, and the mechanical energy is usually delivered in the form of a rotational force that may be used to turn the driveshaft of another machine. The fuel may be burned within the engine, in which case the engine is known as an internal-combustion engine, or the combustion process may occur in a device apart from the engine proper, as it does in a steam power plant. It is desirable that the fuel required by the engine be one that is widely available at low cost and that as much as possible of the heating value of the fuel be converted into useful power.

The desirability of supplying energy directly to the working fluid of a heat engine by combustion within the engine itself was recognized many years before a practical internal-combustion engine was devised. The steam engine, which came into use about 1700, was extremely uneconomical in its use of fuel. Its low efficiency was known to be largely the effect of the indirect application of heat, the fuel being burned under a boiler where water and steam absorbed a small portion of the energy liberated by combustion, and then an even smaller portion of this energy was converted into useful work in the engine. The combined losses incurred in generating the steam, conveying it to the engine, and converting its energy into work were large, much larger than in modern steam equipment. Many of those investigating the problem were convinced that it would be more economical as well as convenient to burn the fuel directly within the working cylinder of the engine. Although the early attempts to accomplish this were unsuccessful, they provided the background for later more successful attempts.

In 1824 Sadi Carnot, one of the outstanding authorities on thermodynamics of his day, published the results of a study of heat-engine cycles in which he discussed the inherent losses caused by the large difference between the temperature of the hot gases under a steam boiler and that of the steam as delivered to the cylinder of a steam engine. His amazingly thorough understanding of the possibilities of the internal-combustion engine at that early date is revealed in his description of a method of operating an engine by compression ignition, the basis of our present Diesel-type engine. A number of other early investigations of the possibilities of various forms of self-contained heat engines are recorded, but none of these studies led to the construction of successful engines employing the principles described in the accounts that were written by these pioneers in the field. The first experimental engines failed to perform satisfactorily, because the methods used were not fundamentally sound, and the details of design were not sufficiently perfected.

The internal-combustion engine as we know it today is the result of years of study and experiment. Ideas contributed by many scientists and inventors have been combined in its step-by-step development. In the early days of experimentation with heat engines, before any practical engine had been conceived, both steam and internal-combustion engines were in the minds of inventors. Steam engines that would actually run were created first, however, because the mechanical difficulties encountered were less perplexing and the small constructive skill of the workmen was equal to the task. Building a practical internal-combustion engine or explosion engine, as they were originally called, required more knowledge of machines than had yet been acquired. Experience with the steam engine increased the knowledge and skill of the workers until only one further step was necessary to burn the fuel directly within the engine cylinder.

It was not until 1860 that an engine was developed to the extent that it could be manufactured and sold as a practical machine. This engine was designed by Lenoir in France and resembled structurally the steam engines of that period, differing basically only in that a combustible charge of fuel and air was supplied to the cylinder of the engine where it was ignited and burned, instead of steam under pressure being supplied from a boiler. This engine was inefficient in its use of fuel and developed very little power in proportion to its size and weight; nevertheless, it was more satisfactory for certain applications than the steam-power plant.

A few years later, another French scientist, Beau de Rochas, published a plan of operating procedure for an internal-combustion engine which differed fundamentally from that of Lenoir and was destined to become the basic principle of our modern engines. He did not build any engines which applied his theory of operation, but in 1876 Otto produced in Germany an engine of this type which operated successfully. The cycle of operation has since been called the Otto cycle, although Otto did not originate the idea.

Later developments include the work of Dugald Clerk in England, who succeeded in supplying the charge to the cylinder in such manner that the necessary processes of the Otto cycle could be completed in one revolution of the crankshaft instead of requiring two turns of the shaft as did the original Otto engine. Dr. Rudolf Diesel of Germany extended the range of operation of the internal-combustion engine and increased its efficiency by reducing to practice the compression-ignition principle that had been investigated theoretically and experimentally by several others who were not successful in carrying their ideas to completion. The adoption of many other advances have similarly been delayed, because the engineers who conceived them failed to correlate all of the factors necessary for success.

3·2   The Lenoir engine.   A study of the working principles of the obsolete Lenoir engine is justified by the theoretical and practical evidence that it affords of the beneficial effect of compression upon the performance of internal-combustion engines. The fuel charge was ignited in the Lenoir engine at practically atmospheric pressure without being previously compressed, and it is therefore classed as a noncompression engine. Early experience with this engine convinced engineers that the compression process that is now a part of the cycle of all reciprocating engines is essential to the efficiency and power capacity of such engines. Starting with the Lenoir engine, which did not compress its charge prior to combustion, the subsequent development of the type of engine which inducts an inflammable fuel–air charge into its cylinder is seen to include a continuous increase in the extent to which the charge is compressed prior to combustion. The high-compression engine of today represents the present level of that trend.

In order to understand the operation of any engine, a knowledge must be acquired of the series of events which is called the cycle upon which the engine operates. By definition, a cycle is a series of events which periodically returns the working parts to their original condition and which, when repeated over and over again, produces regular and continuous operation. Every mechanical device has a cycle which consists of certain movements that occur in regular succession and which, when completed, return all parts of the machine to their original positions ready to start another cycle. This is its mechanical or operating cycle and is distinct from the thermodynamic or theoretical cycle of the engine which consists of the processes undergone by the working fluid or gases that are present in the cylinder during its operation.

Lenoir departed as little as possible from the existing steam-engine designs in constructing his engine. Two slide valves were used to connect the cylinder alternately with the source of fuel–air mixture and the exhaust system. The cylinder was double acting in that both ends of the piston were acted upon by the gases, and a cycle was completed at each end of the cylinder. The cross section shown in Fig. 3·1 illustrates the arrangement of cylinder, valves, piston, and water jacket.

The piston (a) reciprocates in the cylinder (b) which is completely closed at both ends except for the ports through its wall near each end. The movement of the piston is transmitted and controlled by the piston rod (c) through the crosshead and connecting rod to the crankshaft. The slide valves (d and e) are reciprocated by eccentrics on the crankshaft in such manner as to uncover the port leading to the cylinder end from which the piston is moving and form a continuous passage for the charge to flow into the cylinder during the first half of each stroke of the piston. The piston, as shown, is moving toward the head end of the cylinder to the right and the crank-end port is open to the gas line (f) and to the air at (g), the fuel and air being mixed together as they flow through the valve (e). At approximately mid-point in the piston stroke, the port is closed by movement of the valve (e) to the right. The exhaust passage from the cylinder is opened, as the piston approaches the end of its stroke, by movement of the exhaust valve (d). As shown, the head end of the cylinder is open to the exhaust passage.

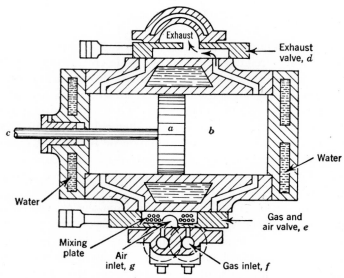

Fig. 3·1 The Lenoir engine cylinder

In operation, a combustible mixture of gas and air is formed in the mixing plate in the intake valve as the charge is drawn into the cylinder by the lowered pressure created by the retreating piston. At the mid-point in the stroke, the port is closed by the valve, and the charge is immediately ignited by an electric spark. Combustion of the charge trapped in the cylinder increases the pressure and causes work to be done by the force acting on the piston. The second half of the forward stroke of the piston is thus the power-producing portion of the cycle, and power is expended in moving the piston during the remainder of the cycle. When the end of the power stroke is approached, the exhaust valve has traveled to the point where its working edge has uncovered the cylinder port and connected the cylinder to the exhaust passage. The return stroke is completed with this connection established, and the movement of the piston displaces the products of combustion from the cylinder. A similar cycle is carried out simultaneously in the opposite cylinder end 180 degrees of crank rotation out of phase with the first.

3·3   The Lenoir cycle.   The operating cycle of an engine is portrayed by an engine indicator in the form of a pressure–volume diagram which is a record of the pressure exerted by the gas and the corresponding volume changes of the working fluid within the cylinder as the strokes are executed. The engine indicator is considered in detail later. A pressure–volume diagram for the Lenoir engine, as traced by an engine indicator, would appear as shown in Fig. 3·2.

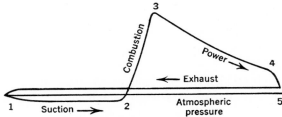

F\ɪɢ. 3·2   Lenoir indicator diagram

Horizontal distances on this diagram represent piston stroke and the corresponding volumes displaced by the piston. The straight line drawn at atmospheric pressure is the datum line from which pressures are measured vertically. The line 1–2 is drawn by the stylus during the first portion of the piston stroke and shows the depression caused by the pumping action of the piston. At the point 2 the valve closes and the charge is ignited, causing the pressure to rise to that of the point 3. Further movement of the piston results in a gradual decrease in pressure to the exhaust opening point 4, after which the pressure drops rapidly until the end of the stroke is reached at 5. The return stroke 5–1 finds the pressure slightly above atmospheric pressure as the products of combustion are being forced from the cylinder by the returning piston. At the point 1 the exhaust closes, and the intake opens, returning all parts of the system to their original condition ready to begin another cycle.

3·4   Lenoir-cycle analysis.   An engine cycle is analyzed by evaluating the heat supplied during the combustion process and either the net work done during the cycle or the heat rejected.

The thermal efficiency of the cycle is the ratio of the useful output to the heat input and may be expressed in equation form as

$$\eta_t = \frac{\text{net work}}{\text{heat supplied}} = \frac{Q_1 - Q_2}{Q_1} \tag{3·1}$$

where Q_1 is the number of Btu supplied by the fuel, and Q_2 is the number of Btu rejected and not used. These quantities may be evaluated for a specific cycle by application of the principles of thermodynamics. An efficiency equation for that cycle can then be derived which contains the factors affecting the theoretical efficiency of any engine operating on a cycle comprising the assumed series of processes.

The theoretical thermal efficiency of an engine operating on the Lenoir cycle may be found by evaluating equation 3·1 in this manner, to depend upon the expansion ratio V_5/V_2, which is the volume ratio by which the products of combustion are expanded after the pressure has been raised by combustion. It is apparent that this expansion ratio cannot be more than approximately 2 without reducing the power capacity of the engine by shortening the first portion of the stroke during which the combustible charge is inducted into the cylinder. The amount of pressure produced by combustion determines the allowable expansion ratio, because any further expansion after the pressure is reduced to that of the surrounding atmosphere would obviously do no work.

The thermal efficiency of an engine of the Lenoir type, as calculated by evaluating equation 3·1 for practical expansion ratios, is about 14 per cent. Since this calculation does not take into account losses caused by imperfections of the engine, which are unavoidable, the efficiency of an actual engine is much less than the theoretical value. It is apparent that only a very small fraction of the heat energy supplied to an engine of this type could possibly be converted into useful work. The actual thermal efficiency of the Lenoir engine is said to have been less than 4 per cent. This is much poorer economy than is attained by modern engines which compress the charge before combustion. Furthermore, the horsepower delivered by a Lenoir engine of a given size and speed was very much less than that of an engine employing compression.

Analysis of the operation of Lenoir's engine reveals two fundamental defects. The intake period, during which charge was drawn into the cylinder, occupied only half a piston stroke and, consequently, supplied to the cylinder only half of the possible charge. The expansion stroke, during which work was done on the piston, occupied only half a stroke and made only a small amount of expansion possible. The small charge and short power stroke resulted in limited capacity and greatly curtailed the power developed by the engine.

The second defect is traceable to the fact that the fuel was burned at low temperature and pressure, and the energy so released was used inefficiently. The fuel consumption of the engine was extremely high in proportion to the power developed. Although this first engine fell far short of attaining the results of later engines, it served an important need in providing a starting point from which to work.

3·5   The Otto engine. The Otto engine differed from the Lenoir engine essentially in that the entire outward stroke of the piston was used to fill the cylinder with charge. Since the piston was then at its greatest distance from the cylinder head, and burning the fuel at the maximum volume of the cycle could not cause any work to be done on the piston, it was necessary to return the piston to its starting point. This was the first possible opportunity that the force resulting from combustion would have to do work by pushing the piston outward. Compression of the charge during a return stroke of the piston was thus necessitated in order to place the piston in position to be acted upon by the energy released by combustion. Additional thermodynamic gains result from compression which make it desirable as well as necessary. Combustion occurred, theoretically, while the piston paused at the end of the compression stroke, and the entire outward stroke was used for expansive work done by the products of combustion. The return of the piston the second time was with the exhaust valve open as in the Lenoir engine.

The differences between these two principles of operation may be summed up as the utilization of an entire stroke for intake of charge instead of half a stroke, compression of the charge by returning the piston to the position of maximum possible expansion after combustion, combustion at minimum cylinder volume, and expansion for an entire forward stroke instead of half a stroke. Since the exhaust strokes were common to both cycles, the additional half-stroke added to the intake period, the half-stroke increase in expansion, and the introduction of a compression stroke increased the number of strokes required to complete the cycle from two to four.   The Otto cycle is thus seen to be a four-stroke cycle that is completed every fourth stroke of the piston and every second revolution of the crankshaft.   The four strokes are *intake, compression, expansion, exhaust,* repeated over and over in that order.   The important disadvantage of this

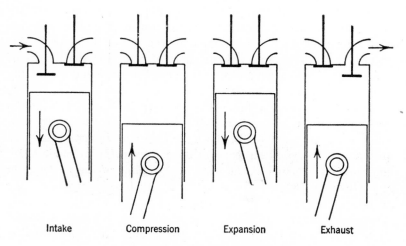

Intake   Compression   Expansion   Exhaust

Fig. 3·3   Four strokes of Otto cycle

cycle is that the power impulses come only half as frequently as in the two-stroke cycle, and only half as much power is, theoretically, possible from an engine of a given size running at a given speed.

The Otto engine differed structurally from the Lenoir engine in the inclusion of a poppet or mushroom valve serving as the exhaust outlet, in addition to a slide valve which communicated alternately with the fuel and air during the intake period.   Later, the slide valve was replaced by a second poppet valve, and this construction is now in general use.   Fig. 3·3 shows a conventional cylinder and piston during each of the four strokes of the Otto cycle of operation.

An indicator diagram, showing the actual pressure–volume relationships during the four strokes, is reproduced in Fig. 3·4.

Ideally the p–V diagram for this cycle would appear as shown in Fig. 3·5, in which the lower loop of the indicator diagram, resulting from the exhaust pressure being higher than atmospheric

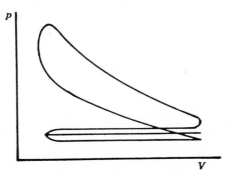

Fig. 3·4   Otto-cycle indicator diagram

pressure and the intake pressure being lower than atmospheric, is eliminated by the assumption that both of these strokes are carried out at atmospheric pressure.   The processes 1–2 and 3–4 follow the theoretical paths for compression and expansion with

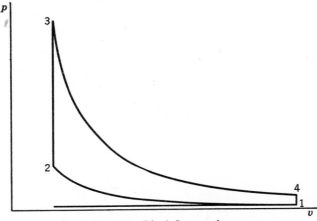

Fig. 3·5   Ideal Otto cycle

no heat transfer to or from the fluid, whereas the indicator diagram shows an appreciable departure from the theoretical paths because of leakage, heat transfer between the gases and the engine parts, and noninstantaneous combustion and valve action. The constant-volume processes 2–3 and 4–1 assume combustion occurring entirely at the inner dead center and an instantaneous pressure release at the outer dead center.

An analysis of the theoretical Otto cycle may be made by evaluating the quantities of heat in Equation 3·1 and the thermal efficiency found to be

$$\eta_t = 1 - \frac{1}{r_e^{k-1}} \qquad (3\cdot2)$$

where r_e is the expansion ratio which is equivalent to the compression ratio, v_1/v_2, of Fig. 3·5, and k is the ratio of specific heats, c_p/c_v, for the working fluid. This expression shows that the

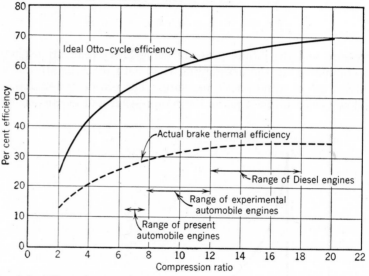

Fig. 3·6   Effect of compression ratio on efficiency of ideal Otto cycle and brake thermal efficiency of actual engines

thermal efficiency of the Otto cycle depends upon the ratio by which the charge is compressed before its combustion.

The upper curve of Fig. 3·6 shows the theoretical thermal efficiencies of the Otto cycle corresponding to compression ratios over the combined ranges of spark-ignition and compression-ignition engines for $k = 1.4$. The lower curve shows the approximate brake thermal efficiencies of typical actual engines. Individual engines may differ slightly from this curve in their performance because of differences in design and operating conditions. It is evident from these curves that important gains in thermal efficiency accompanied increases in compression ratio since the early years of the development of the gasoline engine when compression ratios near 4 were used. Increases above the present automobile-engine compression ratio range of 6.5 to 7.5 will be less effective in improving the efficiency, as is evidenced by the decreased slopes of the curves. It is also apparent that there is little to be gained by the use of compression ratios in the Diesel engine greater than necessary to assure proper ignition of the fuel because the slope in that range is very slight. Since the days of the noncompression Lenoir engine, it has been recognized that the fundamental way to increase thermal efficiency is to increase the compression ratio. Other factors, principally mechanical efficiency, combustion efficiency, and control of heat losses, also affect the performance of engines and cause their thermal efficiencies to be above or below the values of the curve of Fig. 3·6.

Example 1. Find the thermal efficiency of an Otto cycle with an expansion ratio of 6, assuming air as the working fluid.

Solution: If we substitute in Equation 3·2, $r_e = 6$, and $k = 1.4$

$$\eta_t = 1 - \frac{1}{6^{1.4-1}} = 1 - \frac{1}{6^{.4}} = 1 - \frac{1}{2.05} = 1 - 0.486 = 51.4\%$$

The compression ratio of the Otto-cycle engine cannot be increased at will in order to improve the thermal efficiency if it is of the type that inducts an inflammable mixture of fuel and air, because the temperature and pressure at the end of the compression stroke will approach the ignition point of the fuel with the result that self-ignition of the charge will prevent proper control of the combustion process. It is customary to design engines with the highest useful compression ratio, the maximum at which the engine will operate free from objectionable combustion knock without resorting to special fuels.

The compression ratio of an actual engine is established by the amount of space remaining between the piston and the cylinder head of the engine when the piston is at its point of closest approach to the head. Figure 3·7 shows the cylinder with the piston at each of the two extremes of its travel. At *a* the volume of the cylinder above the piston is the minimum or clearance volume, V_c. The volume above the piston in *b* is the maximum or total cylin-

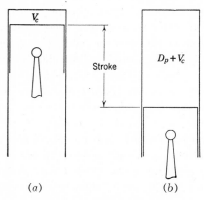

(*a*)   (*b*)

Fig. 3·7   Cylinder volumes

der volume. The difference between these two extremes is the volume swept by the piston in its stroke and is called the piston displacement volume, D_p. It is equal to the product of the area of the piston and its stroke. The compression ratio is the total cylinder volume divided by the clearance volume:

$$r = \frac{\text{total volume}}{\text{clearance volume}} = \frac{D_p + V_c}{V_c} \qquad (3\cdot3)$$

Example 2. An engine of 3.25-in. bore and 4-in. stroke has a clearance volume of 6 cu in. Find the compression ratio.
Solution:

$$D_p = \frac{3.25 \times 3.25 \times 3.14 \times 4}{4} = 33.18 \text{ cu in.}$$

$$r = \frac{33.18 + 6}{6} = 6.53$$

It is customary to express the clearance volume in per cent of the piston displacement. The statement that an engine cylinder has a certain per cent clearance means that the space between the piston and the cylinder head at the inward extreme of piston travel is that per cent of the piston displacement. On a percentage basis, Equation 3·3 becomes

$$r = \frac{D_p + c}{c} = \frac{D_p}{c} + 1 \qquad (3 \cdot 4)$$

where c is the clearance volume in per cent of the piston displacement D_p.

Example 3. Find the compression ratio of an engine which has 20 per cent clearance.
Solution:

$$r = \frac{100 + 20}{20} = 6$$

3·6 The Clerk engine. The Clerk engine operated on the same principle as the Otto engine except that its cycle was completed in two strokes of the piston. The intake and exhaust strokes were eliminated by providing a second cylinder and piston which functioned only as a pump to draw in the fuel–air mixture and place it under a slight pressure in a passage leading to the entrance of the power cylinder. The charge was then transferred to the engine cylinder through inlet ports in the cylinder head that were uncovered by a slide valve near the end of the expansion stroke. A second set of ports in the side of the cylinder wall leading to the exhaust disposal system had been uncovered by the piston an instant earlier, and the products of combustion were forced from the cylinder by the pressure of the incoming charge. Only the compression and expansion strokes were necessary for the completion of the cycle, the transfer of charge into the cylinder and exhaust of products of combustion occurring while the piston was at its most remote point from the cylinder head and occupying the last part of the expansion stroke and the first part of the compression stroke.

The two-stroke cycle as now widely used in Diesel-type engines is a development of the original Clerk cycle. It has the advantage of permitting twice as many cycles to be completed, but requires some form of pump or blower to supply air. It is not so satisfactory for engines that induct a fuel–air mixture because some portion of the charge escapes through the exhaust ports during the transfer period.   Figure 3·8 illustrates an adaptation of the Clerk principle in which the air from the compressor enters through one set of piston-controlled cylinder ports, and the exhaust leaves through a second set.

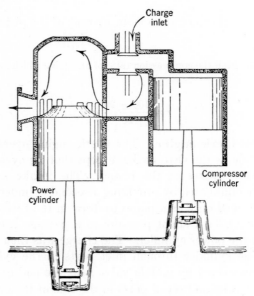

Charge
inlet

Compressor
cylinder

Power
cylinder

Fig. 3·8   Two-stroke-cycle engine

3·7   The Diesel engine.   Ignition of the charge as originally effected by exposing it to a pilot flame or by an electric spark was equally applicable to all types of engines that have been discussed.   The Diesel principle, which was commercialized by Dr. Rudolf Diesel just before the close of the 19th century, eliminates the need for an ignition system by utilizing the temperature rise which accompanies rapid compression to ignite the charge. If sufficiently compressed, the temperature of the air in the cylinder will exceed the ignition point of the fuel, and no spark is needed to ignite it.   Practical Diesel compression ratios cause the air to attain a pressure of approximately 500 psi and a temperature of 1000 F.   When this principle is employed, the charge taken into the cylinder on the intake stroke is air alone, and the fuel is sprayed in near the end of the compression stroke at the precise instant that will cause combustion to occur at the proper point in the cycle.

The early engines of the Diesel type were very large and heavy, running at low speed and with fuel injection and combustion starting at top dead center and continuing during the first portion of the power stroke. The theoretical cycle which approximates the indicator diagram of these engines was first described by Dr. Diesel in 1893 and differs from the Otto cycle only in the heat-addition process. Heat is supplied at constant pressure in the ideal Diesel cycle instead of at constant volume as in the Otto cycle. Figure 3·9 shows the p-v diagram for the Diesel cycle.

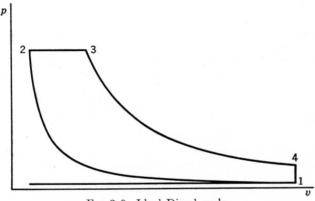

FIG. 3·9 Ideal Diesel cycle

Evaluating the quantities of heat in Equation 3·1 for this cycle yields the thermal efficiency expression

$$1 - \frac{1}{r^{k-1}} \left[\frac{r_c^{\,k} - 1}{k(r_c - 1)} \right] \tag{3·5}$$

where r is the compression ratio, v_1/v_2, of Fig. 3·9, r_c is the cut-off ratio, v_3/v_2, which varies with load, and k is the ratio of specific heats, c_p/c_v. Because v_3 is always greater than v_2, r_c is greater than unity. An increase in the quantity of heat supplied increases v_3 and consequently r_c. The bracketed quantity of Equation 3·5, for any possible values of r_c, is greater than unity and increases with increased cut-off ratio or load. The subtractive portion of the efficiency equation, therefore, increases with the amount of heat supplied and is always greater than $1 - 1/r^{k-1}$, the corresponding quantity for an Otto cycle with the same compression ratio.

The efficiency of the Diesel cycle is shown by Equation 3·5 to depend not only upon the compression ratio, but also upon the amount of heat supplied, increasing with the compression ratio and decreasing with greater heat supply. As the amount of heat supplied approaches zero at light load the efficiency approaches that of the Otto cycle with the same compression ratio, and becomes progressively less than that of the Otto cycle as the heat supplied increases. The efficiency of the Diesel cycle is lower principally because the expansion ratio decreases as the cut-off ratio increases.

Example 4. Find the thermal efficiency of a Diesel cycle with a compression ratio of 16 and a cut-off ratio of 4.

Solution: Substituting in Equation 3·5, $r = 16$, $r_c = 4$, and $k = 1.4$,

$$\eta_t = 1 - \frac{1}{16^{.4}} \left[\frac{4^{1.4} - 1}{1.4(4 - 1)} \right] = 1 - \frac{1}{3.03} \left(\frac{7 - 1}{4.2} \right)$$

$$= 1 - 0.472 = 52.8\%$$

The curve of Fig. 3·6 shows the efficiency of the ideal Otto cycle to be 67.5 per cent for a compression ratio of 16, an efficiency 28 per cent higher than that of the Diesel cycle at this cut-off ratio.

Combustion in the modern high-speed Diesel engine is very rapid and does not extend appreciably into the power stroke. The pressure rises considerably during combustion, and the process more nearly approximates constant volume than constant pressure. Only the extremely large Diesel engines, which run at very low speeds, and particularly those built some years ago when air injection was employed, can be considered to follow the theoretical Diesel cycle. All high-speed Diesels operate with peak cylinder pressures that greatly exceed compression pressures and actually approach the Otto cycle more nearly than does the spark-ignition engine. The thermal efficiency of the Diesel engine is higher than that of the spark-ignition engine because compression ratios of about 16 are employed which are more than double those used with spark ignition.

3·8 Actual thermal efficiency. The thermal efficiency of the cycle, as expressed by the general Equation 3·1 and the special equations for each cycle, represents the portion of the heat consumed by a perfect engine that would be converted into work if there were no losses other than the inherent cycle loss caused by its rejection of the energy remaining in the working fluid at the end of the expansion stroke. No real engine could attain this thermal efficiency, because losses, such as imperfect combustion, heat transfer from the working fluid, leakage, and movement of the piston during combustion, are always present and reduce the work done below the theoretical amount. The actual thermal efficiency of a real engine is found by expressing the heat equivalent of the net work done in per cent of the heat input.

The net work of the actual engine is evaluated by testing the engine in operation. The thermal efficiency is calculated by expressing the heat equivalent of the work done in per cent of the higher heating value of the fuel consumed in the period of the test.

The power developed may be measured in the cylinder of the engine by means of the indicator diagram, in which case it is called the indicated horsepower, or it may be the power delivered by the shaft of the engine, which is called the shaft or brake horsepower. The engine indicator provides a record of the actual pressures existing in the cylinder at the corresponding volumes displaced by the moving piston. An area is enclosed by the lines traced by the indicator stylus (Fig. 3·4) which is proportional, according to the scale to which the diagram is drawn, to the work done on the piston per cycle.

3·9 The engine indicator. Engine indicators are of several types, each of which is suitable for a certain range of operating conditions. The displacement-type indicator, illustrated in Fig. 3·10, is the simplest device available for reproducing the cylinder pressure–volume record. It gives satisfactory results on engines of reasonably large cylinder dimensions operating at moderate speeds. Cylinder diagrams of steam engines, Diesel engines, gas engines, compressors, and pumps are usually made with displacement-type indicators. High-speed small-displacement engines require indicators that do not add an appreciable volume to the cylinder when connected to it and that are capable of responding to extremely rapid changes in cylinder pressure and volume without lag and distortion. The high-speed indicators are usually of the electric type, employing a pressure pickup which generates a small emf that is proportional to the pressure acting upon a small thin steel diaphragm exposed to the gases in the cylinder. A cathode-ray oscilloscope is used to portray the pressure changes, a permanent record of which may be made by photographing the screen.

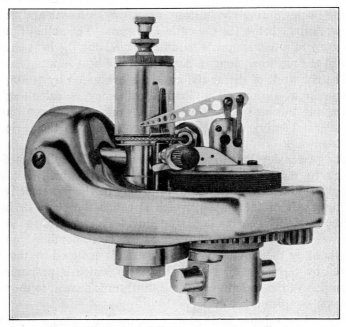

FIG. 3·10 Bacharach bar-spring engine indicator

The displacement-type indicator consists of two essential units, a drum and a cylinder fitted with a piston, spring, and stylus mechanism illustrated in Fig. 3·11. The drum (5) reproduces the volume changes within the cylinder. It is free to rotate slightly less than one full turn about a vertical axis when propelled by the application of tension to the cord (6) which is wrapped about the lower edge. This cord is connected to a reducing-motion mechanism attached to the engine which reproduces exactly the motion of the piston scaled down to less than the circumference of the drum. A spring inside the drum returns it to a stop position and keep the cord taut. A strip of paper;

coated on one side with a metallic compound which causes a brass stylus to produce a black trace, is attached to the cylindrical surface of the drum by means of two spring clips. This strip of paper is customarily referred to as an indicator card.

The cylinder (1) has a normal cross-sectional area of ½ sq in.

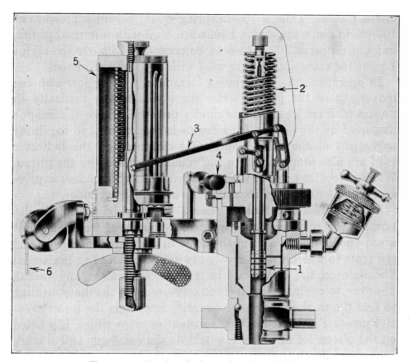

FIG. 3·11 Sectional view of engine indicator

but may be fitted with a smaller bushing rated in terms of the fraction that its area is of the normal half-inch. The lower face of the piston which operates in the cylinder is exposed to the cylinder pressure by a connection to the cylinder head, and its motion is restrained by a calibrated spring (2). A multiplying straight-line linkage connects the piston rod to the brass stylus on the end of arm (3) which can be made to bear against the surface of the card on the drum if the adjustable screw (4) is pressed against a stop. The vertical movement of the stylus will be proportional to the pressure acting on the piston, while the distance it moves will depend upon the scale of the indicator spring. Springs are rated in terms of the pressure in pounds per square inch required to displace the stylus 1 in. when used with a normal-size piston. When a smaller-than-normal piston is used, the scale is increased by dividing by the fractional rating of the piston. Thus, a 100-lb spring would permit a pressure of 100 psi to move the stylus 1 in. when used with a normal piston, but a pressure of 500 psi would be necessary to move the stylus 1 in. if the same spring were used with a $\frac{1}{5}$ normal piston.

In operation, the card moves horizontally in unison with the movement of the piston, while the stylus moves vertically in unison with the changes in cylinder pressure. Since the volume displaced by the piston of the engine is proportional to the linear movement of the piston, horizontal distances on the indicator card are also proportional to the volume displaced by the piston. When placed in contact with the card, the stylus makes a pressure–volume tracing of the cycle executed in the cylinder.

3·10 Mean effective pressure. It would be possible to determine the relationship between foot-pounds of work and unit areas on the diagram from the scale of the indicator spring and the scale to which cylinder volumes are reproduced as horizontal distances on the diagram. It is more convenient and useful, however, to evaluate the average pressure from the diagram than to find the work directly. A quantity known as the mean effective pressure is defined as that constant pressure which, if it acted on the piston for one stroke, would do the same amount of work as is done by the varying pressure during one cycle. It is apparent that this pressure is the average pressure during the return strokes subtracted from the average pressure during the forward strokes.

The mean effective pressure, or mep, is equal to the average ordinate of the area formed by the diagram multiplied by the spring scale of the indicator. The average ordinate may be measured directly by the use of a polar planimeter, or the enclosed area may be evaluated and divided by the length of the diagram parallel to the volume axis.

A better conception of the significance of the average ordinate of the indicator diagram and the corresponding mean effective pressure may be gained from Fig. 3·12. The dotted line encloses a rectangle that is equal in area and length to the diagram traced by the indicator stylus. This equivalent rectangle represents the indicator diagram that would have resulted, had the two strokes of the piston been at the constant pressures corresponding to its upper and lower horizontal boundaries, which are the pressures necessary to do the same amount of work as was done by the

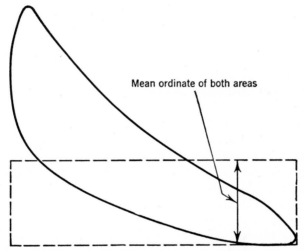

Mean ordinate of both areas

Fig. 3·12   Engine indicator diagram and equivalent rectangle

varying pressures of the actual cycle. The height of this rectangle is found by dividing the area of the actual diagram by its length, and it obviously is equal to the mean ordinate of the original indicator diagram. The difference between the maximum and minimum pressures of this hypothetical cycle is the mean effective pressure indicated by the actual diagram. Evaluation of the mean effective pressure is thus, in effect, the substitution of a constant pressure that would do the same amount of work during the power stroke of the piston for the actual varying pressure of the cycle.

The mean effective pressure is a useful quantity for comparing the performance of two engines, because it is proportional to the work done per cycle per unit of cylinder size. The horsepower capacities of different engines do not indicate how effectively the engines are operating, because the factors of speed and piston displacement are included. Two engines might conceivably develop the same horsepower, but, if one were larger than the other and running at higher speed, its specific output would be less than that of the other. Their mean effective pressures would, in this case, be different and would reveal the extent to which the one was operating more effectively.

Example 5. Find the mep of an engine for which an indicator diagram drawn with a 200-lb spring has an area of 1.65 sq in. and a length of 3.5 in.

Solution: The mean ordinate of the diagram is 1.65/3.5 = 0.471 in. Each inch of mean ordinate corresponds to 200 psi; so 200 × 0.471 or 94.2 psi is the mep.

3·11   Indicated horsepower. The indicated horsepower is the power developed in the cylinders at the faces of the pistons of an engine. It is calculated from the cylinder-pressure information revealed by the engine indicator and receives its name from that fact. The mean effective pressure (mep) of the cylinder in pounds per square inch multiplied by the area of the piston in square inches equals the average total force in pounds acting upon the piston during one stroke. When this force in pounds is multiplied by the length of the piston stroke in feet, the work in foot-pounds done on the piston by the gas during one power stroke is evaluated. One power stroke is completed in each cylinder of a four-stroke-cycle engine while the crankshaft turns through two revolutions and the engine completes one cycle. This product is thus the work done per cycle or per two revolutions of the crankshaft of a four-stroke-cycle engine. Since the two-stroke-cycle engine completes a cycle in one turn of the crankshaft, the work done per cycle is also the work done per revolution.

If the mean effective pressure in pounds per square inch is expressed by P_i, the length of stroke in feet by L, and the area of the piston in square inches by A, the work done per cycle is

$$W = \text{force} \times \text{distance} = P_i L A \text{ ft-lb per cycle} \qquad (3 \cdot 6)$$

If N cycles are completed per minute, the work done per minute is $P_i L A N$ ft-lb per min and, by the definition of a horsepower,

$$\text{Ihp} = \frac{P_i LAN}{33,000} \tag{3.7}$$

N is evaluated by measuring the rpm of the engine and taking into account the cycles completed per revolution. When there are several cylinders in the engine, the average mep of all cylinders may be used for P_i, and N will then be the number of cycles completed per minute by all of the cylinders in the engine. It is also possible to calculate the power developed in each cylinder separately and sum up the total.

Example 6.   Find the ihp of a four-cylinder four-stroke-cycle engine of 3-in. bore and 5-in. stroke when it is running at 1500 rpm with a mep of 90 psi. *Solution:*

$$P_i = 90, \quad L = \tfrac{5}{12}, \quad A = 3.14 \times 1.5 \times 1.5, \quad \text{and} \quad N = 1500 \times \tfrac{4}{2}$$

When substituted in Equation 3.7,

$$\text{Ihp} = \frac{90 \times 5 \times 3.14 \times 1.5 \times 1.5 \times 1500 \times 4}{12 \times 33,000 \times 2} = 24$$

3.12   Brake horsepower.   The brake horsepower (bhp) is the useful power delivered by the engine at the crankshaft coupling. The name comes from the method of loading an engine for test by means of a prony brake or any equivalent device arranged to brake or resist the crankshaft rotation to a controllable and measurable extent. The action of all power-absorbing devices used for testing engines results in converting the rotational tendency of the crankshaft into a tangential force acting at some established distance from the center of rotation.

Figure 3.13 shows a type of prony brake in which the power developed by the engine is converted into heat by friction between the brake shoes and a drum that is rotated by the crankshaft of the engine. The heat generated is absorbed by cooling water circulated through the drum. The torque arm of the brake terminates in a knife-edge located a precise distance r ft from the center of the rotating brake drum. A force F acts upon a pedestal resting on a scale platform, permitting its measurement in pounds. The product Fr is the torque or turning moment in pound-feet which, in conjunction with the rotational speed n, determines the horsepower absorbed by the brake.

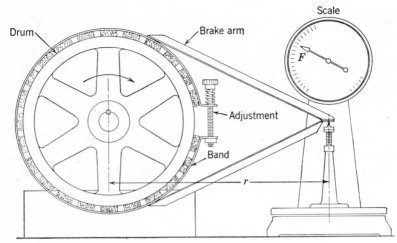

FIG. 3·13 Prony brake

The force F acts tangentially to a circle of radius r and, in one turn of the brake drum, acts through a distance equal to the circumference of the circle, $2\pi r$ ft. Work is done in the amount,

$$W = 2\pi rF \text{ ft-lb per revolution}$$

$$= 2\pi rFn \text{ ft-lb per min}$$

where n is the rpm of the engine shaft.

$$\text{Bhp} = \frac{2\pi rFn}{33,000} \tag{3·8}$$

Since $rF = t$ where $t = $ torque in pound-feet

$$\text{Bhp} = \frac{2\pi tn}{33,000} \tag{3·9}$$

Example 7. An engine is loaded by a prony brake with a 48-in. arm. When it was running at 300 rpm, the scale reading was 60 lb. Find the bhp of the engine loaded by this brake.

Solution:

$$\text{Bhp} = \frac{2\pi rFn}{33,000} \quad \text{from Equation 3·8}$$

$$r = 4, \quad F = 60, \quad \text{and} \quad n = 300$$

$$\text{Bhp} = \frac{2 \times 3.14 \times 4 \times 60 \times 300}{33,000} = 13.7$$

The prony brake is limited to low operating speeds. Its low cost and simplicity make it desirable for testing engines within its speed range, but it is unsatisfactory for higher speeds because of vibration and difficulty in adjusting and maintaining loads. At increased speeds, its convenience of operation and accuracy of power measurement decrease rapidly. Fluid brakes are obtainable in which fluid friction is caused by the shearing action of an impeller rotating within a casing or stator containing water or oil. The stator is cradled by being mounted on trunnion bearings surrounding the impeller shaft, and it tends to rotate under the influence of the friction between the portion of the liquid which rotates with the impeller and that which remains stationary with the stator. The heat produced by friction is dissipated by the fluid being circulated through some form of cooling device. The rotational tendency is measured by the arm attached to the stator which applies the force to scales. The power that can be absorbed at low speeds is usually low, but fluid brakes can operate successfully at high speeds.

Electric dynamometers apply the same fundamental principle as the prony brake. Magnetic linkage between the stator and the rotor replaces the mechanical friction of the prony brake as the means of creating the desired turning effort or load. The torque thus applied to the stator by the rotation of the rotor is transmitted, by means of a horizontal arm attached to one side of the stator, to a sensitive type of weighing scales. The stator is cradled on pedestals and is free to rotate through the small angle necessary to allow the arm to act upon the scale linkage. The rotor or armature is carried on ball bearings mounted in the ends of the stator, which, in turn, are carried on bearings in the supporting pedestals. Thus, any bearing friction between the rotor and stator is included in the force applied to the scales, and need for tare correction in the scale reading is eliminated. The point of contact between the dynamometer arm and the scale linkage tends to rotate in a circle of radius r, which is the distance from the point to the center of rotation, just as in the prony brake.

Electric dynamometers are more generally used for high speeds than other types of brakes. They are of two general types, the eddy current and the motor–generator. The eddy-current dyna-

mometer is, in effect, a magnetic brake in which a toothed steel
rotor turns between the poles of an electromagnet attached to
a trunnioned stator. The resistance to rotation is controlled by
varying the current through the coils and hence the strength of

FIG. 3·14 Dynamatic eddy-current dynamometer

the magnetic field. The flux tends to follow the smaller air gaps
at the ends of the rotor teeth, and eddy currents are set up within
the metal of the pole pieces, resulting in heating the stator. This
heat is removed by circulating cooling water through a jacket
formed in the stator. Figure 3·14 illustrates a Midwest Dynamatic Dynamometer of the eddy-current type which has a capacity of 1100 hp and is capable of operating up to 8000 rpm.

The motor–generator-type dynamometer consists of a cradled
generator that is operated as a generator for loading an engine

and as a motor for cranking or measuring friction horsepower. Torque reaction is applied to scales through a reversible linkage which causes the force at the scales to act in the proper direction, regardless of the direction of rotation of the armature or whether the dynamometer is loading or motoring the engine. Load and speed are controllable both by varying the resistance of the circuit to which the generator terminals are connected and by varying the field strength.

The horsepower absorbed by a dynamometer is calculated in the same manner as when an engine is loaded by a prony brake. The linkage connecting the stator to the scales may be complicated, but its effective length may be determined and substituted in Equation 3·8. It is customary to calculate a constant for a dynamometer such that the horsepower absorbed is equal to the product of the constant, the speed, and the scale reading.

Since the brake horsepower is equal to $2\pi rFn/33{,}000$, calculations of horsepower will be simplified if, in the design of the dynamometer, the arm is given a length r such that $2\pi r$ will equal 33 ft or some simple fraction thereof. If the length of the arm were made equal to 63.02 in. or 5.252 ft, $2\pi r$ would equal 33 ft, and the horsepower expression would become $Fn/1000$. This length, however, is too great for dynamometers of usual size, and so the typical lengths employed are 21 in. or 15.75 in., and the denominators of the above expression become 3000 or 4000. It is customary to express the horsepower determination as

$$\text{Bhp} = CFn \qquad (3 \cdot 10)$$

where C is $\frac{1}{3000}$ for a 21-in. arm and $\frac{1}{4000}$ for a 15.75-in. arm. Either the value of C or the length of the arm will be found on the rating plate attached to the dynamometer by the manufacturer.

Example 8. An automobile engine is attached to an electric dynamometer which has a 15.75-in. arm. When it is running at 3500 rpm, the scale reading is 125 lb. Find the bhp developed by the engine.
Solution:

$$\text{Bhp} = CFn$$

$$C = \tfrac{1}{4000}, \quad F = 125, \quad \text{and} \quad n = 3500$$

$$\text{Bhp} = \frac{125 \times 3500}{4000} = 109.4$$

3·13   Friction horsepower. The indicated horsepower is invariably considerably greater than the brake horsepower. The difference between these two quantities represents the portion of the power developed in the cylinders that was absorbed by the engine and not delivered by its shaft. It includes the power required to overcome friction in the bearings of the engine and between the piston and cylinder walls, the power required to operate such auxiliaries as camshafts, magnetos, oil and water pumps, and fans, in addition to the pumping work done in drawing in the charge and expelling the exhaust gases. These power losses are summed up as the friction horsepower of the engine. The indicated horsepower of slow-speed engines can be accurately determined from the indicator diagrams and the friction horsepower found as the difference between the indicated horsepower and brake horsepower. It is customary to evaluate the friction horsepower of high-speed engines by motoring them with the fuel supply cut off and all operating conditions kept as nearly as possible the same as when the engines are running. The horsepower developed by an electric dynamometer in motoring an engine is a close approximation of its friction horsepower.

The friction horsepower of an internal-combustion engine varies but little with changes in load at constant speed and is essentially a function of the speed of the engine, increasing gradually at low speeds and more rapidly at higher speeds. Figure 3·15 shows a typical relationship of indicated horsepower, brake horsepower, and friction horsepower for an automobile engine.

3·14   Mechanical efficiency. Mechanical perfection is approached as the friction horsepower decreases in proportion to the indicated horsepower. The mechanical efficiency of an engine is evaluated as the brake horsepower in per cent of the indicated horsepower. It is a measure of the mechanical perfection of an engine or its ability to transmit the power developed in the cylinders to the driveshaft. Mechanical efficiency is expressed by the equation,

$$\eta_m = \frac{\text{bhp}}{\text{ihp}} \times 100 \qquad (3\cdot11)$$

The mechanical efficiency of a constant-speed engine, such as a stationary power-plant engine, increases with load, because the approximately constant friction horsepower becomes a smaller per cent of the increasing indicated horsepower. The mechanical efficiency of a variable-speed engine decreases with increased speed, because of the rapid increase in friction horsepower. Mechanical efficiencies of internal-combustion engines usually range from 70 to 90 per cent.

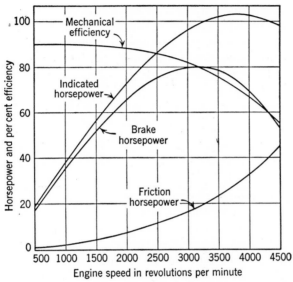

FIG. 3·15   Effect of speed on friction losses of an automobile engine

3·15   Brake mean effective pressure. It is more convenient and accurate to determine the brake horsepower of an internal-combustion engine than the indicated horsepower. Because of the rapidity with which the cylinder pressure changes in high-speed engines, very elaborate engine indicators are necessary for accurate evaluation of mean effective pressures. The friction horsepower can be measured with fair accuracy by motoring an engine with a motor–generator-type dynamometer and calculating the power required to rotate the crankshaft at constant speed from the reaction on the scales. The indicated horsepower can be found as the sum of the brake horsepower and the friction horsepower, instead of by calculating it from the mean effective pressure.

A hypothetical quantity known as the brake mean effective pressure is a widely used index to the pressure developed in the cylinder and, consequently, to the power capacity of the engine per unit of engine size. It may be defined as the constant pressure in pounds per square inch gage which, if acting on the piston through each power stroke, would develop in the cylinder an amount of power equal to the brake horsepower of the engine. It will be seen that the bmep is less than the imep by the ratio of the bhp to the ihp, making it equal to the imep multiplied by the mechanical efficiency. The bmep is found by calculating the bhp in the usual way and then equating it to

$$P_b LAN/33,000$$

Thus, $$P_b = \frac{\text{bhp} \times 33,000}{LAN} \qquad (3\cdot12)$$

where P_b is the bmep in pounds per square inch gage, L is the length of piston stroke in feet, A is the piston area in square inches, and N is the cycles per minute for the entire engine.

3·16   Specific fuel consumption.   The actual thermal efficiency involves the weight of fuel consumed by the engine in an actual test. The fuel burned by the engine during the test period is expressed in pounds per hour and converted into a unit quantity by dividing the total pounds of fuel per hour by the horsepower developed. This quotient is called the brake specific fuel consumption, bsfc, or indicated specific fuel consumption, isfc, depending upon whether the bhp or ihp is used as the divisor.

3·17   Actual thermal efficiency calculation.   The thermal efficiency of an engine is the heat equivalent of the horsepower developed in per cent of the heat supplied to the engine during a test. Since 1 hp delivered for 1 hr is equivalent to 2545 Btu, the product of the specific fuel consumption and the higher heating value of the fuel will be the heat input corresponding to an engine output of 2545 Btu. In equation form,

$$\text{Thermal efficiency, } \eta_t = \frac{\text{work output, Btu per hr}}{\text{energy input, Btu per hr}} \qquad (3\cdot13)$$

$$\text{Brake thermal efficiency, } \eta_{bt} = \frac{\text{bhp} \times 2545}{m_f \times Q_H} \qquad (3\cdot14)$$

Indicated thermal efficiency, $\eta_{it} = \dfrac{\text{ihp} \times 2545}{m_f \times Q_H}$ (3·15)

where m_f is pounds of fuel per hour and Q_H is the higher heating value of the fuel in Btu per pound.

Example 9. An engine loaded by a dynamometer with a 21-in. arm is operated at 500 rpm. When it was tested under load, the scale reading was 72 lb, and, when motored, the reading was 24 lb. It burned 1.8 lb of fuel for which $Q_H = 20,000$ Btu per lb during a 15-min test. Find the efficiencies determined by the test.

Solution:

$$\text{Bhp} = \frac{2\pi r F n}{33,000}$$

$$\text{Bhp} = \frac{2 \times 3.14 \times 1.75 \times 72 \times 500}{33,000} = 12$$

$$\text{Fhp} = \frac{2 \times 3.14 \times 1.75 \times 24 \times 500}{33,000} = 4$$

$$\text{Ihp} = \text{bhp} + \text{fhp} = 12 + 4 = 16$$

$$\text{Fuel consumption} = \frac{1.8 \times 60}{15} = 7.2 \text{ lb per hr}$$

$$\text{Bsfc} = \frac{7.2}{12} = 0.6 \text{ lb per bhp per hr}$$

$$\text{Isfc} = \frac{7.2}{16} = 0.45 \text{ lb per ihp per hr}$$

$$\eta_m = \tfrac{12}{16} \times 100 = 75\%$$

$$\eta_{bt} = \frac{12 \times 2545}{7.2 \times 20,000} = 21.2\%$$

$$\eta_{it} = \frac{16 \times 2545}{7.2 \times 20,000} = 28.3\%$$

3·18 Engine efficiency. The thermal efficiency of a theoretical cycle expresses the per cent of the energy supplied that could be converted into work by a perfect engine operating on that cycle. An engine that carries out a theoretical cycle having a thermal efficiency of 50 per cent would thus be perfect if it converted only half of the energy supplied to it into work. The other half of the energy received is inherently unavailable for conversion into work, and the failure of the engine to use this unavailable portion is not the fault of the engine but of the cycle. Thermodynamic and mechanical imperfections in an engine cause its total losses to exceed these inherent losses. The actual thermal efficiency of an engine, as established by a dynamometer test, must consequently always be lower than the theoretical cycle efficiency by an amount depending upon the imperfections of the engine as a combustion device and a machine.

The brake thermal efficiency of an engine expresses the per cent of the energy received by the engine in the fuel consumed which it has delivered as power at its flywheel or coupling, but it does not indicate, percentagewise at least, how perfect the engine really is as a mechanical device. Actual test values of brake thermal efficiency are usually less than 35 per cent and create the impression that these heat engines are quite inefficient and imperfect. Actually, they are better machines than their thermal efficiencies indicate, because a considerable portion of the energy supplied was inherently unavailable and could not possibly be used to do work.

A more correct measure of the perfection of an engine is obtained by comparing the amount of energy that it converts into work with the amount that is theoretically available for conversion by any engine when operating on the cycle followed. This is done by expressing the useful work output of the engine in per cent of the theoretical net work of the cycle instead of in per cent of the energy supplied. This quantity is usually called engine efficiency or efficiency ratio, but, in the internal-combustion-engine field, it is known as relative efficiency. Engine efficiency is a true indication of the degree of perfection of an engine because it approaches 100 per cent as the losses caused by the imperfections of the engine are decreased by improved design and construction. The brake thermal efficiency curve of Fig. 3·6 is caused to approach the theoretical cycle efficiency curve as improvements are made in the engine other than changes in compression ratio.

The brake engine efficiency of any engine is equal to the brake thermal efficiency expressed in per cent of the corresponding theoretical cycle efficiency. This relationship is derived as follows:

$$\text{Brake engine efficiency} = \frac{\text{bhp}}{\text{theoretical hp}}$$

When both numerator and denominator are divided by the energy supplied, the expression becomes

$$\eta_{be} = \frac{\dfrac{\text{bhp}}{Q}}{\dfrac{\text{theoretical hp}}{Q}} = \frac{\text{brake thermal efficiency}}{\text{cycle efficiency}} \qquad (3 \cdot 16)$$

Figure 3·16 is a flow chart which shows diagrammatically the destination of the energy supplied to a typical engine and makes

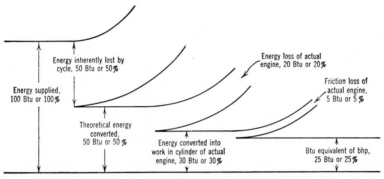

Fig. 3·16   Flow diagram showing destination of energy supplied to an engine

it possible to visualize the various efficiencies that have been discussed. Energy enters the system at the left in the form of fuel. An assumed 100 Btu or 100 per cent of the energy supplied is represented by the width of the stream. The cycle on which the engine operates is shown to be 50 per cent efficient, and the stream, consequently, divides equally between the energy theoretically converted into work and that rejected because it is theoretically unavailable for conversion when following that cycle. The 50 Btu that can be theoretically converted into work suffer a loss of 20 Btu, representing the imperfections of the practical engine as an energy converter. These energy losses are largely the effects of incomplete combustion and heat transfer from the combustion chamber. It should be noted that these losses are considered to be at least partially avoidable, whereas the 50 Btu inherent cycle loss is unavoidable. The remaining energy, 30 Btu, is actually converted into work in the cylinder of the engine and represents the indicated horsepower of the engine. Of these 30 Btu, 5 Btu are lost mechanically by the engine, and the work equivalent of only 25 Btu finally arrives at the flywheel. These last losses are occasioned by the rubbing together of parts, pumping action of the pistons, and such mechanical operations as opening the valves and driving fans, pumps, and other needed accessories.

The various efficiencies indicated by this chart take the form of ratios of energy quantities and, consequently, widths of streams. The theoretical cycle efficiency is the theoretical work in per cent of the energy supplied, $\dfrac{50\ \text{Btu}}{100\ \text{Btu}}$ or 50 per cent. The indicated thermal efficiency is the indicated work in per cent of the energy supplied, $\dfrac{30\ \text{Btu}}{100\ \text{Btu}}$ or 30 per cent. The brake thermal efficiency is the brake or delivered work in per cent of the energy supplied, $\dfrac{25\ \text{Btu}}{100\ \text{Btu}}$ or 25 per cent. The indicated engine efficiency is the energy converted into work in the cylinder in per cent of the theoretical work, $\dfrac{30\ \text{Btu}}{50\ \text{Btu}}$ or 60 per cent. The brake engine efficiency is the Btu equivalent of the brake horsepower in per cent of the theoretical work, $\dfrac{25\ \text{Btu}}{50\ \text{Btu}}$ or 50 per cent. The mechanical efficiency is the Btu equivalent of the brake horsepower in per cent of the Btu equivalent of the indicated horsepower, $\dfrac{25\ \text{Btu}}{30\ \text{Btu}}$ or 83.3 per cent.

3·19 Fuels. Consideration must be given early in the study of internal-combustion engines to the properties of the fuels burned in them. The development of these engines has to a large extent paralleled the progress made in producing fuels suitable for internal-combustion-engine use. Nothing useful is accomplished by designing an engine that is ideally suited to the combustion of a hypothetical but nonexistent fuel. The efforts of the engine designers have, accordingly, been directed toward the creation of engines that would operate as satisfactorily as possible on the fuels that were available on the market at that time. The gasoline engines of 25 years ago represent the best that the engineers of that period knew how to design for operation on the gasolines marketed at that time. The best-performing engines of today would have been useless had they existed then, because they could not have been run on the fuels that were available.

Several important differences between the engines of a generation ago and the best gasoline engines of today are improvements made possible by the acquisition of a better understanding of fuel properties and by the changes in those properties which were the result of technological advances in petroleum production. The fuels engineer strives to produce fuels that will best meet the increasingly severe requirements of the improved engines, while the engine designer modifies his designs to utilize the better characteristics of the improved fuels as fully as possible, both keeping within the limitations imposed by economic and practical considerations.

Since there will probably always be several grades of each of the types of manufactured fuels, there should be engines whose requirements match as closely as practicable the characteristics of each grade and type. Many of the imperfections of the early internal-combustion engines were the result of the designer's lack of knowledge of fuel characteristics, and unsatisfactory performance has frequently been traceable to the operator's lack of knowledge of the fuel requirements of the engine. Effective use of both fuels and engines requires knowledge of the fuels that are available for use. Although it is true that internal-combustion engines may operate on all types of fuels if the necessary provisions are made, only gaseous and liquid fuels have practical significance.

3·20 Gaseous fuels. Gases are very desirable fuels when available at reasonable cost per unit of heating value. Compared with liquid fuels, gases have both good and bad qualities. Aside from the need for removing dirt and other foreign matter, gases need no preparation for combustion other than mixing in appropriate proportions with air. Liquid fuels must be vaporized before they can be burned. Problems also arise in carbureting a liquid-fuel–air charge and in the combustion of partially vaporized mixtures. The advantage of easily preparing a uniform charge of gas and air that is immediately ready to burn is offset to a considerable extent by the disadvantage of its high specific volume which reduces the weight of charge and the power output per unit of engine size. The high ignition points of certain compounds that are frequently present in gaseous but seldom in liquid fuels may cause combustion difficulty. Most fuel gases are mixtures of several elements and compounds in proportions which frequently are not constant with time. Differences in the air requirements and burning characteristics of these varying ingredients may impair the performance of the gas engine.

Four groups or classes of gases are used as fuels for gas engines; natural gas taken from underground deposits, manufactured gas distributed by public-utility organizations, producer gas generated from coal or wood, and by-product gas resulting from certain industrial processes.

Natural gas is now taken from wells in about two thirds of the states in the United States and is distributed by pipe lines over a large portion of the country. It contains amounts of methane, CH_4, as high as 90 per cent, and the remainder of its combustible content is usually ethane, C_2H_6. Its net heating value is commonly 1000 or more Btu per cu ft. About 10 cu ft of air are required for combustion of 1 cu ft of gas, resulting in a heating value of 86 to 87 Btu per cu ft of fuel–air mixture. It is the heating value of the mixture, not that of the fuel alone, which determines the capacity of the engine to produce power from the fuel. The high-ignition point of methane makes natural gas difficult to ignite in Diesel-type engines, but gives it high anti-knock quality in spark-ignition engines.

Manufactured gas is much higher in cost than natural gas and has about half as high heating value. It requires less than half as much air for combustion as natural gas, making the net heating value of the fuel–air mixture not far from 90 Btu per cu ft. It is usually nearly half hydrogen and 25 to 30 per cent methane, with small added amounts of illuminants, C_2H_4 and C_6H_6, completing its combustible content. Several manufacturing processes are employed, the usual basic raw product being coal. Gas is manufactured and distributed principally for heating purposes, but is a satisfactory although uneconomical engine fuel.

Producer gas is made by partial combustion of solid fuel with restricted air supply and frequently with steam passed through the fuel bed. Its net heating value of only about 150 Btu per cu ft is low because of the inert nitrogen which makes up about half of its volume. Because it burns with about an equal volume of air, the net heating value of the fuel–air mixture is relatively high and approaches that of the gas alone more closely than it does for other fuels, reaching 70 to 75 Btu per cu ft of mixture.

A wide variety of gases results from reactions that occur in processing certain commercial products. Blast-furnace gas formed in the production of iron, propane and butane released in refining petroleum oils, and sewage gas liberated in sewage-disposal plants are the most important fuel gases whose production is incidental to industrial processes. Propane and butane are usually liquefied by compression and sold as bottled gas in steel containers. Both have extremely high heating values, butane being evaluated at about 3000 Btu per cu ft, but they require large amounts of air for combustion and produce fuel–air mixtures of about 90 Btu per cu ft. Blast-furnace gas, because of its high inert nitrogen content, releases less than 100 Btu per cu ft and forms combustible mixtures of about 60 Btu per cu ft. Engines operating on blast-furnace gas, other factors being equal, must therefore be much larger than those burning most other fuels.

Operation on by-product gas is usually complicated by variations in the constituents of the gas that occur as the cycle of the process is carried out and may be interfered with even more seriously by intermittent supply. Engines intended to use gases that are not continuously available in sufficient quantities are sometimes equipped for conversion to fuel-oil burning in order that their operation be independent of the gas supply.

3·21 Liquid fuels. A large percentage of all internal-combustion engines burn liquid fuels, most of which are refined from crude petroleum. Fuels processed from certain vegetable materials are quite satisfactory, but cannot compete with petroleum fuels on the present market. Petroleum is a mixture of many hydrocarbon compounds and comes from the oil wells as a brown or black liquid with a peculiar pungent odor. It can be burned in some large slow-speed Diesel engines by merely being centrifuged to remove the sand and water. All other petroleum fuels are refined from the crude oil by processes ranging from those which merely segregate certain groups of hydrocarbons that are already present in the crude oil to those which break down the chemical structure of some of the compounds and form new molecules.

The basis of the separation of the crude oil into the various products that are derived from it is the difference in the boiling points of its hydrocarbon compounds. The lightest constituents of the crude oil boil at temperatures well below zero, whereas the heavy ends are waxes and tarry compounds that are practically nonvolatile. The mixture can be separated into groups containing only compounds whose boiling points lie within a desired temperature range. This process is called fractional distillation and consists essentially in progressively boiling off and condensing fractions that boil below certain temperatures. Highly volatile petroleum ethers are evolved by a slight warming of the crude oil; then other ingredients too volatile for use in gasolines are driven off, followed, at progressively higher temperatures, by gasoline, naphtha, kerosene, light fuel oils or distillates, and lubricating oils. The residue contains the heavy fuel oils and solids.

In the early years of the petroleum industry, kerosene was the product for which the greatest demand existed; gasoline and heavier fuels, having little market value, were sometimes destroyed. Increased use of internal-combustion engines made gasoline the essential product, and refinery practice has progressed in the direction of getting more and better gasoline from the crude petroleum. More recently, the demand for Diesel and oil-burner fuels has necessitated increased yields of these less volatile fuels.

3·22 Hydrocarbon series. A thorough understanding of petroleum fuels and their behavior in the engine requires considerable knowledge of organic and physical chemistry, but a few of the fundamental principles are sufficient to provide a general idea of the relationship of the chemical structure of a fuel to its combustion characteristics. These characteristics, in turn, determine the suitability of the fuel for use in various-type engines.

Hydrocarbons are compounds of carbon and hydrogen of widely varying molecular weight and arrangement of atoms within the molecules. They are classified according to their molecular structure into several series or families, whose members have the same general formula but different molecular weights. Those present in petroleum fuels are paraffins, olefins, diolefins, naphthenes, and aromatics. The important significance of these series lies in their different combustion characteristics and their consequent effect upon engine performance. The eastern crude oils consist largely of paraffins, whereas the western crudes have large aromatic and naphthenic content. Olefins and diolefins are not common in natural petroleums, but are formed at the high temperatures used in some refining operations.

The paraffin series has the general formula C_nH_{2+2}, where n indicates the number of carbon atoms in the molecule. The paraffins are chain compounds, either straight or branched, and range from CH_4 containing only one carbon atom to the waxes containing about 30 carbon atoms. They are classified as saturated compounds, because no additional hydrogen atoms can be attached to the carbon atoms. Normal paraffins have all of the carbon atoms linked together in a straight chain with the hydrogen atoms attached to each side and at each end of the carbon chain. Typical of these is normal pentane which has its five carbon atoms linked together by single bonds and the hydrogen atoms attached so as to satisfy the valence of each. Since carbon has a valence of four and hydrogen of one, there must be 12 atoms in the pentane molecule. The normal pentane molecule may be shown graphically in the following manner:

$$\begin{array}{ccccc} H & H & H & H & H \\ | & | & | & | & | \\ H-C-&C-&C-&C-&C-H \\ | & | & | & | & | \\ H & H & H & H & H \end{array}$$

The chemical formula for pentane is seen to be C_5H_{12}, conforming to the general paraffin formula, C_nH_{2+2}.

Various isomers of the paraffins are formed, differing from the normal paraffins in having branched-chain structures instead of straight chains. Isomers are defined as compounds composed of the same elements and having the same molecular weight as the normal compound but differing in one or more properties, which difference is considered to be the effect of structural rearrangement of the molecule. One such isomer of pentane is called methyl butane or isopentane. It differs from normal pentane structurally only in having four carbons in the chain, with the fifth one attached to one of the others. It may also be considered as differing from normal butane in the substitution of the methyl radical CH_3 for one of its hydrogen atoms.

Normal butane

Methyl butane

The methyl butane molecule contains the same number of each atom and therefore has the same formula and molecular weight as normal pentane, but the different molecular structure effects a change in the properties of the compound evidenced by its different gravity, boiling point, ignition temperature, and other factors affecting its combustion characteristics.

The olefin series has the general formula C_nH_{2n} and differs from the paraffin series by being unsaturated, because two of the carbon atoms in the chain are linked together by a double bond, thereby releasing two hydrogen atoms. The molecular structure of one of the isomeric forms of pentylene, C_5H_{10}, is shown graphically in the following manner.

The diolefin series has the general formula C_nH_{2n-2}. It is more unsaturated than the olefin, two additional hydrogen atoms being omitted from the chain and replaced by a second double-bonded pair of carbon atoms. The molecular structure of one of the diolefins, butadiene, C_4H_6, is shown.

$$\begin{array}{cccc} H & H & H & H \\ | & | & | & | \\ H\!-\!C\!=\!C\!-\!C\!=\!C\!-\!H \end{array}$$

The naphthenes have the same general formula as the olefins, C_nH_{2n}, but are saturated ring-structure compounds, structurally equivalent to a normal paraffin that has been bent around to permit the two ends of the chain to be joined together. The two hydrogen atoms at the ends of the paraffin chain are eliminated in the ring structure. Cyclopentane, C_5H_{10}, is shown graphically.

The aromatics have the ring structure of the naphthenes but are unsaturated and have three double bonds which reduce the number of hydrogen atoms by six, making the general formula C_nH_{2n-6}. The benzene-ring molecule C_6H_6 is shown.

The characteristics of the hydrocarbons which affect their suitability as engine fuels depend upon both their molecular structure and molecular weight. Volatility, as evidenced by decreased boiling point, increases as molecular weight decreases. Ignition temperature increases with decreased molecular weight for any one series of compounds. Ignition temperature also increases as the compactness or complexity of the molecule increases. Volatility and ignition temperature are the principal factors that determine whether a fuel is suitable for a spark-ignition or a compression-ignition engine. Most spark-ignition engines induct a combustible mixture of fuel and air that is prepared outside the cylinder of the engine. The fuel should be sufficiently volatile to permit it to be substantially vaporized during the intake stroke. Gasoline, with a boiling-point range of about 100 to 400 F, meets the volatility requirements of spark-ignition engines of the carburetor type. Some spark-ignition engines use mechanical-injection systems instead of carburetors and can use fuels of lower volatility.

3·23   Spark-ignition combustion. In the spark-ignition engine, combustion originates at the spark-plug points, where a small quantity of fuel is heated above its ignition point by the high temperature of the electric spark. The surface of the particle of fuel that was ignited by the spark presents a tiny incandescent flame front to the particles of fuel adjacent to it, causing them to ignite and, in turn, present a flame front of larger area to the fuel particles surrounding them. This flame front travels through the unburned charge radially across the combustion chamber and, if undisturbed, progressively burns all of the fuel. This process is illustrated in *a*, Fig. 3·17. As each particle of fuel is burned, its chemical energy is released, causing its products of combustion to attain a very high temperature. The resulting expansion of the burned portion compresses the unburned particles by crowding them into a progressively smaller specific volume, and the accompanying temperature rise may cause the ignition point of the fuel to be attained ahead of the flame front. If this happens, all of the remaining unburned fuel will ignite spontaneously, and, instead of burning progressively, it will burn almost instantaneously with a rapid-pressure rise which sets up a high-frequency pressure wave and causes an audible knock that is called detonation. This condition is illustrated in *b*, Fig. 3·17. It should be noted that this combustion irregularity occurs only after burning has progressed considerably, and it involves the last portion of the charge to burn. The higher the ignition point of the fuel, the less possibility there will be for this spontaneous combustion to occur under given combustion-chamber conditions, and the higher its anti-knock quality. Hydrocarbons of relatively low molecular weight and compact or complex structure meet this requirement as they also do the volatility limitation.

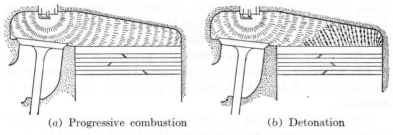

(*a*) Progressive combustion   (*b*) Detonation

Fɪɢ. 3·17 Combustion in the spark-ignition engine

3·24 Octane rating. The compression ratio of the engine determines the temperature and pressure attained by the charge at the end of the compression stroke for given initial conditions. The more nearly the charge approaches self-ignition conditions before being ignited by the flame front created by the spark and the longer it is exposed to these conditions, the greater the possibility of detonation. The factors that control self-ignition include not only temperature and time but also the density and burning rate of the charge. Consequently, the higher the volumetric efficiency of the engine, the higher its compression ratio, and the more powerful the fuel–air ratio of the mixture in the cylinder, the more knock-resistant the fuel must be if detonation is to be avoided. Because the speed of the engine affects the time of exposure to self-ignition temperature, operation at low speed encourages detonation. It naturally follows that, the higher the compression ratio, other factors being equal, the greater the tendency for detonation. The compression ratio at which a fuel can be used without detonation is thus a measure of its anti-knock quality. This fact is utilized in rating the anti-knock quality of gasolines by the octane scale.

The octane method of rating fuels requires an actual test of the fuel in a special knock-rating engine that is so constructed that the compression ratio can be varied while all other operational factors are held constant. The tendency of the fuel to knock can be measured by varying the compression ratio of the test engine until a certain intensity of knock is indicated by a knock meter which measures the rate of pressure rise during the combustion period. This knocking tendency is then matched by preparing a reference fuel composed of iso-octane, a branched-chain paraffin of high anti-knock quality, and normal heptane, a straight-chain paraffin of high knocking tendency, in such proportions that the mixture behaves the same in the engine as the fuel being rated. The higher the percentage of iso-octane in the reference fuel that has the same knocking tendency as the fuel being rated, the higher the anti-knock quality that is indicated.

The octane number of the fuel is expressed as the per cent by volume of iso-octane in a reference blend with normal heptane that has the same anti-knock quality as the fuel. The term 100 octane means a high anti-knock quality equal to that of pure iso-octane, while zero octane means a very low anti-knock quality equal to that of pure normal heptane. If the fuel has higher anti-knock quality than pure iso-octane, as some aviation gasolines now have, this method of testing cannot be used, but approximate octane numbers can be assigned by extrapolation. It should be noted that the octane rating is merely a comparison between the two fuels and does not mean that there is any iso-octane actually present in the gasoline.

3·25 Volatility rating. The volatility of a liquid fuel is determined by a standard distillation test designed to find the lowest or initial boiling point at which the first drop of the fuel distils and the percentage of the original amount of fuel distilled at each chosen increment of temperature rise up to the end point or maximum boiling point. The standard apparatus for this test is illustrated in Fig. 3·18. The fuel sample is placed in the glass flask and heated by the gas burner so that it is boiled off at a prescribed rate. The thermometer inserted in the flask indicates the temperature of the vapor leaving the flask at each interval. The vapor enters the condenser and is cooled to a liquid which drips into the graduated cylinder. The quantity distilled is recorded with the corresponding temperature at each stage.

A volatility curve is plotted from these data which shows, not only the boiling-point range of the fuel, but also the temperature

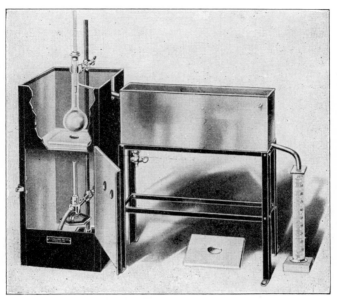

Fig. 3·18   Tag ASTM distillation apparatus

necessary to boil each fraction. Two fuels may have the same boiling range, but differ widely in overall volatility, because the amounts that vaporize when the fuel is heated to each temperature within that range are greatly different. Starting quality, rapidity of warming up, acceleration, power, and completeness of combustion are related to the volatility or distillation curve of a gasoline. Figure 3·19 shows typical distillation curves for a gasoline and a Diesel fuel. Note that the least volatile portion of the gasoline boils at the boiling point of the most volatile portion of the Diesel fuel. These are the boiling points at atmospheric pressure and should not be confused with the evaporation temperatures when atomized and mixed with air. The vapor pressure is then much lower than the total pressure of the mixture, and the temperature of vaporization is correspondingly lower.

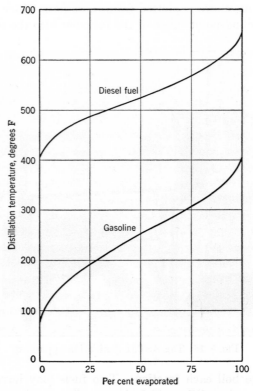

Fig. 3·19   Distillation curves of gasoline and Diesel fuel

3·26   Compression-ignition combustion.   Combustion in the compression-ignition or Diesel-type engine differs extremely from that in the spark-ignition engine.   The compression ratio must be sufficiently high to raise the temperature of the compressed-air charge well above the ignition point of the fuel.   The fuel is sprayed into the combustion chamber as the end of the compression stroke is approached and is distributed in the form of tiny droplets throughout the air charge.   The particles of fuel receive heat by transfer from the air, and their temperature rises to the boiling point of some portion which vaporizes and absorbs additional heat until the ignition point of the most easily ignited particle is reached. Ignition is thus originated at many points throughout the combustion chamber after a certain delay during which the vaporization, heating, and precombustion reactions occur. The length of this delay or ignition lag, as it is called, is not the same for all fuels, and it is a measure of the ignition quality of the fuel. It determines whether or not the engine will run smoothly, because the rate of pressure rise in the cylinder accompanying ignition of the fuel depends upon the amount of fuel that has accumulated in the combustion chamber before ignition.

If the ignition lag is long, a large portion or perhaps all of the fuel will have been injected before any of it ignites. This accumulated fuel will then burn almost instantaneously, and a large amount of energy will be released during the first instant of combustion with a resulting overly rapid rise in cylinder pressure. If this initial burning is too rapid, there will be a combustion knock, and the engine will be rough running and noisy. If the fuel ignites quickly, only a small amount of fuel will be involved in the initial burning, and the remainder will burn progressively as it is sprayed in. Combustion will then start without any audible knock, and the engine will run smoothly. It should then be noted that the knock in a Diesel-type engine occurs at the beginning of combustion instead of at the end as in the spark-ignition type.

3·27   Cetane rating. The ignition quality of a Diesel fuel is rated in the form of a cetane number by a comparison method analogous to the octane rating system. A special variable-compression test engine is used, and the compression ratio is established which causes ignition a certain standard delay period after the injection of the fuel. A reference blend of cetane, a long straight-chain easily ignited paraffin, and α-methyl naphthalene, a closely knit ring-type naphthalene, is then prepared which matches the ignition behavior of the fuel being rated. The per cent by volume of cetane in this reference blend is the cetane number assigned to the fuel. A fuel of high-ignition quality will have a high-cetane number. In order to have a high-cetane number, the molecular structure of a hydrocarbon must be simple and its molecular weight high. This latter requirement limits the volatility range of Diesel fuels to temperatures above those of gasolines.

It is fortunate that the requirements, as to both volatility and ignition temperature of gasoline and Diesel fuel, are directly opposite, because each uses a different group of the hydrocarbons present in petroleum. The high volatility and high-ignition temperature required of gasoline are associated in the same hydrocarbons, whereas the low volatility and low self-ignition temperature required of Diesel fuels are found in other heavier compounds.

3·28 Refining methods. Early refining methods consisted simply in fractional distillation of the crude oil at desired temperature increments which bracketed together the ingredients appropriate to the different products. It was later found that the yield of gasoline from this process was insufficient to meet the demands, as less than 20 per cent of the crude oil was convertible to gasoline. The thermal-cracking process was then devised, whereby the larger and simpler molecules were broken down by heating to high temperatures into lighter molecules in the gasoline range of volatility. More stable molecular structures were also attained by cracking, and gasolines of higher-octane rating were produced besides increasing the yield to nearly 50 per cent of the crude oil. Olefins, diolefins, and aromatics are formed by high-temperature cracking, whereas isomers of the paraffins are formed at lower temperatures.

More recently developed cracking processes employ catalysts which permit accurate control of the compounds formed and produce gasoline of higher-octane number than thermal cracking. Olefins and diolefins, which are unstable in storage and cause gum formation, are not present in catalytically cracked fuels.

Polymerization is a process that is chemically the opposite of cracking and is used extensively to convert hydrocarbons that are too light and volatile for gasoline into heavier compounds of the desired volatility. Numerous other processes for synthesizing desirable molecules from those in the portion of the crude oil that is not suitable for gasoline have been developed by petroleum technologists, and further increases in yield and octane number have resulted, but greater cost of production limits their application.

3·29   Knock inhibitors.   The demand for very high-octane fuels for use in high-compression engines, especially for aviation use, has been met by adding knock inhibitors to gasolines whose molecular structure alone did not provide the desired stability. Tetraethyl lead has proved the most effective of these additives, and it is used extensively.   It should be noted that increasing the octane rating of a gasoline does not increase its energy content, but merely suppresses detonation and permits its use in engines of higher efficiency, gained by increased compression ratios, and does not improve the performance of engines for which lower-octane fuels are suitable.   The octane number indicates only the anti-knock quality and does not evaluate any other property of the gasoline.

Injection of water or mixtures of water and methyl alcohol into the charge in the inlet manifold has proved an effective method of decreasing the octane requirement of high-compression spark-ignition engines.   Devices are available that automatically supply mixtures of alcohol and water, usually in equal proportions, to the inlet manifold when the manifold vacuum falls to a certain point as the load on the engine increases.   There is ordinarily no need for anti-knock agents except when accelerating or when operating at loads requiring a well-opened throttle, especially at low engine speeds.   Anti-detonant injection makes it possible to operate a motor vehicle a large portion of the time on a gasoline that would cause severe knock except at relatively light loads, the additive being supplied only when needed at the higher loads.

The function of water–alcohol mixtures in improving the anti-knock performance of the engine is largely as an internal coolant. The high latent heat of vaporization of water causes it to act as a refrigerant to reduce the temperature rise of the charge before ignition.   Alcohol has a much higher anti-knock rating than ordinary gasoline and also has a higher latent heat, and so it acts both as an octane improver and an internal coolant.   Water alone is unsatisfactory as a year-round additive because the supply would freeze in winter or at high altitude unless blended with alcohol or similar compounds.

The power developed by an unsupercharged engine may increase when a water–alcohol blend is introduced into the inlet manifold because the density of the charge is increased by the cooling effect of vaporization, and a greater weight of charge is inducted. Water–alcohol injection has been used extensively to permit airplane engines to develop increased take-off power by the use of supercharge pressures exceeding the knock limit of the engine on the highest-octane gasoline available. Wide application of anti-detonate injectors to motor vehicles is not likely until the anti-knock characteristics of motor fuels on the market are stabilized so that a standardized device can be developed.

3·30 Nomenclature. In order to read intelligently and understandingly discussions of internal-combustion engines, it is necessary to learn the nomenclature by which the many components of an engine are designated. Some of these terms are descriptive of the parts or their functions, but others are not so readily associated with the devices to which they have been applied. Figure 3·20 illustrates those parts of an automobile engine that would be made visible if it were cut across through one of its cylinders. The more important parts exposed to view by sectioning the engine in this manner are indicated. The following discussion is intended to define the terms that are used to designate the important parts of an engine and to explain their functions.

Cylinder Block. The cylinder block forms the structural framework of the engine except in certain large units that are built up from a foundation or bedplate and in aviation engines with air-cooled cylinders. In the automotive-type engine, the cylinder block is an alloy-iron casting extending ordinarily from the crankshaft vertically to the top of the cylinder bores. Machined surfaces are provided at appropriate places for attaching the bearings that support the crankshaft and for connecting adjacent units of the engine to the block. The upper surface is fitted to retain the cylinder head in position, and the lower extremity is machined for attaching an oil pan which completes the enclosure for the crankshaft and acts as an oil sump for the lubricating system. The extension of the cylinder block below the cylinders is called the crankcase.

The cylinders proper consist of cylindrical passages extending vertically through the block, bored to accurate dimensions, and honed to smooth bearing surfaces. The cylinders are frequently fitted with thin hardened liners which form the cylinder walls instead of these being machined in the block itself. The camshaft

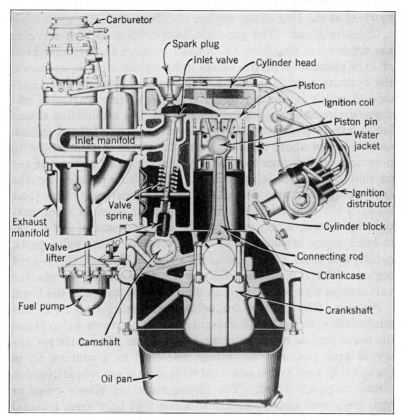

FIG. 3·20 Cross section of automobile engine

which operates the valves is fitted into a passage bored lengthwise of the cylinder block, and suitable guides for the valve lifters are formed above it. The cylinder block illustrated in Fig. 3·20 is of the L-head type and carries the valve passages and valve seats beside the upper extremities of the cylinder bores. Machined faces for attaching the inlet and exhaust manifolds are provided where the valve ports terminate on the side of the block.

Water passages or jackets are cored into the block around the cylinders and valves for cooling. The supports by which the engine is mounted are usually attached to the front cover which encloses the gears or chains by which the camshaft is driven from the crankshaft and to the bell housing which encloses the flywheel at the rear of the engine.

Cylinder Head. The gas-tight compartments which serve as the combustion chambers are formed between the cylinder head and the pistons. With the valves in the cylinder block, as shown, the cylinder head is merely a water-jacketed cover, the underside of which is profiled to form spaces of the exact size and shape desired above each cylinder bore. The combustion chamber is largely concentrated over the valves in the L-head engine, and the space above the far side of the piston is thinned out to provide a quench area to control the temperature of the end gas so that detonation is minimized. Threaded openings for the spark plugs are provided at the proper locations. The joint between the cylinder head and the cylinder block is made gas-tight by a composition gasket. The cylinder head of the valve-in-head engine is complicated by the presence of the valve ports, guides, and seats, which are in the cylinder block of the L-head engine. The supports for the rocker arms which operate the valves must also be provided on top if the valves are in the head.

Pistons. The pistons are cylindrical castings of iron, aluminum alloy, or steel, with one end closed by a crown which forms the lower surface of the combustion chamber. The outer periphery of each piston is accurately machined to a running fit in the cylinder bore and is provided with several grooves into which piston rings are fitted. The piston rings are elastic rings of high-grade cast iron which are so made that they exert a radial force against the cylinder wall and tend to prevent gas leakage through the joint between the piston and the cylinder wall. The upper rings are plain rings, called compression rings, which serve to prevent escape of gases from the combustion chamber. The rings in the lower grooves are vented oil rings that are especially designed to distribute the oil uniformly around the cylinder in a film of proper thickness. The oil rings also scrape excess lubricating oil from the cylinder wall and dispose of it through drain holes leading from the ring grooves to the piston interior.

The pistons are attached to the connecting rods by hardened steel piston pins fitted into bosses cast in opposite sides of the piston. Piston pins are said to be floating when they are free to turn in bearings both in the upper ends of the connecting rods and in the piston bosses but are restrained by suitable retainers from contacting the cylinder wall. In some installations the pin is secured in either the connecting rod or the piston bosses and is not free to turn in both. The portion of the piston below the pin bosses is called the skirt and serves as a bearing surface for the piston.

Connecting Rods. The reciprocating motion of the pistons is adapted to the rotary motion of the crankshaft by forged steel rods which connect them together. The upper ends of the rods are formed into eyes and bushed with bronze or similar bearing material unless the design requires that the piston pins be clamped in the rods. The lower ends are fitted with removable caps that are retained by two or more bolts, and the bored openings are lined with babbitt or similar bearing metal. This lining may be cast in place, or it may be in the form of a precision insert that fits closely within the bore. The rods are usually of I section and may be rifle-drilled to convey lubricant from a passage in the crankshaft to the piston pins.

Crankshaft. The crankshaft is one of the most important parts of the engine and serves to convert the forces applied by the connecting rods into a rotational force. It controls the motion of the pistons and must be designed to cause them to reciprocate in proper sequence. Alloy-steel forgings are usually employed in the crankshaft, although cast-alloy-iron shafts are in common use.

The crankshaft is made up of a throw for each cylinder, or each pair of cylinders if the engine is of the V type, and a suitable number of main bearings located at the two ends and between adjacent throws. The throws are arranged in one or more planes passing through the center of rotation that is common to all of the main bearings. The angles between the throws depend upon the number of cylinders served by the shaft, which determines the firing interval between the cylinders. The location of the throws in the various radial directions depends upon the firing order of the cylinders. The firing order is chosen to distribute the power impulses along the length of the engine, and in the six-cylinder engine the standard sequence is 1-5-3-6-2-4.

Since the crankshaft is made up of rotating masses that are displaced from the center of rotation, centrifugal forces are set up that must be balanced by counterweights opposite the throws. The bearing areas on the crank throws to which the connecting rods are attached are called crankpins, and the radial arms are called cheeks. The distance from the crankpin centers to the main bearing center establishes the stroke of the pistons. The crankshaft is usually drilled to permit oil to be circulated from entrances in the main bearing areas to the crankpins. The main bearing journals operate in soft metal liners similar to those used in the lower ends of the connecting rods.

Valve Mechanism. The camshaft originates the motion that is imparted to the valves and is driven from the crankshaft by a chain or gears. In four-stroke-cycle engines the entire group of valves operates once in two turns of the crankshaft. The camshaft operates each of the valves in one turn and must therefore turn at half the speed of the crankshaft. Each valve requires a cam to open and close it at the proper point in the engine cycle. The complete camshaft for a multicylinder engine consists of a shaft extending the length of the engine with a cam formed adjacent to each valve. The sequence in which the lifting surfaces of the several cams present themselves as the shaft rotates is established by the firing order of the cylinders chosen by the designer. The shape of the cams is established by the valve timing and the lift imparted to the valves.

Associated with the camshaft is a set of cam followers or valve lifters which are reciprocated by contact with the cam surfaces. The valve lifters are interposed between the camshaft and the valves to take the side thrust caused by the rotation of the cams and to provide an adjustment by which the lash in the mechanism can be controlled. Push rods and rocker arms are also included in the camshaft mechanism for valve-in-head engines, because the motion of the lifter must be conveyed to the cylinder head and reversed in direction. The camshaft can be carried on the head above the valves to eliminate this extra linkage.

The valves are mushroom-shaped and are called poppet valves. The bevel-seated heads seal against matching seats in the combustion-chamber wall. The valve stems are closely fitted in guides with which they form gas-tight joints to prevent manifold leakage. Helical springs apply the necessary closing force through spring seats that are attached to the ends of the valve stems by retainers.

Manifolds. The inlet-valve passages in the cylinder head of the valve-in-head engine or in the cylinder block of the L-head engine must be connected to the outlet of the carburetor. The inlet manifold is simply a tube extending along the length of the cylinder block with a branch at each inlet valve and a central inlet at the top to which the carburetor is attached. The principal objectives in the design of the manifold are to provide equal distribution of fuel and air to the several cylinders and to deliver as large a charge as possible when the engine is not throttled.

The exhaust manifold gathers together the streams of products of combustion leaving the exhaust passages of the cylinders and conveys them to the muffler. Minimum possible restriction to flow is desirable.

Fuel Pump. The fuel-supply tank is ordinarily at a lower level than the carburetor, necessitating a pump to supply the fuel to the engine. The usual type of pump employs a diaphragm of impregnated fabric that is displaced on its suction stroke by a lever which bears against one of the cams on the camshaft. It is propelled on its return or delivery stroke by a spring which exerts only sufficient force to push the diaphragm against a fuel discharge pressure of about 4 psi. The pump executes delivery strokes only in accordance with the amount of fuel needed by the carburetor, because the spring can return the diaphragm only as rapidly as the carburetor accepts the fuel.

3·31 Classification. The internal-combustion engine has attained a wide variety of forms in order to meet the requirements of the many widely differing applications to which it has been adapted. Although basically the same in fundamental principle, these engines differ appreciably in structural design, arrangement of components, accessory equipment, and operating characteristics. Any attempt to classify them into clearly defined groups is complicated by the fact that some of the distinguishing features of each type engine are found in varied combinations with certain other features which are distinctive of another type engine. It is necessary to specify a number of things about any engine in order to define its field of application, fuel limitations, and whether it functions in one manner or another. A knowledge of some of the more important functional and constructional differences between these widely diversified engines is essential to the acquirement of a proper background for the study of internal-combustion engines. Some of the more important methods of classifying engines are discussed in the following paragraphs.

Number of Strokes per Cycle. One of the most important differences that may be used as a basis in grouping together certain engines is whether two or four strokes of the pistons are required to complete the operating cycle of the engine. Regardless of their classification on any other basis, engines of all types and for all purposes may be of either the two-stroke-cycle or the four-stroke-cycle type. Actually, the two-stroke engine has not been applied to a wide field because of difficulties in charging and scavenging the cylinders under certain conditions of operation. All high-speed engines are of the four-stroke type with the exception of small outboard marine engines and others of similar structural type intended for different usage. Other than these small gasoline engines, practically all of the two-stroke engines are now of the Diesel or compression-ignition type. The fact that the incoming charge is used to push out the products of combustion remaining in the cylinder at the completion of the power stroke prevents efficient operation on the two-stroke cycle when the incoming charge is a combustible mixture of fuel and air. Some portion of the entering charge invariably escapes with the exhaust gases. This loss of charge to the exhaust is of small consequence if the fuel enters after scavenging is completed, as in the Diesel, but constitutes a serious loss if the fuel has already been mixed with the entering air. The distinguishing feature of the two-stroke engine is the inclusion of some form of pump or blower to place the incoming charge under pressure. This is not necessary in the four-stroke engine unless it is supercharged.

Method of Igniting Charge. All engines may be divided into two groups according to the method of raising the fuel temperature to the ignition point. Those employing compression ratios of between about 14 and 18 cause the air charge to attain a temperature sufficient to ignite ordinary fuels without any supplementary ignition device. Such engines operate on the Diesel principle of compression ignition which requires that the charge inducted into the cylinders be noninflammable and that the fuel be injected late in the compression stroke at the precise instant that will properly time combustion. The second group employs compression ratios that are limited to a maximum of about seven to avoid self-ignition. The fuel and air must be combined to form an inflammable mixture before the combustion period. Ignition is by means of an electric spark.

Fuel Systems. Engines have been designed for operation with three general types of fuels: solid, liquid, and gaseous. Solid fuel, in the form of pulverized coal, has been burned with some success, but the abrasive nature of the ash presents a problem that has not been mastered. Liquid fuels are burned either by carburetion or injection. Gases require no conversion preparatory to combustion and permit the use of a simple mixing valve.

Fuel systems are necessarily adapted, not only to the type of fuel used, but also to the operating cycle of the engine. Volatile fuels may be aspirated into the air stream as it flows through a carburetor, or they may be injected at moderate pressure into the air as it enters each cylinder or directly into the cylinders after the air has entered. Nonvolatile fuels, whether burned by compression ignition or spark ignition, are injected into the engine cylinder. Compression ignition requires a more elaborate injection system, because extremely high fuel pressures are necessary to atomize the fuel, and accurate timing must be maintained.

Number and Arrangement of Cylinders. Whether an engine has but one cylinder or several depends to a large extent upon the purpose for which the engine is intended. When a relatively small power output is required at slow speed under stationary power-plant conditions, a single-cylinder engine of quite large dimensions may be appropriate. When flexibility and smoothness of operation are important, six or eight small cylinders may be a more logical choice, even for power requirements that could easily be met with fewer and larger cylinders. Extremely large power capacity necessitates an increase in the number of cylinders, because the power that can be developed in each cylinder is limited by practical considerations. Engines having as many as 24 cylinders are produced for aviation use.

Single-cylinder engines may be built with the axis of the cylinder horizontal, but usually the cylinder is mounted vertically. Multicylinder designs permit a wide latitude in cylinder arrangement. The inline type has all cylinders in a single row, and they may be vertical, as in many automobile engines, or horizontal, as in some truck and bus engines that are disposed beneath the body to permit full space utilization above. V-type engines have half the cylinders in one line or bank and the other half in a second bank, with a common crankshaft at the intersection of the planes of the axes of the two rows of cylinders. Two connecting rods are attached to each throw of the crankshaft, and each cylinder in one bank is thus paired with the opposite cylinder in the other bank. The crankshaft has as many throws as there are cylinders in one bank. The angle between the two banks is determined by the application of the engine and the number of cylinders. It may be as small as 45 degrees or it may be 180 degrees, in which case it is classed as an opposed cylinder engine rather than a V-type.

Figure 3·21 shows a cross section of an eight-cylinder 90-degree V-type Studebaker engine of the valve-in-head design. This engine is representative of the compact short-stroke design that has been found desirable in providing the greater rigidity necessitated by the higher pressures encountered in engines of high compression ratio.

Several arrangements of cylinders are used in combining more than ordinary numbers of cylinders into a single engine. Engines with four banks of cylinders and only one crankshaft are called X-type engines. Four banks of cylinders are also combined with two crankshafts in the form of a double V. Multicylinder engines with all of the connecting rods attached to a single crank throw are called radial engines. They may have two such rows with as many as nine cylinders in each row.

Valve Type and Location. Most engines now employ poppet or mushroom valves that are held in the closed position by helical springs and are operated by a camshaft and associated linkage. The seat of the poppet valve is usually beveled at an angle of either 30 or 45 degrees with the plane of the valve head. Double-

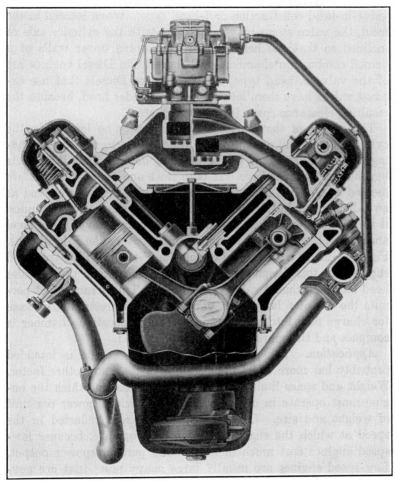

Fig. 3·21 Cross-sectional view of Studebaker V-8 engine

sleeve-valve engines, in which two reciprocating cylindrical sleeves containing inlet and exhaust ports were interposed between the piston and the cylinder wall, were quite widely used several years ago but are seldom seen now. Single-sleeve-valve types in which the sleeve has a combined reciprocating and oscillating motion are used by a few foreign manufacturers.

The inlet and exhaust valves of the four-stroke engine may both be inverted over the top of the piston in the widely used valve-in-head construction or I-head type. When located in the head, the valve stems may be parallel with the cylinder axis or inclined so that the heads lie in the sloping upper walls of a domed combustion chamber. All four-stroke Diesel engines are of the valve-in-head type, and two-stroke Diesels that use exhaust valves have them located in the cylinder head, because the resulting clearance space is more compact.

The valves of the four-stroke engine may be located in the cylinder block and open upward into pockets formed by extending the clearance space in the cylinder head so that it projects beyond the cylinder bore. If both inlet and exhaust valves are located at one side of the cylinder bore, the engine is classed as an L-head type, but, if they are on opposite sides of the cylinder, it is a T-head engine. Some engines have one valve in the head and one on the side in an arrangement known as the F-head type. Figure 3·22 is a cross section of the F-head Willys-Overland engine. In this design the inlet valve is located in the cylinder head and the exhaust valve in the block. This arrangement permits the use of a large inlet valve with an unrestricted passage for charge flow into the cylinder. The combustion chamber is compact and the spark plug favorably located.

Application. The purpose for which an engine is intended probably has more effect upon its design than any other factor. Weight and space limitations dictate the speed at which the engine must operate in order to develop sufficient power per unit of weight and size. Cost limitations are also reflected in the speed at which the engine is designed to operate, because low-speed engines cost much more to build per horsepower output. Low-speed engines are usually large heavy units that are governed to maintain a relatively constant speed. They are largely of the Diesel type, although most gas engines are also in this classification. Large marine and stationary power applications are the principal fields of the low-speed type.

Automotive applications require the light weight and flexibility of the high-speed multicylinder type. High-speed gasoline engines, such as the automobile type, commonly operate over a wide range of speeds with top speeds well above 4000 rpm. High-speed Diesel engines intended for automotive applications oper-

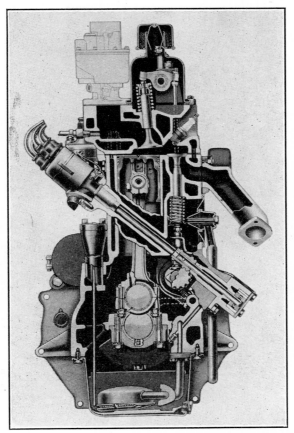

Fig. 3·22   Cross-sectional view of F-head Willys-Overland engine

ate at speeds that would be medium speed for gasoline engines, and few go higher than 2500 rpm. Diesels of this type are extensively used for truck and tractor propulsion. Figures 3·23 and 3·24 illustrate a Cummins high-speed Diesel engine. It is representative of the type that is applicable to heavy-duty automotive, portable, stationary, and marine uses. It differs from the automobile engine of Fig. 3·20 in that it is of the valve-in-head type, has a Diesel fuel-injection system instead of a carburetor, has removable cylinder liners, and is of heavier more rugged construction throughout.

Aviation engines operate under conditions that impose very

Fig. 3·23 Cummins truck-type Diesel engine

special requirements. The need for large horsepower capacity, light weight, and absolute reliability justifies construction costs that would be considered prohibitive for other uses. High-strength alloys are used for highly stressed parts and lightweight alloys contribute further weight savings at other points. Super-chargers are necessary to enable the engine to obtain sufficient weight of charge at high altitudes where the specific weight of the air is low. Aviation engines are usually of the V-type or the radial type and may be either air- or liquid-cooled.

3·32 Power processes. The function in the internal-combustion engine is to convert heat released by combustion of fuel into mechanical energy or power. Regardless of type: spark

Fig. 3·24   Cut-away view of Cummins Diesel engine

ignition or compression ignition; four-stroke cycle or two-stroke cycle; gas, gasoline, or fuel-oil burning; all must in some way complete certain processes which are essential to this conversion

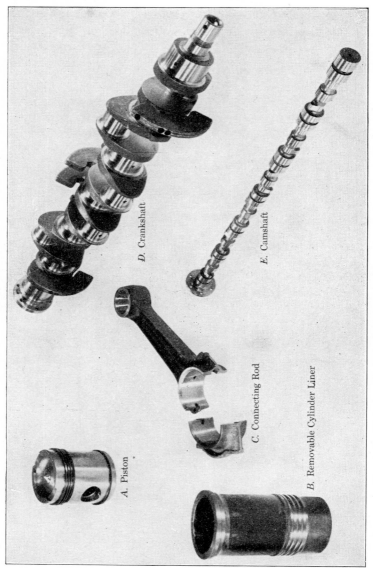

FIG. 3·24 (*Continued*)   Some of the working parts of Cummins Diesel engine

of stored chemical energy into power. Some of these processes play a direct part in completing the engine cycle, whereas others, although equally necessary for its operation, do not carry out any of the actual steps that make up the cycle. The essential processes of the internal-combustion engine may be grouped as cylinder charging, mixture making, cylinder treatment of charge, internal temperature control, lubrication, and regulation.

3·33 Cylinder charging. The first step that must be taken in order to burn a fuel–air mixture within the cylinder of an engine is to supply the charge to the cylinder. Air will not flow into an engine cylinder of its own accord. It must be pumped in quantities of 100 or more cu ft per hr for each horsepower developed by the average engine. The first function of the engine is therefore that of an air pump to supply oxygen to the cylinders to react with the fuel. This function includes forcing from the cylinder the products of combustion which must be removed to make room for the next air charge, either by direct pumping action of the piston, as in the four-stroke cycle, or by requiring the entering air charge to push out the exhaust gases under the influence of the air-supply pump, as in the two-stroke cycle.

The pumping mechanism of the four-stroke-cycle engine consists of a system of inlet and exhaust valves that are mechanically actuated in phase with the movement of the piston. The exhaust valve must be held open during the inward stroke of the piston following the power stroke, and the inlet valve must be open during the next outward stroke.

Theoretically, the opening and closing events of the valves would occur at the crankshaft dead-center positions coincident with the beginning and ending of the piston strokes, but the time necessary for opening and closing the valves and the effects of high speeds upon the flow of the gases require that these events be displaced somewhat from the dead-center points. The intake and exhaust periods of the cycle are therefore not truly intake and exhaust strokes, since each includes 50 or more degrees of crank rotation in excess of a full piston stroke, and the two periods actually overlap to some extent. The most desirable timing of the valve operation is determined experimentally for

each engine. A typical automobile-engine valve-timing spiral is
shown in Fig. 3·25a.

This diagram shows all four valve events, inlet opening, inlet
closure, exhaust opening, and exhaust closure, to be displaced
appreciably from the top and bottom dead-center points, where
they would theoretically occur. Opening events are earlier and
closing events later to allow for time required to open and close

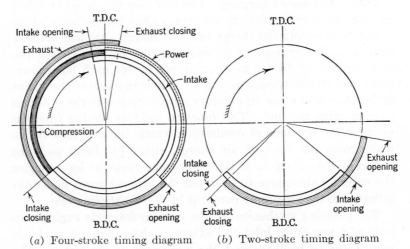

(*a*) Four-stroke timing diagram   (*b*) Two-stroke timing diagram

FIG. 3·25   Timing of intake and exhaust events

the valves without excessive inertia loading or slamming. Ramps
are provided on each cam to start the valve lift gradually and to
slow down the valve return motion slightly before the seat is
contacted. Of still greater significance, however, are the advance in opening timing and delay in closure for the purpose of
utilizing the inertia of the flowing gases and for other practical
considerations.

The exhaust valve is shown to open about 45 degrees before the
piston reaches its bottom dead center. This so-called release
point occurs well before the end of the power stroke in order to
provide a blow-down period, during which the pressure in the
cylinder is reduced by outflow of products of combustion to nearly
that of the exhaust manifold by the end of the piston stroke.

This results in some loss of work done on the piston by the expanding gases, but effects a greater reduction in the negative work that the piston must do in being pushed up against the back pressure of the gases during the early part of the exhaust stroke. The optimum exhaust-opening point is that at which the net work of the cycle is a maximum.

The exhaust valve is allowed to remain open some 10 to 20 degrees after the piston has reached its top dead-center position in the typical high-speed engine. The exhaust gas flows rapidly from the cylinder during the entire exhaust stroke, and the moving column has considerable kinetic energy because of its high velocity. Flow will thus continue outward after the piston is no longer pushing the gases. If the valve is still open, this inertia effect will reduce the pressure in the combustion chamber appreciably below exhaust-manifold pressure, thereby decreasing the weight of spent gases retained in the clearance space to dilute the incoming charge. This inertia effect of the outflowing exhaust gases is also the reason for opening the inlet valve before the end of the exhaust stroke. A partial vacuum is formed in the cylinder behind the moving column of exhaust gases, and this vacuum can be used to start the flow of fresh charge into the cylinder by opening the inlet valve at the point in the cycle at which the cylinder pressure is reduced to that of the inlet manifold. This valve-overlap period results in improved scavenging of the clearance space and more complete filling of the cylinder with fresh charge.

The inlet valve is allowed to remain open 50 degrees or more after bottom dead center to utilize the ram effect resulting from the kinetic energy of the column of rapidly moving charge in the inlet manifold. The flow of fresh charge persists after the piston has started upward on the compression stroke, and at some point, depending upon the engine speed and the flow characteristics of the induction system, a maximum weight of charge will have entered the cylinder. The inlet valve should close late enough to utilize the ram effect of the charge column in the manifold, but not so late as to permit some of the charge already inducted to be returned to the manifold by the rising piston. In general, the higher the speed at which the power of the engine is desired to reach its peak, the farther all of the valve events will depart from the dead-center points.

The two-stroke-cycle engine requires a pump external to the working cylinder to force the air into the cylinder and the exhaust gases out. This pump may consist of the underside of the power piston and a closed crankcase, a second cylinder with a pump piston driven from the engine crankshaft, or a rotary pump of either the centrifugal or positive-displacement type. This pump or compressor places the air charge under sufficient pressure to force the required amount of air through the inlet ports in the cylinder wall against the back pressure of the outgoing exhaust gases within the allotted portion of the cycle. Figure 3·26 illustrates the scavenging action of a modern uniflow Diesel engine with air supplied by a Roots blower. Instead of more than 200 degrees of crank angle available for pumping in air and a similar period for pumping out exhaust products, as in the four-stroke cycle, the entire transfer of air and gases must be completed in about 130 degrees in the two-stroke-cycle engine. The timing circle for a two-stroke-cycle engine is shown in Fig. 3·25b.

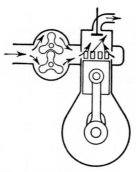

FIG. 3·26 Uniflow scavenged two-stroke engine

The exhaust valve or port is shown to open somewhat earlier than the release point of the four-stroke cycle because the blow-down period must now be completed before the inlet-port opening point. Unless the pressure in the cylinder is reduced to that maintained on the fresh charge by the scavenging blower, back flow of exhaust gases into the air box surrounding the inlet ports will result. This necessarily early release is a defect of the two-stroke cycle because it shortens the effective power stroke and decreases the mean effective pressure. Both inlet and exhaust passages are open for nearly 100 degrees, and the exhaust valve is then closed a few degrees before the inlet ports are again covered by the rising piston. This period during which the inlet remains open after the exhaust closure is referred to as a supercharging period, but it is doubtful that the high-speed two-stroke-cycle engine can be supercharged to any great extent by additional charge flow during so short an interval of time unless exceedingly high blower pressure is employed.

Engines of the back-flow-scavenged type differ from the uniflow type of Fig. 3·26 in that two sets of cylinder ports are provided at opposite sides of the cylinder bore, one serving as the inlet and the other as the exhaust passage, both opened and closed by the piston motion. The fresh air entering one of the ports is deflected sharply upward toward the cylinder head by a baffle formed on the piston crown, and the combustion products from the previous cycle flow downward on the opposite side of the cylinder bore, leaving via the exhaust ports. The inlet and exhaust timing of these engines is symmetrical in that the exhaust ports are covered by the piston at the same point on the compression stroke at which they were uncovered on the power stroke. This is also true for the inlet ports, and, since a blowdown period is necessary before the inlet opens, the exhaust must open before the inlet and close later than the inlet. This late exhaust closure is a defect of this type engine because some air charge will be lost from the cylinder after the inlet closes.

The opposed-piston-type two-stroke-cycle engine of Fig. 3·27 has two pistons in the same cylinder, and each controls a set of ports extending entirely around its circumference. By advancing one of the crankshafts with respect to the other and properly locating the ports in the cylinder walls, the timing of events is made similar to that of Fig. 3·25b. The large port areas made possible by this construction, the compact combustion chamber resulting from the high stroke–bore ratio, and the nearly perfect balance of reciprocating parts are advantages of the opposed-piston-type Diesel engine. The flow of gases during scavenging and charging of the cylinder is in one direction, resulting in less mixing of fresh air with exhaust gases than in engines wherein the two gases flow in opposite directions. The use of two crankshafts and the need for a means of connecting them together makes the opposed-piston engine somewhat complicated mechanically. The engine illustrated has bevel gears on the front ends of the two crankshafts which mesh with gears on a vertical connecting shaft.

A comparison of Fig. 3·25a and Fig. 3·25b shows that, although the pumping operations of the two cycles are aimed at the same accomplishment, that of replacing the products of combustion in the cylinder by a fresh charge, the portions of the two cycles devoted to this exchange are quite different, as are the methods and mechanisms employed.

Fig. 3·27 Fairbanks-Morse opposed-piston Diesel engine

3·34 Volumetric efficiency. The time during which air flows into the cylinder of an engine is not ordinarily sufficient to permit complete filling. Since the extent to which the cylinder is filled with air limits the amount of fuel that can be burned in the engine, a measure of the effectiveness of the engine as an air pump in charging itself will serve as an index to its possible power output. The weight of air inducted into the cylinder expressed in per cent of the weight required to completely fill the piston-displacement volume at outside temperature and pressure is known as the volumetric efficiency of a four-stroke-cycle engine. When the air entering the inlet system is measured volumetrically at atmospheric conditions, the volumetric efficiency is this measured volume in per cent of the volume displaced by the pistons during the same interval of time. High-speed engines usually show an increase in volumetric efficiency with increased speed to a peak value of about 80 per cent at about half speed and then a decrease at an increasing rate at higher speeds. Improvements in valve timing, intake-manifold design, valve design, carburetor design, and engine cooling are responsible for much higher volumetric efficiencies at high speeds than were formerly possible.

Example 10. A four-stroke engine has six cylinders of 3-in. bore and 4-in. stroke and runs at 3000 rpm. The air entering the carburetor was metered at 110 cu ft per min at outside temperature and pressure. Find the volumetric efficiency.

Solution: The piston-displacement volume of the engine is 1.5 × 1.5 × 3.14 × 4 × 6 = 169.5 cu in. The engine completes a cycle in two revolutions of the crankshaft, so that in 1 min 169.5 × 3000/2 or 254,000 cu in. are required to fill the cylinders completely.

$$110 \times 1728 = 190,000 \text{ cu in. supplied}$$

$$\eta_v = \frac{190,000}{254,000} = 74.8\%$$

The volumetric efficiency curve of Fig. 3·28 is typical of modern high-speed automobile engines. The weight of air supplied to the cylinders per cycle at full throttle when running at 1800 rpm is shown to exceed considerably that at 4000 rpm. Since the fuel burned per cycle depends upon the amount of air inducted, the energy released during each combustion period decreases as the engine speed increases above that at which the volumetric efficiency curve peaks. The mean effective pressure curve consequently follows the descent of the volumetric efficiency curve because the decreased weight of charge burned results in lower cylinder pressures during each power stroke. Torque is mathematically related to mean effective pressure, and the curves are therefore similar.

The equation for brake horsepower

$$\text{Bhp} = \frac{2\pi t n}{33,000} = \frac{t n}{5252}$$

indicates that the horsepower delivered would increase linearly with speed if the torque remained constant. Because the torque decreases at speeds above the peak of volumetric efficiency, the horsepower increases less rapidly than it does at the lower speeds where the torque is rising. When the speed is reached at which

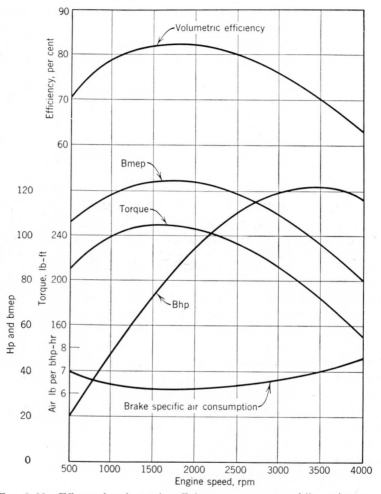

Fig. 3·28   Effect of volumetric efficiency upon automobile-engine performance

the rate of decrease in torque equals the rate of increase in speed, their product no longer increases, and the maximum horsepower of the engine is reached. At speeds above this peak, the torque is decreasing faster than the speed is increasing, and the horse-power falls off. The shape of the full-throttle horsepower curve is thus seen to depend upon how well the volumetric efficiency is maintained at increasing speed, and, consequently, the speed at which maximum horsepower is developed will be higher if the high-speed pumping effectiveness of the engine is improved.

The weight of air flowing into the cylinder per hour divided by the brake horsepower developed is expressed as the brake specific air consumption of the engine. The specific air consumption curve of Fig. 3·28 correlates the pumping capacity of the engine with the power developed. The fewer pounds of air consumed for each horsepower developed, the more effectively the cylinder charge is being used. Just as the specific fuel consumption is a measure of the economy of operation, the specific air consumption is a measure of the power-developing effectiveness of the engine. Designers of engines whose horsepower capacity is of primary importance are more interested in the specific-air-consumption curve than in the specific-fuel-consumption curve.

3·35 Supercharging. In certain-type engines it has been found desirable to incorporate an auxiliary pump or blower to supplement the pumping action of the cylinders. A notable example of the application of this idea is in supercharging the cylinders of an aviation engine in order to increase its output per unit of size and weight and particularly to offset the loss in power at altitude caused by the decreased specific weight of the air. Diesel engines for marine, locomotive, and truck propulsion are sometimes supercharged to permit more horsepower output from a given space and weight limitation.

Supercharging appears to have greater advantages when used with compression ignition than with spark ignition, because it causes higher temperatures and pressures at the end of compression which increase the tendency of the spark-ignition engine to detonate and raise its gasoline octane requirement, whereas ignition is improved in the compression-ignition engine and its cetane requirement decreased by these same factors.

The supercharger merely raises the intake-manifold pressure, making it possible to fill the cylinders at a greater charge density. Since the density of the charge is intentionally reduced to regulate the input to the engine at partial loads, supercharging is necessary only when the engine operates at full load. The possibility of driving the supercharger blower by an exhaust turbine makes the idea even more attractive, incorporating as it does the utilization of otherwise wasted heat.

Supercharged engines differ from those that are naturally aspirated in that a pump or blower discharging into the intake manifold is incorporated. Blowers of the Roots type (Fig. 3·26) are usually employed for supercharging relatively small Diesel engines where the blower is geared to and driven by the crankshaft of the engine. The centrifugal-type blower is often geared to the crankshafts of aviation engines and, to a lesser extent, engines for other applications where the speeds are fairly constant and high manifold pressures are maintained.

Turbocharging, in which a centrifugal blower is driven by a gas turbine operated by the exhaust gas from the engine cylinders, is rapidly increasing in use. A majority of the large Diesel engines of the four-stroke-cycle type now manufactured are turbocharged, and their specific output is thus made to compare favorably with the power capacity of two-stroke-cycle Diesels. Locomotive Diesels of the four-stroke-cycle type are all turbocharged, in one instance the horsepower being doubled by increasing the inlet pressure to 22 psig pressure. When the blower is geared to the crankshaft, the friction horsepower of the engine is considerably increased, and it is not likely that the fuel economy of the engine will be improved by supercharging. The turbocharged engine, however, operates at improved mechanical efficiency and lower brake specific fuel consumption. It is conceivable that all four-stroke-cycle Diesel engines will eventually be supercharged as a means of decreasing the weight and cost per horsepower.

3·36   Mixture making.   In carburetor-type engines the fuel–air mixture necessary for combustion is created at the entrance to the intake manifold through which the charge is led to the cylinders. In injection-type spark-ignition engines the mixing of fuel and air is started either at the inlet valve as the air flows in or later within the cylinder. It is desirable that the fuel and air be brought into contact as early as possible in the cycle of the spark-ignition engine so that the liquid particles of fuel may have opportunity to vaporize and mix with the air. The carburetor excels other fuel-feeding devices in this respect but is inferior to injection systems in other respects. Injection of fuel directly into the combustion chamber immediately before the spark occurs offers the advantage that the fuel is exposed to high temperatures for a shorter time before its combustion and is, consequently, less likely to attain its self-ignition temperature and detonate. It is also possible to stratify the charge in the combustion chamber by direct injection of the fuel as a means of controlling detonation and operating on lean mixtures.

3·37 Mixture requirements. The chemical reactions that occur when a hydrocarbon fuel is burned can be expressed in the form of combining-weight equations which make possible determinations of the relative amounts of fuel and air that are theoretically necessary for combustion. The most important internal-combustion-engine fuels are mixtures of many hydrocarbons, and the equation for the combustion of each compound would be necessary for an accurate analysis of their combustion requirements. It is customary, since the identity and proportions of the various ingredients are never known for fuels such as gasoline, to assume that the mixture is a single compound having the approximate molecular weight and carbon–hydrogen ratio of the mixture. Gasoline may, without great error, be considered to be octane, C_8H_{18}, and its combustion may be expressed by the equation:

$$C_8H_{18} + 12.5O_2 + 47.5N_2 = 9H_2O + 8CO_2 + 47.5N_2$$

If we multiply by molecular weights,

$$114 \text{ lb} + 400 \text{ lb} + 1330 \text{ lb} = 162 \text{ lb} + 352 \text{ lb} + 1330 \text{ lb}$$

When we divide by 114,

$$1 \text{ lb } C_8H_{18} + 3.51 \text{ lb } O_2 + 11.66 \text{ lb } N_2$$

$$= 1.42 \text{ lb } H_2O + 3.09 \text{ lb } CO_2 + 11.66 \text{ lb } N_2$$

$$1 \text{ lb } C_8H_{18} + 15.17 \text{ lb air} = 16.17 \text{ lb products of combustion}$$

These equations show that 1 lb of gasoline requires slightly over 15 lb of air to form a mixture of chemically correct proportions. If such a mixture were completely burned, there would be no oxygen or fuel in the products of combustion. Such perfect combustion is not possible under the conditions existing in an engine cylinder where mixing is not sufficiently complete to bring each fuel particle into contact with its quota of the air, and the time available for combustion is not always great enough to allow the reaction to go to completion.

The exhaust gases from the internal-combustion engine always contain fuel in the form of CO, CH_4, and H_2, and some oxygen is also present. The amount of unburned fuel discharged from the engine may be decreased by supplying additional air in excess of the chemically correct amount, and it has been found experimentally that air–fuel ratios of around 17 lb of air to 1 of fuel are most economical to burn except at light loads. Greater economy is possible when so-called lean mixtures are burned, because combustion is more complete if excess air is supplied, and mixing need be less perfect. It has been found experimentally that the maximum horsepower that an engine is capable of delivering is reduced when the air–fuel mixture is lean. This is explainable because the total volume of charge that can be inducted by natural means into the cylinder is fixed by the cylinder dimensions, and the space occupied by the excess air reduces that remaining for fuel–air mixture. Any increase in the amount of air supplied will result in a decrease in the amount of fuel that can be supplied. Consequently, the amount of energy liberated by combustion will decrease in spite of more complete combustion. This same effect makes it possible to increase the amount of energy released by combustion of rich mixtures containing a deficiency of air, in spite of the lowered efficiency of such combustion. Experiment has proved that air–gasoline mixtures of about 12 to 1 ratio produce the most horsepower from an engine. This difference in air–fuel ratios necessary for maximum economy and maximum power makes it impossible for full power to be developed by a spark-ignition engine without a sacrifice in fuel economy and prevents full-load operation at maximum economy.

Because the charge in a spark-ignition engine is burned by being ignited at one point and sending a flame front across the combustion chamber, the charge must consist of fuel and air in such proportions as will support combustion. There are definite limits of inflammability for fuel–air mixtures which impose both a rich limit and a lean limit beyond which the proportions of the charge cannot go or it will not burn under cylinder conditions. The clearance space in the cylinder is seldom scavenged of exhaust gases to any extent, and the inert material carried over tends to dilute the next charge. At light-load conditions the proportionate effect of this neutral dilution is much greater than at heavier loads and necessitates enriching the mixture at light loads. Thus, the maximum-power, maximum-economy, lean-

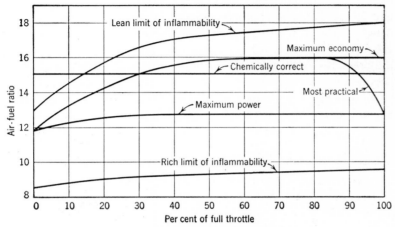

FIG. 3·29   Engine mixture requirements

limit, and rich-limit mixtures are all richer at light loads than at heavy loads to compensate for this dilution.

These factors all combine to require that the charge supplied to a spark-ignition engine contain fuel and air in precise proportions which are different for different loads and operating conditions if optimum performance is to be had. Compression-ignition engines are not limited in this respect and do not require inflammable mixture ratios for their operation. Very high air–fuel ratios result at light loads in such engines, because the amount of air supplied is not varied with the fuel supplied at different loads.

Individual spark-ignition engines have different mixture requirements because of the effects of differences in the design of various functional parts. Figure 3·29 shows a typical range of mixture ratios.

3·38   Carburetion. The function of the carburetor is to atomize and meter the liquid fuel and mix it with the air as it enters the induction system of the engine, maintaining under all conditions of operation fuel–air proportions appropriate to those conditions. The process of carburetion is complicated by the wide range of fuel–air ratios required for best performance under different load and speed conditions. Automatic metering of fuel and air over a wide range of charge quantities by devices based upon hydraulic-flow principles is not easily accomplished when one of the fluids is a liquid and the other a compressible gas. Much of the difficulty in carburetion arises from the failure of the liquid gasoline to behave the same as the air under the changing pressures produced in the carburetor as the quantity of charge supplied varies.

All modern carburetors are based upon Bernoulli's theorem which leads to the equation,

$$V^2 = 2gh \qquad (3·17)$$

where V is the velocity in feet per second at which a fluid flows, g the acceleration of gravity in feet per second per second, and h is the head causing the flow expressed in feet of height of a column of the fluid.

The quantity in cubic feet per second of fluid flowing in a stream having a cross-sectional area of A sq ft and flowing at a velocity of V fps equals the product of A and V. Multiplying this volume rate of flow by ρ, the density of the fluid in pounds per cubic foot, converts the quantity to pounds mass per second. Substitution of $\sqrt{2gh}$ for V then makes the equation for mass rate of flow:

$$m = \rho A \sqrt{2gh} \qquad (3·18)$$

Figure 3·30 shows diagrammatically a simple elementary carburetor. A is the float chamber in which a constant gasoline level is maintained by the float valve B, and C is the jet from which the gasoline is sprayed into the air stream as it enters the carburetor at the inlet G and passes through the throat or venturi E. The gasoline level is slightly below the outlet of the jet when the carburetor is inoperative. All modern carburetors are basically of this type. Functioning is automatic in that no gasoline is discharged except when air is flowing through the carburetor. The gasoline and air mixture leaves the carburetor through the throttle valve F and enters the inlet manifold at D.

Air flowing through the carburetor air passage is accelerated by the constriction at the throat E, with a resulting pressure drop caused by conversion of a portion of its pressure head to kinetic energy. The total pressure exerted by the air equals its static pressure plus its velocity head. The total pressure at the Venturi throat equals the total pressure at the entrance, but the velocity head is increased at the throat because acceleration is necessary when the same amount of air passes through the smaller throat area. The static pressure at the throat is correspondingly decreased as the velocity increases; the kinetic energy increases while the total energy remains unchanged. This energy conversion reduces the pressure at the throat section E below that at the entrance G by an amount

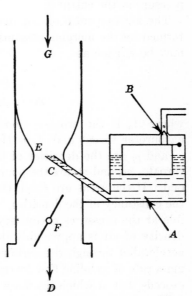

Fig. 3·30   Elementary carburetor

related to the rate of air flow, in accordance with Equation 3·18. Since the fuel jet has its outlet C at the point where the air pressure is reduced by the air flow, and the surface of the fuel in the float chamber A is under atmospheric pressure, a head, h of Equation 3·18, is applied to the fuel, causing it to flow from the jet into the air stream and to form a mixture with the air as it enters the inlet manifold at D. The throat pressure, being a function of the velocity at which the air is flowing, the head on the fuel, and the consequent flow of fuel will depend upon the rate of flow of air. The amount of charge supplied to the engine is regulated in accordance with the needs of the engine by varying the position of the throttle valve F.

Equation 3·18 applies to both the flow of air through the throat of the carburetor and the flow of fuel through the jet. In the case of the air flow, the quantity of air is drawn through the carburetor by the pumping action of the pistons in the engine cylinders. In flowing through the smaller area at the carburetor throat, the air pressure is decreased by an amount h below the pressure at the entrance.

The air–fuel ratio on the mass or weight basis of the mixture formed by the merging streams of fuel and air in the carburetor may be written as

$$\frac{m_a}{m_f} = \frac{\rho_a A_a \sqrt{2gh_a}}{\rho_f A_f \sqrt{2gh_f}}$$

where A_a is the cross-sectional area of the air stream at the carburetor throat and A_f is that of the fuel stream at the jet. ρ_a and ρ_f are the densities of the air and fuel at the carburetor throat. m_a and m_f are the pounds of air and fuel flowing per second. If the areas are fixed, the air–fuel ratio will depend upon the constancy of the densities. Because gasoline is not compressible at the pressures encountered in the carburetor, whereas the density of air is appreciably decreased by its expansion as it is accelerated through the carburetor throat, the rate at which the mass rate of gasoline flow increases in response to opened throttle exceeds that at which the mass rate of air flow increases.

The elementary carburetor proportions the volumes of air and fuel according to the relative sizes of the air orifice E and the fuel jet C and serves as an accurate volumetric metering device. Because the density of the air at the throat of the carburetor becomes progressively less as the pressure is decreased by increasing rates of flow, the mass ratio of fuel to air increases, and the mixture supplied becomes richer in fuel. Fuel-jet and air-orifice sizes that provide a fuel–air mass ratio which meets the needs of the engine at one rate of charge flow will not maintain that ratio at other rates of flow, although the volume ratio will be unchanged.

The curves of Fig. 3·31 illustrate the effect of the compressibility of air upon the metering accuracy of the simple elementary carburetor. Air enters the carburetor at 0.075 lb per cu ft density and expands to progressively lower density as the rate of flow increases. At a flow rate that causes a throat pressure 60 in. of water below atmospheric pressure the air weighs only 0.0615 lb per cu ft. The actual pounds of air flowing per unit of time is indicated by the solid line, and the dotted curve shows the pounds that would flow if the air did not expand under the

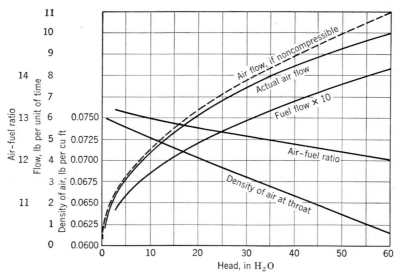

FIG. 3·31   Effect of compressibility of air on air–fuel ratio of charge delivered by simple elementary carburetor

reduced throat pressure. This latter quantity of air is the amount necessary to maintain the air–fuel ratio at the initial value, and the difference between these two curves represents the deficiency in air supply which causes the mixture delivered by an uncompensated carburetor to become richer in fuel at higher rates of operation. No fuel is delivered to the air until sufficient air flow occurs to raise the fuel level to the discharge outlet and overcome the surface tension of the liquid. For this reason the fuel flow and air–fuel ratio curves do not start at the zero of air flow. The enriching effect accompanying increased charge flow is indicated by the decrease in air–fuel ratio from 13.2 to 12 in the range covered by the curves.

This tendency of the simple elementary carburetor to supply an increasingly rich mixture at increased rates of charge flow is a fundamental defect which makes it unsatisfactory for use with an engine that requires varying quantities of charge as loads and speeds are changed. Since few engines operate at constant input and output, the designer has had to conceive compensating devices to eliminate the need for readjustment of the size of the air or fuel passage whenever changes in engine output occur. The problem is further complicated by the fact that a constant air–fuel ratio would not be satisfactory for all operating conditions, even if a carburetor capable of providing a constant ratio were obtainable, because of the factors explained in Article 3·37.

When operating at constant loads and speeds within the middle portion of its total operating range, the engine should receive a mixture having as nearly as possible the maximum-economy ratio of air to fuel. At heavy loads, the mixture should be enriched to provide a maximum-power ratio, and at light loads it should again be enriched to compensate for greater neutral dilution. At idling conditions, the velocity at which the reduced amount of air flows through the carburetor is not sufficient to cause fuel to issue from the fuel jet, and it is necessary to equip the carburetor with an additional idling jet which functions only when the throttle is nearly closed. It must also be equipped to provide a greatly enriched mixture for starting a cold engine when the low temperature will not vaporize the heavier portions of the fuel, and, consequently, they will not enter into the mixture that has to be ignited in the cylinder. Rapid acceleration, as demanded of an automobile engine, also requires a momentarily enriched and more powerful mixture.

The inlet manifold, which connects the carburetor outlet to the inlet ports of the several cylinders of a multicylinder engine, introduces additional carburetion problems. Increased throttle opening raises the absolute pressure in the manifold, whereas closing the throttle produces a higher manifold vacuum. These changes in pressure occur because the restriction to flow into the manifold varies with the throttle position, while the vacuum-creating pumping action of the pistons does not change until the engine speed changes. The boiling points of the various fuel constituents are increased with the pressure rise that accompanies greater throttle opening. The normal operating temperature maintained in the inlet manifold causes slightly more than half of the gasoline in the charge to vaporize before it reaches the cylinders. Any increase in manifold pressure resulting from throttle manipulation will cause condensation of such fuel constituents as have boiling points that were only slightly exceeded at the previous pressure. The mixture arriving at the cylinders immediately after the throttle is opened will thus be leaner than it was when formed in the carburetor, some of its fuel remaining in the manifold to establish equilibrium at the higher pressure. Closing the throttle has an opposite effect, and the charge gains fuel in passing through the manifold. During acceleration, additional fuel must be supplied by the carburetor to compensate for the momentary loss of fuel from the charge in the manifold in order that the mixture arriving at the cylinders will not be so lean as to cause misfiring or so slow burning as to cause popping back through the carburetor.

The major differences between commercial carburetors as they are now produced are in the mechanisms provided for compensating for the inherent enriching tendency of increased flow and for varying the mixture proportions to meet the special needs of operation under varying loads, speeds, and temperatures.

3·39 Carburetor systems. The following illustrations are sectional views of a Stromberg carburetor, a typical automobile engine device. Figure 3·32 depicts the float mechanism which maintains the fuel at the proper level, just slightly below the main discharge jet, by means of a needle valve which is pressed horizontally against its seat when the float rises to a predetermined height. A passageway formed in the cover casting connects the space above the fuel in the float chamber to a small tube, shown at the air entrance, which serves as a vent to maintain the same pressure on the fuel and the air entering the carburetor.

The throttle is shown in the closed or idle position. The velocity of the air through the Venturi is now too low to produce enough head to raise the fuel to where it will flow from the main discharge jet. The idle system, shown in Figs. 3·32 and 3·33, controls the mixture under idling and slow-speed conditions until the throttle is opened sufficiently to cause the main metering system to function. A passage, terminating at a point below the throttle plate, extends vertically to the air entrance above the Venturi. A horizontal opening near the upper end of this passage connects it to a second vertical tube in the float chamber, called the idle tube, which extends down below the fuel level to a point above the outlet of the main metering jet. This tube is kept filled with gasoline by the passageway through the main metering jet

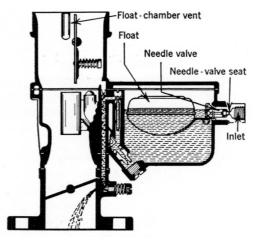

Fig. 3·32   Float system

and the metering orifice in the idle tube. The air opening at the top is partially restricted by the inserted idle bleed, while the outlet below the throttle plate is provided with an adjustable needle valve as a means of so regulating the flow of fuel that a proper mixture ratio can be established. Two discharge holes leading to the main air tube are provided, one above and one below the throttle plate when in its closed position.

The idle system functions only when the throttle is closed, as in idling, or when operating at very low speed and light load. Under these conditions, the pressure in the inlet manifold and in the region below the throttle plate is very low, a vacuum of about 18 in. of Hg commonly existing when idling. This low outlet pressure causes the fuel to be forced through the idle system by the atmospheric pressure acting in the float chamber and to flow from its lower discharge hole, as shown in Fig. 3·32 at closed throttle. When the throttle is slightly opened, as in Fig. 3·33, the region of high vacuum is extended upward to include the upper discharge hole, and fuel then flows from both holes in increased amount to compensate for the greater amount of air now flowing. When it is opened beyond a certain point, the pressure at the throttle will have risen until there is not enough head to operate the idle system and fuel discharge will cease.

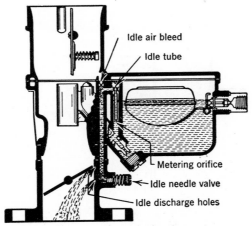

FIG. 3·33 Idle system (second stage)

Figure 3·34 shows the main metering system, which controls the flow of fuel during the intermediate or part-throttle range. Fuel flow, in this system, is from the float chamber through the main metering jet and up through the inclined passage and inserted jet tube to the main discharge jet. An enlarged section of this jet tube and associated parts is shown in Fig. 3·35. The annular space around this tube *A* communicates with the interior of the tube through a row of small holes arranged along its length and also opens vertically to a high-speed bleeder *B* at the Venturi entrance. The main discharge jet *C* is located in a small boost Venturi, which is so mounted in the center of the main Venturi that its mouth or exit is at the throat of the main Venturi. The pressure at the throat of the boost Venturi will thus drop more rapidly with increased air flow than that at the throat of the main Venturi. The restriction to air flow of this double

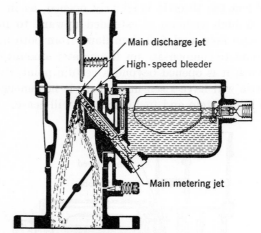

FIG. 3·34 Main metering system

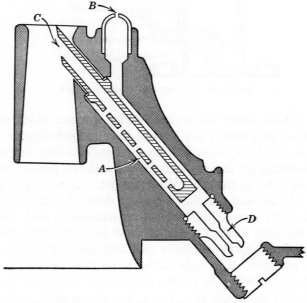

FIG. 3·35 Enlarged section of air-bled carburetor jet

Venturi is less than that of a single Venturi of the size that would produce the same throat pressure at the same rate of air flow.

As the rate of air flow through the carburetor increases with increased throttle opening, the pressure at the main discharge jet becomes progressively lower. The pressure in the passage leading to the main discharge jet will decrease correspondingly, and the level of the gasoline in the annular space surrounding the jet tube will be depressed by the pressure of the air entering at the high-speed bleeder. At a certain rate of air flow through the carburetor throat, the fuel level outside the jet tube will drop below the highest of the holes leading into the tube and air will then flow from the high-speed bleeder, through this hole into the jet tube, and accompany the fuel through the main discharge jet. At further increases in the rate of operation, the level will continue to drop, and the other holes will be uncovered in sequence, admitting additional air to flow with the fuel. The effect of this air entrance to the fuel stream will be to partially break the vacuum in the tube and prevent the pressure at the exit from the metering jet D from dropping as rapidly as it drops at the main discharge jet C in response to increased rates of air flow through the carburetor throat. The head across the metering jet will, consequently, not increase so much for a given increase in air flow as it otherwise would and, since the gasoline flow varies with the head across the metering jet, the mixture will not become so rich as it does in the simple elementary carburetor with no air bleed. This air-bleeding system is, therefore, a compensating device which automatically maintains a reasonably constant air-fuel ratio throughout the intermediate range of operation. The rate of fuel flow in this range can be adjusted to meet the requirements of the engine by substitution of different-size main and air-bleeder jets.

For smooth and rapid acceleration it is necessary to supply momentarily an extra quantity of fuel when the throttle is suddenly opened. In most designs, the accelerating pump (Fig. 3·36) is directly connected to the throttle, so that, when the throttle is closed, the pump piston moves up, taking in a supply of fuel from the float chamber through the inlet check valve into the pump cylinder. When the throttle valve is opened, the piston on its down stroke has a tendency to compress the fuel in the cylinder, which action closes the inlet check valve, forces open the by-pass jet, and discharges a metered quantity of fuel through the pump-discharge nozzle. This occurs only momentarily during the accelerating period. The pump duration spring provides a follow-up action so that the discharge carries out over a period of time.

The stroke of the accelerating pump plunger is made adjust-

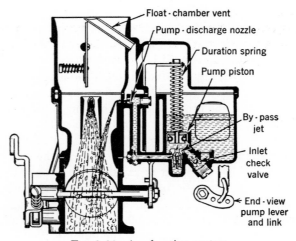

Fɪɢ. 3·36   Accelerating system

able by providing three holes in the pump lever on the throttle shaft. When the pump link is placed in the center hole, as shown, the plunger has a medium stroke. Should conditions require, as in cold weather, the link may be moved to the outer hole and the stroke increased, whereas, in warm weather, the inner hole may provide sufficient accelerating enrichment.

For maximum power operation, a richer mixture is required than that necessary for part-throttle operation at lighter loads. A vacuum-controlled piston (Fig. 3·37) automatically operates the power by-pass jet in accordance with the engine load condition. At light loads, the engine speed is high in proportion to the throttle opening, a high manifold vacuum is present, and the vacuum piston is moved to its "up" position against the tension of the spring. When the load on the engine is so heavy that the throttle must be opened beyond a certain point to maintain the engine speed, the manifold vacuum decreases sufficiently so that the spring on the piston assembly moves the piston down and thereby opens the power by-pass jet to feed additional fuel into the main metering system. When the manifold vacuum is high, fuel flows only from the main metering jet, and a maximum-economy air–fuel ratio supplied. When the manifold vacuum is

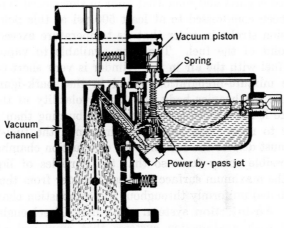

Fig. 3·37 Power system

low, fuel flows from the by-pass jet and the main jet, their combined flow enriching the mixture to the maximum-power ratio.

The butterfly valve shown in the air entrance at the top of the carburetor serves as a choke valve to supply the greatly enriched mixture necessary when starting a cold engine. When the choke is fully closed, a mixture of approximately equal weights of fuel and air will leave the carburetor. Only a small fraction of the gasoline entering the cylinders will vaporize at low starting temperatures. If as little as 8 per cent of the liquid fuel vaporizes when the carburetor is fully choked, an ignitable air–vapor mixture will be formed, and the engine will start. The spring-loaded poppet valve shown in the lower portion of the choke valve will open automatically when the engine starts, thus making the control of the choke less sensitive.

3·40   Fuel injection.   The fuel charge is injected into the cylinder of the compression-ignition engine after the air has been inducted into the cylinder and compressed.   The time at which fuel is injected is so chosen that the pressure rise accompanying combustion will occur approximately at the piston upper dead-center position.   Allowance for the ignition lag and the initial pressure rise to occur before dead center usually makes the injection period start about 25 degrees before top dead center in high-speed engines and somewhat later in slow-speed types.   The air has been compressed to at least 500 psi at this point in the compression stroke in order that its temperature exceed the ignition point of the fuel.   The time available to vaporize and mix the fuel with the air in the cylinder is very short compared with the mixture-preparation period in the spark-ignition engine, while the heavier body and lower volatility of the Diesel fuel make it more difficult to prepare for burning than gasoline. In order to meet these severe requirements, the fuel-injection system must deliver the fuel into the combustion chamber in the finest possible spray form so that the particles of liquid will present the maximum surface for heat transfer from the air and be distributed uniformly throughout the combustion chamber.

3·41   Air-injection system.   The first Diesel engines were equipped with air-injection systems that employed air under about 1000 psig pressure to carry the fuel into the cylinder against the back pressure offered by the compressed-air charge. Excellent atomization of the fuel is obtained by this means, even with exceedingly heavy fuels.   The multistage air compressor necessary to maintain the supply of injection air, however, adds greatly to the cost, size, and weight of the engine, besides consuming an appreciable amount of power and requiring frequent maintenance attention.   These factors have limited the use of air injection to large slow-speed engines.

The injectors used with air injection comprise an orifice, behind which a cavity is formed for the fuel, and a cam-operated valve to time the admission of air.   A fuel-metering pump is used to measure out accurately the amount of fuel needed per cycle under each load condition and deliver it to the injector at some time earlier in the cycle than the injection period.   At the proper time, the air valve is lifted from its seat by the cam mechanism, and the blast of high-pressure air passing through the injector picks up the fuel and discharges it at high velocity from the orifice or spray nozzle into the combustion chamber. The expansion of high-pressure air as it enters the air of lower pressure in the combustion chamber carries the fine particles throughout the clearance space of the cylinder and rapidly associates them with the combustion air.

3·42   Mechanical injection systems.   In the year 1910 the mechanical or solid injection system was introduced and is now used on all high-speed engines of the Diesel type as well as on many of the larger slow-speed engines. Its greater simplicity more than offsets its failure to attain the excellent atomization of the air-injection system. Basically, all mechanical injection systems work on the same principle, that of placing the liquid fuel under an extremely high pressure, 30,000 psi in some systems, and forcing it through a spray nozzle having very small openings leading to the combustion chamber. The high velocity at which it flows from the spray nozzle breaks up the particles of oil and distributes them in a pattern dependent upon the number and type of openings in the nozzle. Because the fuel is not so finely atomized or perfectly distributed, engines designed for solid injection frequently have specially formed combustion chambers that cause rapid movement or turbulence of the air charge to assist in the mixing process.

The most commonly used injection systems employ a small plunger-type pump for each cylinder of the engine, either located separately adjacent to each cylinder or combined in a single multipump unit and driven from the crankshaft. The injection pump is small in comparison with the engine cylinder and usually has a displacement of about 1/10,000 of the piston displacement of the power cylinder. Because of the high pressure and the need for extreme accuracy in metering the fuel, the injection pump must be made of high-grade materials, and the standards of workmanship and tolerances in fitting parts are much more exacting than in other units of the internal-combustion engine.

The metering function of the injection pump imposes one of its most difficult requirements. The maximum amount of fuel injected per cycle is usually less than 1 cu mm per cu in. of piston displacement, and at light loads it is proportionately less.

Smooth running of the engine is dependent upon a high degree of precision in balancing the amount of fuel injected into the several cylinders of a multicylinder engine and in equalizing the successive injections in each cylinder. Measuring these minute quantities of fuel with the accuracy demanded at varying loads and under the high pressures and high speeds now encountered is a problem that has required the utmost skill and ingenuity of the designer.

A variety of metering methods have been and many still are used, ranging from mechanisms for varying the actual stroke of the pump plunger so that its displacement is changed in accordance with the load on the engine, to valve and port arrangements which vary the effective stroke of the plunger by preventing delivery during either the initial or final portion of the stroke. The present trend appears to be toward the type that uses a spirally recessed plunger which covers a port through the wall of the pump barrel during a portion of its stroke which is varied by rotating the plunger.

Figure 3·38 shows five sectional views of the plunger and barrel assembly of an injection pump of the type in which the effective stroke is lengthened or shortened by rotating the plunger to different positions. The complete pump unit into which this plunger and barrel assembly is fitted may be of three types. Each single barrel may be housed in a separate pump body containing the helical spring which retracts the plunger and the rack and pinion which position the plunger angularly. This unit is then mounted adjacent to the camshaft of the engine, and the plunger is actuated by an additional cam formed on the camshaft. The second construction is to provide a single housing for as many barrels as there are cylinders in the engine, including a camshaft to be driven by an accessory shaft. The third arrangement is to combine the barrel with the spray-nozzle body into a unit injector operated by a rocker arm from the camshaft as in Fig. 3·24.

The Bosch injection pump of Fig. 3·39 is widely used by Diesel engine builders and is representative of the second construction type. This six-cylinder unit is driven by gears from the crankshaft of the engine and provides a self-contained multipump unit. The plunger and barrel pump elements are similar in principle to those of Fig. 3·38.

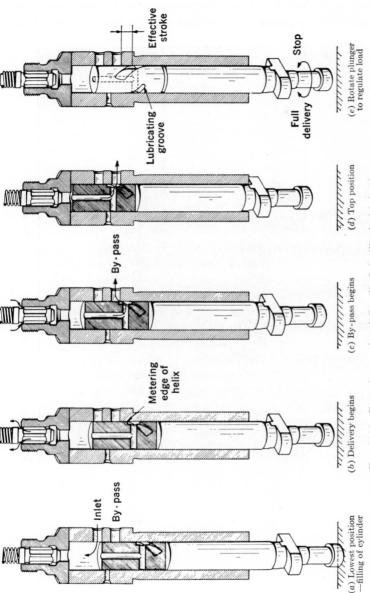

Fig. 3·38 Pumping cycle of Bendix-Scintilla fuel-injection pump

(a) The pumping chamber has been filled; the upstroke begins. (b) All ports are closed, and discharge through the delivery valve begins. (c) By-pass of fuel begins; delivery valve closes by spring pressure. (d) By-pass continues to end of stroke. (e) Rotation of the plunger changes the effective stroke which is the vertical distance between the upper edge of the metering helix and the lower edge of the by-pass port when the inlet port is just closed. In stop position all fuel is by-passed

Figure 3·40 shows a similar four-cylinder unit with the necessary additional elements of a complete Diesel fuel system. The

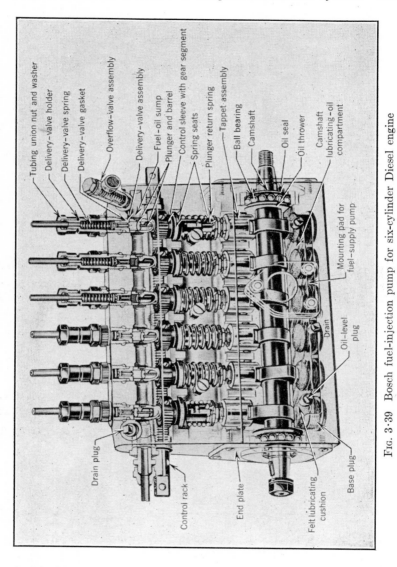

Tubing union nut and washer
Delivery-valve holder
Delivery-valve spring
Delivery-valve gasket
Overflow-valve assembly
Delivery-valve assembly
Fuel-oil sump
Plunger and barrel
Control sleeve with gear segment
Spring seats
Plunger return spring
Tappet assembly
Ball bearing
Camshaft
Oil seal
Oil thrower
Camshaft lubricating-oil compartment
Mounting pad for fuel-supply pump
Drain
Oil-level plug
Base plug
Felt lubricating cushion
End plate
Control rack
Drain plug

Fig. 3·39 Bosch fuel-injection pump for six-cylinder Diesel engine

fuel is drawn from the tank by the supply pump, passed through a three-stage filter system for removal of dirt that would damage the pumps and nozzles, and delivered to the injection pumps.

The high-pressure delivery lines then convey the fuel to the nozzle assemblies by which it is sprayed into the combustion chambers of the engine.

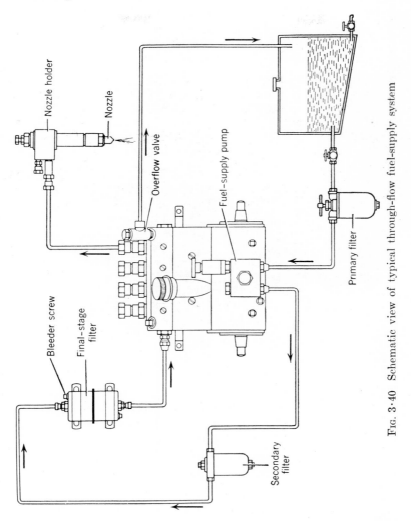

FIG. 3·40 Schematic view of typical through-flow fuel-supply system

Figure 3·41 illustrates a multicylinder pump in which the plungers are arranged along the ordinates of a cylinder and reciprocated by a swash plate. Control of injection in this pump is by a rotating valve in the center of the group of pump units which rotates with the swash plate. Fuel enters the several barrels through passages drilled radially from the central valve chamber. These passages are closed in sequence by the trapezoidal land on the rotating valve as the delivery stroke of each plunger is executed. Fuel is delivered to the spray nozzle during the portion of the stroke that the valve prevents its return to the

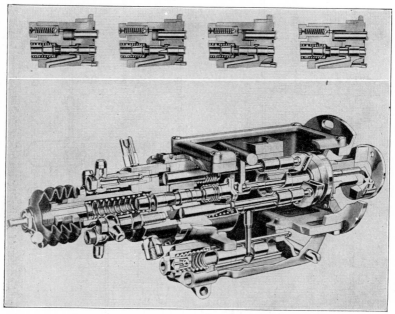

Fig. 3·41 Ex-Cell-O Diesel fuel-injection pump

central chamber, and the length of that portion is varied by moving the valve axially and causing a wider or narrower portion of the trapezoidal land to be adjacent to the passages leading to the pump barrels. This pump construction also provides a change in the timing of injection by advancing or retarding the position of the rotary valve with respect to the driving shaft.

Spray nozzles are frequently of the multihole type, in which orifices of from 0.005-in. diameter upward are drilled in such manner that about six jets of fuel are discharged along ordinates of a cone. Conical spray nozzles of the pintle type are also widely used, in which the orifice is an annular one formed by a pin centered in a hole about 0.001 in. larger in diameter than the pin. This construction provides a nozzle that is easier to produce and maintain than those with several very small openings. Figure 3·42 illustrates a nozzle of this type. Fuel delivery is prevented until sufficient pressure is built up by the pump to force the spring-loaded valve from its seat. A predetermined opening

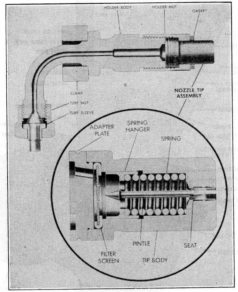

Fig. 3·42   Ex-Cell-O fuel spray nozzle

pressure is established in the design of the valve, and its closure when the pressure drops serves to produce a sharp end to the injection period, preventing dribbling fuel into the cylinder between injections. The fuel is conveyed to the spray nozzle from the injection pump by a heavy-walled steel tube of small internal diameter which must be rigid to resist expansion under the high fuel pressure.

Some manufacturers combine the pump and nozzle assemblies into unit injectors, thus eliminating the high-pressure fuel lines and delivering the fuel directly from the pump barrels to the spray nozzles. Others use distributors to index the several spray nozzles in proper sequence to a single injection pump. The common-rail system is also used in which fuel under high pressure is maintained in an accumulator with leads to each of the spray nozzles which are controlled by cam-operated valves.

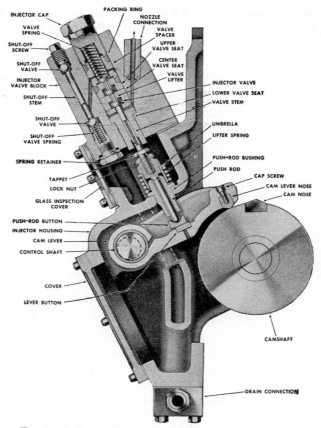

Fig. 3·43   Cooper-Bessemer common-rail fuel injector

Figure 3·43 shows a sectional view of the injector valve unit of the common-rail injection system used on the Cooper-Bessemer engine illustrated in Fig. 3·51. The injector valve consists of the three flat disk valves shown, arranged in series, which are raised from their seats at the proper instant for injection by a cam-actuated push rod. The amount of fuel delivered to the spray nozzle depends upon the length of the period the valves are open, which is varied by increasing or decreasing their lift. The cam lever interposed between the camshaft and the push rod is pivoted on eccentric bearings on a control shaft. The cam lever pivot is moved closer to or farther away from the camshaft by rotating the control shaft about its center which is not the center of the cam-lever bearing. This movement shifts the point at which the push rod contacts the cam lever, thus changing the lever-arm ratio and the portion of the cam lift that is transmitted to the pump plunger. When the cam lever is shifted to the left, the valves are held off their seats for a longer period than when it is shifted to the right, and more fuel passes from the high-pressure supply above the valve seats to the nozzle connection. The control shaft is rotated by the governor in accordance with the fuel requirements of the engine. Fuel enters the injector through the shut-off valve from the high-pressure header where injection pressure is maintained by a supply pump.

The relationship between the injector valve unit of Fig. 3·43 and the other components of the common-rail system is shown in the diagram of Fig. 3·44. The injector is interposed between the accumulator, in which fuel is maintained under injection pressure by the supply pump, and one of the spray nozzles that it supplies. Three additional delivery lines, not shown, lead from the injector to the nozzles in the other three cylinders of the engine that are served by the unit. Two similar injector units are employed on each bank of the 16-cylinder Cooper-Bessemer Diesel engine of Fig. 3·51.

3·43 Gasoline injection. The failure of the carburetor to meter the gasoline accurately into the air stream and the difficulty in delivering equal amounts of charge of uniform fuel and air proportions to the several cylinders of a multicylinder engine cause one of the most serious imperfections of the gasoline engine. By injecting the fuel, either directly into the engine cylinders or into the air stream at the entrance to each cylinder, the distribution of the charge can be greatly improved, much greater accuracy in metering can be maintained, and the atomization of the fuel can be improved. These accomplishments tend to increase the power output of the engine and to lower its specific fuel consumption, the two important objectives of the engine designer.

Compared with the carburetor, the gasoline-injection system is more complicated and expensive to produce, and this factor has delayed its application to any except highly refined types of engines, such as military aviation engines. Improved designs permitting lower production cost and simplification to reduce

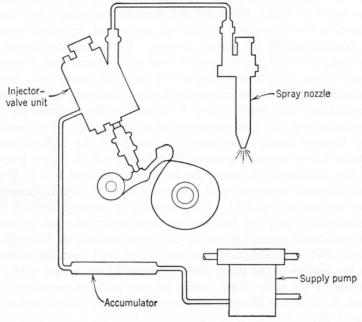

Injector-valve unit

Spray nozzle

Supply pump

Accumulator

Fig. 3·44   Schematic diagram of Cooper-Bessemer common-rail fuel-injection system

mechanical operating difficulties will extend the use of gasoline injection to other engines.

The fundamental principle of the gasoline injector is the same as that of the Diesel injector, and the general construction features are the same. The lower back pressures against which the fuel is injected, the greater ease of atomizing and vaporizing the fuel, and the elimination of the need for accurate timing and control of the rate of injection simplify the requirements appreciably, but lubrication of the injection pump by the fuel itself, as is done in Diesel systems, presents a difficulty arising from the gasoline's lack of lubricating body.

Figure 3·45 illustrates the Excello gasoline-injection system. The injection-pump unit comprises three essential parts, the supply pump, the fuel-metering valve, and the combined pumping

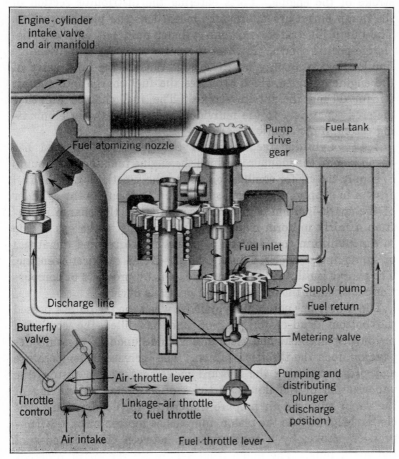

Engine-cylinder intake valve and air manifold

Fuel atomizing nozzle

Pump drive gear

Fuel tank

Fuel inlet

Discharge line

Supply pump

Fuel return

Butterfly valve

Metering valve

Air-throttle lever

Throttle control

Linkage-air throttle to fuel throttle

Air intake

Fuel-throttle lever

Pumping and distributing plunger (discharge position)

Fig. 3·45 Flow diagram and section view of Ex-Cell-O gasoline-injection system

and distributing plunger. The gear-type supply pump takes the fuel from the storage tank and delivers it through the metering orifice to the barrel in which the plunger operates. The metering orifice varies in size with movement of the throttle valve in the air inlet, thus proportioning the amount of fuel delivered to the amount of air flowing to the cylinders. The cams formed on the upper face of the plunger gear cause it to reciprocate as it rotates and execute a delivery stroke in phase with each suction stroke of the engine. Ports entering the distributor section of the pump barrel are alternately indexed as the plunger rotates. The pump illustrated is a four-cylinder unit, but only one discharge port is shown. Each of the ports connects to a discharge line leading to a spray nozzle located outside the inlet valve of the engine cylinder which atomizes the fuel charge into the air stream during the intake stroke. The fuel charges are thus metered separately to the individual cylinders, largely eliminating errors in distribution.

3·44 Cylinder treatment of charge. Consideration has been given to the manner in which the engine functions as a pump to supply the air for combustion and to the functioning of the fuel system in supplying the necessary fuel. As it enters the cylinder of the spark-ignition engine, the condition of the charge ranges from a fairly uniform mixture of fuel and air in the gas engine to a nonuniform combination of somewhat segregated quantities of liquid fuel, vaporized fuel, and air in the carburetor engine. The charge is diluted to a varying extent by products of combustion retained in the cylinder from previous cycles.

The charge has entered the cylinder when the piston has passed the bottom dead-center position and has filled the combined piston displacement and clearance volume under a pressure depending upon the throttle position. The increase in temperature and pressure during the upward movement of the piston, the vaporization of the liquid particles of gasoline, and mixing of the vapor with the air prepare the charge for combustion. The charge is ignited, as the piston approaches top center on the compression stroke, by a spark passing between the electrodes of the spark plug. The flame front set up by the spark proceeds across the combustion chamber, releasing the energy that was stored in the fuel.

3·45 Ignition. The methods used to ignite the charge in the cylinder have passed through an interesting cycle which started with the battery, distributor, induction coil, and spark plug used in a crude form in the Lenoir engine and returned to a fundamentally similar high-voltage electric system after several other methods were used during the intervening years. The early electric systems were erratic in operation because of the low output of the Bunsen battery, the only source of electricity available for the purpose at that time, and the poor electrical insulating materials used. There was also greater difficulty in igniting the charge at the low temperature and pressure of the noncompression engine. Pilot gas flames, located in ports exposed to the charge by opening valves at the time of ignition, incandescent wires or tubes similarly cut off from the cylinder except at the instant of ignition, and low-voltage electric systems of the so-called make-and-break type were used in the interval between the first electric igniter and the modern high-voltage spark system.

Two forms of ignition systems are now in use, the magneto and the battery and distributor systems. The magneto is a self-contained device which generates its own electric power, times the occurrence of the sparks, and distributes them to the spark plugs in proper sequence. It requires only the spark plugs and the wires connecting them to the magneto to complete the system. The magneto is the same in principle as the battery and distributor system except for the source of electric energy and the arrangement of parts. Both types provide all of the electrical devices necessary to produce a voltage sufficient to cause a spark to pass across a gap of 0.025 to 0.040 in. against the resistance of the compressed charge in each cylinder at the precise instant when needed.

Figure 3·46 shows the component units of a four-cylinder battery and distributor system and the electric circuit. One terminal of the battery is grounded to the frame of the engine, and the other is connected through the ignition switch to one primary terminal of the induction coil. The other primary terminal is connected to one of the contact points of the circuit breaker and through the closed points to the ground. The primary circuit of the coil is thus completed when the contact points of the circuit breaker are together and the switch is closed. The secondary terminal of the coil is connected to the central contact of the distributor and thence to the distributor rotor. Each spark plug is connected to one of the outer contacts of the distributor to be contacted in proper sequence by the turning rotor. The other end of the secondary winding is connected within the coil to the primary winding.

The battery is the source of electric energy for the ignition system in conjunction with the generator which maintains it in a charged state. The storage battery also serves to operate the starting motor and, in many installations, supplies electricity

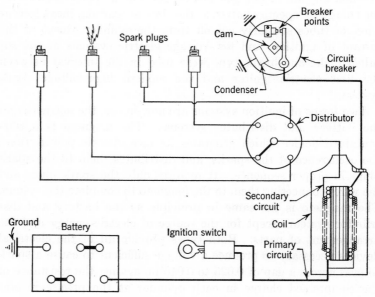

Fig. 3·46 Ignition system

for lights and accessories. Batteries of six to eight volts are ordinarily used for this purpose.

The distributor assembly is a double unit, comprising the distributor proper, which is a rotary switch whose function is to connect the secondary of the coil alternately to each of the several spark plugs in their firing sequence, and the circuit breaker by which the current in the primary winding of the coil is controlled. The two devices are not electrically connected within the distributor assembly and are combined only because both must be driven at the same speed by a shaft connection to the engine crankshaft. The distributor is located on the outer end of the spindle which passes through the assembly and is driven by gears from the camshaft or crankshaft. A cam mounted just beneath the distributor is formed with as many lobes as there are cylinders in the engine and operates the primary circuit breaker, the second unit of the distributor assembly. The breaker points are held in contact by a spring except when forced apart by the lobes of the cam. The cam rotates at half

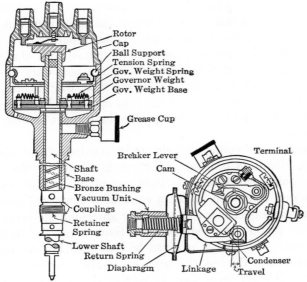

Rotor
Cap
Ball Support
Tension Spring
Gov. Weight Spring
Governor Weight
Gov. Weight Base

Grease Cup

Breaker Lever
Cam
Terminal

Shaft
Base
Bronze Bushing
Vacuum Unit
Couplings
Retainer Spring
Lower Shaft
Return Spring
Diaphragm
Linkage
Condenser
Travel

FIG. 3·47 Ignition distributor

crankshaft speed on four-stroke-cycle engines and breaks the primary circuit once for each cylinder in the engine during one complete cycle of the engine. The distributor assembly is shown in Fig. 3·47.

The ignition coil is merely a special form of step-up transformer to raise the battery voltage, which is far too low to jump the spark-plug gap, to the necessary 8000 to 20,000 volts. It consists of a primary winding of a relatively few turns of copper wire wound about a soft-iron core and a secondary winding of a great many turns of very fine wire wound over the primary winding. Both ends of the primary winding are brought out to exterior terminals. One end of the secondary winding is connected to the primary winding, and the other is brought out to the high-voltage terminal of the coil.

When the primary circuit is closed, the current flows through the primary winding of the coil and creates a magnetic field through the core. When the primary circuit is opened by the action of the circuit breaker, the magnetic field rapidly collapses, and a high voltage is induced in the secondary winding because of the high rate of change in the magnetic flux through the coil. A high voltage is thus built up across the secondary winding at each instant that the circuit-breaker points separate.

The distributor rotor is mounted in phase with the circuit-breaker cam so that it has established the secondary circuit to one of the spark plugs at the instant that the breaker points open. When the next lobe of the cam opens the breaker points, the distributor rotor has advanced to the contact leading to the next spark plug.

A considerable voltage is built up by self-inductance when the primary circuit is broken, and a spark results at the circuit-breaker points which tends to burn and pit the contact surfaces. A capacitor, commonly called a condenser, connected across the contact points quenches this spark by absorbing the surge which otherwise would jump between the contacts at the instant of separation. The charge received by the capacitor immediately discharges back through the primary winding of the coil in the opposite direction from that in which the current flows while the points are closed. The capacitor and the inductive primary-coil winding are now in series, completing a resonating circuit with a high-frequency characteristic. An oscillating current of damped sine-wave form flows until its amplitude drops to zero when the stored energy in the capacitor is dissipated. Without the capacitor, the contact points would be short lived, and less energy would be delivered to the spark plugs because of the energy drained from the coil to maintain the arc at the contact points.

The spark plug is essentially a pair of electrodes insulated from each other by an insert of fused aluminum oxide or similar heat-resistant material of high electrical resistance. One electrode is attached to the metal body of the plug which is threaded to screw into the cylinder of the engine whereby it is electrically grounded. The central electrode extends outside the plug through the insulator and provides a connecting terminal for the high-voltage lead from the distributor.

In operation, the coil is energized when the breaker contacts close, and a magnetic field is established. This field collapses when the contacts open, and the resulting high voltage sends a current to the distributor which selects the spark plug whose turn it is to fire. Very little current flows through the secondary circuit during this discharge, but considerable energy is expended at the spark-plug gap because of the high voltage.

The spark must be timed precisely with the cycle of the engine, and this is accomplished by adjusting the relationship between the circuit-breaker cam and the engine crankshaft. Changes in engine speed and load change the optimum point in the cycle at which the spark should occur. Since an earlier timing of spark is needed at higher speed, a simple fly-weight mechanism is incorporated in the distributor assembly beneath the breaker mechanism to advance the relative position of the cam with respect to the driving shaft as the speed increases. The charge in the cylinder burns more rapidly at heavy load conditions than at light load because of the higher pressure and temperature and relatively less dilution with exhaust gas from previous cycles. It is desirable, therefore, to retard the timing of the spark as the load increases. Since the vacuum in the intake manifold is higher with the throttle partly closed than at full throttle, this vacuum can be used to advance the spark timing at light loads. This is accomplished by a diaphragm attached to the breaker plate so as to rotate the contact points relative to the cam and cause the points to separate earlier as the manifold vacuum increases at lighter loads. These control devices are shown in Fig. 3·47.

3·46 Internal temperature control. Provision must be made in all internal-combustion engines to remove a portion of the heat released within the combustion chamber and dissipate it to the surroundings. Although the objective of the combustion system is to liberate as much heat as is possible from the fuel that is burned, only a fraction of the heat supplied by the fuel can be converted into useful work. That fraction, represented by the thermal efficiency of the engine, seldom exceeds 30 per cent, and the remainder is waste heat and must be removed or the engine will overheat.

The instantaneous temperature attained by the burning gases in the combustion chamber probably exceeds 4000 F when an engine operates under load. If the unused portion of the heat in the cylinder is not removed from the engine, the temperature of the metal parts will rise rapidly and approach that of the gases. The major portion of the rejected heat is carried away by the exhaust gases, radiated, or unaccounted for, but a considerable amount, usually about 30 per cent of the heat input to the engine, must be removed from the metal of the cylinders by a cooling system.

The amount of heat dissipated by the cooling system should be the minimum that will prevent the temperature of the engine from becoming too high for proper functioning. The limiting temperature at which the combustion-chamber walls of a well-designed spark-ignition engine will permit satisfactory operation is that at which preignition and detonation are avoided. Compression-ignition engine temperatures are limited only by the ability of the parts to function properly, since the normal combustion process is aided rather than interfered with by high cylinder temperature. In any case, cooling must be sufficient to prevent excessive loss of strength, erosion, warpage, overexpansion, and lubrication difficulties which accompany high temperatures. The parts that are most likely to suffer from overheating are exhaust valves, spark-plug electrodes, and piston crowns. Cooling is a matter of equalization of internal temperatures to prevent local overheating as well as one of removing sufficient heat to maintain a practical overall working temperature.

There are two systems of cooling in use: liquid and air. Each has certain advantages, and each is especially adapted to engines intended for certain applications. Marine engines are logically liquid-cooled, and aviation engines are very successfully air-cooled. The principal problem in liquid cooling is that of finding a coolant that has a high boiling point and a low freezing point and is chemically inert. Although water is largely used for this purpose, its low boiling point requires the engine to operate at lower than optimum temperatures, and its high freezing point necessitates the addition of anti-freeze agents in cold weather. Ethylene glycol has a much wider temperature range in the liquid phase than water, but is to some extent chemically active and is quite expensive.

Passages called cooling jackets are cored in the cylinder and cylinder-head castings of liquid-cooled engines. These jackets are so arranged that cool water can be forced in through an entrance at the lower extremity, pass around the cylinder walls, and flow upward into the cylinder-head jackets, and the heated water can be discharged through an outlet at the top. A radiator is commonly used to transfer the heat absorbed by the coolant to air that is circulated through the openings in the radiator core. A pump circulates the coolant at a rate sufficient to effect the necessary heat transfer. A thermostat is usually placed at the water outlet from the engine to regulate the flow and maintain the jacket temperature constant, regardless of the load and speed of the engine and the temperature of the surrounding air.

The principal problem in air cooling is to expose sufficient cooling surface to the air and to circulate the necessary amount of air without the expenditure of large amounts of power. The area of the cooling surface of the engine cylinder and cylinder head is increased by forming thin fins, either integrally by machining them on the outer walls of the parts or by attaching separate fins to them. Except in airplanes where the high speed and the propeller wash provide the necessary cooling air, the power required to circulate the air consumes an appreciable portion of the power developed by the engine.

The portion of the heat liberated by the burning fuel that is dissipated by the cooling system varies from one installation to another and changes slightly with load and speed in each engine. Less heat must be removed by the cooling system of a Diesel engine than by that of a spark-ignition engine of lower efficiency. The usual range is 20 to 35 per cent of the heat supplied by the fuel or 2000 to 3500 Btu per hp-hr.

3·47 Lubrication. Lubrication of the parts of an engine that have relative motion is necessary in order to reduce friction and wear that would quickly destroy the parts. The importance of proper lubrication of any mechanical device can hardly be overestimated, because successful operation without lubrication is impossible. Friction converts mechanical energy into heat, thereby consuming a portion of the power developed in the cylinders of the engine and causing heating of the parts. If friction is excessive, the heat generated will become so intense that the metal surfaces will seize and prevent further motion.

The theory of lubrication is to interpose a fluid film between the moving surfaces, such that metallic contact between the parts is prevented. Fluid friction between the many microscopically thin layers of oil that may be considered to make up the oil film is substituted for the rubbing friction between the metal parts. The forces pressing the surfaces together tend to squeeze out the lubricant and may prevent the maintenance of an oil film of sufficient thickness to eliminate metallic contact entirely. The resulting partial film will not eliminate friction so fully as a complete film but will permit the parts to function with only moderate heating and wear. Depending upon the load carried by the bearing, its lubrication may be so perfect that the moving part is entirely floated on an oil film, it may operate under a boundary condition with a film so thin that there is partial metallic contact, or the load may be so great that extreme-pressure lubricants are necessary which react with the metal to plate it with a slippery compound and do not interpose an oil film. Friction is never entirely eliminated, but is reduced to a very much smaller amount varying with the thickness of the oil film, the characteristics of the bearing surface, and the fluid friction of the lubricant.

The principal objective of the lubricating system of an internal-combustion engine is to restore continuously the oil film on all the bearing surfaces of the engine so that friction and wear are reduced to the minimum permitted by operating conditions. Several other purposes are served by the lubricating system, however. When the usual circulating system is employed, the lubricant serves as a coolant and picks up heat from the metal surfaces and permits its dissipation to the surroundings. Particles of metal, resulting from wear, and other contaminants, such as carbon that may form on cylinder walls, are flushed from the bearing surfaces and carried away. Leakage between the piston and cylinder walls is more effectively blocked, and noise resulting from contact between moving parts is reduced by the cushioning action of the oil film.

Lubricants suitable for engine use are refined from petroleum stocks after the various fuels are removed. The refining process removes impurities, such as dirt, asphalt, and wax, and also certain portions of the oil itself that are undesirable, because they are unstable and tend to oxidize or deteriorate otherwise under the severe conditions encountered in the engine. The purified oils are graded according to their body or viscosity and marketed under SAE number classifications ranging from 5W to 70. The lighter-bodied lower-numbered oils are suitable for cold-weather lubrication of automobile engines, and progressively higher-numbered oils are required for operation at higher temperatures, with the air-cooled aviation engines using the highest ones. The 5W, 10W, and 20W oils meet certain flow requirements at zero temperature, and each is suitable for starting and operating down to a subzero temperature limit. Greater mechanical clearances provided in the engine design or resulting from wear require higher-viscosity oils for proper lubrication and must be taken into consideration in addition to the temperature.

The SAE lubricants code specifies three types of motor lubricants. Regular-type oil is of a quality suitable for engines operating under moderate conditions. Premium-type oil has the oxidation stability and bearing-corrosion-preventive properties necessary for more severe operating conditions than are imposed by regular duty. Heavy-duty type oil has oxidation stability, corrosion resistance, and detergent-dispersant characteristics which meet the requirements of both high-speed Diesel and gasoline engines under heavy-duty operating conditions. The special requirements of the premium and heavy-duty types are met by chemical additives which are compounded with the mineral-oil base. Manufacturers prescribe the proper grade and type of lubricant to be used in their engines when operating under conditions of varying severity.

Physical and chemical tests are made in the laboratory with test apparatus designed and operated according to ASTM lubricant test codes. These tests form the basis for specifications which limit certain properties or characteristics of the oil to narrow ranges that have been found by experience to be proper for the application covered by the specification. Viscosity, which is probably the most important of the items included, is expressed as the number of seconds required for 60 cc of the oil to flow through the Saybolt universal viscosimeter at standard temperatures specified in the code. The viscosity index of an oil, which is a measure of the rate of change in viscosity with temperature, is another indication of its desirability. Viscosity index is important because excessive flow resistance at low temperature seriously hinders starting and early lubrication; conversely, excessive thinning at high temperature impairs lubrication and increases oil consumption. Straight mineral oils refined from Pennsylvania crude oils have been assigned a viscosity index of 100, and Gulf Coast oils, which lose viscosity at increased temperature to a much greater extent, have an index of 0. A comparison with the characteristics of these two oils establishes the viscosity index of any oil. Viscosity-index improvers are added to some commercial lubricants, and the oils refined by solvent processes have high viscosity indexes. Also related to the viscosity is the pour point of an oil. The lowest temperature at which an oil flows determines its pour point. The crankcase oil must have an appropriate pour point if an engine is to be started readily and without damage after exposure to extremely low temperature. Dewaxing operations in the refining process and the addition of pour-point depressants are the methods used to procure oils with low pour points.

Detergent-dispersant additives are desirable in oils used in Diesel engines or in spark-ignition engines operated under unusually severe conditions. They impart cleansing properties to the oil and cause it to pick up and retain in suspension particles of carbon, dirt, and oxidized hydrocarbons, which would otherwise accumulate in the piston-ring grooves, resulting in stuck rings when solidified by the high temperature, or be deposited on metal surfaces in the form of lacquer. Corrosion inhibitors, antifoam agents, and anti-oxidants are among the other chemical additives used in heavy-duty oils to meet the needs of some modern engines.

Lubrication systems differ considerably between extreme types of engines. Large slow-speed engines commonly use mechanical lubricators consisting of a large number of metering pumps which deliver an adjustable number of drops of oil to each separate lubricated surface. Automotive-type engines use circulating systems in which a quantity of oil is carried in a sump formed in the lower extremity of the crankcase. A pump, usually of the gear type, takes oil from the sump and delivers it under pressure to a system of tubes and passages leading to the bearings of the engine. In most instances the crankshaft is drilled so that the oil which is delivered to its main bearings flows through drilled passages in the cheeks of the crank to the crankpin bearings. Frequently, the connecting rods have oil passages drilled through them to convey oil up to the piston pins. In other instances, the oil that issues from the crankshaft bearings and is sprayed throughout the engine enclosure reaches the cylinder walls in sufficient quantities to lubricate the pistons.

Figure 3·48 shows a typical system applied to a four-cylinder gasoline engine. Various parts of the engine, such as the valve mechanism and front-end gears or chains, are supplied with oil by suitable connections. After passing through the engine, the oil drains back to the sump to be recirculated. The filter, shown in the diagram, continuously by-passes a portion of the oil pumped and passes it through a filtering medium which removes the more injurious particles of foreign matter picked up by the oil, thus maintaining it in good condition. The pressure under which the oil is circulated is regulated by a spring-loaded relief valve to prevent excessive pressures at high speed.

The lubricating oil in an engine tends to oxidize and form solid compounds that are called sludge. When the sludge concentration becomes too great, lubrication is interfered with. There is also a possibility that decomposition will yield corrosive substances. The quality of the oil also suffers from contamination by products of combustion and heavy ends of unburned fuel that pass the piston rings. Because of these accumulations, the oil must be purified and renewed at regular intervals, or it will fail to protect the working parts against damage.

3·48 Regulation. The fuel input to an engine must be regulated in accordance with the load applied and the desired speed. The speed will increase with decreases in load unless the amount of fuel supplied is decreased proportionately. The fuel admitted to the cylinder of the internal-combustion engine may be adapted to the load and speed requirements by two methods known as quantity and quality governing.

The gasoline engine is regulated by a throttle or butterfly valve

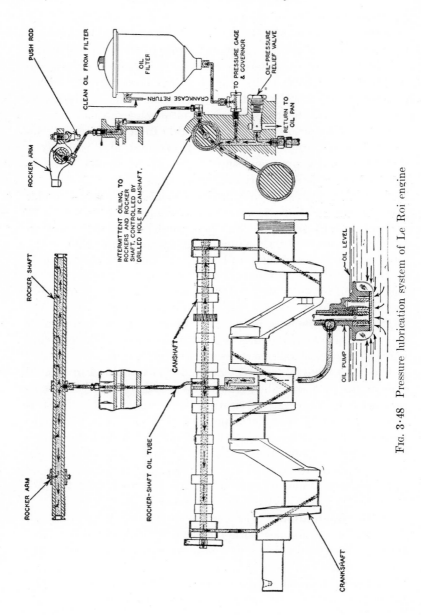

Fig. 3·48 Pressure lubrication system of Le Roi engine

at the entrance to the intake manifold. This throttle valve is incorporated in the carburetor and in the control unit of the gasoline-injection device. The throttling method of regulation is called quantity governing, because the fuel and air supplied to the engine are both varied in substantially constant proportion.

Compression-ignition engines do not use throttle valves in the air-induction system, but are controlled by varying only the amount of fuel supplied. This type of regulation changes the air–fuel proportions and is called quality governing, since the mixture becomes richer in fuel at increased loads. The air–fuel ratio of the gasoline engine varies with throttle position only by the amount necessary to meet the changes in mixture requirements and remains within a narrow range above and below the chemically correct ratio. The Diesel engine always operates with excess air, and the air–fuel ratio varies from about 20 to 25 at maximum load to several hundred at light load because of quality governing.

Throttling causes a drop in inlet pressure below the outside condition, and the cylinder is filled at the end of the intake stroke at a reduced pressure. The charge volume is the same at all loads, but the pressure is progressively lower as the throttle is closed. The decreased pressure lowers the specific weight of the charge, and the cylinder is filled with an expanded charge of smaller weight. A corresponding reduction in the weight of fuel is brought about by the metering action of the carburetion device.

Throttling is not an efficient means of regulating an engine. Compression begins at a much lower cylinder pressure at light load than at full load because of throttling action, and the pressure at ignition is correspondingly lower. The entire cycle is thus executed at lower temperatures and pressures which result in lower efficiencies and increased specific fuel consumption. The fuel economy of the Diesel engine is not decreased so much at light load as that of the gasoline engine because of its more efficient method of regulation.

The controls which regulate an engine may be operated manually by a throttle lever or by the accelerator pedal of a vehicle. Constant speed may be automatically maintained, if desired, by a mechanical or hydraulic governor. Stationary and marine en-

gines operate at governed speeds that are maintained with the
degree of accuracy demanded by the installation. Diesel engines
of all types, stationary, marine, or automotive, are equipped with
governors which may be of the constant-speed type, or they may
permit the operator to select any speed within the useful range
of a variable-speed engine. The accelerator pedal of a Diesel-
powered vehicle acts on the governor which, in turn, acts on the
fuel-injection pumps, but that of a gasoline-powered vehicle acts
directly on the throttle valve of the engine. Speed governors are
incorporated in the fuel-injection units used by several Diesel
manufacturers, and others use separate governing units.

3·49   Performance.   The performance of an engine is expressed by the relationship of its power, speed, and fuel consumption. Several other relationships based upon the power, size, and
weight of the engine are of interest, because they affect the usefulness of the engine for exacting applications. Among these are
the ratio of the engine weight in pounds to the horsepower delivered and the horsepower developed per cubic inch of piston displacement. The brake mean effective pressure is also used as a
standard for measuring the effectiveness of the engine.

At any speed within the operating range of an engine, which
may be a very narrow range in the stationary power-plant engine
or may cover a wide range in the automobile-type engine, it is
capable of developing a certain definite amount of power at full
throttle. Since the speed at which cycles are executed in the
cylinders is a factor in determining the power developed, more
power is produced at increased speeds, provided other factors
remain unchanged. When the speed becomes extremely high,
however, the ability of an unsupercharged engine to draw in as
full a charge as at lower speeds causes the mean effective pressure
in the cylinders to decrease and offset, to some extent, the effect
of increased speed. A point is eventually reached above which
the mean effective pressure decreases at a rate higher than that
at which the speed increases, and the peak horsepower of the
engine is reached. At speeds above that at which the maximum
horsepower is developed, the effect of reduced mean effective
pressure will predominate, and the full-throttle power output will
be less with further increases in speed.

The relationship between the full-throttle brake horsepower of an automobile engine and its speed in revolutions per minute is shown by the brake-horsepower curve in Fig. 3·49. This curve is typical of those plotted from data taken in testing an automo-

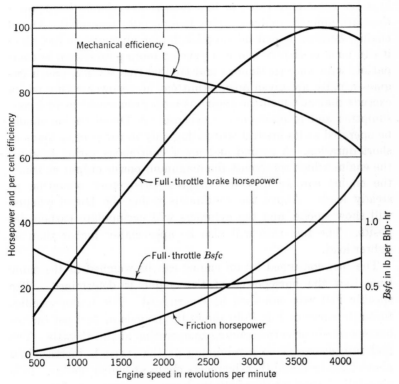

Fig. 3·49   Automobile-engine performance curves

bile engine loaded by a dynamometer. It shows that for any speed within the range tested there is a corresponding horsepower which is the maximum the engine can develop. Any amount of power less than the maximum can be developed by partially closing the throttle, but more than that cannot be produced at that speed. Below the speed at which the horsepower curve peaks, more power can be had by increasing the speed, but, when that peak is reached, the full-power capacity of the engine is being developed. The curve shows that the engine for which it was plotted attained its maximum output of 100 bhp at 3800 rpm. Those values of horsepower and speed would ordinarily be stated as the rating of the engine.

Heavy-duty engines intended for continuous operation at full load are commonly rated at less than the maximum horsepower they are able to produce. This is especially true of the Diesel engine, because it can be supplied larger amounts of fuel than it can burn efficiently and can develop more power than is compatible with long continuous and trouble-free service. Such engines usually are given an intermittent horsepower rating which exceeds that at which the engine is most economical in fuel consumption and in maintenance expense. A Diesel engine should be operated at its intermittent rating only to carry peak loads of short duration. A second and lower continuous rating is given the engine which represents the maximum power output at which the engine can be expected to give satisfactory operation at steady loads. Above the continuous rating the Diesel exhaust will show smoke, and the cylinders will accumulate carbon deposits. The fuel rate will also be appreciably higher than at lighter load.

The fuel consumed by an engine can be weighed at the same time that the horsepower of the engine is determined. The specific fuel rate can then be determined. The brake-specific-fuel-rate curve of Fig. 3·49 shows the pounds of fuel per brake-horsepower-hour corresponding to operation at full throttle. The fuel rate decreases to a minimum as the speed is increased to about 2200 rpm and then increases again at higher speeds. It is especially important that both the horsepower curve and the fuel-rate curve shown in this diagram be recognized as those of full-throttle conditions only. Partially closing the throttle at any speed will decrease the horsepower below the values plotted and will also cause important changes in the fuel rate.

Figure 3·50 shows the effect of load upon the fuel rate at any constant speed. The typical engine is most economical at about 75 to 85 per cent load. The fuel rate usually increases slightly as the load is increased to 100 per cent, and it increases at a progressively faster rate as the load is decreased, becoming much higher at very small loads than the minimum rate. This curve indicates that it is very uneconomical to operate an engine at small percentages of its full-throttle output and that it should operate at slightly less than maximum capacity if its fuel consumption is to be low.

Since the fuel economy is a function of both load and speed, it is evident that there is some intermediate speed and per cent load at which the combined effects of speed and load will produce the best fuel economy of which the engine is capable. This speed and load combination is not likely to be the one at which an engine would be selected to operate, however, because a larger and more costly engine would be required for a given power output than if it were operated at a higher speed. The speed

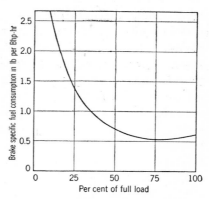

Fig. 3·50 Variation in fuel rate of automobile engine with changing load at constant speed

ratio by which an engine is connected to its load must be carefully chosen in order that the engine may operate at favorable load and speed combinations as much as possible. Because of the increased fuel rates at light load, it is frequently desirable to install several small engines instead of one large one for fluctuating loads. The minimum number of engines necessary to carry the load can then be operated with each carrying an economical load.

The minimum fuel rate attained depends upon the size, type, and speed of the engine. In general, the large slow-speed Diesel engines have better fuel economy than other engines. The average engine of this type will operate at a fuel rate of 0.39 lb per bhp-hr or less at its best operating range. High-speed Diesels do not ordinarily operate at fuel rates lower than about 0.45 lb per bhp-hr, and many engines of this type consume more than that amount of fuel. A range of 0.47 to 0.60 lb per bhp-hr may be taken as the range of minimum fuel rates for gasoline engines of the ordinary types, but high-output aviation engines are known to show superior economy on high-octane fuel under optimum conditions.

In comparing the fuel consumption of Diesel and gasoline engines, the fact that fuel rates are calculated on a weight basis whereas fuels are marketed on a volume basis should be considered. Diesel fuels are higher in specific weight than gasoline by a ratio of about 7 to 6, their approximate respective weights per gallon. The somewhat lower cost per gallon of Diesel fuel, the greater weight per gallon, and the lower specific fuel consumption all combine to make the cost of fuel per power unit substantially less for the Diesel than for the gasoline engine. This saving is partially offset in competing fields by the higher initial investment in the Diesel, resulting from its more expensive construction throughout. The net saving of the Diesel increases with increased output in horsepower-hours over a period of time.

Weight–horsepower ratios range from 0.85 lb per bhp for modern aircraft engines to about 200 lb per bhp for stationary Diesels where no attempt is made to reduce weight. Horsepower–displacement ratios range from about 0.02 bhp per cu in. for slow-speed engines to about 2.0 bhp per cu in. for high-output automotive engines. Brake mean effective pressures at rated load are between 75 and 125 psi for a wide range of engines. Aircraft-engine brake mean effective pressures of 250 psi are not unusual, and values much higher than that are obtained experimentally.

The lowest fuel cost per brake horsepower-hour of any type engine is attained by Diesel engines operating on gaseous fuel, usually natural gas or by-product gases. In geographical regions near gas wells and along pipe lines, natural gas is quite low in price and is the most economical fuel to burn. All hydrocarbon gases have relatively high self-ignition temperatures, resulting from their small compact molecular structure. Consequently, their use in compression-ignition engines caused ignition difficulties and, for many years, gas-burning internal-combustion engines were limited to the spark-ignition type. Gases are very suitable for spark-ignition engines because of their high-octane ratings.

The ignition problem, which prevented satisfactory use of gases in Diesel engines, has now been solved by the injection of a pilot charge of ordinary Diesel fuel oil, which is easily ignited, into the gaseous mixture. In operation, the gas Diesel inducts a charge of air and gas into the cylinders during the intake stroke. The mixture is very lean, partly because the Diesel is inherently a lean-mixture engine, and also because the gaseous charge is only a fraction of the total fuel to be burned, the remainder being

FIG. 3·51   Sixteen-cylinder V-type Cooper-Bessemer Diesel engine

supplied later in the pilot charge of fuel oil. The fuel-injection pumps are timed to deliver the pilot charge at the proper point in the compression stroke to cause combustion at the optimum time. The inducted charge of gas and air does not ignite at the temperature of compression to which it is exposed before the injection of the pilot charge because of the low fuel–air ratio and the high self-ignition temperature of the gas.

Most of the large stationary power-plant Diesels now manufactured are equipped to burn gas because of the large savings in power costs effected. Figure 3·51 illustrates a large stationary engine of the gas- or oil-burning type. The unit is a model LSV 16 Cooper-Bessemer turbosupercharged four-stroke-cycle gas-Diesel engine with 16 cylinders arranged in two banks of 8 forming an angle of 36 degrees. The cylinders are of 15.5-in. bore and 22-in. stroke. Two exhaust-gas-driven turbochargers are provided, one at each end of the engine serving separate banks of cylinders. The engine is equipped with a complete Diesel-fuel system and also with gas-admission equipment, permitting operation entirely on Diesel fuel or on proportions of fuel oil and gas up to 96 per cent gas and 4 per cent pilot fuel oil. At any time while the engine is running, the fuel mixture may be changed to the proportions desired. Gas is taken into the cylinders with the intake air, where it is ignited by the pilot oil. A governor controls the quantity of the two fuels needed to meet engine demands. Because of its lower cost, the gaseous portion of the charge is normally made as large as possible, but at times the available gas may be inadequate to supply the power demanded of the engine and it is necessary to increase the proportion of fuel oil in order to carry the load.

The heating value of the charge that can be burned in a gas Diesel is less than that of the fuel-oil charge of the conventional Diesel, and the horsepower rating is therefore lower. The rating of the engine illustrated, when supercharged, is 3700 hp when burning fuel oil at 327 rpm and 3300 hp when burning 96 per cent gas at the same speed. Unsupercharged, the rating is 2300 hp. These ratings correspond to brake mean effective pressures of 135, 120, and 85 psi, respectively. The engine is 37 ft 7 in. long and at maximum rating, develops over 12 hp per sq ft of floor space occupied.

Figure 3·52 shows the brake specific fuel consumption of the Cooper-Bessemer LSV engine. When it is operating on gas, the fuel rate is expressed in Btu per brake horsepower-hour and is calculated on the basis of the lower heating value of the gas plus the higher heating value of the pilot fuel oil. The scale of pounds of fuel oil per brake horsepower-hour applies to the curves for operation on fuel oil and is approximately equivalent to the Btu scale on the higher-heating-value basis. Compared to the automobile-engine performance of Fig. 3·49, these curves show that, at its most economical load, the Diesel operating turbocharged on fuel oil uses less than three-fourths the weight of fuel per brake horsepower-hour that is used by the automobile engine at its most economical load. The economy of the engine when burning gas is especially high at heavy loads, but the fuel rate increases more at light loads than it does on fuel oil. Since the price of natural gas in many parts of the United States is somewhat lower per Btu than that of fuel oil, appreciable savings in the cost of power generation are effected by engines of this type. The turbosuper-

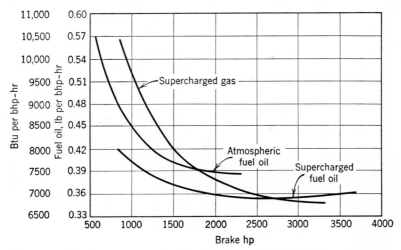

Fig. 3·52 Fuel-rate curves for 16-cylinder model LSV Cooper-Bessemer Diesel engine

charger is also shown to reduce substantially the fuel consumption of this engine.

The performance of an engine is best analyzed by means of an energy balance. A summation of energy quantities for the Cooper-Bessemer LSV engine running on gas and minimum pilot fuel can be made from routine power-plant data as follows:

	Btu per Bhp-Hr	Per Cent
Energy utilized in bhp	2545	37.5
Energy dissipated by jacket water	1200	17.7
Energy dissipated by oil coolers	285	4.2
Energy dissipated by aftercoolers	150	2.2
Energy to exhaust, radiation, etc.	2620	38.4
Energy supplied	6800	100

The brake thermal efficiency of 37.5 per cent indicated is based upon the lower heating value of the gas burned plus the higher heating value of the fuel-oil pilot charge, and would be decreased if the higher heating values of both were used. It is customary in the United States to charge engines with the higher heating value of the fuel, assuming that it is a fault of the engine that it cannot utilize the latent heat of the water vapor formed by burning hydrogen.

A more detailed energy balance may be calculated from test data in the same manner as is discussed in Article 2·21. The results of a complete test of an automobile engine are stated in the following data and the energy balance determined by the accompanying calculations.

Example 11. An automobile engine developing 100 bhp at 3600 rpm at full throttle burns 8.9 gal of gasoline per hr. Cooling water enters the jacket at a rate of 66 gpm at a temperature of 70 F and leaves at 180 F. Fuel analysis by mass: 15.8% hydrogen and 84.2% carbon. Specific gravity of fuel: 0.731. Higher heating value of fuel: 20,750 Btu per lb. Exhaust gas analysis by volume: 11.5% CO_2, 4.1% CO, 0.4% O_2, 2.3% H_2, 0.2% CH_4, and 81.5% N_2. Exhaust temperature, 1100 F. Ambient temperature, 70 F.

Solution: Contents of 100 moles of exhaust gas:

	Dry Gases	Carbon	Hydrogen
CO_2	$11.5 \times 44 = 505$	$11.5 \times 12 = 138$	
CO	$4.1 \times 28 = 115$	$4.1 \times 12 = 49.2$	
O_2	$0.4 \times 32 = 12.8$		
H_2	$2.3 \times 2 = 4.6$		$2.3 \times 2 = 4.6$
CH_4	$0.2 \times 16 = 3.2$	$0.2 \times 12 = 2.4$	$0.2 \times 4 = 0.8$
N_2	$81.5 \times 28 = 2280$		
	100.0 moles = 2920.6 lb	189.6 lb	5.4 lb

$$\text{Lb of dry gas per lb fuel} = \frac{\text{lb of 100 moles of dry gas}}{\text{lb of C in 100 moles of gas}} \times \text{lb of C per lb fuel}$$

$$= \frac{2920.6}{189.6} \times 0.842 = 13 \text{ lb dry gas per lb fuel}$$

$$\text{Lb of fuel per 100 moles of dry gas} = \frac{\text{lb of C in 100 moles of dry gas}}{\text{lb of C per lb fuel}}$$

$$225.2 = \frac{\text{\#}}{100 \text{ moles}}$$

$$= \frac{189.6}{0.842} = 225.2 \text{ lb fuel}$$

Lb of H in fuel per 100 moles of dry gas = lb of fuel per 100 moles of dry gas $\times$ lb of H_2 per lb fuel = $225.2 \times 0.158 = 35.6$ lb H_2 in fuel

Lb of H_2 in water vapor formed by combustion = lb of H_2 in fuel − lb of H_2 in dry gas = $35.6 - 5.4 = 30.2$ lb H_2 in water vapor

9 lb water vapor are formed per lb H_2

$9 \times 30.2 = 271.8$ lb water vapor in exhaust per 100 moles of dry gas

Lb of water vapor per lb fuel $= \dfrac{271.8}{225.2} = 1.2$ lb H_2O per lb fuel

Lb dry gas $+$ lb H_2O $-$ 1 lb fuel $=$ lb air per lb fuel

$13 + 1.2 - 1 = 13.2$ lb air per lb fuel

Bsfc $= \dfrac{\text{lb fuel per hr}}{\text{bhp}} = \dfrac{8.9 \times 0.731 \times 8.33}{100} = 0.548$ lb per bhp-hr

Fuel burned per min $= \dfrac{0.548 \times 100}{60} = 0.9133$ lb *MIN.*

Energy utilized, Btu per lb fuel $= \dfrac{\text{Btu per hp-hr}}{\text{bsfc}} = \dfrac{2545}{0.548} = 4644$ Btu *#fuel*

% of energy supplied utilized in Btu $= \dfrac{4644}{Q_H} = \dfrac{4644}{20{,}750} = 22.38\%$ *HHV*

Energy absorbed by coolant $= 66 \times 8.33 \times 10 = 5498$ Btu per min

Energy to coolant per lb fuel $= \dfrac{5498}{0.9133} = 6022$ Btu *# fuel*

% of energy supplied absorbed by coolant $= \dfrac{6022}{20{,}750} = 29.02\%$ *loss to cooling H_2O*

Dry-gas loss $=$ (exhaust-gas temperature $-$ air temperature) $\times$ specific heat
      of gas $\times$ lb gas per lb fuel $= (1100 - 70)\ 0.254 \times 13.2 = 3634$ Btu *3400*

% of energy supplied lost in sensible heat $= \dfrac{3634}{20{,}750} = 17.51\%$ *16.38%* *sp. heat of ex. gas*

Heating value of combustibles in exhaust $= Q_H$ for each combustible con-
      stituent $\times$ lb of each constituent per lb fuel

$Q_H = 4330$ Btu per lb CO, 62,000 Btu per lb H_2, and 23,700 Btu per lb CH_4

Heating value of CO in exhaust $= 4330 \times \dfrac{115}{225.2} = 2210$ Btu per lb fuel

Heating value of H_2 in exhaust $= 62{,}000 \times \dfrac{4.6}{225.2} = 1265$ Btu per lb fuel

Heating value of CH_4 in exhaust $= 23{,}700 \times \dfrac{3.2}{225.2} = 327$ Btu per lb fuel

Energy in combustibles in exhaust $= 2210 + 1265 + 327 = 3812$ Btu

% of energy supplied in combustibles in exhaust $= \dfrac{3812}{20{,}750} = 18.37\%$

Energy in H_2O formed by combustion of H_2 in fuel = lb of H_2O $(1066 + 0.5$
$\times$ exhaust temperature $-$ air temperature$)$ = 1.2 $(1066 + 0.5 \times 1100$
$- 70)$ = 1.2 $\times$ 1546 = 1855 Btu per lb fuel

% of energy supplied in H_2O formed by combustion = $\dfrac{1855}{20,750}$ = 8.94%

Radiation and unaccounted for losses, by difference = 783 Btu

% of energy supplied unaccounted for = $\dfrac{783}{20,750}$ = 3.78%

Summary

	Btu per Lb Fuel	Per Cent of Energy Supplied
I. Energy utilized, Btu	4,644	22.38
II. Losses		
1. Loss due to sensible heat in dry gaseous products	3,634	17.51
2. Loss due to combustibles in dry gaseous products	3,812	18.37
3. Loss due to heat transfer to jacket cooling water	6,022	29.02
4. Loss due to water vapor formed from the hydrogen in the fuel	1,855	8.94
5. Loss due to radiation and unaccounted for losses	783	3.78
Totals	20,750	100.00

PROBLEMS

1. An engine of 3.75-in. bore and 4-in. stroke has 7.0 cu in. clearance volume. What is the thermal efficiency of an Otto cycle as applied to this engine?

2. A gasoline-engine cylinder has 17 per cent clearance. What is the Otto-cycle efficiency for this engine?

3. A Diesel-type-engine cylinder has 6.25 per cent clearance. What is the Otto-cycle efficiency for this engine?

4. A Diesel-engine indicator diagram drawn with a 180-lb spring and a one-half normal size piston has an area of 0.56 sq in., and its length is 2.6 in. What is the mep of the cylinder?

5. A four-cylinder four-stroke-cycle engine has a bore of 4 in. and a stroke of 5 in. What ihp is produced when it is running at 1750 rpm with 95 psig mep?

6. An engine loaded by a prony brake with a 60-in. brake arm runs at 500 rpm, and the net scale reading is 130 lb. What are the torque in lb-ft and the bhp delivered?

7. A dynamometer with a 21-in. torque arm indicates a force of 200 lb when absorbing the output of an engine running at 1800 rpm. What is its bhp?

8. An engine under test delivers 78 bhp when its ihp is 95. Find the fhp and the mechanical efficiency.

9. If the engine of Problem 7 is motored by the dynamometer, and a reactive force of 20 lb is produced on the scales at 1800 rpm, what are the fhp and the ihp when it is delivering 60 bhp?

10. A six-cylinder four-stroke engine of 3.25-in. bore and 4-in. stroke delivers 40 bhp at 1500 rpm. Find the bmep.

11. An engine burns 1.75 gal of gasoline in a 15-min test while delivering 72 bhp. What is its bsfc if gasoline weighs 6.1 lb per gal?

12. Find the brake thermal efficiency of an engine that burns 1.8 gal of gasoline in 12 min while delivering 92 bhp. Assume 20,000 Btu per lb heating value.

13. Write the combining-weight equation for combustion of heptane, C_7H_{16}, in air. Find the weight of air required to burn 1 lb of heptane in chemically correct proportions.

14. Heptane vapor has a higher heating value of 5475 Btu per cu ft. Find the heating value of 1 cu ft of a chemically correct heptane and air mixture.

15. The Ford engine has eight cylinders of $3\frac{3}{16}$-in. bore and $3\frac{3}{4}$-in. stroke. When it was running at 2300 rpm, it was found to consume 140 cu ft of air per min, which was metered at 120 F and 14 psia. If the room temperature was 70 F and the barometric pressure 29.2 in. Hg, what volumetric efficiency was indicated?

16. If the engine of Fig. 3·49 develops 60 hp at 2500 rpm, and the curve of Fig. 3·50 is assumed to be plotted for that speed, find the gal of gasoline it will consume per hr.

17. Find the thermal efficiency of a theoretical Diesel cycle with a compression ratio of 15 and a cut-off ratio of 5.

18. Find the thermal efficiency of a Diesel cycle when applied to an engine of 5 in. bore and 6 in. stroke which has 9 cu in. clearance volume with cut-off occurring when the piston has descended 1 in. on its stroke.

19. An engine operating on the Otto cycle has a compression ratio of 7.5 and a bsfc of 0.48 when burning cracked fuel oil of 36 degrees API gravity. Find its brake thermal efficiency and brake engine efficiency.

20. Determine the length of dynamometer arm for which the constant C in the horsepower equation is equal to $\frac{1}{5000}$.

21. The General Motors six-cylinder two-stroke-cycle Diesel engine has a bore of 4.25 in. and a stroke of 5 in. When it is delivering 100 bhp at 1000 rpm, its fuel rate is 0.46 lb per bhp-hr. The blower delivers a volume of air, measured at the outside temperature of 70 F and pressure of 14.7 psia, 35 per cent in excess of the piston displacement volume. Q_H for the fuel is 19,600 Btu per lb, and specific gravity is 0.85.

(*a*) Find the brake thermal efficiency.

(*b*) Find the air–fuel ratio supplied to the engine. Note that this is not the actual air–fuel ratio of the mixture burned because not all of the air remains in the cylinder.

(*c*) Find the volume of fuel in cu mm supplied to each cylinder per cycle.

22. A six-cylinder automobile engine of 3.25 in. bore and 4.375 stroke with a compression ratio of 7 is tested on a dynamometer which has a 15.75 in. arm. The scale reading of the dynamometer is 100 lb when loading the engine at 3600 rpm and 30 lb when motoring the engine at the same speed; 8 gal of gasoline are burned per hr. $Q_H = 20,000$ Btu per lb. Find (a) the bhp delivered, (b) the bmep, (c) the torque, (d) the ihp, (e) the mechanical efficiency, and (f) the brake engine efficiency. The license rating used in many states as the basis for fees assumes that the bhp per cylinder equals 40 per cent of the square of the cylinder bore in in. (g) Find the license rating of this engine, and compare with the actual bhp.

23. An eight-cylinder automobile engine of 3.375 in. bore and 3.25 in. stroke with a compression ratio of 7 is tested at 4000 rpm on a dynamometer which has a 21 in. arm. During a 10-min test at a dynamometer scale beam reading of 90 lb, 10 lb of gasoline for which Q_H is 20,000 Btu per lb are burned, and air at 70 F and 14.7 psia is supplied to the carburetor at the rate of 12 lb per min. Find (a) the bhp delivered, (b) the bmep, (c) the bsfc, (d) the brake specific air consumption, (e) the brake thermal efficiency, (f) the brake engine efficiency, (g) the volumetric efficiency, and (h) the air–fuel ratio.

24. A supercharged six-cylinder four-stroke-cycle Diesel engine of 4.125 in. bore and 5 in. stroke has a compression ratio of 15. When it is tested on a dynamometer with a 21 in. arm at 2500 rpm, the scale beam reads 180 lb, 6.3 lb of 19,700 Btu per lb Q_H are burned during a 6-min test, and air is metered to the cylinders at the rate of 24 lb per min. Find (a) the bhp developed, (b) the bmep, (c) the bsfc, (d) the air–fuel ratio, (e) the brake thermal efficiency, and (f) the brake engine efficiency based on the theoretical Otto cycle.

25. A 200-hp gasoline truck engine operates at an average 50 per cent load and bsfc of 0.72 lb per bhp-hr. Find the saving in fuel cost that would result during an 8-hr run if a Diesel engine of the same rating were substituted with a bsfc of 0.52 under the same conditions. Assume gasoline of 0.73 specific gravity at 25 cents per gal and fuel oil of 0.85 specific gravity at 16 cents per gal.

26. A Diesel engine burns 9.6 gal of fuel oil per hr while delivering 150 bhp at 2000 rpm. A total of 70 gal of cooling water per min enters the jackets at 154 F and leaves at 165 F. The fuel contains 15.2 per cent hydrogen and 84.8 per cent carbon by weight, has a specific gravity of 0.85, and Q_H of 19,650 Btu per lb. The exhaust gas analysis by volume is 9.1% CO_2, 8.0% O_2, 0.04% CO, 0.05% CH_4, and 82.81% N_2. The exhaust-gas temperature is 900 F, and the ambient temperature is 70 F. Calculate an energy balance for the engine.

27. An engine loaded by a prony brake with a 4-ft arm runs at 300 rpm, and a platform-scale beam indicates a net torque reaction of 150 lb. The acceleration of gravity at the location is 30 ft per sec². Find the bhp.

4 · Fuel-Burning Equipmnet

4·1 Introduction. The combustion of fuel in the cylinder of an internal-combustion engine and the conversion into work of part of the energy thus released have been discussed in Chapter 3. This present chapter is concerned primarily with the principles involved and the equipment used for the economical combustion of fuel for steam generation. The functions of the furnace, the construction and methods of cooling furnace walls, the behavior of fuels on grates and in furnaces, and the equipment used to burn solid, liquid, and gaseous fuels are considered. Although the discussion is concerned primarily with the combustion of fuel under steam boilers, either for power generation or for steam heating, the same principles apply, and the same equipment with modifications is used in industrial heating furnaces such as drying or baking ovens; ceramic, cement, or lime kilns; soaking pits; open hearth furnaces; annealing furnaces; forge furnaces; and even domestic heating plants.

From the standpoint of ease of regulation, cleanliness, and control of combustion, gas is the ideal fuel. It is used in many industrial furnaces even though it is often necessary to manufacture it from coal. Gas can be burned efficiently if a *burner* is provided to proportion and mix the gas with the air required for its complete combustion and to introduce this mixture into a hot *furnace* or insulated compartment of sufficient size and shape to permit the combustion reactions to proceed to completion. Liquid fuels are atomized in burners which are designed to produce a fine spray of oil intimately mixed with air. This mixture is introduced into a hot furnace and burned in suspension like a gaseous fuel. Coal may be pulverized or reduced to a fine dust, mixed with air, and burned in suspension in a suitable furnace in a manner similar to the burning of oil or gas. Lump coal is placed, either by hand or mechanically, on a *grate* through which air may pass to react with the combustible constituents of the coal. Although part of the heat is released by combustion in the fuel bed, the gases which leave the fuel bed may contain as much as 40 to 60 per cent of the heating value of the fuel, and a furnace or combustion space of proper design is necessary if the fuel is to be burned completely.

4·2   Furnaces. A furnace is a fairly gas-tight and well-insulated space in which gas, oil, pulverized coal, or the combustible gases from solid-fuel beds may be burned with a minimum amount of excess air and with reasonably complete combustion. Near the exit from the furnace, at which place most of the fuel has been burned, the furnace gases will consist of inert gases such as CO_2, N_2, and H_2O vapor, together with some O_2 and some combustible gases such as CO, H_2, hydrocarbons, and particles of free carbon (soot). If combustion is to be complete, the combustible gases must be brought into intimate contact with the residual oxygen in a furnace atmosphere composed principally of inert gases. Also, the oxygen must be kept to a minimum if the loss due to heating the excess air from room temperature to chimney gas temperature is to be low. Consequently, *the major function of the furnace is to provide space in which the fuel may be burned with a minimum amount of excess air and with a minimum loss due to the escape of unburned fuel.*

The design of a satisfactory furnace is based upon the "three T's of combustion": *temperature, turbulence,* and *time.*

For each particular fuel, there is a minimum *temperature,* known as the *ignition temperature,* below which the combustion of that fuel in the correct amount of air will not take place. The ignition temperature of a fuel in air as reported by various investigators depends somewhat upon the methods used to determine it and, for some common gases, is as follows:

Hydrogen (H_2)	1075–1095 F.
Carbon monoxide (CO)	1190–1215 F.
Methane (CH_4)	1200–1380 F.
Ethane (C_2H_6)	970–1165 F.

If the combustible gases are cooled below the ignition temperature, they will not burn, regardless of the amount of oxygen present. A furnace must therefore be large enough and be maintained at a high enough temperature to permit the combustible gases to burn before they are cooled below the ignition temperature. In other words, the relatively cool heat-transfer surfaces must be so located that they do not cool the furnace gases below the ignition temperature until after combustion is reasonably complete.

Turbulence is essential if combustion is to be complete in a furnace of economical size. Violent mixing of oxygen with the combustible gases in a furnace increases the rate of combustion, shortens the flame, reduces the required furnace volume, and decreases the chance that combustible gases will escape from the furnace without coming into contact with the oxygen necessary for their combustion. The amount of excess oxygen or air required for combustion is decreased by effective mixing. Turbulence is obtained, in the case of oil, gas, and powdered coal, by using burners which introduce the fuel–air mixture into the furnace with a violent whirling action. High-velocity steam or air jets and mixing arches may be used to increase the turbulence in furnaces fired with coal on hand-fired grates or stokers.

Since combustion is not instantaneous, *time* must be provided for the oxygen to find and react with the combustible gases in the furnace. In burning fuels such as gas, oil, or pulverized coal, the incoming fuel–air mixture must be heated above the ignition temperature by radiation from the flame or hot walls of the furnace. Since gaseous fuels are composed of molecules, they burn very rapidly when thoroughly mixed with oxygen at a temperature above the ignition temperature. However, the individual particles of pulverized coal or atomized oil are very large in comparison with the size of molecules, and many molecules of oxygen are necessary to burn one particle of coal or droplet of oil. Time is required for the oxygen molecules to diffuse through the blanket of inert products of combustion which surrounds a partially burned particle of fuel and to react with the unburned fuel. Consequently, oil and pulverized coal burn with a longer flame than gaseous fuels.

The required furnace volume is dependent, therefore, upon the kind of fuel burned, the method of burning the fuel, the quantity of excess air in the furnace, and the effectiveness of furnace turbulence. The shape of the furnace depends upon the kind of fuel burned, the equipment used to burn the fuel, and the type of boiler used to absorb the heat if the fuel is burned for steam generation. Typical furnaces are illustrated in Figs. 4·3, 4·15, 5·11, 5·13, 5·17, 5·20, 5·28, 5·30, and 5·31.

Vertical furnace walls are often constructed of *fire brick*, a brick that has been developed to withstand high furnace tempera-

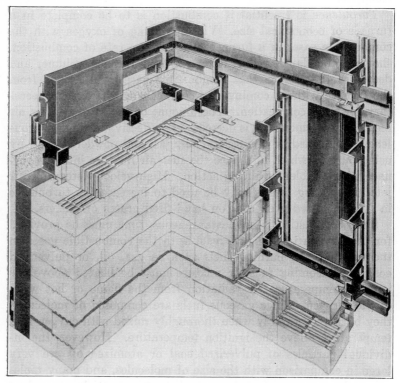

FIG. 4·1   Sectionally supported refractory wall

tures without softening, to resist the erosive effects of furnace atmospheres and particles of ash, and to resist spalling when subjected to fluctuating temperatures. Brick walls may be constructed, as shown in Figs. 5·9, 5·13, and 5·20. Where furnace walls are high, the weight of the brick wall and the strains caused by unequal expansion contribute to high maintenance cost if the wall is of solid brick construction. Under such conditions, a sectionally supported brick wall constructed as illustrated in Figs. 4·1 and 4·3 may be used. Heat-resisting alloy iron hangers are attached to a steel framework surrounding the furnace. Each hanger has a flat horizontal supporting pad upon which a set of specially shaped fire bricks or tiles may be supported. These tiles are slotted to engage the vertical T-shaped ribs of the hangers which hold the tiles in vertical alignment. The tiles are grooved to form interlocking joints. The wall may be air-cooled by encasing the supporting structural-steel framework in a gas-tight steel jacket and blowing air through the space between the brick and the casing. If the air required for combustion is circulated

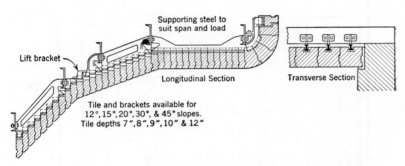

Fig. 4·2 Construction of suspended furnace arches

through the air space, most of the heat which flows through the brick wall can be returned to the furnace, thereby improving the efficiency of the unit.

Where it is necessary to provide a brick roof over part of a furnace, or where brick mixing or reflecting arches are required, the suspended arch as shown in Fig. 4·2 may be used. Slotted refractory tile are hung from T-headed supporting castings which are attached to a structural-steel framework. Some industrial furnaces employ this type of suspended-arch construction for flat or inclined roofs up to 20 ft or more in width and over 80 ft in length. Figure 5·17 shows the installation of suspended arches in a stoker-fired furnace.

Figure 4·3 illustrates an oil-fired furnace with sectionally supported air-cooled furnace walls and a suspended front arch. The path of the gases from the burners through the furnace is indicated. The furnace is so designed as to provide maximum length of flame travel without flame impingement on furnace walls or boiler surface and with good utilization of the total furnace volume for combustion space. The weight of the sectionally supported walls is carried on the steel framework surrounding the furnace. Each group of nine rows of refractory tile can be

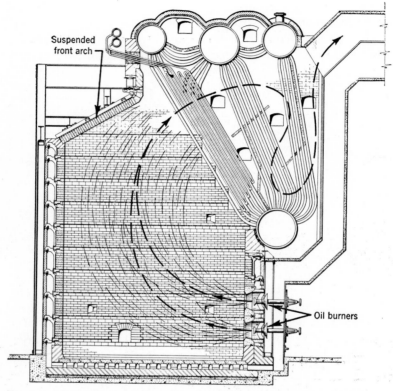

Fig. 4·3 Oil-fired boiler unit equipped with sectionally-supported, air-cooled side, front, and rear walls, suspended arch and air-cooled floor

removed for replacement without disturbing the wall above or below that section.

When furnaces are operated at high capacities, the temperature may be high enough to melt or fuse the ash which is carried in suspension by the furnace gases. Molten ash will chemically attack and erode the fire brick with which it comes into contact. Also, if the ash particles are not cooled below the temperature at

which they are plastic and sticky before they are carried into the
heat-transfer surfaces of the boiler, they may adhere to these
surfaces, obstruct the gas passages, and force a shutdown of the
unit. These difficulties may be overcome by constructing the

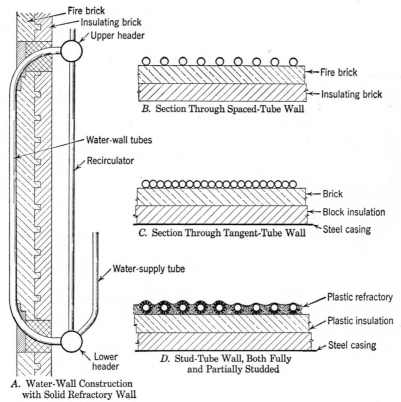

Fire brick
Insulating brick
Upper header

B. Section Through Spaced-Tube Wall

Fire brick
Insulating brick

Water-wall tubes
Recirculator

C. Section Through Tangent-Tube Wall

Brick
Block insulation
Steel casing

Water-supply tube

D. Stud-Tube Wall, Both Fully
and Partially Studded

Plastic refractory
Plastic insulation
Steel casing

Lower
header

A. Water-Wall Construction
with Solid Refractory Wall

FIG. 4·4 Details of water-wall construction

furnace walls of boiler tubes. Figure 4·4*A* shows a vertical section through a brick wall which is cooled by boiler tubes. Water
from the boiler is supplied to the lower water-wall header by
means of supply or downcomer tubes. The lower and upper
headers are connected by tubes, generally about 3¼ in. in outside diameter, which are bent to extend through the furnace walls
and placed to form a bank of parallel tubes adjacent to the

furnace side of the refractory wall. The heat which is absorbed by these tubes from the hot furnace produces steam bubbles that rise in the furnace-wall tubes, thus creating circulation from the lower to the upper header. The steam generated in the tubes is delivered through risers to the boiler drum. Recirculator tubes may connect the upper and lower headers outside of the furnace so that part of the water which flows upward in the furnace tubes may be returned to the lower header. The water in the furnace-wall tubes is normally at some temperature between 400 and 600 F, depending upon the boiler pressure, and a considerable part of the steam generated in the unit may be produced in these furnace-wall tubes.

Where a moderate amount of furnace cooling is desired, the tubes may be placed on 6- to 14-in. centers as shown in Fig. 4·4B. Complete water cooling of the wall may be obtained by using the tangent tube construction of Fig. 4·4C. These tubes are frequently backed by a thin layer of refractory tile, insulation, and a steel casing, all supported from the furnace tubes by means of studs welded to the back side of the tubes.

In some sections of the furnace it may be desirable to limit the heat absorption by the water-wall tubes in order to maintain rapid ignition of the incoming fuel, to protect the tubes against excessive heat-transfer rates, or for other reasons. This may be done by using a furnace-wall construction as shown in Fig. 4·4D. Short studs are welded to the furnace tubes, and a refractory material is pounded into place and anchored by these studs. Either complete or partial coverage of the furnace wall tubes is possible. Bare or refractory faced cast-iron blocks can also be bolted from the rear to the furnace side of tubes to control heat absorption. Water-cooled furnaces are illustrated in Figs. 4·15, 5·18, 5·28, 5·30, 5·31, and 5·32. Partial or complete cooling of furnace walls by boiler tubes has been found to be economical in practically all pulverized-coal-burning installations, in most high-capacity stoker installations, and in high-capacity oil- or gas-fired furnaces. Where furnaces are designed to burn the fuel with a high degree of turbulence and especially where the fusing temperature of the ash is low, complete water cooling of the furnace walls is generally necessary.

The furnace heat-release rate is expressed in Btu per hour per cubic foot of furnace volume. It is computed by multiplying the quantity of fuel burned per hour by the heating value per pound of fuel and dividing this product by the furnace volume in cubic feet. Furnaces used for steam generation are usually proportioned for a heat-release rate of 20,000 to 50,000 Btu per hr per cu ft. Excessive maintenance of furnace brick work, troubles due to clinker formation on stokers, and plugging of gas passages between boiler tubes by particles of plastic ash can be avoided by the use of liberal furnace volumes and adequate water cooling of furnace walls. Large pulverized-coal-fired furnaces intended for long periods of trouble-free operation are usually designed for a furnace heat-release rate of about 20,000 Btu per hr per cu ft, especially if the ash has a low fusing temperature. Higher values of furnace heat-release rates may be used in small units, stoker-fired installations, cyclone burners and furnaces burning oil or gas which is relatively free of ash.

4·3 Gas burners. Gas is burned in many industrial furnaces because of its cleanliness, ease of control of furnace atmosphere, ability to produce a long slow-burning flame with uniform and gradual heat liberation, and ease of temperature regulation. Natural gas is used for steam generation in gas-producing areas and in areas served by natural-gas transmission lines where coal is not available at a competitive price. It is also burned extensively in coal- or oil-fired units during the summer months in districts served by natural-gas pipe lines, at which time the absence of the domestic heating load creates a temporary surplus of natural gas. By-product gas such as blast-furnace gas may be available at the steel mills for steam generation. Because of the variable or seasonal supply of gaseous fuels, combination burners have been developed to permit the simultaneous burning of the available gas together with pulverized coal or oil in an amount sufficient to produce the required steam. These multifuel burners are discussed in Article 4·10.

When a molecule of combustible gas is mixed with the oxygen necessary for its combustion at a temperature above the ignition temperature, combustion is practically instantaneous. For steam generation, where a short flame is desired in order to reduce the required furnace volume, the burner should provide for rapid and thorough mixing of the fuel and air in the correct proportions for good combustion. For such applications, a good burner is primarily a proportioner and mixing device. In industrial furnaces where long "lazy" flames are desired, slow and gradual mixing of the air and fuel in the furnace is necessary. Figure 4·5 shows the construction of a number of typical gas burners. In the burner illustrated in Fig. 4·5*A*, the gas, under pressure in the supply line, enters the furnace through a burner port and induces

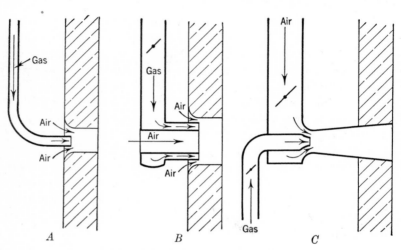

FIG. 4·5 Typical gas burners

a flow of air through the port. Mixing is poor, and a fairly long flame results. The flame can be shortened by use of the ring burner (Fig. 4·5*B*) in which the gas flows through an annular ring and induces air flow both around and within the annulus of gas. Where both air and gas are under pressure, an arrangement as shown in Fig. 4·5*C* may be used. In each of these burners, the gases must flow through the port into the furnace at a velocity high enough to prevent the flame from burning back into the burner, or, in other words, the velocity must exceed the "rate of flame propagation." The arrangement of burners and the shape of the furnace should be such that the flame does not impinge on the furnace walls or the heat-transfer surfaces.

4·4   Oil burners. Most of the fuel oil that is used for steam generation is the residuum that remains after crude petroleum has been refined to produce gasoline, kerosene, Diesel-engine fuels, and lubricants. Because of the ease of storage and handling, smaller storage space required compared with coal, absence of ash, high capacity obtainable from small furnaces, and small amount of labor required, oil is the only fuel used for steam generation in naval vessels and many merchant-marine ships. It is burned in locomotives and stationary steam power plants in regions where the price is competitive with the price of coal. Since the residual fuel oil that is used for steam generation contains the ash and most of the sulphur originally present in the

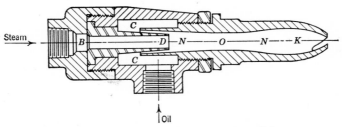

FIG. 4·6 National Airoil steam-atomizing oil burner

crude petroleum before refining, serious difficulties with corrosion and slag formation on furnace walls and boiler tubes have been encountered with some grades of fuel oil.

To burn fuel oil successfully, it must first be atomized or broken up into very small droplets of oil. In a hot furnace, these small drops of oil will be partially vaporized to form gases which will burn very rapidly if mixed with the correct amount of air. The complex hydrocarbon molecules of which the oil is composed are unstable at high temperatures and may decompose upon heating to form gaseous compounds which are readily burned and carbon particles which burn slowly with a long flame. Decomposition of molecules to form carbon can be kept to a minimum by thorough mixing of the fuel with an adequate supply of air. A successful oil-burning installation is one that produces a spray of finely atomized oil which is thoroughly mixed with air in a furnace hot enough to vaporize the oil quickly and large enough to permit combustion to be completed without flame impingement on the boiler-tube bank or on the furnace walls.

The *steam-atomizing* oil burner, as illustrated in Fig. 4·6, is used extensively for burning oil in stationary steam power plants and locomotives. Steam from the boiler is expanded through the nozzle *BD* and enters the combining tube *NON* at high velocity. Oil is supplied to the burner under a pressure up to 60 psig and flows around the steam nozzle from the space *C* into the combining tube *NON*. The mixture of oil and steam is churned into an emulsion in the chamber *K* and is discharged into the furnace through the flat orifice at the tip of the burner. This burner delivers a thin flat horizontal fan-shaped spray of oil into the furnace about a foot above and parallel to the furnace floor. Air is admitted through openings in the furnace floor beneath the fan-shaped spray of oil. Wide furnaces may be fired by several oil burners set side by side, but care must be exercised in their installation to avoid overlapping of the oil sprays, or incomplete combustion due to insufficient air will result. The steam-atomizing burner requires oil at a maximum pressure of about 70 psig which permits the use of simple and inexpensive pumping equipment. It may be necessary to heat the heavier grades of oil to about 150 F in steam heaters in order to increase the fluidity of the oil and promote good atomization. The steam required should not exceed 1.5 to 2.0 per cent of the boiler output if the burners are well designed and carefully operated.

Mechanical atomizing oil burners were developed for marine applications where the loss up the chimney of the steam required in a steam-atomizing burner could not be tolerated since steam cannot be generated in steam boilers from untreated sea water. A mechanical atomizing oil burner and air register is illustrated in Fig. 4·7. All of the air required for combustion is supplied to the burner through the air register. The air, which is normally supplied under slight pressure by a fan, flows through adjustable air doors in the register in such a manner as to impart a whirl to the air. The position of the air doors is shown in the left cutaway section of the front view of the register. Oil at a pressure up to 300 psig is admitted to the mechanical atomizer which is essentially a tube with a removable sprayer plate in the tip through which the oil is delivered in a finely atomized spray having the shape of a hollow cone. An impeller is mounted on a hollow distance piece within which the mechanical atomizer is placed. It may be moved in or out of the burner throat to control the amount of air passing through and around the impeller.

A minimum oil pressure at the burner tip of about 100 psig is necessary for proper atomization of the heavy grades of fuel oil. With a maximum oil pressure of 300 psig, the range of capacity of the mechanical atomizing burner is about 1.0 to 1.7; that is, the maximum capacity is 170 per cent of the minimum capacity. Greater capacity ranges are obtainable by changing sprayer plates or by cutting burners in or out of service. Since all of the air is admitted through the registers, several rows of

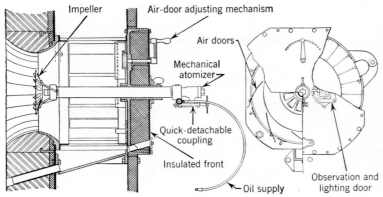

FIG. 4·7   Mechanical atomizing oil burner

burners can be installed across a boiler front, as shown in Fig. 4·3, and removing a burner from service is easily done. Wide-range mechanical atomizing burners have been developed with a range of 1 to 4 with a single sprayer plate and with a range of 1 to 7 by using steam to atomize the oil at the lower capacities. Steam-atomizing burners producing thin hollow conical sprays may also be used interchangeably with the mechanical atomizers in the air registers. Mechanical atomizing burners are standard equipment on sea-going vessels, although they require more expensive pumping equipment and oil heaters than are required by steam-atomizing burners.

4·5   Hand-fired grates. Although mechanical stokers have replaced the hand firing of coal in all except small installations, a large amount of coal is still burned on hand-fired grates, and an understanding of the combustion of coal on hand-fired grates is essential to a study of stoker performance.

A *grate* is a flat surface upon which coal or other solid fuel may be placed. It is provided with many small openings through which air is supplied to burn the fuel. Figure 4·8 shows several common types of grate bars. These bars are not over 3 ft in length and may be assembled into grates of any desired width

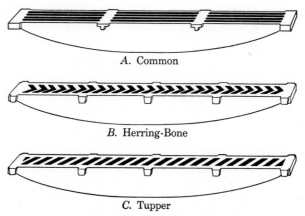

A. Common

B. Herring-Bone

C. Tupper

FIG. 4·8 Bars for hand-fired grates

and of lengths not over 6 ft for bituminous coal and 12 ft for anthracite. From 25 to 50 per cent of the grate area is open for the passage of air, the finer sizes of coal requiring less opening to prevent sifting of coal through the grate. The ash is deposited on the grate as the coal burns. The fine particles of ash will

FIG. 4·9 Dumping grate

fall into the ashpit through the grate openings, but the clinkers or fused lumps of ash must be raked out of the firing door periodically. Dumping grates, as shown in Fig. 4·9, are composed of rocking segments which can be rotated about supporting shafts through a sufficient angle to provide clearance for the discharge of the ash through the grate, thereby facilitating the disposal of the ash.

A level fuel bed of coal, fired by hand and free of blow holes, is illustrated in Fig. 4·10. The grate is covered with a layer of ash through which the *primary air* is supplied from beneath the grate. The lowest zone of the active fuel bed is an oxidizing zone in which nearly all of the oxygen combines with carbon to form

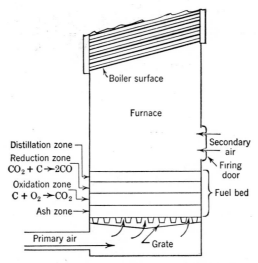

FIG. 4·10   Zones in a hand-fired fuel bed

CO_2. Above the oxidizing zone is a reducing zone in which the carbon combines with CO_2 to form CO. The freshly fired coal is placed on top of the fuel bed and forms a distillation zone in which the volatile matter is being distilled from the coal by heat from the hot fuel bed below. The combustible gases rising from the fuel bed consist of CO and volatile matter and may represent *40 to 60 per cent of the total heating value of the fuel.* These gases are burned in the furnace by *secondary air* supplied over the fuel bed through openings in the firing door, or by leakage through holes in the fuel bed.

Figure 4·11, based on experiments of the U. S. Bureau of Mines, shows the composition of gases in a level hand-fired fuel bed of coal. Practically all of the oxygen will disappear within

2½ to 4 in. of the grate, regardless of the rate of burning or the kind of coal. The CO_2 content reaches a maximum at the point where most of the oxygen has combined with the carbon, after which the percentage of CO_2 decreases, owing to the reaction $CO_2 + C = 2CO$. The combustible gases at the surface of the

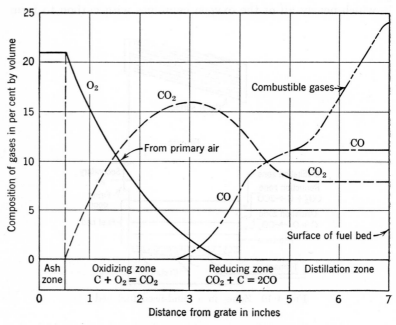

Fig. 4·11 Composition of gases in a hand-fired fuel bed

fuel bed consist of the CO formed in the reducing zone plus the volatile matter driven out of the coal in the distillation zone. The line labeled "combustible gases" in Fig. 4·11 represents the condition in the fuel bed shortly after firing. Three or four minutes later, most of the volatile matter will have been distilled from the coal, leaving fixed carbon, and the line labeled "CO" more nearly represents the combustible gases leaving the fuel bed. It is apparent that only part of the carbon is burned in the fuel bed, that much of the carbon is gasified to CO, and that this CO plus the volatile matter must be burned in the furnace by secondary air supplied over the fuel bed.

Figure 4·12 shows a typical hand-fired grate installed under a boiler. Coal is thrown onto the grate by hand through a firing door provided with adjustable openings for the admission of secondary air. Primary air is supplied to the ashpit under the grate. A bridge wall at the rear of the grate serves as a support and back wall for the grate and a mixing device for the gases.

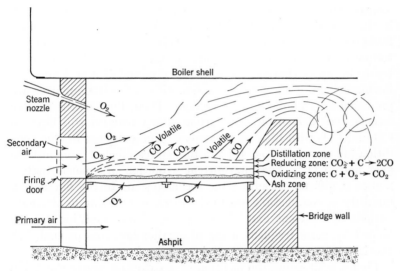

Fig. 4·12 Combustion of coal in a hand-fired setting

A horizontal combustion space extends for a distance of 10 to 15 ft behind the bridge wall. The combustible gases from the fuel bed, which in many cases have a heating value of more than 50 per cent of the heating value of the fuel, mix in the furnace with secondary air and air leaking through holes in the fuel bed and burn in the furnace if the necessary temperature, time, turbulence, and oxygen are provided.

It is difficult to burn high-volatile bituminous coal in an installation of this type without producing objectionable *smoke*. Black smoke is caused by particles of carbon floating in the colorless gases such as CO_2, CO, O_2, and N_2. *These carbon particles are caused by the cracking or thermal decomposition of the unstable hydrocarbon compounds which are distilled from the* *coal as volatile matter. If these compounds can find the oxygen and temperature necessary for their combustion as soon as they are driven from the coal, they will burn to CO_2 and H_2O. If this oxygen is not present, they will decompose to form soot which is almost impossible to burn once it is formed.* It should be noted that in a hand-fired installation the green coal is thrown on top of the hot fuel bed where it is *heated rapidly in the absence of oxygen,* all of the primary oxygen having combined with carbon in the oxidizing zone of the fuel bed. Conditions are therefore favorable for the decomposition of this volatile matter and the formation of free carbon or soot. If the coal is fired intermittently in heavy charges, there will be a period of 3 or 4 min following firing during which large quantities of volatile matter are produced and smoke will be heavy. Then, the volatile matter having been driven off, the carbon which remains will burn to CO and CO_2 with little or no smoke. The extremes of this condition are shown in Fig. 4·11 in the curves labeled "combustible gas" and "CO." The intermittent evolution of volatile matter makes it difficult to adjust the secondary air to the fluctuating quantity of combustible gas in the furnace, resulting in alternate periods of deficient and of excess air. This condition can be helped by more frequent firing of smaller amounts of coal, but this involves more labor.

Figure 4·12 shows the location of a steam jet above the firing door. Steam may be discharged from the nozzle at high velocity, thereby inducing a high-velocity stream of air through the opening in the front wall and delivering this secondary air into the furnace in a manner to increase turbulence. Frequent firing of small amounts of coal, steam jets, and large furnaces will help to reduce the smoke problem, but the mechanical firing of coal by a well-designed stoker is usually the best solution to the smoke problem when high-volatile bituminous coal is being burned.

4·6 Chain-grate stokers. The chain-grate stoker as illustrated in Figs. 4·13, 4·14, 4·15, 5·13, and 5·17 consists of an endless moving chain or grate upon the top surface of which coal may be placed, conveyed through the furnace and burned, with provision for discharge of ash and refuse from the rear end of the stoker. As shown in Fig. 4·13, a front driving shaft with sprockets and a rear idler drum are mounted in bearings in a frame composed of heavy side plates and cross girders. Longitudinal skid bars attached to the cross girders support the grate surface and fuel bed. The grate bars, made of heat-resistant castings in the form of links of a chain, provide a flat undisturbed surface for the fuel bed. Air is supplied through openings around each link. As the chain passes around the rear drum,

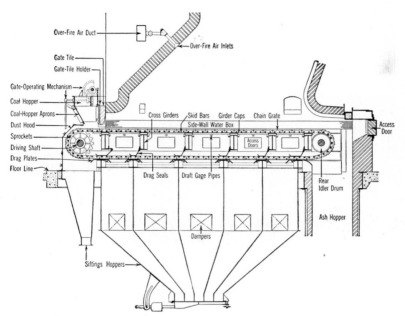

Fig. 4·13 Forced-draft chain-grate stoker

the shearing action between links as shown in Fig. 4·14 cleans them of adherent refuse.

The speed of the grate is controlled by a variable-speed drive to give grate speeds from about 4 to 20 in. per min. The depth of the fuel bed is adjustable by the position of a fuel gate in the coal hopper (Fig. 4·13). This gate is hung by chains from a shaft which can be rotated to raise or lower the gate and produce a fuel bed of uniform thickness, usually between 3 and 8 in. deep, depending upon the kind of fuel being burned.

Most modern chain-grate stokers are of the forced-draft type; that is, air is supplied beneath the grate under pressure by means of a fan. In Fig. 4·13, the grate area is divided into five compartments into each of which air is supplied under adjustable pressure through a damper. Drag seals attached to the cross girders ride on the lower run of the chain and reduce air leakage between compartments to a negligible quantity. The correct air pressure to be carried in each compartment depends upon the kind of fuel being burned and upon the load. If the load is light,

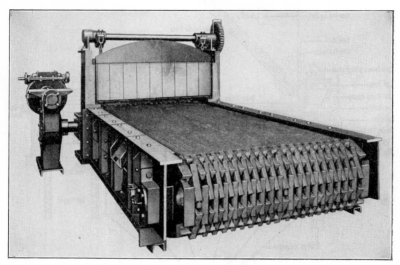

Fig. 4·14   Rear view of chain-grate stoker

the fuel may be burned out over the front three or four zones, and the air may be shut off from the rear zones. Small stokers, as illustrated in Fig. 5·17, may be supplied with air between the upper and lower runs of the chain through adjustable dampers located in the side frames of the stoker.

A side-wall water box or clinker chill is often located in the side walls of the furnace at the grate line, as shown in Figs. 4·13 and 5·13. This water box is connected into the boiler circulation and is kept relatively cool by the evaporation of boiler water. This cool zone prevents clinker adhesions on the side walls at the grate line.

Chain-grate stokers are set in furnaces provided with front and rear arches which control the fuel ignition and promote furnace turbulence and good combustion. The green coal on the front end of the stoker must be ignited by downward penetration of heat radiated from the flame or from brick arches in the furnace. High-moisture coals such as lignite and subbituminous coals are slow to ignite and require a furnace which is "bottled up" by brick arches, as illustrated in Fig. 5·17, in order that the furnace temperature may be as high as possible above the ignition zone. High-volatile bituminous coal may be burned in a furnace having shorter arches, as shown in Fig. 5·13, since heat may be radiated to the fuel bed from the high-temperature flame in the furnace. If the fine sizes of anthracite were to be burned in a furnace such as the one illustrated in Fig. 5·13, much of the fine particles of fuel would be blown into the furnace from the front of the grate, would fall onto the rear of the stoker, and would be dumped into the refuse pit before they could be burned. The furnace shown in Fig. 4·15 is used for burning the anthracite fines. The long rear arch carries the fine particles forward instead of toward the discharge end of the stoker, so that the carbon loss in the refuse can be kept to a low value.

The gases from the front end of the stoker where ignition and distillation are taking place are normally deficient in oxygen and rich in combustible gases while the gases from the rear of the stoker have a liberal supply of air. An important function of the furnace arches is to mix these furnace gases in such a manner as to produce good combustion. Secondary or overfire air is normally admitted to the furnace through the front arch at high velocity to improve turbulence, supply oxygen to the rich gases from the front end of the stoker, and reduce arch maintenance. Typical installations of overfire air nozzles are shown in Figs. 4·13 and 5·13.

The *traveling-grate* stoker is similar in general appearance and operation to the chain-grate stoker except that individual grate bars or keys are mounted on carrier bars which extend across the width of the stoker and are attached to and driven by several parallel chains. Since adjacent grate bars have no relative motion with respect to each other, this stoker is particularly applicable to the burning of the fine sizes of anthracite and coke breeze in which all of the fuel may pass through a screen having $\frac{3}{16}$-in. round openings.

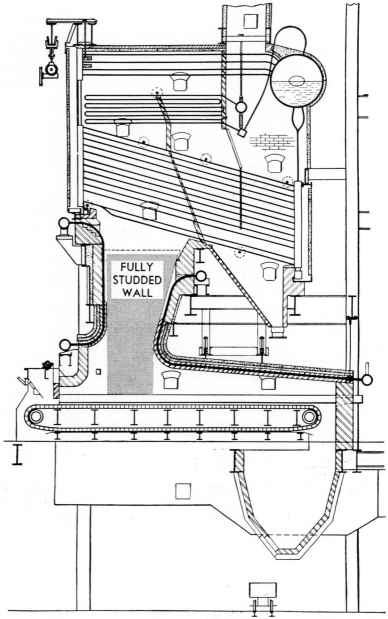

FULLY
STUDDED
WALL

FIG. 4·15   Forced-draft chain-grate stoker and setting for burning anthracite and coke breeze

The chain- and traveling-grate stokers are particularly adapted to the burning of the free-burning or noncaking bituminous coals of the Midwest, lignite, and the steam sizes of anthracite and coke breeze. Since there is no means of mechanically agitating the fuel bed, caking coals should be avoided. The fuel should preferably contain at least 8 per cent of ash in order to provide a protective covering for the grate. Combustion rates of 30 to 45 lb of coal per sq ft of grate area per hr are common with peak burning rates of 60 lb. This stoker has been built in sizes large enough to generate 250,000 lb of steam per hr. Since the fuel feed is continuous and the fuel is ignited from above by the downward penetration of the heat, air under pressure can be supplied at the place where the volatile matter is being evolved, and secondary air can be supplied through the arches so as to achieve efficient and smokeless combustion of the high-volatile midwest bituminous coals.

4·7 Spreader stokers. The spreader stoker is designed to throw coal *continuously* onto a stationary or moving grate. Figure 4·16 shows a spreader stoker equipped with a moving grate which travels toward the feeder mechanism and discharges the refuse continuously. Coal is fed from the hopper by means of a reciprocating feeder plate having a variable speed drive which for best performance should be regulated automatically to feed coal in accordance with the demand for heat. The coal is delivered by the feeder to a rapidly revolving drum or rotor on which are fastened specially shaped blades which throw the fuel into the furnace and distribute it uniformly over the grate. Coal can be distributed thus for a total distance of about 22 ft. The feeder mechanism is built in standardized widths, and several units may be installed across the front of the larger furnaces.

Air is supplied by means of a blower to the space under the moving grate through an adjustable damper. The active fuel bed is normally not over 1½ in. deep so that an adequate supply of air can penetrate the fuel bed and enter the furnace. Active fuel beds much thicker than 1½ in. will produce excessive amounts of smoke. Much of the volatile matter is distilled from the coal before it strikes the fuel bed, and the caking properties of the fuel are thus destroyed, thereby making it possible to burn even the strongly caking bituminous coals. Since the fuel bed is thin and undisturbed and the ash is cooled by the flow of air through it, trouble with clinkering or fusing of the ash is uncommon, and this stoker can burn almost any kind of bituminous coal. Since the finer sizes of coal are burned in suspension, large furnaces are required, and objectionable quantities of dust may be discharged from the installation if it is not designed correctly and if dust collectors are not installed to clean the gases leaving the steam-generating unit. Also, it is standard practice to install high-

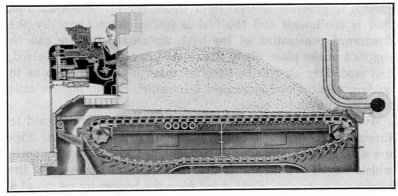

Fig. 4·16   Spreader stoker with continuous ash discharge

velocity steam jets in the furnace to promote turbulence, improve combustion, and reduce smoke.

Large units provided with continuous ash-discharge grates as shown in Fig. 4·16 are capable of burning 10 to 12 tons of coal per hr. Figure 5·18 shows a smaller spreader stoker equipped with a hand-operated dump grate similar to the grate illustrated in Fig. 4·9. Dump grates may also be actuated by a power cylinder and piston supplied with steam, air, or oil under pressure. Small units may have stationary grates with clean-out doors through which the ashes may be removed with a hoe.

The spreader stoker is simple in construction and reliable in operation. It can burn a wider variety of coal successfully than any other type of stoker. Maximum continuous combustion rates of 45 to 60 psf of grate area per hr are normally used. When provided with automatic regulation of fuel and air in accordance with the demand for heat, this stoker is very responsive to rapidly fluctuating loads. However, it is not so adaptable to light load operation as other types of stokers because of the difficulty of maintaining ignition and combustion in the very thin fuel bed with a cold furnace.

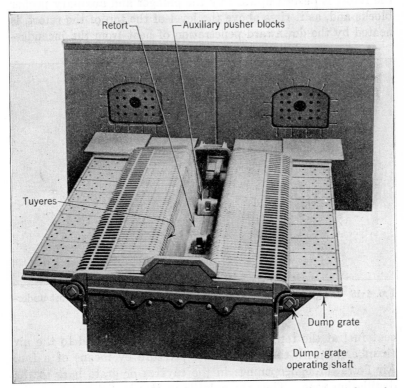

Fɪɢ. 4·17 Single-retort underfeed stoker as seen from above and at the rear of the stoker

4·8 Single-retort underfeed stokers. Figure 4·17 shows a photograph taken from the rear and looking down on a single-retort underfeed stoker before installation in a furnace. Figures 4·18 and 4·19 are longitudinal and cross sections, respectively, of this type of stoker. Coal is fed from a hopper by means of a reciprocating plunger into a horizontal retort or trough. Auxiliary reciprocating pusher blocks in the bottom of the retort have an adjustable stroke and are designed to assist in pushing the coal upward out of the retort and in distributing it uniformly along the length of the retort, as indicated in Fig. 4·18.

The behavior of the fuel on the single-retort underfeed stoker may be understood by reference to Fig. 4·19. The raw coal in the retort is pushed upward by the plunger and auxiliary pusher blocks and, as it rises above the level of the top of the retort, is heated by the downward penetration of heat from the incandes-

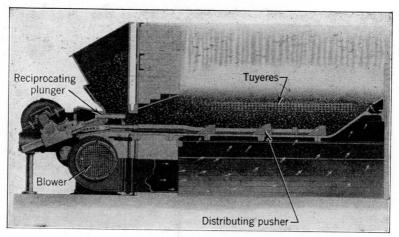

Fig. 4·18 Longitudinal section through the retort of a single-retort under-feed stoker

cent fuel at the top of the fuel bed. Air is supplied to the air chamber beneath the retort under pressure by means of a fan. Air flows through openings in the tuyères or grate bars to the distillation zone. Thus the volatile matter is distilled from the coal *uniformly in the presence of air,* and the combustible mixture which results from this process is heated to the ignition temperature and burned as it travels upward through the high-temperature fuel bed above the distillation zone. The coke which remains after distillation of the volatile matter from the coal is forced upward and to the sides where it receives air through the grates and burns. The ash and some unburned carbon accumulate on the dumping grates. Air can be supplied to the dumping grates periodically to burn out the carbon before the grates are rotated about a shaft to drop the refuse into the ashpit.

A constant-speed motor drives the blower or fan and the crankshaft at uniform speed. Dampers on the fan inlet and lost-motion adjustments on the plunger operating rod permit variable feed of air and coal as needed. Smaller stokers are often provided with a rotary-feed screw instead of a reciprocating plunger and distributing blocks. Larger stokers often have some lateral reciprocating motion of the side grates to assist in the distribution of the burning coke over a wider grate.

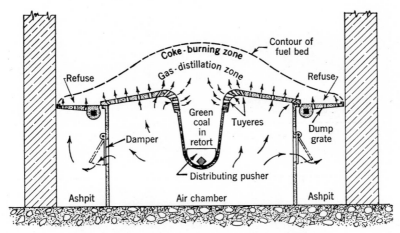

Fig. 4·19   Cross section through the retort of a single-retort underfeed stoker

Single-retort stokers have been built in sizes from domestic stokers to units capable of burning over 3000 lb of coal per hr. They require little more head room than good hand-fired grates and have largely replaced the hand-fired grates for small and medium-sized industrial power boilers and for apartment house and industrial heating boilers because of their ability to burn bituminous coal efficiently and smokelessly with a minimum of attention. Maximum continuous combustion rates of 20 to 30 psf of grate area per hr are recommended, the higher rates being used on the wider stokers and with the better coals.

4·9   Multiple-retort underfeed stokers. The multiple-retort underfeed stoker as illustrated in Figs. 4·20 and 4·21 consists of several parallel retorts (seven retorts are shown in Fig. 4·21) set at an angle with the horizontal in order that gravity may

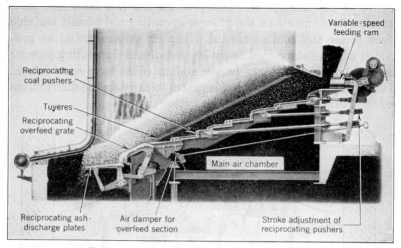

FIG. 4·20 Multiple-retort underfeed stoker

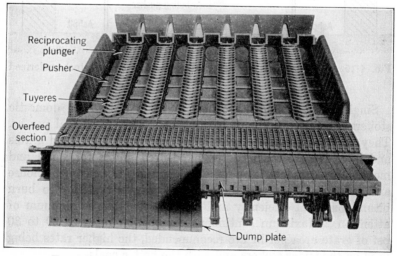

FIG. 4·21 Rear view of multiple-retort underfeed stoker

assist in the distribution of coal and the discharge of refuse. The coal is fed into the retorts by means of reciprocating plungers driven from a variable-speed crankshaft. The bottom of each retort has a number of reciprocating pushers, the motion of which can be controlled by lost-motion adjustments from the front of the stoker. The longitudinal distribution of the coal and the contour of the fuel bed are regulated by the motion of these pusher blocks. The tuyères through which the air is admitted under pressure from a blower consist of fan-shaped castings mounted one above the other on the retort side walls. The tuyère castings have deflecting ribs on their lower sides to produce air jets which penetrate the fuel being forced upward from the retorts. The retorts are deep at the front of the stoker, become shallower toward the lower end, and terminate in an overfeed section of reciprocating grate bars and an ash-discharge apron.

As the green coal is forced upward from the retort, it is heated from above by the incandescent fuel bed. The volatile matter is distilled in the presence of air from the tuyères and burns as the gases rise through the hot fuel bed, thereby producing a short flame with little smoke. The carbon which remains is carried to the surface of the fuel bed and toward the rear of the stoker where it burns, leaving the ash and clinker to be discharged from the lower end. Since the ash is carried to the top of the fuel bed where the temperatures are high, it will fuse to form clinkers which will be carried to the rear as a result of the reciprocating action of the coal distributors in the bottom of the retort and the motion of the overfeed section of the grate.

Air is supplied beneath the retort section of the stoker by a fan at an adjustable pressure up to 6 or 7 in. of water in order to overcome the resistance of the deep fuel bed on the stoker. The air supply to the overfeed section can be regulated by a damper between the main air compartment and the space under the overfeed section. A water-cooled rear wall absorbs heat from the fuel bed and furnace, thereby reducing furnace maintenance and clinker troubles. The rear-wall tubes are armored with cast-iron blocks at the fuel-bed level to protect them from the erosive action of moving clinkers. As shown in Fig. 4·21, the stoker should be so operated as to form a bed of refuse on the ashpit apron which will produce an air seal with the rear wall and cause the air from the ashpit to flow through the refuse on the apron where the residual carbon in the refuse can be burned out.

Because the fuel-bed agitation provided by the reciprocating action of the feed plunger and reciprocating pusher blocks will break up masses of coke, the multiple-retort underfeed stoker is particularly applicable to the burning of the *coking or caking bituminous coals* which are found throughout the eastern coal-producing region extending from Pennsylvania and Ohio to Alabama. In general, these coals are high-grade bituminous coals, low in ash and of fairly high ash-fusing temperature, so that excessive clinker formation of a troublesome nature can be avoided. Because of the deep fuel bed on these stokers, they respond readily to rapidly changing loads. They have been built in sizes large enough to generate 500,000 lb of steam per hr. Maximum continuous combustion rates of 40 to 60 psf of grate area per hr are recommended, the higher combustion rates being used for low-ash coal having a high ash-fusing temperature. In recent years, the spreader stoker has been selected in preference to the multiple-retort underfeed stoker for many new installations because of lower cost and less maintenance.

4·10 Pulverized coal. Coal may be pulverized or ground to a dust, mixed with air, blown into a hot furnace, and burned in suspension. In the furnace, the combustion of a particle of coal takes place in four steps as follows: (1) evaporation of any moisture, (2) gasification of the volatile matter, (3) combustion of the gaseous volatile matter, and (4) combustion of the residue of coke dust. These four steps are not distinct but tend to overlap. Even with fine grinding of the coal, the size of the individual particles is great compared with the size of a molecule of gas, and each particle of coal dust will require for its complete combustion a volume of air equal to about *14,000* times its own volume. As combustion progresses, the particle of fuel is surrounded by a layer of products of combustion, consisting mainly of CO_2 and N_2, through which the oxygen in the furnace atmosphere must penetrate by diffusion or turbulence in order to react with the carbon on the surface of the particle of coke dust. Considering the relative volumes of air and coke dust involved in the combustion process, it is apparent that combustion of powdered coal does not occur so rapidly as the combustion of gas or oil and that large furnaces are required. A high degree of turbulence is necessary in a pulverized-coal furnace to accelerate the process of bringing the oxygen into contact with the suspended particles of coke dust if a furnace of reasonable size is

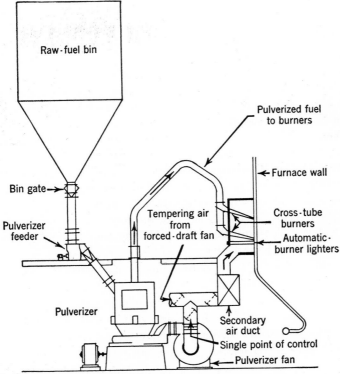

Fig. 4·22 Unit system of firing pulverized coal

to be used. Fine grinding of the coal is also necessary, and it is customary to pulverize the coal so that 60 to 80 per cent will pass through a 200-mesh sieve, that is, a screen having 40,000 openings per sq in. In general, the low-volatile coals require finer grinding than coals containing 25 per cent or more of volatile matter, and finer grinding requires additional power.

There are two systems of firing pulverized coal: the *unit system* and the *storage system*. The *unit system* is shown diagrammatically in Fig. 4·22. Raw coal which has been crushed to pass through a screen having ¾-in. openings is supplied as needed by a feeder to a pulverizer or mill. Practically all pulverized-coal installations are equipped with air heaters in which the air for combustion is heated to between 350 and 600 F by the hot products of combustion before they are discharged to waste up a chimney. Hot primary air is supplied to the pulverizer by means of a fan, as shown in Fig. 4·22. In passing through the mill, the hot air dries the coal and also picks up the fine particles of pulverized coal and carries them in suspension to the burners. The use of preheated air in the pulverizer is essential to satisfactory operation, since the power consumption is greatly reduced and the capacity of the mill is much higher when dry coal is pulverized. In the system shown in Fig. 4·22, the amount of fuel delivered to the burners is determined by the amount of air that the fan blows through the pulverizer. A tempering air damper on the suction side of the fan permits control of the inlet-air temperature to the pulverizer by adding air at room temperature to the hot air supplied by the air heater. The primary air and fuel from the pulverizer are mixed with secondary air at the burners which are designed to deliver the fuel and air to the furnace with a high degree of turbulence.

In the *storage* system of firing pulverized coal, the coal from the pulverizer is delivered to a storage bin from which it is fed to the burners as necessary by variable-speed feeders. The simplicity and lower cost of the unit system and the development of pulverizers which operate satisfactorily under conditions of rapidly fluctuating loads have resulted in the choice of the unit system for practically all recent installations.

A number of different types of pulverizers or mills have been developed for pulverizing coal, of which two types are shown in Figs. 4·23 and 4·24. The air-swept tube mill shown in Fig. 4·23 consists essentially of a horizontal cylindrical steel housing closed by heads with integral trunnions and lined with replaceable corrugated liners. The trunnions are mounted in bearings, and the mill is rotated around a horizontal axis through gearing by a motor. The mill is partially filled with steel balls, and the liners are so constructed as to distribute the balls by size along the axis of the mill with the large balls at the entrance end and the small

balls at the discharge end. The rotation of the mill carries the
balls around by centrifugal force to a point where they are thrown

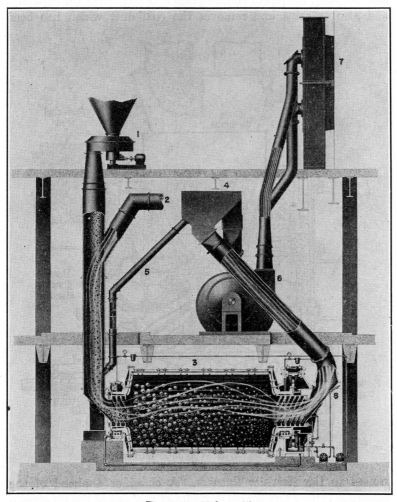

FIG. 4·23 Tube mill

down on the particles of coal which are crushed by the impact of
the balls.

Coal is fed to the mill by a variable-speed feeder 1 as needed to
maintain a predetermined level of coal in the mill. Hot preheated

air is supplied to the mill through duct 2 and flows through the mill to the exhauster fan 6. The hot air dries the coal in the mill, thus reducing the power consumption and increasing the capacity, and also entrains and removes the coal dust which has been

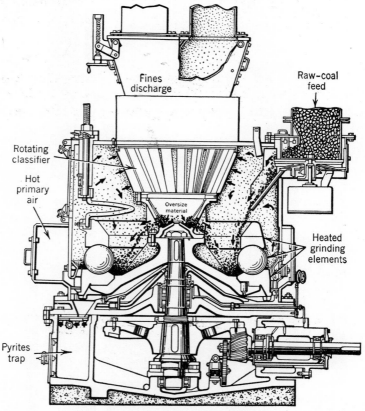

Fines discharge

Raw-coal feed

Rotating classifier

Hot primary air

Oversize material

Heated grinding elements

Pyrites trap

FIG. 4·24 B & W type-E pulverizer

ground to the requisite fineness. A classifier 4 ahead of the exhauster throws any coarse particles of coal out of the air stream and returns them to the mill through the return duct 5 for further grinding. The output of the mill is controlled by varying the air flow through the mill, either by a damper in the air duct or by a variable-speed exhauster fan. The pulverized coal and primary air are delivered to the burner 7 where the secondary air is added and the mixture is introduced into the furnace. This type of mill is particularly adaptable to the grinding of hard fuels such as anthracite and coke.

The pulverizer illustrated in Fig. 4·24 operates on the principle of the ball bearing. A set of balls roll between a stationary top grinding ring and a rotating bottom grinding ring which is driven by a vertical shaft geared to a motor. Adjustable springs load the stationary grinding ring from above and control the pressure on the balls. The raw coal is admitted through a feeder to maintain automatically the desired coal supply in the mill. Preheated air is admitted at the bottom of the mill, passes upward around the balls where it dries the coal and entrains the pulverized-coal particles, flows upward through a rotating classifier where the oversize particles of coal are rejected to the mill for further grinding, and is discharged from the top of the mill to the burners.

The power consumption of pulverizers and the blowers associated with them varies from 9 to 16 kw-hr of electric energy per ton of coal pulverized, depending upon the type of mill, the moisture content of the coal, the required fineness of pulverization, and the "grindability" of the coal.

Although there is a wide variety of pulverized-coal burners, most of them operate on the principle that the stream of hot primary air and coal from the mill is mixed thoroughly with the preheated secondary air at the burner and the mixture is introduced into the hot furnace with a maximum degree of turbulence. Many of these burners operate on the same principle as the mechanical atomizing oil burner as illustrated in Fig. 4·25. The primary air and pulverized coal enter the burner through a central tube. The preheated secondary air is given a rotary motion as it flows through the secondary-air doors and is mixed thoroughly with the primary air and coal in the burner throat. An oil-atomizing tube is located in the center of the burner, and an annular gas ring having a row of holes for the discharge of gas surrounds the burner throat. In this burner, either coal, oil, or gas, or a combination of any two or all three of these fuels may be burned simultaneously. Such burners are particularly adapted to those installations in which by-product gas or oil are available in variable quantities or where fluctuation in the price of the various fuels makes it advisable to change from one fuel to another from time to time. Where only pulverized coal is to be burned, the oil and gas burners may be omitted from the installation.

The success of a pulverized-coal installation depends largely on the furnace design. Since all of the ash in the coal is in suspension in the furnace, the successful removal of this ash is one of the most important factors to be considered in designing the furnace. Furnaces may be designed for operation as *dry-bottom*

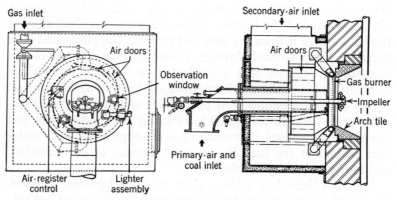

FIG. 4·25 Circular multifuel burner for burning gas, oil, and pulverized coal

furnaces or as *wet-bottom* or *slag-tap furnaces*. For burning coal having a fairly high ash-fusing temperature, it may be possible to place a sufficient area of relatively cool boiler tubes in the furnace walls to absorb enough heat to keep the furnace gases below the fusing temperature of the ash, thus permitting part of the ash to settle to the bottom of the furnace as a dry dust. The rest of the ash will be carried out of the furnace with the products of combustion, also as a dry dust. Dry-bottom furnaces are shown in Figs. 5·28 and 5·31. The furnaces are constructed of boiler tubes, and the front and rear walls are shaped to form a hopper through the bottom of which the dry ash falls into the ashpit.

For burning coals with a low ash-fusing temperature such as the midwestern bituminous coals, many of the high-capacity furnaces are designed to operate at temperatures that will melt the ash. Such a slag-tap furnace is illustrated in Fig. 5·30. In this installation, the burners are located near the bottom of the furnace in the four corners and are set to discharge their air and coal streams toward an imaginary circle in the center of the furnace. This imparts a violent whirling motion to gases in the bottom of the furnace and results in very rapid combustion with a resultant furnace temperature high enough to melt the ash. The molten ash flows from an opening in the floor of the furnace. A high water-cooled furnace is used so that the ash which is carried upward by the gases will be cooled and solidified before it strikes the convection-tube bank at the top of the furnace. If this is not accomplished, the ash will adhere to the tubes in the superheater, obstruct the gas passages, and interfere with transfer of heat from the hot gases to the tubes.

Although it is possible to burn a wide variety of coals in pulverized form with higher sustained efficiencies than are obtainable from stoker-fired installations, the greater power consumption required for pulverizing the fuel offsets part of this advantage. Also, as much as 80 per cent of the ash in the coal may be discharged from the chimney in a pulverized-coal installation unless steps are taken to reclaim this dust. Cyclone separators and electrostatic precipitators are usually installed to collect most of the dust and prevent its discharge, although such equipment adds to the cost of the plant.

4·11 The cyclone burner. The cyclone burner has been developed to burn the coals having a high content of low-fusing-temperature ash with maximum recovery of ash in the burner. The coal is crushed to $\frac{1}{4}$ in. size as compared to the pulverized-coal installation in which the coal must be ground to a fineness such that 60 to 70 per cent will pass through a 200-mesh sieve.

Figure 4·26 shows a schematic arrangement of the cyclone burner, and Fig. 4·27 shows the essential features of the actual installation. A mixture of primary air and crushed coal is introduced tangentially into the inlet end of the burner at very high velocity. A small amount of tertiary air is admitted to assist in ignition of the fuel. This burning mixture is then discharged into the cylindrical burner where the secondary air is admitted tangentially at high velocity. Thus a very violent whirling or cyclonic action is maintained in the burner.

The cyclone burner is a cylindrical combustion chamber of water-cooled construction. Bent tubes form the cylindrical burner wall and are connected to top and bottom headers which in turn are connected into the boiler circulating system. Burner-wall tubes are also formed to produce a re-entrant outlet of smaller diameter through which the gases are discharged into a larger furnace of conventional construction. The cyclone burner

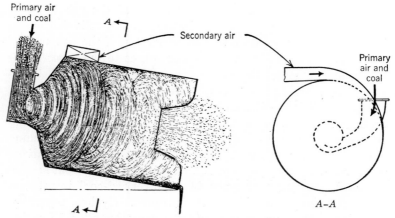

Fig. 4·26   Diagrammatic arrangement of the cyclone burner

is set at a small angle with the horizontal so that the molten ash may be drained out of the burner at the low point.

The temperature in the burner is above 3000 F, and the ash is melted and forms a layer of flowing viscous slag on the entire surface of the cylindrical burner wall. Particles of fuel are trapped on the surface of this molten slag where they float like pieces of wood in a stream of water. The intense scrubbing action between the particles of fuel and the whirling air in the cyclone burner promotes rapid and complete combustion with only 8 or 10 per cent of excess air. Owing to the scrubbing action of the whirling gases, the layer of molten slag moves slowly toward the discharge end of the cyclone burner where the re-entrant throat holds it in the furnace and allows it to flow through an opening at the low point in a continuous liquid stream. About 85 per cent of the ash in the coal is removed from the cyclone

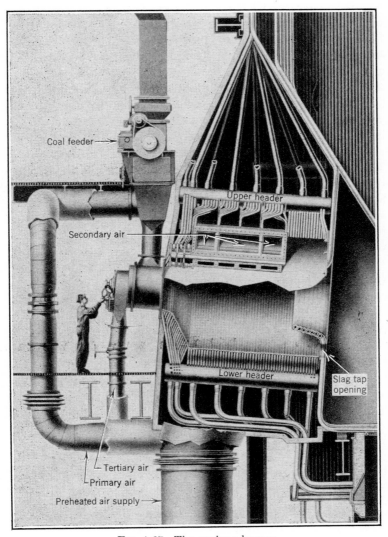

Fig. 4·27 The cyclone burner

burner in the liquid state, thereby reducing the size of the dust-removal apparatus which is necessary with practically all pulverized coal and many stoker installations.

The cyclone burner as presently constructed is completely assembled in the manufacturer's shop and is attached to the lower end of a water-cooled furnace of rather conventional design as shown in Fig. 5·32. It is being constructed in standardized sizes, and large capacities are obtainable by installing several units across the front of the furnace. Most of the installations that have been made have employed one cyclone burner for each 175,000 to 200,000 lb per hr of total steam-generating capacity. The power consumption for preparation of the fuel is much less than that required in a pulverized-coal plant, but the very high air velocities necessary in the cyclone burner require high-pressure fans with so much power input that the total power requirement is not greatly different from that required in a pulverized-coal installation.

Although there are exceptions to all rules, it may be stated in general that stoker firing is usually preferred for units having a capacity of 60,000 lb of steam per hr or less, pulverized coal is usually preferred for capacities in excess of 250,000 lb of steam per hr, whereas local conditions will lead to selection of either stokers or pulverized coal for the intermediate range of capacities. However, for burning high-ash coals of low fusing temperature, such as the midwest bituminous coals, in installations having a capacity of 350,000 lb per hr or more, the cyclone burner is gaining wide acceptance.

PROBLEMS

1. A company wishes to install a steam-generating unit having a maximum continuous output of 150,000 lb of steam per hr. A total of 1100 Btu is absorbed in converting one lb of feedwater into steam. The unit is to be designed for an efficiency of 80 per cent at maximum load (Efficiency = heat absorbed ÷ heating value of fuel burned). After consideration of the characteristics of the available coals and the nature of the load, it has been decided that a continuous-ash-discharge spreader stoker should be installed. Experience with this type of installation when fired with the coals available to this plant indicates that the maximum continuous combustion rate on the stoker should be limited to an energy release rate of 700,000 Btu per sq ft of stoker area per hr (lb of fuel burned per sq ft per hr × heating value of fuel in Btu per lb). Also, experience indicates that, with the fuels available, the maximum furnace heat-release rate should be limited to 26,000 Btu per cu ft per hr. (*a*) Calculate (1) the grate area, and (2) the furnace volume required to satisfy these conditions. (*b*) Calculate the mean vertical distance from the grate to the boiler tubes, assuming a furnace with vertical walls closed at the top by a bank of inclined straight boiler tubes.

2. An oil-fired furnace is to be designed for a steam boiler having a maximum continuous output of 75,000 lb of steam per hr. A total of 1150 Btu is absorbed in converting 1 lb of feedwater into steam. Experience indicates that, for the fuels available and the type of furnace construction and service required, the furnace heat-release rate should be limited to 45,000 Btu per cu ft per hr. The unit is to be designed to operate at an efficiency of 78 per cent when burning fuel oil having a gravity of 18 degrees API. The heating value of the fuel is 148,000 Btu per gal. Calculate (*a*) the gal of oil required per hr, and (*b*) the furnace volume required in cu ft.

3. A pulverized-coal-fired furnace is being designed for a steam-generating unit capable of producing a maximum continuous output of 500,000 lb of steam per hr with an efficiency of 85 per cent. A total of 1150 Btu is absorbed in converting 1 lb of feedwater into steam. The furnace is of completely water-cooled construction, 26 ft long by 22 ft wide with vertical walls. Experience indicates that, with the coals available, trouble-free operation for long periods of time requires that the furnace heat-release rate should not exceed 21,000 Btu per cu ft per hr. The furnace is to be designed to burn coal having a heating value of 11,000 Btu per lb. It has been found by experience that an average of 13 kw-hr of electric energy will be required to pulverize 1 ton of this coal. Calculate (*a*) the required furnace volume, (*b*) the required furnace height, and (*c*) the power input to the coal pulverizer.

4. A boiler having a maximum continuous output of 70,000 lb of steam per hr is to be fired by a chain grate stoker. A total of 1130 Btu is absorbed in converting 1 lb of feedwater into steam. Experience in similar plants burning the same fuels as are available to this plant under comparable conditions has shown that, for trouble-free reliable service, the maximum combustion rate should be limited to 55 lb of coal per sq ft of grate area per hr, and the maximum furnace heat-release rate for the type of furnace under consideration should be limited to 28,000 Btu per cu ft per hr when burning the available coals which have an average heating value of 10,500 Btu per lb. The unit is to be designed for an efficiency of 78 per cent. Calculate the minimum required grate area and furnace volume.

5 · Steam Generation

5·1 Introduction. Steam is generated for the production of power or for the heating of buildings or for supplying the heat required in manufacturing processes. Two thirds of the electric energy generated in the United States for general distribution to the public and most of the power generated in industrial plants are produced from steam. The growth of the electric load in the larger cities and industrial districts of the country has necessitated the development of steam-generating units capable of delivering from 500,000 to 1,400,000 lb of steam per hr. Most of the large units that have been installed in recent years have been designed for operation at pressures between 800 and 2000 psi with steam temperatures up to 1050 F since the work obtainable from 1 lb of steam increases with both initial pressure and temperature.

Many industrial plants require large quantities of steam at moderate pressures for manufacturing operations. Such plants normally generate steam at a pressure high enough to permit the production of their needed power upon expansion of high-pressure steam in turbines or engines to the low pressure at which it is required for process purposes. Other plants require steam for space heating.

Although the Diesel-electric locomotive is replacing the steam locomotive, about 40,000 steam locomotives are still in use on the railroads in the United States. The locomotive type of boiler is also used extensively in construction work where portability is necessary, as in the oil fields.

The surface fighting ships of the Navy, from destroyers to large battleships and aircraft carriers, require from 50,000 to over 200,000 hp per ship and are steam-driven. An important factor in the success of the United States Navy in the war against

Japan where great distances were involved was the use of high-pressure high-temperature steam with a resulting reduction in fuel consumption and increased radius of operation.

In this chapter, the more important and commonly used types

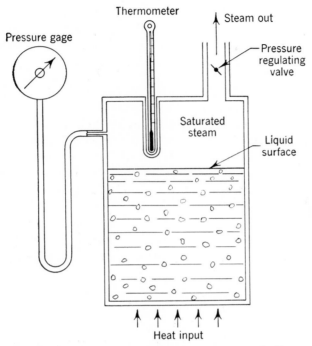

Fig. 5·1 Steam generation in a simple steam boiler

of steam-generating equipment are described. Since the calculation of the performance of such equipment involves some knowledge of the thermodynamic properties of steam and the use of the steam tables, a study of the mechanism of steam generation is included. The reader should strive to develop facility in the use of the steam tables through the solution of numerous problems.

5·2 The mechanism of steam generation. Figure 5·1 illustrates a steel vessel partially filled with water and provided with a pressure gage, thermometer well and thermometer, an adjustable discharge valve, and a source of heat. Let the discharge valve be wide open to the atmosphere which is assumed to be at standard atmospheric pressure or 14.696 psia, and let heat be supplied to the vessel. It will be observed that the thermometer reading will increase to 212 F, at which point it will remain constant while steam escapes to the atmosphere through the discharge valve. If the rate of heat input is increased or decreased, the rate of discharge of steam will be changed correspondingly but the temperature will remain constant at 212 F if the pressure in the vessel remains constant and equal to standard atmospheric pressure. If the walls of the vessel are of glass, it will be observed that the steam bubbles which are formed on the heated bottom of the vessel rise through the water, break at the liquid surface, and discharge their steam into the space above the surface. The steam in the space above the liquid surface is called *saturated steam*. If the source of heat is removed momentarily so that all of the steam bubbles rise to the surface of the water, the bubble-free water will be *saturated water*, and it will be found that the *saturated water* is at the same temperature as the *saturated steam*. This temperature is known as the *saturation temperature*.

If heat is supplied and the discharge valve is partially closed so as to restrict the escape of saturated steam to the atmosphere, the pressure will rise, and the temperature of the saturated steam will increase also. It will be observed that at each pressure there is only one temperature of the saturated steam. This saturation temperature is plotted against steam pressure in Fig. 5·2.

The thermal properties of saturated water and saturated steam have been measured accurately, and these properties are arranged in brief tabular form in Table A·1 and Table A·2 of the Appendix since they cannot be represented by simple equations. In Table A·1 the independent variable is the temperature of saturated steam; in Table A·2 the independent variable is the absolute pressure of saturated steam. Identical results may be obtained by the use of Tables A·1 and A·2, and the choice of the table to be used will depend upon whether the temperature or the pressure of saturated steam is specified.

The following data were obtained from these tables and should be verified by the student for practice in using the tables:

FROM TABLE A·1		FROM TABLE A·2	
Temperature, F	Pressure, Psia	Pressure, Psia	Temperature, F
170	5.992	6.0	170.06
212	14.696	14.696	212.0
250	29.825	30.0	250.3
280	49.203	50	281.01
320	89.66	90	320.27
400	247.31	250	400.95
705.4	3206.2	3206.2	705.4

If, in the apparatus shown in Fig. 5·1, the rate of heat input is low so that the liquid surface is only slightly disturbed by the bursting steam bubbles which are rising through the water, the steam that is produced will be free of entrained droplets of

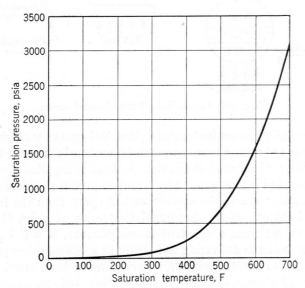

FIG. 5·2 Saturation temperature and pressure of steam

water and is known as *dry saturated steam*. However, at high rates of heat input, the liquid surface will be violently disturbed by the rapidly bursting steam bubbles, and droplets of water will be entrained with the steam and carried out through the discharge valve. Such steam is called *wet steam*. This wet steam will be at the saturation temperature corresponding to the steam pressure, because the saturated water and saturated steam are at the same temperature. The *quality* of wet steam may be defined as the weight of dry steam present in 1 lb of the mixture of dry saturated steam and entrained water and is designated by the symbol x. Thus, if $x = 98\%$, the wet-steam mixture delivered from the boiler in Fig. 5·1 is composed of 2 parts by weight of saturated water, usually in the form of a fine mist, and 98 parts by weight of dry saturated steam.

Let Fig. 5·3 represent a simple steam boiler in the form of

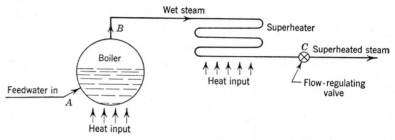

Fig. 5·3 Generation of superheated steam

an externally heated horizontal cylindrical drum to which water is supplied at such a rate as to maintain a constant water level at about the mid-point of the drum. As heat is supplied, the water is evaporated into steam. The steam so produced will normally be wet steam due to the entrainment of spray from the bursting steam bubbles. If the flow-regulating valve at point C is adjusted to maintain a constant steam pressure, it will be found that the boiler is delivering wet steam at a constant temperature at the boiler outlet, point B. Variations in heat input to the boiler will change the rate of evaporation, but, no matter how rapidly the water is evaporated, the steam temperature will remain constant if the pressure is held at a uniform value by adjustment of the flow-regulating valve. If the wet steam is allowed to flow through an externally heated coil, called a *superheater* (Fig. 5·3), it will be found by suitable temperature-measuring devices that the temperature of the wet steam will remain constant (if pressure drop in the superheater is neglected) until all of the entrained moisture has been evaporated and dry steam has been produced. Further addition of heat in the superheater will cause the temperature of the steam to rise above the saturation temperature, and it is then said to be *superheated steam*. The temperature of the steam at the superheater outlet may be several hundred degrees above the saturation temperature of the steam if sufficient heat is supplied in the superheater. The difference between the temperature of the superheated steam and the saturation temperature at the pressure of the steam is called the *degrees of superheat*. It should be noted that superheating does *not* increase the pressure of the steam. In fact, in an actual case, it results in a decrease in pressure due to the frictional resistance to the flow of steam through the superheater coil. It should be noted further that the addition of heat to saturated water or wet steam at constant pressure results in evaporation at the saturation temperature if any water is present, and that superheating will only occur when *heat is added to dry steam in the absence of water*. The thermal properties of superheated steam are given in brief form in Table A·3 of the Appendix.

If heat is removed from superheated steam at constant pressure, the temperature will decrease to the saturation temperature at which point condensation will begin. No further reduction in temperature can occur at constant pressure until the steam has been condensed to saturated water. Thus condensation takes place at the same temperature as evaporation occurs for any given pressure and is, in fact, the reverse process of evaporation.

5·3   The specific volume of water and steam. The specific volume of a fluid is the volume occupied by a unit mass of the fluid and, in the English system of units, is expressed in cubic feet per pound and is given the symbol v. The following symbols will be used for the specific volume of water and steam:

v_f = specific volume of saturated water, cu ft per lb

v_g = specific volume of dry saturated steam, cu ft per lb

$v_{fg} = v_g - v_f$ = increase in specific volume when saturated water is converted into dry saturated steam

v_x = specific volume of wet steam, cu ft per lb

v_s = specific volume of superheated steam, cu ft per lb

The specific volume, enthalpy, internal energy, and entropy of water and steam are tabulated in the steam tables for 1 mass pound since 1 mass pound is a definite quantity of matter, regardless of location, whereas the weight or gravitational force acting on a pound of mass is dependent upon the local acceleration of gravity.

In Table A·1 and Table A·2 of the Appendix, it may be noted that the specific volume of saturated water and dry saturated steam at 212 F are, respectively, as follows: $v_f = 0.01672$ cu ft per lb, and $v_g = 26.80$ cu ft per lb. Similarly for any other temperature or pressure the specific volume of saturated water and dry saturated steam may be obtained from Table A·1 or Table A·2.

The specific volume of *wet steam* may be computed by considering that 1.0 lb of wet steam having a quality x is composed of x lb of dry saturated steam and $(1 - x)$ lb of saturated water if x is expressed as a decimal.

Then, $$v_x = x v_g + (1 - x) v_f \qquad (5 \cdot 1)$$

Example 1. Compute the specific volume of wet steam at 212 F if the quality is 98 per cent.

Solution: One pound of wet steam at 212 F and 98 per cent quality may be considered as a mixture of 0.98 lb of dry saturated steam and 0.02 lb of saturated water.

Then

$$v_x = 0.98(v_g) + 0.02(v_f)$$

or $$v_x = 0.98(26.80) + 0.02(0.01672)$$

or $$v_x = 26.284 + 0.000334$$

The volume of the saturated water in the wet-steam mixture is negligible in this problem. For most engineering problems involving slide-rule computations and steam of more than 95 per cent quality at ordinary pressures, the volume of the saturated water may be neglected, and the specific volume of wet steam may be computed as follows:

$$v_x = x v_g \text{ (approximately)} \qquad (5 \cdot 2)$$

The specific volume of *superheated steam* may be determined from Table A·3 when the pressure and temperature are known. Thus, at a pressure of 100 psia, the specific volume of superheated steam, v_s, is found from Table A·3 to be 4.937 at 400 F, 5.589 at 500 F, 6.835 at 700 F, and 8.656 at 1000 F. Values for pressures and temperatures not given in the abridged Table A·3 may be found by interpolation or by reference to *Thermodynamic Properties of Steam* by Keenan and Keyes, published by John Wiley & Sons.

5·4 Enthalpy. Before proceeding further, the reader should thoroughly review Articles 1·20, 1·21, and 1·22.

In Article 1·21, *enthalpy* was introduced as a property of the substance and was defined as follows:

$$h = u + \frac{pv}{J} \qquad (5·3)$$

In Article 1·22, the application of the first law of thermodynamics to heat-transfer apparatus such as a steam boiler resulted in the following equation:

$$Q = h_2 - h_1 \qquad (5·4)$$

where Q = heat absorbed, Btu per lb of fluid flowing through the apparatus

h_1 = enthalpy of the fluid entering the apparatus, Btu per lb

h_2 = enthalpy of the fluid leaving the apparatus, Btu per lb

The following symbols will be used in designating the specific enthalpy or enthalpy per pound of fluid:

h_f = enthalpy of saturated water, Btu per lb

h_g = enthalpy of dry saturated steam, Btu per lb

$h_{fg} = h_g - h_f$ = increase in enthalpy when saturated water is converted into dry saturated steam = latent heat of evaporation, Btu per lb

h_x = enthalpy of wet steam at quality x, Btu per lb

h_s = enthalpy of superheated steam, Btu per lb

h_c = enthalpy of compressed water, Btu per lb

Since the engineer is concerned with the change in enthalpy when a fluid flows through some apparatus, and since the total enthalpy of a substance could only be evaluated by reducing it to absolute zero, it is customary to select some convenient reference point as a zero of enthalpy and to compute enthalpies with respect to this reference point in much the same way as Fahrenheit temperatures may be measured above and below a convenient zero point. For water and steam, it is customary to select saturated water at 32 F as the zero or reference point and to compute the enthalpy of water and steam in Btu per pound from this reference state. For the common refrigerants, the zero of enthalpy is taken as saturated liquid at −40 F.

In Table A·1 for each of the temperatures listed and in Table A·2 for each of the pressures given, the enthalpy of saturated water, h_f; the enthalpy of dry saturated steam, h_g; and the latent heat of evaporation, h_{fg}, are given in Btu per pound of fluid. Thus, in Table A·1, at 212 F, $h_f = 180.07$ Btu per lb, $h_g = 1150.4$ Btu per lb and $h_{fg} = 970.3$ Btu per lb. The same data will be found in Table A·2 at a pressure of 14.696 psia.

The enthalpy of superheated steam, h_s, can be determined from Table A·3 when the pressure and temperature are known. Thus, at 100 psia, the enthalpy of superheated steam is 1279.1 Btu per lb at 500 F, 1428.9 Btu per lb at 800 F, and 1530.8 Btu per lb at 1000 F.

5·5 Enthalpy of compressed water. Compressed water may be defined as water under a pressure higher than the saturation pressure corresponding to its temperature. Thus, water at 212 F and 14.696 psia is saturated water whereas water at 212 F and 1000 psia is compressed water. It is also called subcooled water since it is at a temperature less than the saturation temperature corresponding to its pressure. In the enthalpy equation, $h = u + pv/J$, the pressure term is greater than the saturation pressure corresponding to its temperature, the specific volume is somewhat less than the specific volume of the saturated water because water is slightly compressible, and the internal-energy term is also less because the slight reduction in volume due to compression of the water reduces the mean distance between molecules and thus decreases the molecular potential energy.

The difference between the enthalpy of compressed water, h_c, at a given temperature and pressure and the enthalpy of *saturated water, h_f, at same temperature*, may be determined from Fig. 5·4. The following example illustrates the method of calculation:

Example 2. Determine the enthalpy of 1 lb of water at 200 F and 2000 psia.

Solution: From Table A·1, at 200 F, $h_f = 167.99$ Btu per lb, and the saturation pressure is 11.526 psia. The enthalpy correction for 200 F and 2000 psia from Fig. 5·4 is found to be 4.5 Btu per lb. Therefore,

$$h_c = 167.99 + 4.5 = 172.5 \text{ Btu per lb}$$

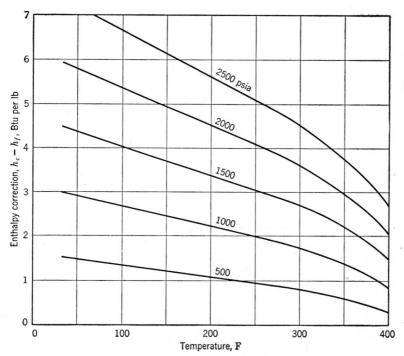

Fɪɢ. 5·4   Enthalpy correction for determination of the enthalpy of compressed water

Plotted by permission of the authors from *Thermodynamic Properties of Steam* by Keenan and Keyes; John Wiley & Sons, publishers

The feedwater is supplied to practically every boiler and economizer as compressed water and not as saturated water since it is under a pressure at least equal to the boiler pressure. However, for most engineering calculations, especially those involving the use of the slide rule, the enthalpy correction for compressed water may be neglected for pressures below 400 psia and the enthalpy of saturated water at the given *temperature* may be used directly.

5·6 Enthalpy and quality of wet steam. Steam having a quality, x, may be considered as steam in which each pound is composed of x lb of dry saturated steam and $(1 - x)$ lb of saturated water where x is expressed as a decimal.

Then $\qquad h_x = xh_g + (1 - x)h_f \qquad\qquad\qquad (5\cdot5)$

or $\qquad h_x = xh_g + h_f - xh_f = h_f + x(h_g - h_f)$

$\qquad\qquad\quad = h_f + xh_{fg} \qquad\qquad\qquad\qquad (5\cdot6)$

Equation 5·6 may be interpreted as follows: The enthalpy of saturated water is h_f; to completely vaporize 1 lb of saturated water requires the addition of the latent heat of evaporation, h_{fg}; to vaporize a part of 1 lb, x, requires xh_{fg} Btu; therefore,

$$h_x = h_f + xh_{fg}$$

Also, $\qquad h_x = h_f + xh_{fg} = (h_g - h_{fg}) + xh_{fg}$

$\qquad\qquad\quad = h_g - (1 - x)h_{fg} \qquad\qquad\qquad (5\cdot7)$

Equation 5·7 may be interpreted as follows: The enthalpy of dry saturated steam is h_g Btu per lb; to condense 1 lb of dry saturated steam requires the removal of the latent heat of evaporation, h_{fg} Btu; to condense $(1 - x)$ lb requires the removal of $(1 - x)h_{fg}$ Btu; therefore, $h_x = h_g - (1 - x)h_{fg}$.

Since the quality of steam is normally more than 95 per cent, Equation 5·7 gives the most accurate results when a slide rule is employed although Equation 5·6 is used more frequently by most engineers. The use of these equations may be illustrated by an example.

Example 3. Compute the enthalpy of 1 lb of wet steam at 100 psia and 97 per cent quality.

Solution: Obtain the enthalpy values from Table A·2 of the Appendix for 100 psia and compute as follows:

$h_x = xh_g + (1 - x)h_f = 0.97(1187.2) + 0.03(298.40) = 1160.5$ Btu per lb

$h_x = h_f + x(h_{fg}) = 298.40 + 0.97(888.8) = 1160.5$ Btu per lb

$h_x = h_g - (1 - x)h_{fg} = 1187.2 - 0.03(888.8) = 1160.5$ Btu per lb

Where the quality of the steam is relatively high as in the case of steam generated in a modern boiler, a *throttling calorimeter* may be used to determine the enthalpy and quality. Before proceeding further, the reader should review thoroughly Article 1·27 dealing with the application of the first law of thermodynamics to the throttling process. Since no work is done in the apparatus and it is assumed that the apparatus is so constructed and insulated that there is no significant change in kinetic energy of the fluid and no heat transfer, then

$$h_1 = h_2 \qquad (5 \cdot 8)$$

The following data pertaining to the enthalpy of dry saturated steam at various pressures may be obtained from Table A·2:

Steam Pressure, Psia	Enthalpy, h_g
14.7	1150.4
100	1187.2
200	1198.4
400	1204.5

Therefore, if dry saturated steam at ordinary boiler pressures is throttled to atmospheric pressure, the steam will become superheated since its enthalpy is greater than the enthalpy of dry saturated steam at atmospheric pressure. Also, if steam having only 2 or 3 per cent of moisture, that is, a quality of 98 or 97 per cent, is throttled from ordinary boiler pressures to atmospheric pressure, its enthalpy is high enough to produce superheated steam at the lower pressure. If the steam after throttling is superheated, the enthalpy, h_2, can be found by measuring its pressure and temperature in the calorimeter and referring to the superheated steam tables for the enthalpy at the measured pressure and temperature. Figure 5·5 is a plot of the enthalpy of superheated steam at temperatures and pressures normally found in throttling calorimeters and may be used in place of the abridged steam tables. Once the enthalpy of the steam at the lower pressure and temperature has been determined, the initial quality of the steam may be computed as follows:

Since
$$h_1 = h_2 \qquad (5 \cdot 8)$$

then
$$h_{f1} + x_1 h_{fg1} = h_2 \quad \text{and} \quad x_1 = \frac{h_2 - h_{f1}}{h_{fg1}} \qquad (5 \cdot 9)$$

where h_2 = enthalpy of superheated steam in the calorimeter
h_{f1} = enthalpy of saturated water at the initial pressure p_1
h_{fg1} = enthalpy of evaporation at the initial pressure p_1
x_1 = quality of the wet steam at the initial pressure p_1

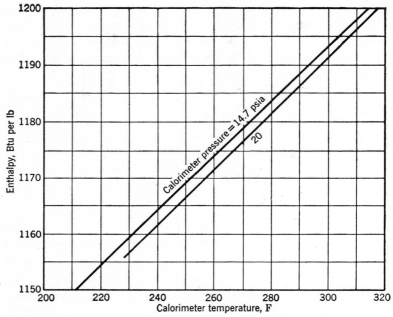

FIG. 5·5   Enthalpy of superheated steam in the normal range of the throttling calorimeter

Plotted by permission of the authors from *Thermodynamic Properties of Steam* by Keenan and Keyes; John Wiley & Sons, publishers

Example 4. Determine the quality of steam at 200 psia if the steam after throttling to 20 psia is found to be at a temperature of 260 F.

Solution: From Fig. 5·5, h_2 at 20 psia and 260 F = 1172 = h_1. Then, from Table A·2 at 200 psia,

$$h_1 + x_1 h_{fg1} = 355.36 + x_1(843.0) = h_2 = 1172$$

$$x_1 = 96.9\%$$

Figure 5·6 illustrates a simple calorimeter which may be made from standard pipe fittings. It must be well insulated to reduce heat losses and must be suitably supported to prevent strain on the sampling tube. The sample of steam should be obtained from a vertical pipe at a point some distance from sharp turns or valves which would disturb the flow pattern in the pipe and cause an unequal distribution of the droplets of moisture across the pipe. A sampling tube consisting of a short length of pipe having holes drilled in its wall and plugged at the far end should be screwed into the pipe line and connected to the calorimeter through a shut-off valve. A pressure gage must also be connected to the pipe line near the sampling tube for the purpose of measuring the steam pressure at the point where the quality and enthalpy are desired. The steam is throttled through the orifice nipple to atmospheric pressure after which it flows through a

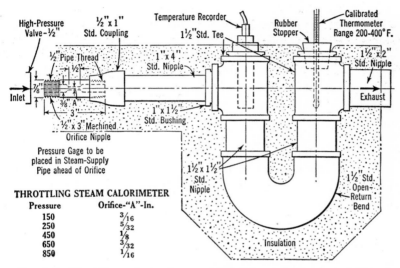

THROTTLING STEAM CALORIMETER

Pressure	Orifice-"A"-In.
150	$\frac{3}{16}$
250	$\frac{5}{32}$
450	$\frac{1}{8}$
650	$\frac{3}{32}$
850	$\frac{1}{16}$

Fig. 5·6 Throttling calorimeter constructed from standard pipe fittings

U-shaped path to the thermometer and then to the atmosphere. Since the steam is at atmospheric pressure at the thermometer, it is only necessary to read this thermometer and, from the upper curve of Fig. 5·5, to determine the enthalpy of the steam at the temperature indicated by the thermometer. The temperature-recorder bulb shown in Fig. 5·6 may be omitted by plugging the opening in the tee with a standard pipe plug.

If the quality of the high-pressure steam is too low to produce superheated steam in the calorimeter, the throttling calorimeter cannot be used, and some other form of calorimeter must be employed. However, a properly operated steam boiler should produce steam of quality high enough to permit the use of the throttling calorimeter.

5·7 Entropy and the Mollier diagram. In Article 1·23, it was pointed out that the ideal expansion of a fluid in a prime mover is a frictionless expansion without heat transfer between the fluid and its cooler surroundings. When such an ideal expansion occurs, a property of the fluid known as *entropy* is constant, and the ideal expansion is frequently referred to as an *isentropic* or *frictionless adiabatic expansion.*

As in the case of enthalpy, the entropy of 1 lb of saturated water at 32 F is assumed to be zero, and the entropy values in the steam tables have been determined for 1 lb with respect to this reference point. The entropy of saturated water, s_f; the entropy of dry saturated steam, s_g; the increase in entropy during evaporation, s_{fg}; and the entropy of superheated steam, s_s, are determined from the steam tables in the same manner that corresponding values for enthalpy and specific volume are found. The entropy of wet steam of quality x can be determined by the use of equations similar to Equations 5·5 to 5·7 which were used in computing the enthalpy of wet steam. Thus, for the entropy of 1 lb of wet steam the following equation has the same form as Equation 5·7:

$$s_x = s_g - (1 - x)s_{fg} \qquad (5·10)$$

A very useful chart, known as the Mollier diagram, may be constructed by plotting the enthalpy of 1 lb of steam as ordinate against the entropy of 1 lb of steam as abscissa. Such a skeleton diagram is illustrated in Fig. 5·7, and a working diagram suitable for the solution of simple problems is shown in the Appendix as Fig. A·1. A much larger diagram will be found in Keenan and Keyes's *Thermodynamic Properties of Steam.*

Lines of constant pressure extend diagonally across the chart from the lower left-hand corner to the upper right-hand corner as shown in Fig. 5·7. Across the center of the diagram is a curved line known as the "saturation line" which is a plot of h_g versus s_g from the tabular values in Table A·2. The enthalpy and entropy of 1 lb of *dry saturated steam* at any pressure can be read directly from the chart by locating the point of intersection of the saturation line and the appropriate constant-pressure line.

The saturation line divides the chart into a region below this curve which is the wet-steam region and a region above the curve which is the superheat region. A series of lines of constant-moisture content are located below and roughly parallel to the saturation line. The line of 5 per cent moisture is a line of 95 per

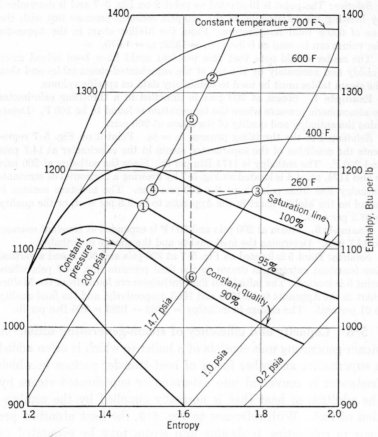

FIG. 5·7 Mollier diagram for steam

cent quality. A series of constant-temperature lines is plotted in the superheat region of the chart.

The use of this chart may be illustrated by a few examples.

Example 5. Determine the enthalpy and entropy of 1 lb of wet steam at 95 per cent quality and 200 psia.

Solution: The point is illustrated as point 1 on Fig. 5·7 and is determined by locating the intersection of the 200-psia constant-pressure line with the line of 95 per cent quality. From the Mollier chart in the Appendix (Fig. A·1) the values can be read as follows: $h_x = 1156$; $s_x = 1.495$.

Example 6. Determine the enthalpy and entropy of 1 lb of superheated steam at 200 psia and 600 F.

Solution: The point is illustrated as point 2 on Fig. 5·7 and is determined by locating the intersection of the 200-psia constant-pressure line with the line of 600 F total temperature. From the Mollier chart in the Appendix the values can be read as follows: $h_s = 1322$; $s_s = 1.676$.

The reader should note that this problem could have been solved more quickly and accurately by the use of the superheated-steam tables and that the steam tables must be used to obtain any data on specific volume.

Example 7. Steam at 200 psia is throttled in a throttling calorimeter to atmospheric pressure where the temperature is found to be 260 F. Determine the enthalpy and quality of the steam at 200 psia.

Solution: For the throttling process, $h_1 = h_2$. Point 3 on Fig. 5·7 represents the condition of the superheated steam in the calorimeter at 14.7 psia and 260 F. The enthalpy is 1174 Btu per lb. Since the enthalpy at 200 psia is also 1174, point 4 is located on Fig. 5·7 by drawing a horizontal or constant-enthalpy line from point 3 to the 200-psia line. The moisture content is found on the Mollier chart in the Appendix to be 2.8 per cent, or the quality is 97.2 per cent.

Example 8. Steam at 200 psia and 500 F is expanded at constant entropy to 14.7 psia. Determine the final quality and the change in enthalpy.

Solution: Point 5 is located on Fig. 5·7 at 200 psia and 500 F and a vertical line (constant entropy) is drawn to the final pressure line, 14.7 psia where point 6 is located. The initial and final enthalpies are found from the Mollier chart in the Appendix to be 1269 and 1063, respectively, and the final quality is 91 per cent. The change in enthalpy = 1269 − 1063 = 206 Btu per lb.

5·8 Capacity and efficiency of steam-generating units. A steam-generating unit consists of a boiler to which is often added a superheater and other forms of heat-transfer surface in which feedwater is converted into saturated or superheated steam by the addition of heat that is normally supplied by the combustion of fuel. With reference to Fig. 5·3, the heat absorbed per hour in converting feedwater into steam may be computed as follows:

$$\text{Heat absorption, Btu per hr} = m_s(h_2 - h_c) \qquad (5·11)$$

where m_s = lb of steam generated per hr

h_2 = enthalpy of steam leaving the unit, Btu per lb (at point C of Fig. 5·3)

h_c = enthalpy of compressed feedwater entering the unit (at point A, Fig. 5·3)

For low and moderate pressures (below 400 psia in this text) the enthalpy of *saturated water* h_f at the given feed-water *temperature* may be used instead of the enthalpy of compressed water because of the small error introduced in neglecting the correction factor from Fig 5·4.

Example 9. A total of 10,000 lb of steam is generated per hr in a boiler operating at a pressure of 200 psia. A throttling calorimeter connected to the boiler outlet indicates a steam temperature of 260 F for a calorimeter pressure of 20 psia. Feedwater is supplied at 220 F. Compute the heat absorption in Btu per hr.

Solution: From the calorimeter pressure and temperature given, $h_2 = 1172$ (see Fig. 5·5). At 220 F, $h_f = 188$ (from Table A·1). Then,

Heat absorption = 10,000 (1172 − 188) = 9,840,000 Btu per hr

Example 10. A total of 150,000 lb of steam is generated per hr at a pressure of 1000 psia and a final steam temperature of 900 F from feedwater at 200 F. Compute the heat absorption in Btu per hr.

Solution: For 1000 psia and 900 F, $h_2 = 1448.2$ from Table A·3.

For 200 F feedwater at 1000 psia, $h_c = h_f$ at 200 F + correction from Fig. 5·4 = 167.99 + 2.2 = 170.2. Then,

Heat absorption = 150,000 (1448.2 − 170.2) = 191,700,000 Btu per hr

The *rated capacity* of steam-generating units was originally expressed in terms of boiler horsepower, 1 boiler hp being equal to 10 sq ft of heating surface. Thus, a boiler having 5000 sq ft of heating surface was *rated* as a 500-hp boiler. This arbitrary rating has been abandoned, and steam-generating units are now rated in terms of the steam they can deliver continuously in pounds per hour. It is now standard practice in large central-station power plants to install one steam-generating unit per turbine and to operate the group as a unit. Where this is done, the capacity of the steam-generating unit is sometimes expressed in kilowatts equal to the kilowatt rating of the turbine generator to which it supplies the steam.

The *output* of steam-generating units was originally expressed in terms of *boiler horsepower* where 1 boiler hp was defined as the absorption of 33,475 Btu per hr. Since no work is done in a boiler, the work being done by the expansion of the steam in an engine or turbine, the term "boiler horsepower" is a misnomer and has been abandoned. The output of steam-generating units is now expressed as the heat absorption per hour in units of 1000 Btu, this unit being given the symbol kB.

The *output* of a steam-generating unit may be computed as follows:

$$\text{Output} = \frac{\text{heat absorbed per hr in generating steam}}{1000} \, kB \quad (5 \cdot 12)$$

Example 11. Express the output of the steam-generating unit of Example 10 in kB.

Solution: From Example 10,

$$\text{Heat absorption} = 191,700,000 \text{ Btu per hr}$$

Then

$$\text{Output} = \frac{191,700,000}{1000} = 191,700 \, kB$$

The *efficiency* of a steam-generating unit,

$$\eta = \frac{\text{output}}{\text{input}}$$

or

$$\eta = \frac{\text{heat absorbed, Btu per hr}}{\text{heating value of fuel burned per hr}}$$

or

$$\eta = \frac{m_s(h_2 - h_c)}{m_f Q_H} \times 100 \text{ in } \% \quad (5 \cdot 13)$$

where m_f = fuel burned, lb per hr

Q_H = higher heating value of the fuel, Btu per lb

Example 12. Compute the efficiency of the steam-generating unit of Example 10 if 21,000 lb of coal having a heating value of 12,000 Btu per lb are burned per hr.

Solution:

$$\eta = \frac{\text{output}}{\text{input}} = \frac{191,700,000}{21,000 \times 12,000} \times 100 = 76.3\%$$

The efficiency obtainable from a steam-generating unit depends upon the kind of fuel burned, the method of firing the fuel, the characteristics of the furnace, the arrangement and extent of heat-absorbing surfaces, the load on the unit, and the care exercised in operating it. The efficiency will vary from less than 60 per cent for some hand-fired installations and locomotives operated at very high loads to 90 per cent for modern pulverized-coal-fired steam-generating units designed to burn high-grade low-sulphur fuel.

It is the function of the fuel-burning equipment including the furnace to release or develop all of the energy in the fuel through the process of complete combustion with a minimum amount of excess air. It is the function of the steam-generating unit to absorb as much as possible of the energy released by combustion and to transfer it to steam. The extent to which this is done is determined by the flue-gas temperature at which the products of combustion are discharged to waste. Since most fuels contain sulphur, the minimum allowable flue-gas temperature is the temperature below which the condensation of water vapor from the products of combustion containing SO_2 and SO_3 may cause corrosion of the heat-transfer surfaces. This minimum temperature is usually between 275 and 350 F, depending upon the sulphur content of the fuel. To attain such low exit-gas temperatures requires the installation of a large amount of economizer and air-heater surface, as discussed in Articles 5·20 and 5·21 of this chapter. Such equipment can be justified when the unit is operated almost continuously under heavy load conditions when burning relatively high-priced fuel so that the fuel saving in dollars per year is sufficient to pay for the extra cost of the heat-recovery surfaces. Where fuel is cheap, loads are variable and light over much of the year, or the unit is small, the fuel savings in dollars per year may not justify the installation of heat-transfer surfaces to cool the products of combustion to temperatures below 500 to 600 F. It is for this reason that steam-generating units may be designed to produce efficiencies that are generally between the limits of 73 and 90 per cent.

The computation of an energy balance for the combustion of fuel was discussed in Article 2·21. These calculations, together with the computations for determination of the capacity and efficiency of a steam-generating unit, are illustrated in Example 13 as applied to a typical set of test data.

Example 13. The following data were collected during the test of a steam-generating unit consisting of a stoker-fired boiler, superheater, and air heater:

Ultimate analysis of coal, %: C = 66.0; H = 4.4; O = 7.9; N = 1.5; S = 11.; ash = 7.6; moisture = 11.5; total 100%

Heating value of coal = 11,780 Btu per lb

Orsat analysis of dry gaseous products of combustion, %: CO_2 = 14.5; CO = 0.2; O_2 = 4.4; N_2 = 80.9; total = 100%

Coal burned = 6480 lb per hr

Dry refuse collected = 622 lb per hr; 21% carbon in dry refuse

Steam generated = 55,000 lb per hr

Feed-water temperature = 300 F; feed-water pressure = 800 psig

Boiler pressure = 605 psig

Calorimeter pressure and temperature at boiler outlet = 5 psig and 310 F, respectively

Superheater outlet pressure = 585 psig; superheater outlet temperature = 800 F

Barometric pressure = 29.9 in. of Hg = 14.7 psia

Air temperature = 70 F; exit flue-gas temperature = 400 F

Compute (a) Heat absorbed in boiler per lb of steam generated.
   (b) Heat absorbed in superheater per lb of steam generated.
   (c) Heat absorbed in steam-generating unit per lb of steam generated.
   (d) Output of steam-generating unit in kB.
   (e) Efficiency of steam-generating unit.
   (f) Energy balance.

Solution: (a) Enthalpy of compressed feedwater at 300 F and 800 psig = h_f at 300 F plus correction factor for 815 psia from Fig. 5·4 = 269.6 + 1.5 = 271.1 Btu per lb of feedwater

Enthalpy of wet steam at the boiler outlet can be determined from the pressure and temperature in the throttling calorimeter. At 310 F and 19.7 psia, h_2 = 1196.5 Btu per lb = h_1

Then the heat absorbed in the boiler = 1196.5 − 271.1 = 925.4 Btu per lb of steam generated

(b) Enthalpy of the steam leaving the superheater at 599.7 psia (585 psig + 14.7 psi barometric pressure) = 1407.7 Btu per lb

Then the heat absorbed in the superheater = enthalpy of steam leaving superheater − enthalpy of steam leaving boiler = 1407.7 − 1196.5 = 211.2 Btu per lb of steam

(c) Heat absorbed in steam-generating unit per lb of steam generated = enthalpy of steam leaving superheater − enthalpy of feedwater = 1407.7 − 271.1 = 1136.6 Btu per lb of steam generated

Check: heat absorbed in boiler + heat absorbed in superheater = 925.4 + 211.2 = 1136.6 Btu per lb of steam generated

(*d*) Output of steam-generating unit in kB

$$= \frac{\left\{\begin{array}{l} \text{55,000 lb of steam generated per hr} \times \text{1136.6 Btu} \\ \text{absorbed per lb of steam generated} \end{array}\right\}}{1000} = 62{,}513 \ kB$$

(*e*) Efficiency of steam-generating unit

$$= \frac{\text{Heat absorbed, Btu per hr}}{\text{Heating value of fuel supplied, Btu per hr}}$$

$$= \frac{\left\{\begin{array}{l} \text{55,000 lb of steam generated per hr} \times \text{1136.6 Btu} \\ \text{absorbed per lb of steam} \end{array}\right\}}{\text{6480 lb of coal burned per hr} \times \text{11,780 Btu per lb of coal}} \times 100$$

$$= 81.8\%$$

(*f*) Energy balance; computed for 1 lb of fuel:

Carbon input = 6480 lb of coal burned per hr × 66% C in coal = 4275 lb of C per hr

Carbon in refuse = 622 lb of dry refuse per hr × 21% C in refuse = 131 lb of C per hr

Carbon burned to CO and CO_2 per lb of coal, C_b

$$= \frac{\text{4275 lb of C in fuel} - \text{131 lb of C in refuse}}{\text{6480 lb of fuel}}$$

$$= 64 \text{ lb of C per lb of fuel}$$

Dry flue-gas analysis, %	Lb per 100 Moles	Lb of C in 100 Moles
CO_2 = 14.5	14.5 × 44 = 638	14.5 × 12 = 174
CO = 0.2	0.2 × 28 = 6	0.2 × 12 = 2.4
O_2 = 4.4	4.4 × 32 = 141	
N_2 = 80.9	80.9 × 28 = 2265	
Total 100.0	3050	176.4

Dry products of combustion per lb of fuel

$$= \frac{\text{3050 lb of dry gas per 100 moles}}{\text{176.4 lb of C per 100 moles}} \times 0.64 \text{ lb of C per lb of fuel}$$

$$= 11.05 \text{ lb of dry gaseous products of combustion per lb of fuel}$$

(1) Loss due to sensible heat in dry gaseous products of combustion = lb of dry flue gas per lb of fuel × $c_p \ (t_g - t_a)$ = 11.05 lb of dry gas per lb of fuel × 0.24 (400 − 70) = 876 Btu per lb of fuel

(2) Loss due to CO in dry products of combustion

$$= \frac{2.4 \text{ lb of C in CO per 100 moles of dry gas}}{176.4 \text{ lb of C in CO and CO}_2 \text{ per 100 moles of dry gas}}$$

$\times$ 0.64 lb of C per lb of fuel

$\times$ 10,160 Btu per lb of C in the form of CO

$= 89$ Btu per lb of fuel

(3) Loss due to C in the refuse

$$= \frac{131 \text{ lb of C in refuse} \times 14,600 \text{ Btu per lb of C}}{6480 \text{ lb of coal burned}}$$

$= 292$ Btu per lb of fuel

(4) Loss due to evaporating moisture in fuel
$= 0.115$ lb of moisture in fuel $(1089 + 0.46t_g - t_a)$
$= 0.115 (1089 + 0.46 \times 400 - 70) = 138$ Btu per lb of fuel

(5) Loss due to water vapor formed from H $= 0.0444$ lb of H per lb of fuel
$\times$ 9 lb of H_2O per lb of H $\times (1089 + 0.46t_g - t_a) = 0.0444 \times 9 \times 1203$
$= 482$ Btu per lb of fuel

(6) Energy absorbed in generating steam

$$= \frac{55,000 \text{ lb of steam generated per hr} \times 1136.6 \text{ Btu per lb of steam}}{6480 \text{ lb of coal burned}}$$

$= 9640$ Btu per lb of fuel

The energy balance may be summarized as follows in Btu per lb of fuel and in per cent of the heating value of the fuel:

	Btu per Lb	Per Cent
I. Energy absorbed	9,640	81.8
II. Losses:		
1. Sensible heat in dry flue gas	876	7.4
2. CO in dry flue gas	89	0.8
3. Unburned C in refuse	292	2.5
4. Moisture in coal	138	1.2
5. Water vapor formed from hydrogen	482	4.1
6. Radiation and unaccounted for (by difference)	263	2.2
Total	11,780	100.0

5·9   The steam boiler. The steam boiler is a pressure vessel in which feedwater can be converted into *saturated steam* of high quality at some desired pressure. When other heat-transfer surfaces such as superheater, air heater, or economizer surfaces are combined with boiler surface into a unified installation, the name *steam-generating unit* is applied to the complete unit.

Since the *function of the boiler is to convert water into relatively dry saturated steam,* it must be so constructed that the steam bubbles can be separated from the water effectively. This is normally accomplished in a cylindrical horizontal boiler drum in which a definite water level is maintained, either manually or automatically. The drum must have sufficient steam-disengaging surface or separator capacity to allow the steam to escape without entraining very much water in the form of a mist or fog. The boiler must be so designed as to have as much heat-absorbing surface as possible for the amount of steel in the boiler. This surface is usually in the form of tubes which are 2 to 4 in. in outside diameter (OD) with a wall thickness that depends upon the steam pressure at which the unit is designed to operate. The heating surfaces must be so arranged as to provide adequate circulation of the boiler water in order to prevent overheating of the metal at high rates of heat transfer.

Boilers in which the water is inside the tubes are called *water-tube* boilers, whereas boilers that have the hot products of combustion in the tubes and the water outside of the tubes are called *fire-tube* boilers. Boiler heating surface is defined as that surface which receives heat from the flame or hot gases and is in contact with water. The area is based on the surface receiving the heat: that is, the outside area of water tubes and the inside area of fire tubes.

Because of the large energy storage in boiler water under pressure and the disastrous results of a sudden release of the pressure in a boiler explosion, the American Society of Mechanical Engineers has developed a boiler construction code which specifies the design rules, methods of construction, and materials to be used in boilers. Most states have laws that require all boilers installed within their borders to be constructed in accordance with this code. Within the limits of the code, many arrangements of drums and heating surfaces are possible. Some of the more important types of boilers are discussed in subsequent articles of this chapter. These discussions are limited to power boilers: that is, boilers designed for pressures above 15 psig.

5·10   The vertical tubular boiler.   The vertical tubular boiler as illustrated in Fig. 5·8 is a small self-contained *internally fired* boiler.   It consists of an outer cylindrical shell closed at the top by a tube sheet; a set of fire tubes; and an internal furnace formed by the grate, a water leg, and a crown sheet.   The water leg is made by riveting to the outer shell and the crown sheet, a short cylindrical shell of smaller diameter.   Vertical tubes, generally about 2 in. OD extend from the lower or crown sheet to the upper tube sheet.   During construction, the tube holes in the sheets are drilled and reamed to size, and the tubes are inserted loosely and are then rolled or expanded to form a tight seat in the tube sheet.   A pressure gage indicates the steam pressure, and a spring-loaded safety valve will allow the steam to escape to the atmosphere in case of excessive pressure.   The water level in the boiler is indicated by a glass gage; three cocks are also installed within the limits of the glass gage as a means of checking the water level.   It is necessary for the operator to maintain a water level within the limits of the water-level gage, to supply fuel as needed, and to regulate the rate of combustion with a damper in the flue-gas-outlet pipe so as to maintain the steam pressure within the desired limits.

The boiler is called an *internally fired* boiler because the furnace is built into the boiler.   The efficiency of the unit is low, and it is seldom constructed for more than 150 psig pressure.   It is used on construction work and other applications where a compact and portable boiler of small size is needed.

5·11   The horizontal-return tubular boiler.   The horizontal-return tubular (HRT) fire-tube boiler is illustrated in Figs. 5·9, 5·10, and 5·11.   The boiler shell is a horizontal cylinder closed at each end by a flat tube sheet or head.   The shell may be of riveted construction with riveted heads as shown in Fig. 5·9, or it may be made of welded construction as shown in Fig. 5·10.   The ASME boiler construction code requires that all welds must be X-rayed to discover defective welds, and the welded drum must be stress-relieved in an annealing oven.

The fire tubes which are usually 3 to 4 in. in diameter extend through the boiler from one tube sheet to the other and are rolled or expanded into the tube sheets at each end, thus serving not only as flues through which the hot gases flow but also as tie rods

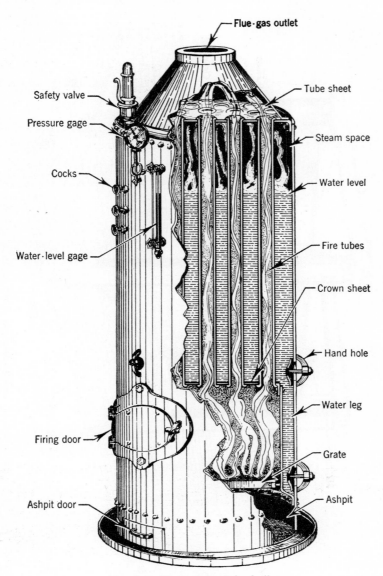

Flue-gas outlet

Safety valve

Pressure gage

Cocks

Water-level gage

Firing door

Ashpit door

Tube sheet

Steam space

Water level

Fire tubes

Crown sheet

Hand hole

Water leg

Grate

Ashpit

FIG. 5·8 Vertical fire-tube boiler

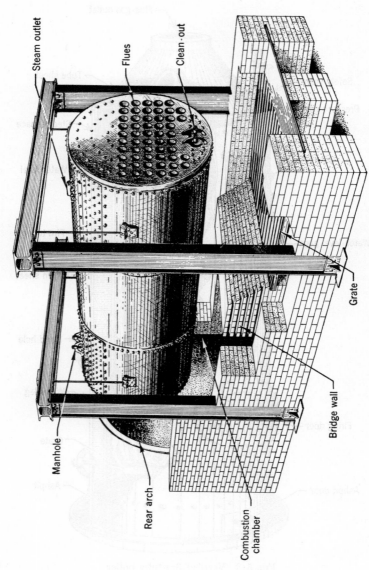

Steam outlet

Flues

Clean-out

Manhole

Rear arch

Combustion chamber

Bridge wall

Grate

Fig. 5·9 Horizontal-return tubular boiler

to hold the flat tube sheets in place against the steam pressure in the boiler. The flat surfaces of the heads above the tubes are tied to the boiler shell by diagonal braces.

The boiler may be suspended on a steel frame as shown in Fig. 5·9 or may be supported on the brick side walls by means of brackets attached to the boiler drum. The brick side walls of Fig. 5·9 are carried up to a level somewhat above the center line of the drum. This boiler is called an *externally fired* boiler

Fig. 5·10 Welded horizontal-return tubular boiler

since it is supported over a brick furnace. A furnace of adequate size can be obtained by supporting the boiler a reasonable distance above the grate. The illustration shows a hand-fired grate under the front end of the boiler. The products of combustion pass over the bridge wall which extends across the setting behind the grate and into a combustion chamber under the rear of the boiler. They then flow upward behind the boiler under the rear arch, forward through the fire tubes, and upward through a flue connection not shown in Fig. 5·9 at the front end of the boiler. The water level is maintained above the upper row of fire tubes in order to cover them with water and prevent them from being burned out. However, the water level is carried only a short distance above the tubes so as to provide adequate surface for the separation of the steam from the water and to permit the delivery of steam of high quality.

A longitudinal section and a cross section of an HRT boiler and setting are shown in Fig. 5·11. The boiler is fired by a single-retort underfeed stoker. The path of the gases from the stoker to the rear under the boiler shell and back to the front through the fire tubes is indicated. A blow-off line at the rear of the boiler is protected from direct contact with the hot gases by a small brick pier. The boiler may be drained through the blow-off line. In normal operation, the blow-off line will be opened periodically as necessary in order to blow down the water level several inches and wash out the suspended material in the boiler water which will form scale if allowed to concentrate in the boiler. A perforated dry pipe extends for some distance within the boiler drum as far above the water level as possible and is connected to the boiler-outlet nozzle. The function of the dry pipe is to equalize the steam removal over a considerable length of the drum in order to keep the moisture entrainment to a minimum.

A water column is connected to the boiler by two pipes, one above and one below the normal water level. A blow-off line from the bottom of the water column may be opened periodically to wash out any scale and dirt from the piping. This arrangement is necessary to insure that the level of the water in the water column is the same as the water level in the boiler at all times. The water level in the water column is indicated by a glass tube connected to it, and three cocks are also installed on the column to check the water level as indicated in the glass tube.

The HRT boiler is built in drum diameters from 48 to 90 in. and in lengths from 14 to 20 ft, the longer lengths being associated with the larger diameters. The boiler is usually designed for steam pressures from 100 to 150 psig with a maximum evaporative capacity of about 10,000 lb of steam per hr. This range of pressures and capacities meets the requirements of many small industries which need steam for power and heat. The large water-storage capacity results in stable operation with a minimum of attention. When stoker-fired with an adequate furnace, efficiencies of 70 to 75 per cent are obtainable. Consequently, the HRT boiler is one of the commonest types of boilers to be found in small installations.

5·12   The locomotive boiler. The locomotive boiler is designed to occupy a limited height and width and to have a high

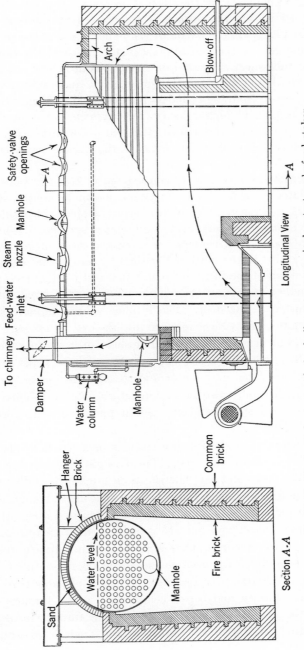

FIG. 5·11 Horizontal-return tubular boiler set over a single-retort underfeed stoker

evaporative capacity for the space it occupies. It is an *internally fired* boiler in that the furnace is surrounded by the boiler. As shown in Fig. 5·12, the barrel of the boiler is composed of cylindrical and conical sections of steel plates closed at the front end by a flat tube sheet. A cast-iron smoke box attached to the front end of the boiler contains the smokestack and exhaust nozzle. Exhaust steam from the cylinders is discharged vertically through the smokestack at high velocity, thus creating an intense draft which draws the air through the fuel bed on the grate and draws the products of combustion through the furnace and the fire tubes.

The furnace side walls are constructed of two parallel nickel-alloy plates from 5 to 8 in. apart as shown in section *A-A* of Fig. 5·12. These parallel plates form a water-cooled side wall for the furnace and are held together by stay-bolts spaced in rows on about 4-in. centers. The crown sheet or roof of the furnace is tied to the outer boiler shell by long radial stay-bolts. The rear wall of the furnace is constructed of parallel steel plates tied together with stay-bolts with an opening flanged into the plates for the firing door. The furnace volume is increased by extending the crown sheet forward into the cylindrical part of the boiler and attaching a semi-circular sheet to it as shown in section *B-B*. Since the space between the furnace walls and the boiler shell is filled with water and steam under boiler pressure, these surfaces must also be tied together with stay-bolts. The flat plates and stay-bolt construction limit the boiler pressure to about 350 psig.

The front end of the furnace consists of a flat flue sheet into which the flues are fastened. The straight flues or fire tubes connect the front and rear flue sheets in a manner similar to the construction used in the HRT boiler. The flue arrangement is shown in section *C-C*. The water level is carried above the top of the crown sheet and flues to protect them from overheating.

A row of five inclined tubes is placed in the furnace over the grate, and a fire-brick arch is supported on these tubes. The function of the arch is to increase the length of flame travel and to promote mixing and better combustion in the furnace. The path of the gases from the grate through the furnace to the flues is indicated on Fig. 5·12. Most of the modern coal-burning

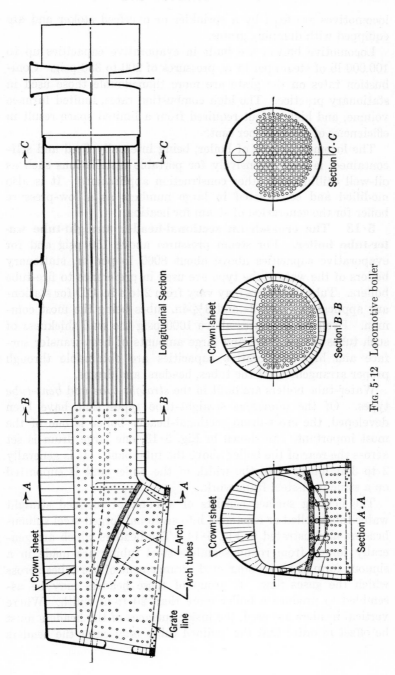

FIG. 5·12 Locomotive boiler

locomotives are fired by a sprinkler or overfeed stoker and are equipped with dumping grates.

Locomotive boilers are built in evaporative capacities up to 100,000 lb of steam per hr at pressures of 200 to 350 psig. Combustion rates on the grate are more than double those used in stationary practice. The high combustion rates, limited furnace volume, and high output required from a limited space result in efficiencies of about 60 per cent.

The locomotive type of boiler, being internally fired and self-contained, is used extensively for portable installations such as oil-well drilling and other construction applications. It is also modified and constructed in large numbers as a low-pressure boiler for the generation of steam for heating.

5·13   The cross-drum sectional-header straight-tube water-tube boiler.   For steam pressures above 150 psig and for evaporative capacities above about 8000 lb per hr, stationary boilers of the water-tube type are used in preference to fire-tube boilers. Tube diameters may vary from 2 to 4 in. OD for stationary applications with 3- and 3¼-in. tubes being the most common. Even for pressures above 1000 psig the wall thickness of such tubes is moderate, and large amounts of heat-transfer surface and high evaporative capacities are obtainable through proper arrangement of the tubes, headers, and drums.

Water-tube boilers are built in the *straight-tube* and *bent-tube* types. Of the numerous straight-tube types that have been developed, the cross-drum sectional-header boiler is one of the most important. As shown in Fig. 5·13, one large drum is set across the rear of the boiler above the tube bank. It is generally 2 to 3 ft longer than the width of the boiler and is supported on a structural-steel framework.

The heating surface consists of a bank of inclined straight water tubes rolled or expanded into sectional forged-steel sinuous headers as illustrated in Fig. 5·14. The headers which are generally forged from round seamless steel tubing are made in a sinuous form to give a staggered arrangement of the tubes across which the gases flow. A group of these headers may be assembled to produce a boiler more than 20 ft in width. Where vertical headers are used, the inside surfaces of the headers must be offset in order that the inclined tubes may enter the headers perpendicular to the seating surfaces into which the tubes are rolled. An elliptical hand hole, closed by a gasket, cover, and clamp, is machined in each header opposite each tube to provide access to the tube for cleaning, inspection, and replacement.

As shown in Fig. 5·13, the rear or lower headers are connected

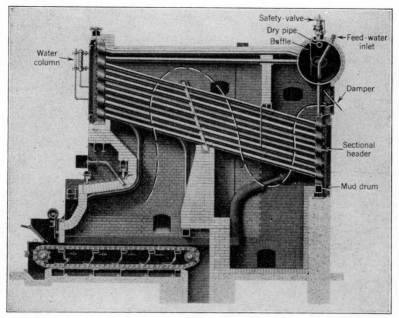

FIG. 5·13 Cross-drum sectional-header boiler and forced-draft chain-grate stoker

to the steam drum by vertical tubes, and the front headers are connected to the drum by horizontal tubes. A mud drum is connected to the low point of each of the rear headers. The mud drum is blown down periodically to remove the sediment which settles at the low point in the system.

As steam is generated in the inclined water tubes, the steam bubbles which tend to rise create an upward circulation to the front headers from which the steam–water mixture is delivered by the horizontal circulator tubes to the drum. Feedwater is distributed across the width of the boiler by means of a distributor located in the bottom of the drum. Water circulates down the connecting tubes from the drum to the lower headers to supply the inclined tubes in which the steam is generated. Steam is removed from the drum through a dry pipe, and a baffle in the drum assists in the separation of the steam and water.

Figure 5·13 shows the boiler set over a furnace fired by a

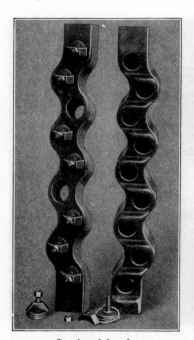

Header and tube assembly

Sectional header Section through sectional header showing hand-hole closure assembly

Fig. 5·14 Details of header construction and assembly of sectional-header straight-tube boiler

forced-draft chain-grate stoker and designed to burn bituminous coal. The path of the products of combustion is indicated by a dotted line. Tile and brick baffles guide the gas stream through the boiler without short-circuiting the heat-transfer surface in what is known as *three passes*. The cross-sectional area for the flow of the gases decreases with the decreasing gas temperature and volume so that the gas velocity may be maintained throughout the tube bank. The flow of gases across the staggered tubes in each pass results in excellent heat transfer and a low exit-flue-gas temperature. This type of boiler has been built in capacities in excess of 500,000 lb of steam per hr and for steam pressures up to 1400 psig.

5·14 Bent-tube boilers. Bent-tube boilers are generally constructed with one lower or mud drum and one to three upper drums. The drums are drilled radially to receive the tubes which are bent to enter the drums radially. Drum diameters vary from 24 to 72 in. The lower or mud drum is made as small as possible, the diameter being determined by ligament strength between

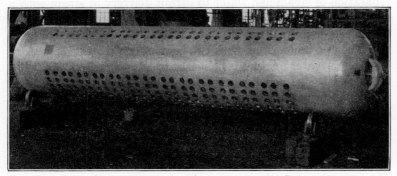

Fig. 5·15 Shop view of a drum for a bent-tube boiler

tube holes. The size of the upper or steam drums must be sufficient to permit separation of steam from the water so that the boiler will deliver relatively dry steam.

Boiler drums are fabricated from flat steel plates which are trimmed to width and length and rolled into a cylinder or half-cylinder. Boiler manufacturers have equipment for bending plates up to 7 in. thick and 42 ft long. The longitudinal seam or seams are electric-arc-welded by automatic welding machines. Forged-steel heads are welded to the ends of the cylinder, forged-steel nozzles are welded into place for piping connections, all welds are X-rayed for defects, and the drum is stress-relieved in an annealing oven. A manhole in one end of the drum is closed by a door which opens inward and is held on its seat by yokes and bolts and the steam pressure. After the radial tube holes have been drilled, the drum appears as in Fig. 5·15.

The upper drums are usually supported by structural steel while the lower drum is generally suspended from the upper drums by the boiler tubes and is free to move as the tubes expand and contract. The tubes are normally 2, 3, or $3\frac{1}{4}$ in. OD. They are bent to shape at the tube mill and are inserted into the drums and rolled to a tight fit after the drums have been erected in place on the job. Because of modern methods of fabricating fusion-welded boiler drums, the bent-tube boiler is usually cheaper than the sectional-header straight-tube boiler and has largely replaced other types of water-tube boilers in recent years.

Since the major function of the upper or steam drums is the separation of steam and water to permit delivery of steam with a quality as close to 100 per cent as possible, separating devices have been developed for installation in the steam drum. Figure 5·16 shows a boiler drum with two rows of centrifugal separators. The steam–water mixture is delivered to the drum from the boiler tubes and is directed by means of baffle plates to a battery of centrifugal separators. The mixture of steam and water enters the centrifugal separators tangentially at high velocity. The water is thrown outward by centrifugal force and flows downward while the steam rises and passes through a battery of corrugated scrubber plates to which the remaining droplets of water adhere. The separators greatly increase the steam-separating capacity of the drum and permit the construction of high-capacity steam boilers with only one steam drum.

5·15   The low-head three-drum bent-tube boiler.   Figure 5·17 shows a typical three-drum bent-tube boiler of the low-head type, fired by a forced-draft chain-grate stoker set in a brick furnace designed to burn high-moisture coal such as lignite. The tubes are bent to enter each drum radially, and this particular boiler has 17 different shapes of tubes which are not interchangeable.

Feedwater is supplied to the upper or steam drum at such a rate as to keep this drum about one third full of water. The water passes downward to the bottom or mud drum, flows through the inclined tubes to the front drum, and returns through the upper tubes to the steam drum. Most of the steam is generated in the tubes connecting the mud drum to the front drum. The steam bubbles which are formed in these inclined tubes tend to rise and create good circulation. A baffle and dry pipe in the steam drum help to separate the steam from the mixture of steam and water which is discharged into this drum above the water level, thereby resulting in the delivery of relatively dry steam. Tile baffles are installed below the steam drum and in the lower tube bank to

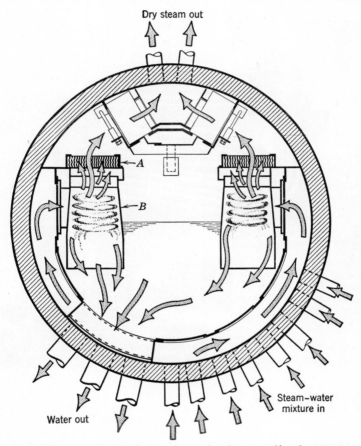

FIG. 5·16   Section through boiler drum showing centrifugal separators *B* and scrubber plates *A*

direct the flow of gases across the tube banks in the path indicated in Fig. 5·17. A blow-off line with two valves in series is connected to the bottom of the mud drum. By opening one manhole in each drum, a man can enter the boiler drums to inspect and clean them and can push a rotating tube cleaner through the tubes to remove any scale that may have accumulated in them.

Most of the three-drum low-head boilers are built for pressures between 160 and 250 psig with capacities between 5000 and 30,000 lb of steam per hr, although some have been built

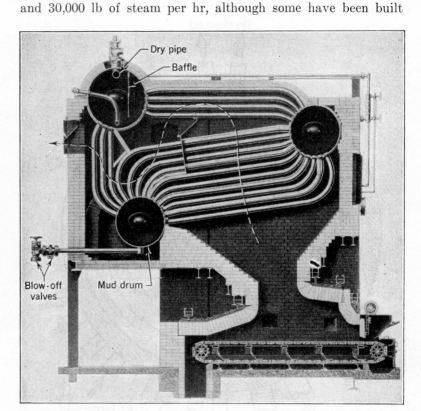

Dry pipe

Baffle

Blow-off valves

Mud drum

Fig. 5·17   Low-head three-drum boiler with forced-draft stoker and setting for lignite or subbituminous coal

for pressures up to 450 psig and capacities up to 50,000 lb of steam per hr.

5·16   The two-drum bent-tube boiler.   Figure 5·18 shows a two-drum bent-tube boiler with water-cooled furnace, fired by a spreader stoker equipped with a hand-operated dump grate. By means of baffles which are attached to the boiler tubes, the gases are forced to follow a path from the furnace to the boiler exit as indicated by the dotted lines.   A water level is maintained slightly below the mid-point in the upper or steam drum. Water circulates from the steam drum to the mud drum through the six rows of tubes in the rear of the boiler-tube bank. Circulation is

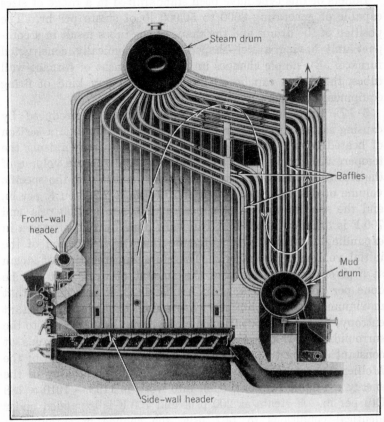

Fɪɢ. 5·18   Two-drum bent-tube boiler with spreader stoker and water-cooled furnace

from the mud drum to the front drum through the front boiler tubes and also through the furnace-wall tubes. The side-wall furnace tubes are supplied with water from the mud drum by means of circulators connected to rectangular water boxes located in the side walls at the level of the grate. Water for the front-wall tubes is supplied to the round front-wall header by down-comer tubes connected to the upper drum and insulated from the furnace by a row of insulating brick. Most of the steam is generated in the furnace-wall tubes and in the first and second rows of boiler tubes which can "see" the flame in the furnace.

Boilers of this type have been standardized in a range of sizes capable of generating 8000 to 50,000 lb of steam per hr. The position of the drums and the shape of the tubes result in a compact unit having a well-shaped and economically constructed furnace. By simple changes in the arrangement of furnace-wall tubes, the design can be adopted to almost any kind of firing equipment and fuel.

5·17 Superheaters. Superheated steam is produced by causing saturated steam from a boiler to flow through a section of heated tubing as illustrated in Fig. 5·3, thereby raising the temperature and increasing the enthalpy and specific volume of the steam. As may be noted from the steam tables, the specific volume of dry saturated steam at 200 psia is 2.288 cu ft per lb, and the specific volume of superheated steam at 200 psia and 700 F is 3.380 cu ft per lb. The work done by 1 lb of steam in expanding through a given pressure range is a function of the initial volume of the steam. Therefore, superheating of steam at a given pressure increases the amount of work that can be done per pound of steam. In Article 1·23, it was shown that maximum work was obtained when a fluid expanded at constant entropy, that is, without friction and without heat transfer to the surroundings. If dry saturated steam at 200 psia expands at constant entropy to 14.7 psia, it can be shown by means of the Mollier diagram (Fig. A·1) that the change in enthalpy or the energy available for conversion into work is $1198 - 1010 = 188$ Btu per lb. If steam at 200 psia and 700 F is expanded under identical conditions to 14.7 psia, the change in enthalpy is $1374 - 1128 = 246$ Btu per lb or an increase of 30.8 per cent in the amount of energy that could be converted into work under ideal conditions. It should be noted that superheating does not increase the steam pressure but in fact causes some *decrease* in pressure, owing to fluid friction in the superheater tubing.

In addition to the theoretical gain in output due to the increased volume and enthalpy which results from superheating, the efficiency of steam engines is also improved by the use of superheated steam through reduction in initial condensation as discussed in Article 8·9. In a steam turbine, serious erosion of blades will occur if the steam is discharged from the turbine with a quality less than about 88 per cent. The first law of thermodynamics states that all work done by the turbine comes from the energy in the steam flowing through the turbine. Thus, if steam enters a turbine with an enthalpy of 1300 Btu per lb and the work done in the turbine is equivalent to 300 Btu per lb, the enthalpy of the exhaust steam will be 1300 − 300 = 1000 Btu per lb, neglecting heat transfer to the surroundings. If sufficient energy is converted into work to reduce the quality of the steam leaving the turbine to less than 88 per cent, blade erosion results. Also, each 1 per cent of moisture in the steam reduces the efficiency of that part of the turbine in which the wet steam is expanding by from 1 to 1½ per cent. It is necessary, therefore, that high-efficiency steam turbines be supplied with superheated steam. The minimum recommended steam temperature at the turbine throttle of condensing turbines for various initial steam pressures is as follows:

Throttle Steam Pressure, Psig	Minimum Steam Temperature, F
400	725
600	825
850	900
1250	950
1450	1000
1800	1050

The decreased strength of steel at high temperature makes it necessary to use alloy steels for superheater tubing where steam temperatures exceed 800 F. Alloy steels containing 0.5 per cent of molybdenum and 1 to 5 per cent of chromium are used for the hot end of high-temperature superheaters at steam temperatures up to 1000 F, and austenitic steels such as those containing 18 per cent chromium and 8 per cent nickel are used for higher temperatures.

Superheaters may be classified as convection or radiant superheaters. *Convection* superheaters are those that receive heat by direct contact with the hot products of combustion which flow around the tubes. *Radiant* superheaters are located in furnace walls where they "see" the flame and absorb heat by radiation with a minimum of contact with the hot gases.

A typical superheater of the *convection* type is shown in Fig. 5·19. Saturated steam from the boiler is supplied to the upper or inlet header of the superheater by a single pipe or by a group of circulator tubes. Steam flows at high velocity from the inlet to the outlet header through a large number of parallel tubes or elements of small diameter. Nipples are welded to the headers

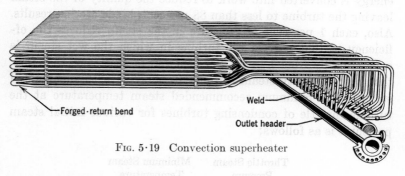

Forged-return bend

Weld

Outlet header

FIG. 5·19 Convection superheater

at the factory, and the tube elements are welded to the nipples in the field, thus protecting the headers from temperature stresses due to uneven heating during field welding. In the superheater shown in Fig. 5·19, the individual elements are fabricated from tubes whose ends are connected by forged return bends. When space permits the forged return bends may be replaced by 180-degree U bends.

The amount of surface required in the superheater depends upon the final temperature to which the steam is to be superheated, the amount of steam to be superheated, the quantity of hot gas flowing around the superheater, and the temperature of the gas. In order to keep the surface to a minimum and thus reduce the cost of the superheater, it should be located where high-temperature gases will flow around the tubes. Since the tubes are kept below dangerous temperatures by the steam which is flowing through them, they must be protected from excessive rates of heat input. Consequently, convection superheaters are so located as to have a few rows of boiler tubes between them and the furnace to shield them from direct radiation by the hot flame in the furnace. The location of superheaters in various types of boilers is discussed in the succeeding articles in this chapter.

5·18   The four-drum Stirling boiler with superheater. The four-drum Stirling boiler is one of the most popular types of boilers for medium pressures and capacities. Figure 5·20 shows such a boiler installed in an oil-fired brick setting. The upper drums are supported on structural-steel beams and are located 15 to 30 ft above the mud drum. The mud drum is supported by the boiler tubes, is free to move in all directions as the tubes expand or contract, and is protected from the hot furnace by a bridge wall.

Feedwater is supplied to a distributing trough in the upper rear drum in order to insure uniform distribution across the entire width of the boiler. The upper rear drum is normally about one third full of water. The feedwater passes down the tubes in the rear bank to the mud drum. Water circulation is from the mud drum up the front bank of tubes to the front drum, through the row of water circulators below the center line of the front drum to the center drum and back to the mud drum by way of the four rows of rear tubes from the center drum. Water also rises in the center-tube bank between the mud drum and the center drum and returns to the mud drum by way of the three rows of tubes in the rear-tube bank. Steam which is liberated in the front and middle drums is conveyed to the rear drum where much of the suspended moisture is thrown out. Saturated steam from the rear drum flows through a group of tubes to the superheater inlet header which in Fig. 5·20 is a rectangular header located directly behind the front drum. The superheater is located in the space between the front and center boiler-tube banks with the discharge header located adjacent to the center drum.

The boiler is baffled by a set of tile mounted on the front and rear rows of boiler tubes of the center and rear tube banks. The gases are thereby forced to follow the path indicated in Fig. 5·20 by the dotted lines. A manhole in each drum gives access to all boiler tubes for cleaning and inspection. The large number of

tubes, their steep slope, and the vertical distance between the
mud drum and the steam drums insure excellent circulation. The

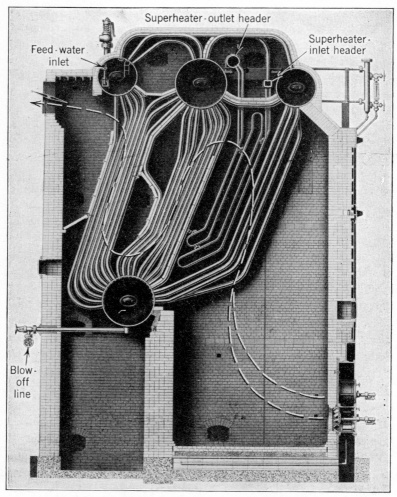

Fɪɢ. 5·20   Four-drum Stirling boiler with superheater

three steam drums provide sufficient steam disengagement area to
produce relatively dry steam.   For industrial plants and power
stations which require steam at pressures up to about 1000 psig
and in capacities up to 900,000 lb per hr, the four-drum Stirling

boiler is used in large numbers, particularly under poor conditions of feedwater and for wide swings in load.

5·19 The two-drum bent-tube steam generator. The two-drum bent-tube steam generator (Fig. 5·21) has been de-

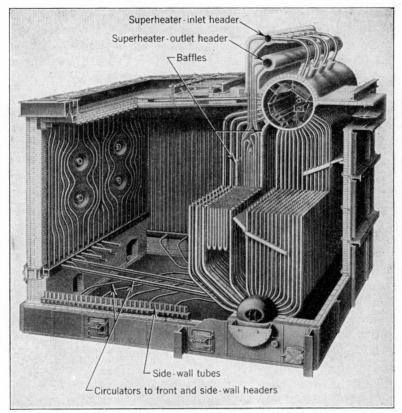

Fig. 5·21 Two-drum bent-tube steam generator

veloped to provide a compact unit of standardized design with a water-cooled furnace built into the unit as as integral part of the design. It was designed originally for firing with pulverized coal, oil, or gas, either singly or in any combination, and by modification of the furnace it can be fired by any of the common types of stokers.

Two drums are used with the steam drum supported directly

above the mud drum. The front and side walls of the furnace are protected by vertical boiler tubes which are connected to bottom and top headers. The bottom headers are supplied with water from the mud drum through circulators which serve as a floor screen through which the ash may fall onto a cool floor. The ash may be removed through clean-out doors at the bottom of the side walls. The upper wall headers discharge steam and water to the steam drum through tubes which form the roof of the furnace. The boiler proper in Fig. 5·21 consists of a front bank of three rows of 3-in. tubes with a baffle attached to the third row of tubes, two additional rows of 3-in. tubes with another baffle attached to the first row of these tubes, and a closely spaced rear bank of 2-in. tubes through which the water flows from the upper to the lower drum. The superheater is located between the third and fourth rows of 3-in. tubes with the inlet and outlet headers placed in a housing above the steam drum. The path of the gases is up the front bank of 3-in. tubes, down through the superheater, up and across the rear tube bank, and out through the damper behind the steam drum.

Most of the steam is discharged into the steam drum through tubes which deliver their steam–water mixture above the water line in the upper drum, thereby making it unnecessary for the steam to rise through the water in the drum. This feature, combined with effective baffles in the steam drum, insures the delivery of relatively dry steam, although only one steam drum is used in this boiler. This type of unit may be built in capacities from 30,000 to 300,000 lb of steam per hr for pressures up to 1000 psig and for steam temperatures up to 900 F.

5·20 Economizers and air heaters. It has been pointed out in Articles 2·21 and 5·8 that the largest loss that occurs when fuel is burned for steam generation is the sensible heat carried away in the flue gas and that the efficiency of a steam-generating unit provided with good fuel-burning equipment is a function of the flue-gas temperature.

Theoretically, the minimum temperature to which the products of combustion may be cooled is the temperature of the heat-transfer surface with which they are last in contact. In the conventional boiler, the theoretical minimum flue-gas temperature would be the temperature of the saturated water in the boiler tubes. This saturation temperature is plotted against boiler pressure in Fig. 5·22. In general, it is not economical to install sufficient boiler surface to cool the gases to within less than 150 F of the saturation temperature of the water in the tubes, because sufficient heat cannot be transmitted to the tubes at such low temperature differences to pay for the cost of the boiler surface. The curve labeled "minimum flue-gas temperature from boiler"

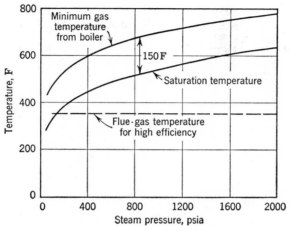

Fɪɢ. 5·22   Minimum flue-gas temperature from conventional boiler

in Fig. 5·22 is 150 F above the saturation temperature. The minimum gas temperature increases with boiler pressure and is from 600 to 800 F in the range of boiler pressures used in efficient plants, that is, 400 to 2000 psi. To allow the gases to escape at such high temperatures would be very wasteful.

As mentioned in Article 5·8, the minimum allowable flue-gas temperature is 275 to 350 F, depending upon the sulphur content of the fuel, and is the temperature below which corrosion of heat-transfer surfaces will take place. In Fig. 5·22, the desirable flue-gas temperature has been assumed to be 350 F. The gases must be cooled from the boiler exit-gas temperature shown in Fig. 5·22 to the flue-gas temperature required for high efficiency (350 F) by means of heat exchangers supplied with fluids at temperatures less than the saturation temperature at the boiler pressure. This can be done in an *air heater* supplied with the air required for combustion at room temperature or in an *econo-mizer* supplied with boiler feedwater at a temperature consider-ably below the saturation temperature, or both. In many in-stallations, it is economical to install a small boiler and a large economizer and air heater and to deliver the gases to the econo-mizer at temperatures as high as 900 F rather than to cool the gases to lower temperatures by a larger boiler.

A typical economizer is shown in Fig. 5·23. Feedwater is

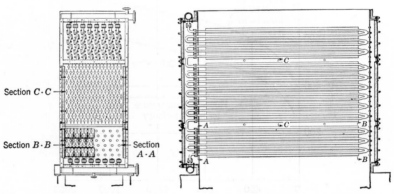

Fɪɢ. 5·23 Front and longitudinal sections through Elesco fin-tube economizer

supplied to the inlet header from which it flows through a number of parallel circuits of 2-in. OD tubes of considerable length to the discharge header. If the inlet header is at the bottom so that the water rises as it flows from tube to tube, the hot gas normally enters at the top and flows downward. Thus the coldest gas will be in contact with the coldest tubes, and it is possible to cool the gas to within 125–150 F of the temperature of the *inlet water* if sufficient surface is installed. In the economizer of Fig. 5·23, the right-hand ends of each pair of tubes are connected by a forged-return bend which is supported by a welded-on bolt to the cast-iron casing. At the left end, two parallel tubes are connected by a forged bifurcated joint into a single flanged outlet which is connected to the next pair of tubes above by a flanged-return bend, as shown in Fig. 5·24. The use of bifurcated tubes reduces by one half the number of flanged joints required to give access to the interior of the tubes for cleaning. In order to increase the

heat absorption per linear foot of tube, fins are welded to the top
and bottom sides of each tube, as shown in Fig. 5·23 and Fig.
5·24. The closely packed 2-in. fin tubes with staggered arrangement and gas flow at right angles to the tubes result in good heat-
transfer rates.

Where scale-free feedwater is available, the flanged-return
bends may be eliminated, and the tubing may be welded into a

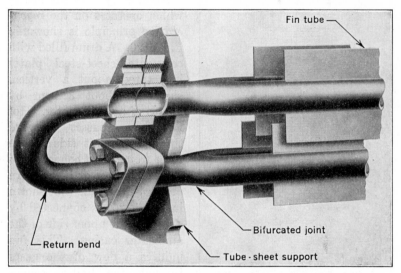

Fig. 5·24 Return-bend construction of bifurcated fin-tube economizer

continuous circuit without flanged connections between headers.

The tubular air heater, as illustrated in Fig. 5·25, is constructed
by expanding vertical tubes into parallel tube sheets which form
the top and bottom surfaces, respectively, of the gas inlet and
outlet boxes. The tube bank is enclosed in an insulated casing
so constructed that the inlet air at room temperature can be
admitted to the heating surfaces at the upper end from a fan or
blower. The air passes downward around the tubes in a direction
opposite to the flow of the hot gases and leaves the air heater at
the lower end of the tube bank. Deflecting baffles are installed
to guide the air and reduce frictional resistance at the turns. A
by-pass damper and baffle permit by-passing the air around the
upper half of the tube surface on light loads when there is danger

of corrosion due to low flue-gas temperatures. Long tubes closely spaced to maintain high air and gas velocities and countercurrent flow of gases and air make it possible in many installations to cool the gases to a temperature 100 to 200 F below the temperature at which the hot air is discharged.

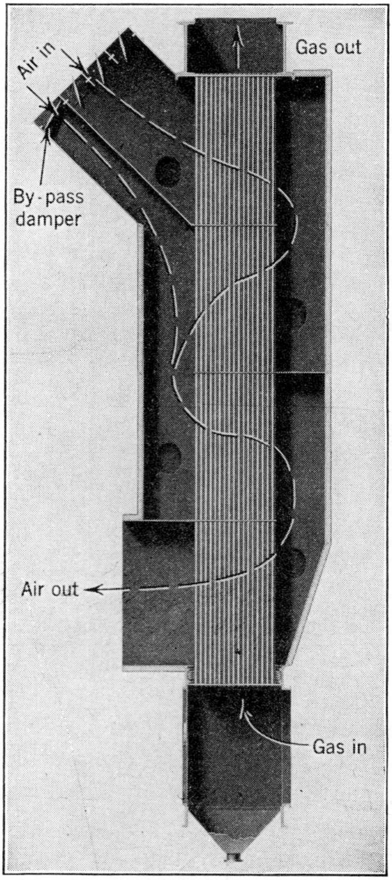

Another type of air heater which operates on the *regenerative* principle is shown in Fig. 5·26. A drum filled with corrugated-sheet-steel plates is rotated about a vertical shaft at about 3 rpm by means of a small motor. Hot flue gas passes upward through the left side of the rotor from a duct connected to the economizer or boiler. An *induced-draft fan* (not shown in Fig. 5·26) is connected by a duct to the upper side of the air-heater casing. This fan induces a flow of the gases through the boiler, economizer, and air-heater surfaces, and discharges them to waste up the chimney. The cold air from a *forced-draft* fan flows downward through the right side of the rotor in Fig. 5·26 where the air is heated, after which it is delivered through suitable duct work to the

Fig. 5·25 Tubular air heater with by-pass damper for light load operation

stoker or burner in the furnace. Any point on the corrugated sheet-metal surface of the rotor is rotated alternately into the hot ascending gas stream and the cold descending air stream, thus transferring heat from the hot gas to the cold air. Radial seals with rubbing surfaces on them are mounted on the rotor and make contact with a flat section of the casing between the hot-gas and cold-air ducts, thus minimizing leakage between the two streams of fluid. The depth of the rotor is normally between

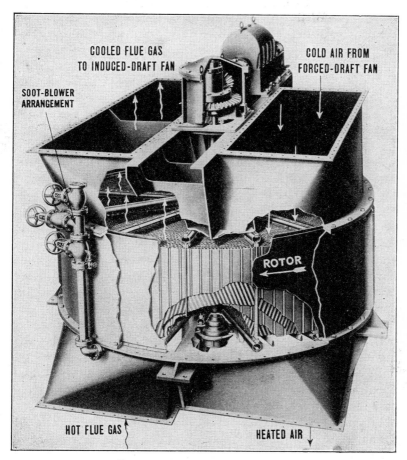

Fig. 5·26   Regenerative air heater

3 and 4 ft. The unit is also made for operation about a horizontal shaft with horizontal flow of gas and air where building space makes such an arrangement desirable.

The maximum air temperature that can be used in stoker-fired installations without increasing grate maintenance is about 300 F, since the grate surface which supports the hot fuel bed must be cooled by the air to a temperature below which the iron grates will not be damaged. Air temperatures of 600 F are often used with pulverized coal. Since the stoker limits the heat-recovery possibilities of the air heater, both economizers and air heaters are usually installed in stoker-fired high-pressure steam-generating units. Where oil, gas, or pulverized coal is burned, an air heater is often installed without an economizer, although in many high-pressure units it may be more economical to reduce the boiler surface and use an economizer. The air heater is necessary in modern pulverized-coal plants since the coal is dried in the pulverizer by hot air to reduce power consumption and increase the capacity of the mill.

5·21 High-efficiency high-capacity steam-generating units. The reliability of modern steam-generating units is such that they may be operated continuously for several months at a time. Since the cost of one large unit is considerably less than the cost of two smaller units of the same total capacity, the trend in recent years has been toward the installation of one steam-generating unit for each turbine. In large power plants, such units have steam-generating capacities of 300,000 to 1,000,000 lb per hr with several installations of 1,300,000-lb-per-hr capacity in operation. The majority of recent installations have been for boiler pressures between 900 and 2000 psi and for superheater outlet temperatures of 900 to 1050 F. One unit has been operating for several years at 2400 psi and 960 F. Coal burned in such units at rated capacity will be 15 to 60 tons per hr, depending upon the size of the unit. Because of the large annual operating cost for fuel, a considerable amount of money can be spent to obtain maximum efficiency, and such units are normally designed for an efficiency of 85 to 90 per cent.

In Fig. 5·27, the enthalpy of saturated water, the enthalpy of dry saturated steam, and the enthalpy of superheated steam at 1000 F have been plotted against steam pressure. The vertical distance between the curves of the enthalpy of saturated water and the enthalpy of dry saturated steam represents the latent heat of evaporation of water. It is the primary function of the boiler to supply this latent heat, and it will be noticed that this quantity decreases with increase in pressure. A curve has been drawn to show the enthalpy of feedwater at 375 F, it being assumed that the feedwater has been heated from a condensate temperature of 79 to 375 F in regenerative heaters supplied with

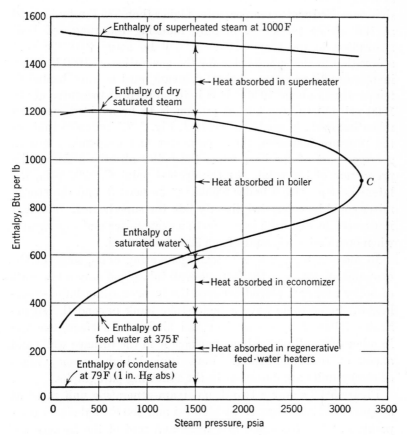

FIG. 5·27 Heat absorption in economizer, boiler, and superheater as affected by steam pressure

steam from the main turbine, as discussed in Chapter 6. The vertical distance from the line representing the enthalpy of the feedwater to the enthalpy of saturated water represents the heat that can be absorbed in the economizer. Some economizers are designed with upward flow of water and are capable of generating steam, thereby increasing their heat-absorbing capacity, but most economizers are designed to deliver the water to the boiler at a temperature below the saturation temperature. According to Fig. 5·27, the allowable heat absorption in the economizer is greater at high pressures than at the lower pressures, although it is possible that feed-water temperatures higher than 375 F may be used at the higher pressures, thereby reducing the range of heat absorption in the economizer. It will be noted that the heat absorption in the superheater for the generation of 1000 F steam increases with pressure. Actually, steam must be superheated to temperatures above 1000 F if it is to be used at pressures above 1500 psi and turbine bucket erosion is to be avoided, unless a reheating cycle is used. In general, Fig. 5·27 indicates that, as the pressure increases, the superheater and economizer absorb a larger part of the heat while the boiler absorbs a decreasing proportion of the total. At the critical point C, 3206 psia, the latent heat is zero, a boiler would not be needed, and the economizer could be connected directly into the superheater. The unit illustrated in Fig. 5·35 is in effect an economizer and superheater when operated at pressures from 3206 to 3500 psi.

In modern high-pressure steam-generating units, most of the evaporation occurs in the furnace-wall tubes, and only a few rows of boiler tubes are placed between the furnace and a large superheater. Some units have a boiler-tube bank beyond the superheater followed by economizer and air-heater surface, whereas in other units all of the boiler surface is in the furnace walls and ahead of the superheater. Four typical high-capacity high-efficiency units are described in the following paragraphs.

Figure 5·28 shows a two-drum steam-generating unit rated at 300,000 lb of steam per hr at 1325 psi and 960 F final steam temperature. The front and side walls and roof of the furnace are covered with bare boiler tubes which feed their steam–water mixture into the upper boiler drum. Baffles supported on one row of boiler tubes separate the furnace from the space in which the convection superheater is mounted and protect the superheater from excessive temperatures. The path of the gases from the pulverized-coal burners through the furnace, superheater, convection boiler-tube bank, economizer, and air heater is indicated by arrows. Steam from the upper boiler drum is carried by a row

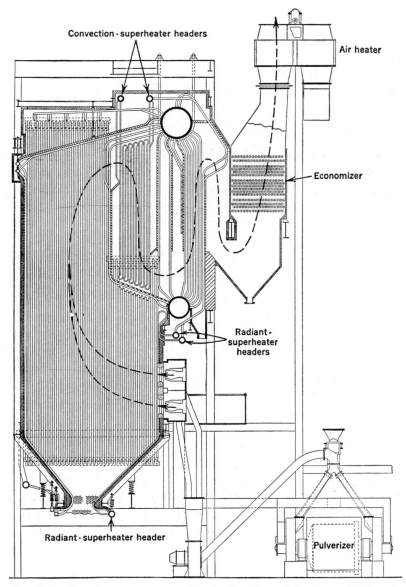

Convection-superheater headers

Air heater

Economizer

Radiant-superheater headers

Radiant-superheater header

Pulverizer

FIG. 5·28 Two-drum steam-generating unit with combination radiant and convection superheaters and hopper-bottom pulverized-coal furnace. 300,000 lb of steam per hr at 1325 psig and 960 F

of tubes in the rear boiler-tube bank to a superheater inlet header located beneath the lower boiler drum. The steam flows downward through a radiant superheater in the burner wall and the sloping hopper floor to a lower header below the hopper throat from which it flows back through more radiant-heat-absorbing surface in the burner wall to the outlet header under the lower boiler drum. The steam then flows upward through tubes in the rear boiler-tube bank to the convection-superheater inlet header which is located above and behind the boiler steam drum. The steam then flows through the convection superheater where heat is absorbed from the hot gases leaving the furnace.

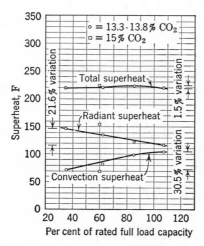

FIG. 5·29 Characteristic performance of combination radiant and convection superheater

It is characteristic of a convection superheater that the outlet steam temperature increases with load, whereas the outlet temperature of a radiant superheater decreases with load, as shown in Fig. 5·29. By combining the two types of superheaters in series, it is possible to obtain uniform final steam temperature at all loads above 30 per cent of rated capacity.

The hopper bottom furnace is designed with sufficient heat-absorbing surface in the walls to keep the ash below the fusing temperature and to permit removal through the hopper throat of such dry ash as settles out in the furnace.

Figure 5·30 shows a steam-generating unit which is based on a three-drum boiler. It has a continuous capacity of 1,000,000 lb of steam per hr at 1625 psi and 955 F. Pulverized coal is delivered to burners located in the four corners of the furnace. The burners discharge the coal–air mixture into the furnace tangentially to an imaginary circle in the center of the furnace, thus producing a violent whirling motion in the furnace. The

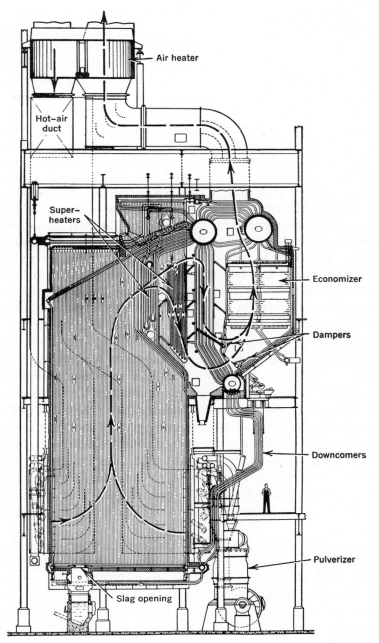

Air heater

Hot–air duct

Super– heaters

Economizer

Dampers

Downcomers

Pulverizer

Slag opening

Fɪɢ. 5·30   1,000,000-lb-per-hr steam-generating unit with slag-tap furnace

completely water-cooled furnace is operated at a temperature so high that the ash is melted and runs out of the slag opening in the water-cooled floor in a continuous stream. The furnace walls are constructed of bare vertical boiler tubes in which most of the steam is generated. Water from the lowest or mud drum flows downward through a battery of circulating tubes or downcomers to the bottom headers which supply water to the furnace-wall tubes. The steam–water mixture rises in the furnace-wall tubes and is discharged into the front or left upper drum. Steam flows from this drum to the upper rear or right drum where any residual moisture is removed in separators. The superheater is divided into a primary section of closely spaced tubes which receives steam from the boiler drum and a secondary section of widely spaced tubes adjacent to the furnace where the final steam temperature is reached in tubes that are surrounded by the hottest gases. The tubes in the hot end of the superheater are widely spaced to reduce any tendency of plastic-ash particles to build up on the superheater tubes and choke the gas passages. An economizer is located in the space beneath the dry-steam drum, and a regenerative air heater is placed above the furnace.

As the hot gases leave the furnace, they are divided into two paths in order to provide control of the steam temperature leaving the superheater. At light loads, the gases flow downward around the primary superheater and up through the economizer. At heavy loads, excessive steam temperature at the outlet of the superheater is prevented by by-passing part of the gases across the top of the primary superheater and down the boiler-tube bank which connects the upper front and mud drums. The dampers which control the temperature of the superheated steam are located at the exit point of the convection-tube bank where the gas temperature is low enough to avoid damage to uncooled dampers.

Figure 5·31 shows front and side sections of a steam-generating unit which is designed for a maximum continuous output of 1,300,000 lb of steam per hr at 1500 psi and 1050 F at the turbine throttle valve when supplied with feedwater at 410 F. A single-drum boiler is used with the boiler drum located 130 ft 9 in. above the floor, a distance approximately equal to the height of a 12-story office building.   In order to burn high-grade eastern coal without melting the ash, two hopper-bottom completely water-cooled furnaces are used as shown in the front section. The added furnace cooling, which results from a common water-cooled division wall between the two furnaces, greatly increases the ratio of cooled furnace-wall surface to furnace volume, as compared to a single furnace of equal volume, and prevents the furnace temperatures from becoming high enough to melt the ash. Consequently, much of the ash settles out of the furnace and is removed as a dry dust through the openings in the hopper-shaped bottom of the furnaces.

Water from the boiler drum flows downward through a battery of tubes located outside of the front wall of the furnace to the bottom headers which supply the furnace-wall tubes.   Circulation is up the vertical bare furnace-wall tubes to the steam drum. Rear-wall furnace tubes are bent inward below the secondary superheater to form a partial roof for the furnace. Part of these tubes make a vertical screen in front of the secondary super-heater, and the remainder of the tubes are bent to form the floor, rear wall, and roof of the space enclosing the secondary super-heater.   Steam from the boiler drum flows through the primary superheater and then through the secondary superheater to the turbine.   An economizer is located below the primary superheater and is built in two sections separated by a vertical division wall. Gas-control dampers are located below the economizer to by-pass some of the hot gas around the primary superheater at heavy loads through the path indicated by the dotted lines on Fig. 5·31*B*, thereby obtaining close regulation of the steam temperature leaving the secondary superheater.

A regenerative type of air heater is installed below the economizer.   Air from a forced-draft fan is delivered vertically through the air heater to a horizontal duct which carries the preheated air around the furnace to the pulverized-coal burners, eight of which are installed in the front wall of each furnace.

Figure 5·32 illustrates a steam-generating unit fired by cyclone burners.   This unit is designed for a continuous maximum capacity of 830,000 lb of steam per hr at 1850 psi and 1010 F with reheat to 1010 F when supplied with feedwater at 465 F.   It is

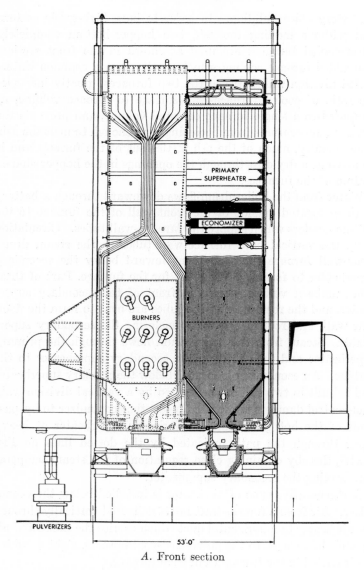

PRIMARY
SUPERHEATER

ECONOMIZER

BURNERS

PULVERIZERS

53'-0"

A. Front section

FIG. 5·31 Large steam-generating unit with double furnace

Continuous steaming capacity   1,300,000 lb per hr
Pressure 1500 psi   Final steam temperature 1050 F

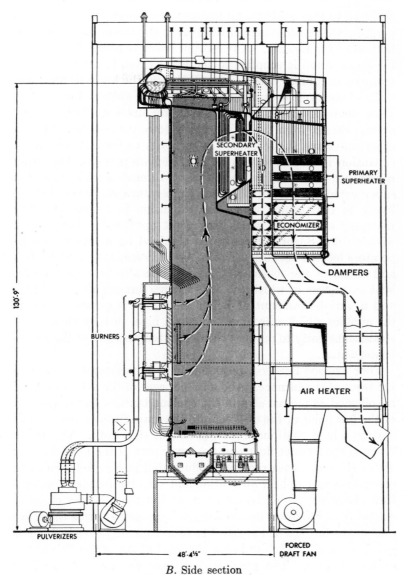

B. Side section

FIG. 5·31 (*Continued*)

designed to burn midwest bituminous coal of low ash-fusing temperature with maximum ash removal in the liquid form from the
bottom of the furnace. A two-drum boiler is used. Water from
the steam drum is supplied to the lower drum through unheated
downcomer tubes. Water is supplied from the lower drum to the
walls of the cyclone burners and to the four walls of the furnace.
These tubes discharge a mixture of steam and water to the steam
drum. Steam from the boiler drum flows through the primary
superheater and the secondary superheater to the turbine. After
expansion in the turbine to an intermediate pressure, the steam
is returned to the unit where it passes through a reheater and is
superheated to the initial steam temperature of 1010 F for delivery to the turbine where the expansion is completed. The
reheating cycle upon which this plant operates is discussed in
Article 6·9. Superheat control is obtained by means of attem-
perators located between the primary and secondary superheaters
and ahead of the reheater. The attemperator is a double-pipe
heat exchanger in which the steam flows through the inner pipe
and a variable amount of boiler feedwater is pumped through
the annulus which surrounds the steam pipe, thereby cooling the
steam sufficiently to produce the design temperature at the superheater outlet.

Four cyclone burners are mounted in a horizontal row across
the front of the furnace. About 85 per cent of the ash in the coal
is collected as molten slag in the cyclone burners and drains out
of the low point of the cyclone into the main furnace from which
it drains in a continuous stream into a slag tank. The boiler
tubes in the furnace floor and the lower part of the main furnace
are of stud-wall construction as illustrated in Fig. 4·4D so as to
control the rate of heat absorption and keep the furnace temperature above the fusing temperature of the ash. Banks of tubes
extend from the lower header diagonally upward across the lower
part of the furnace and are bent to form a gas-tight baffle, the low
point of which is slightly below the level of the center line of the
cyclone burner. The gases which leave the cyclone are thus
forced to follow a U-shaped path downward, across the furnace
floor, and upward into the vertical portion of the furnace as shown
by the arrows in Fig. 5·32. As the gases flow upward in the
vertical bare-tube section of the furnace, they are cooled to a

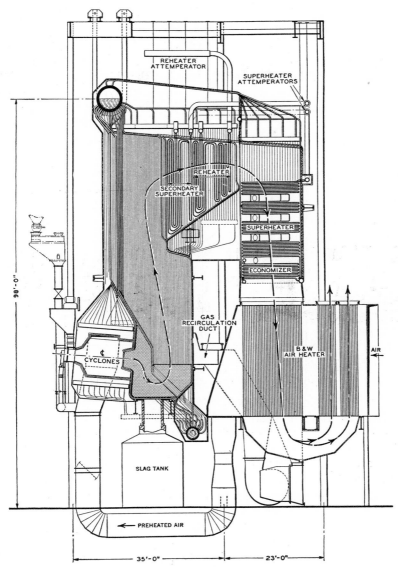

FIG. 5·32 Steam-generating unit with cyclone furnace

Maximum continuous capacity 830,000 lb per hr
Operating pressure 1850 psi
Temperature at superheater outlet 1010 F
Reheat steam temperature 1010 F

temperature that causes any residual particles of ash to solidify before striking the superheater tubes. The gases then flow through the secondary superheater, reheater, primary super-heater, economizer, and a tubular air heater to the dust collector (not shown), the induced-draft fan, and the chimney.

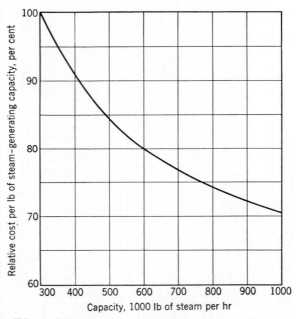

FIG. 5·33   Effect of capacity of steam-generating units upon the cost per unit of capacity

Modern high-capacity steam-generating units such as those described in this article have been developed to the point that with intelligent operation they can be depended upon to carry heavy loads continuously for months at a time. Their reliability is approximately equal to that of modern steam turbines. Consequently, most new central-station power plants are built on the unit system: that is, with each turbine generator supplied with steam from its own steam-generating unit. Thus, turbine-generator units in capacities up to 200,000 kw are being supplied with steam from a single steam-generating unit. One of the major reasons for this arrangement is the decreased cost per unit of capacity which results from increased size. Figure 5·33 shows how the cost per pound of steam-generating capacity decreases with increased size for a line of modern steam-generating units which are alike except for size, and which operate at the same steam pressure and temperature, feed-water temperature, and

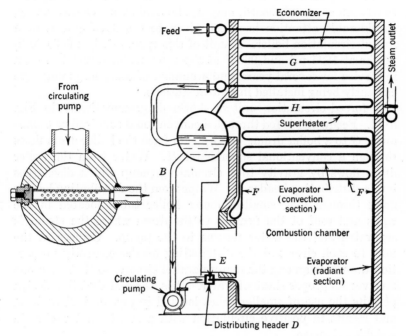

Fig. 5·34 Diagrammatic arrangement of forced-circulation steam generator

efficiency. The cost per unit of capacity of turbine-generator units likewise decreases with increased size. Moreover, doubling the size of a unit requires only a moderate increase in building space, building and foundation cost, piping cost, erection expenses, and operating labor. The installation of large units has made it possible to build new central stations in 1950 at an investment not much greater per kilowatt of capacity than was required before World War II and is one of the major reasons why electric energy is still being sold at approximately prewar rates in spite of the greatly increased cost of fuel and labor.

5·22   **Forced-circulation and once-through steam-generating units.** Natural-circulation boilers depend for circulation on the upward flow of a steam–water mixture in inclined or vertical heated tubes. At high pressures the difference between the specific weight of steam and water decreases. Also, natural circulation requires high head room at high pressure which, in some applications such as on shipboard, may not be available. Consequently, considerable attention has been given to the development of a forced-circulation boiler. A unit of this type, rated at 650,000 lb per hr at 1825 psi and 960 F at the superheater outlet has been in service for several years, and a number of other large units are currently being installed in central stations.

A forced-circulation unit is shown diagrammatically in Fig. 5·34. Feedwater is fed through a conventional counterflow economizer G to a boiler drum. Also, steam from the boiler drum flows through a conventional superheater H. Water from the boiler drum flows by gravity to a circulating pump which discharges into a distributing header D. Water from the distributing header flows through long small-diameter boiler tubes located in the walls and roof of the furnace to the drum where the steam is separated and the water returns to the pump. Orifices at the inlet to each circuit at the distributing header correctly proportion the water among the many parallel circuits so that each one receives its proper share of water. It is asserted that this design permits the use of smaller tubes located in any desired position and results in positive circulation with a substantial saving in weight and space.

Figure 5·35 shows the once-through experimental steam-generating unit installed in the Purdue University laboratory. This unit is designed for operation at any desired pressure from 1500 to 3500 psi and at a maximum superheater outlet temperature of 830 F. It differs from the forced-circulation units in that it has no drum and consists entirely of seamless steel tubing through which the water flows once in being converted into superheated steam. It is essentially a counterflow economizer set over an oil-fired radiantly heated water- and steam-cooled furnace. Feedwater is supplied to the economizer inlet at the top of the unit and flows through two parallel circuits of seamless steel tubing downward counter to the upward flow of the hot gases from the furnace. The hot water from the economizer section then enters the bottom of the furnace-wall section and flows upward through two parallel circuits of seamless tubing which constitute the furnace walls. Steam may be delivered from the radiant furnace-

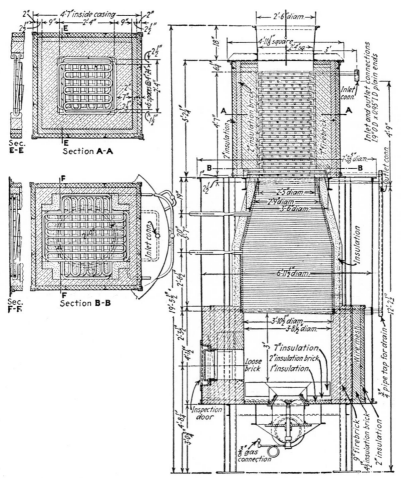

Fig. 5·35   Purdue University once-through steam-generating unit

wall coils as wet steam or as superheated steam at any temperature up to 830 F, depending upon the amount of oil burned per pound of steam generated. The heating surface is composed of 1-in. OD seamless steel tubes having a wall thickness of ¼ in.

Figure 5·36 shows the temperature of the steam and water as

it flows through the furnace-wall circuit at discharge pressures of approximately 2500 and 3500 psi. As shown by the horizontal line of curve A, at 2500 psi a definite evaporating zone exists in the circuit in which the water is being converted into saturated steam at the saturation temperature. After the water has been

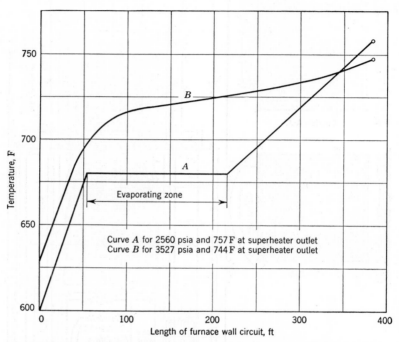

Fig. 5·36 Water and steam temperatures in the furnace-wall circuits of the Purdue high-pressure steam-generating unit

evaporated, the steam temperature increases in the superheater zone. As indicated in curve B, a constant temperature or evaporating zone does not exist at a discharge pressure of 3500 psi since this pressure is above the critical pressure (3206.2 psia) and the latent heat is zero. Under these conditions, the unit is essentially an economizer connected to a superheater; there is no "boiler" since there is no evaporation or boiling at constant temperature.

The elimination of the boiler drum, which results in a substantial saving in weight, makes it necessary to control both pressure and temperature since there is no definite amount of superheater surface in the unit. Also, any impurities in the feedwater must be carried through the unit and must leave in the steam if they are not deposited on the heat-transfer surfaces, and they may cause trouble by depositing on turbine blades.

PROBLEMS

1. Determine from the steam tables the saturation pressure at each of the following temperatures: (a) 70 F, (b) 250 F, (c) 500 F.

2. Determine from the steam tables the saturation temperature at each of the following pressures: (a) 2 in. Hg abs, (b) 2 psia, (c) 500 psia, (d) 10.3 psig when the barometric pressure is 29.9 in. of Hg, (e) a vacuum of 11 in. of Hg when the barometric pressure is 29.4 in. of Hg.

3. Determine from the steam tables the specific volume of saturated water and dry saturated steam at each of the following temperatures: (a) 80 F, (b) 200 F, (c) 500 F.

4. Determine from the steam tables the specific volume of saturated water and dry saturated steam at each of the following pressures: (a) 4.1 in. of Hg abs, (b) 4 psia, (c) 20 psia, (d) 1000 psia.

5. Compute the specific volume of steam at 200 psia and 95 per cent quality.

6. Compute the specific volume of steam at 400 F and 96 per cent quality.

7. According to Equation 5·1, for wet steam, $v_x = xv_g + (1-x)v_f$. Prove that (a) $v_x = v_f + x(v_{fg})$, and (b) $v_x = v_g - (1-x)v_{xg}$.

8. Determine from the steam tables the specific volume of superheated steam at (a) 20 psia and 600 F, (b) 400 psia and 800 F, and (c) 2000 psia and 1000 F.

9. Determine from the steam tables the enthalpy of saturated water, the enthalpy of dry saturated steam, and the latent heat of evaporation for steam at (a) 100 psia, (b) 500 psia, (c) 100 F, and (d) 400 F.

10. Compute the enthalpy of 1 lb of steam at 200 psia and 95 per cent quality, and check with the Mollier chart.

11. Compute the enthalpy of steam at 300 F and a quality of 90 per cent.

12. Steam at 200 psia is throttled in a calorimeter to a pressure of 20 psia at which point the temperature of the steam is found to be 260 F. Compute the quality and enthalpy of the steam at 200 psia, and check with the Mollier chart.

13. Steam at 300 psia is throttled in a throttling calorimeter to a pressure of 14.7 psia at which point the temperature of the steam is 240 F. Compute the enthalpy, quality, and specific volume of the steam at 300 psia.

14. Steam at 100 psia is throttled in a calorimeter to a pressure of 14.7 psia at which pressure the temperature is 300 F. Determine the initial enthalpy and specific volume of the steam.

15. What is the enthalpy of water at 100 F and 2000 psia?

16. How much heat must be supplied to convert 1 lb of water at 1000 psia and 200 F into steam at 500 psia and 800 F?

17. How much heat must be supplied to convert 1 lb of steam at 620 psia and 97 per cent quality into steam at 600 psia and 900 F?

18. Feedwater at 2000 psia and 300 F is converted into steam at 2000 psia and 1000 F. How much heat is supplied per lb of steam generated?

19. Steam at 900 psia and 900 F flows through a pipe having an internal diameter of 12 in. at the rate of 400,000 lb per hr. Calculate the average steam velocity in the pipe.

20. Compute (a) the heat absorbed in Btu per hr, (b) the output in kB, and (c) the efficiency of a boiler operating under the following conditions: feed-water temperature, 190 F; boiler pressure, 150 psig; barometric pressure, 14.7 psia; a throttling calorimeter connected to the boiler outlet line shows 240 F at a calorimeter pressure of 5 psig; 20,000 lb of steam generated per hr; 2400 lb of coal burned per hr; heating value of the coal, 13,000 Btu per lb.

21. The following data were obtained during a test of a steam-generating unit: feed-water temperature, 260 F; feed-water pressure, 1500 psig; boiler pressure, 1250 psig; calorimeter pressure at boiler outlet, 5 psig; calorimeter steam temperature, 260 F; superheater outlet pressure, 1185 psig; superheater outlet temperature, 900 F; 400,000 lb of steam generated per hr; 42,800 lb of coal burned per hr; heating value of coal, 13,500 Btu per lb. Compute (a) heat absorbed in the boiler in Btu per hr, (b) heat absorbed in the superheater in Btu per hr, (c) heat absorbed in the steam-generating unit in Btu per hr, (d) output of the unit in kB, and (e) efficiency of the steam-generating unit.

22. The following data were obtained from tests of coal-fired steam-generating units:

Item		Unit 1	Unit 2	Unit 3	Unit 4
Steam generated, lb per hr		80,000	100,000	120,000	324,500
Coal fired, lb per hr		9,850	11,300	12,800	30,690
Ash-pit refuse, lb per hr		970	1,150	700	2,510
Carbon in ash-pit refuse, %		20	15	10	20
Ultimate analysis of coal as fired, %:	C	67	68	76	80.6
	H	5	4	5	4.2
	O	6	7	5	2.9
	N	2	2	2	1.3
	S	2	2	1	1.2
	Ash	8	9	5	6.6
	Moisture	10	8	6	3.2
Heating value of fuel, Btu per lb		12,500	11,900	12,700	14,120
Orsat analysis of dry flue gas, % by volume:	CO_2	13.4	14.0	14.5	14.7
	O_2	6.2	5.8	5.2	3.8
	CO	0.2	0.1	0.1	0.02
Air temperature, F		80	70	90	54
Flue-gas temperature, F		440	380	360	360
Feed-water temperature, F		190	350	280	250
Feed-water pressure, psig		500	1,200	750	600
Superheater-outlet pressure, psig		385	890	585	411
Superheater-outlet temperature, F		750	900	800	720

For each of the sets of test data, compute (a) the output of the unit in kB, (b) the efficiency, and (c) a complete energy balance.

23. The following data were obtained from a test on the Purdue high-pressure boiler: Volumetric analysis of dry flue gas in per cent: $CO_2 = 12.0$; $O_2 = 5.8$; $CO = 0.1$; $N_2 = 82.1$; barometric pressure = 29.3 in. of Hg; feed-water pressure = 2790 psia; feed-water temperature = 245 F; steam-outlet pressure = 2560 psia; final steam temperature = 751 F; water evaporated per hr = 2225 lb; 97 F air temperature; 50 per cent relative humidity; 165 F oil temperature; 850 F flue-gas temperature; 171 lb of oil burned per hr; ultimate analysis of oil in per cent: C = 88.54; H = 10.75; N = 0.14; S = 0.57; heating value of the oil = 18,650 Btu per lb. Compute (a) the output in kB, (b) the efficiency of the unit, and (c) a complete energy balance.

24. The following data were obtained from a steam-generating unit fired by natural gas: Volumetric analysis of fuel in per cent: $H_2 = 2$; $CO = 1$; $CH_4 = 93$; $O_2 = 2$; $N_2 = 2$; heating value = 900 Btu per cu ft at 14.7 psia and 58 F; volumetric analysis of dry products of combustion in per cent: $CO_2 = 10.5$; $O_2 = 2.0$; $N_2 = 87.3$; $CO = 0.2$; temperature of air = 90 F; temperature of fuel gas = 70 F; temperature of flue gases = 350 F; feed-water temperature = 300 F; feed-water pressure = 1500 psia; superheater-outlet temperature = 900 F; superheater-outlet pressure = 1200 psia; steam generated = 200,000 lb per hr; fuel burned = 325,000 cu ft per hr measured at 70 F and 16.3 psia. Compute (a) the output of the unit in kB, (b) the efficiency, and (c) a complete energy balance.

6 · Steam Power-Plant Cycles

6·1   Introduction.   In the spark-ignition internal-combustion engine, a charge of fuel and air is drawn into the cylinder of the engine, compressed, ignited, and heated to a high temperature and pressure by the release of energy through the combustion process. The high-pressure gases then expand and do work, after which they are exhausted to the atmosphere and cooled in the atmosphere to the initial temperature. The process of compression, heating, and expansion all occur within the cylinder of the engine.

In the steam power plant, water is compressed by a pump to a pressure that will permit it to flow into a boiler. In the boiler, the heat released by burning fuel converts the water into high-pressure steam which then flows through a steam pipe to the engine or turbine where it is expanded to the exhaust pressure. Work is done as the pressure of the steam decreases and its volume increases during expansion. The exhaust steam from the engine or turbine may be discharged to the atmosphere, into a heating system, or into a condenser where it is converted into water again. Thus, to do work in a steam power plant, at least three different pieces of equipment are needed. They are the boiler feed pump, the boiler, and the engine or turbine, often called the prime mover. These pieces of equipment must be connected by suitable piping so that the working fluid may flow from the pump through the boiler to the prime mover to the atmosphere or condenser as the water or steam is successively compressed, heated, expanded, and cooled.

A cycle is a series of operations that is repeated again and again with the working fluid returning to its initial state at the end of each cycle. The steam power-plant vapor cycle is composed of the sequence of operations (compression, evaporation, expansion, and condensation) through which the working fluid passes as it flows through the pump, steam-generating unit, prime mover, and condenser. It is customary to analyze the vapor cycle by determining the energy changes that occur as 1 lb of the fluid undergoes each of the operations that constitute the cycle. The efficiency of the cycle is the ratio of the net work done to the heat supplied per pound of fluid completing the cycle.

In this chapter, the theoretical efficiency of the ideal Rankine cycle is considered first since this cycle may be used as a yardstick for determining the best performance obtainable in a simple steam power-plant cycle operating under specified steam pressures. A discussion of the more complex theoretical cycles will be found in standard textbooks on thermodynamics. The remainder of the chapter is concerned with the arrangement of equipment and the actual performance of the common power-plant cycles and a discussion of the methods of expressing the overall performance of steam power plants from entering fuel to net power delivered.

6·2 The Rankine cycle. The simplest ideal or theoretical power-plant vapor cycle is the Rankine cycle which is illustrated in Fig. 6·1. The system contains the following apparatus: (1) a steam-generating unit (Fig. 6·1 shows a boiler only, but a superheater and economizer may be added), (2) a prime mover (a steam engine or steam turbine), (3) a condenser, and (4) a boiler feed pump.

The following assumptions are made for the Rankine cycle:

1. The working fluid, usually water, is pumped into the boiler, evaporated into steam in the boiler, expanded in the prime mover, condensed in the condenser, and returned to the boiler feed pump to be circulated through the equipment again and again in a closed circuit under *steady-flow conditions;* that is, at any given point in the system, the conditions of pressure, temperature, flow rate, etc., are *constant.*

2. All of the heat is added in the steam-generating unit, all of the heat that is rejected is transferred in the condenser, and there is no heat transfer between the working fluid and the surroundings at any place except in the steam-generating unit and the condenser.

3. There is no pressure drop in the piping system; there is a constant high pressure, p_1, from the discharge side of the boiler feed pump to the prime mover, and a constant low pressure, p_2, from the exhaust flange of the prime mover to the inlet of the boiler feed pump.

4. Expansion in the prime mover occurs without friction or heat transfer; in other words, it is a frictionless adiabatic or

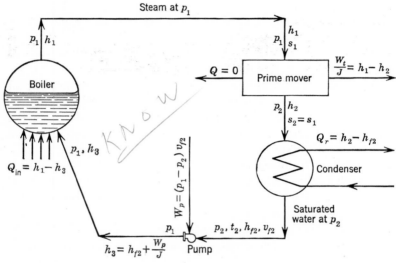

Steam at p_1

$p_1 \mid h_1$

Boiler

$p_1 \mid h_1$ s_1

$Q = 0$ Prime mover

$\dfrac{W_t}{J} = h_1 - h_2$

$p_2 \mid h_2$ $s_2 = s_1$

$Q_r = h_2 - h_{f2}$

Condenser

p_1, h_3

$Q_{in} = h_1 - h_3$

$W_p = (p_1 - p_2) v_{f2}$

Saturated water at p_2

p_1 p_2, t_2, h_{f2}, v_{f2}

$h_3 = h_{f2} + \dfrac{W_p}{J}$ Pump

FIG. 6·1   Rankine cycle

isentropic expansion in which the entropy of the fluid leaving the prime mover equals the entropy of the fluid entering the prime mover.

5. The working fluid leaves the condenser as liquid at the highest possible temperature, which is the *saturation temperature* corresponding to the exhaust pressure p_2.

If, as shown in Fig. 6·1, the steam-generating unit is a boiler only, the steam that it delivers will be wet, and its quality and enthalpy can be determined by a throttling calorimeter, as discussed in Article 5·6. If a superheater is included in the steam-generating unit, the steam that is delivered will be superheated, and its enthalpy can be determined from its pressure and temperature by use of the superheated steam tables or the Mollier chart.

In the prime mover, which is usually a turbine, the steam is assumed to expand at *constant entropy*, and, in accordance with the discussion in Article 1·23,

$$\frac{W_t}{J} = h_1 - h_2 \tag{6·1}$$

where W_t = work done in the turbine, ft-lb per lb of steam
h_1 = enthalpy of steam entering the turbine, Btu per lb
h_2 = enthalpy of steam leaving the turbine after *isentropic* expansion to the exhaust pressure, Btu per lb

The enthalpy of the exhaust steam, h_2, after isentropic expansion, can be found most easily by using the Mollier diagram as discussed in Article 5·7 and illustrated in Example 8 in that article.

The condensate leaving the condenser and entering the boiler feed pump is always assumed to be *saturated water at the condenser pressure*, and its enthalpy, h_{f2}, can be found from the steam tables at the given condenser pressure. The heat rejected in the condenser per pound of steam, Q_r, is then given by the equation

$$Q_r = h_2 - h_{f2} \tag{6·2}$$

It is necessary to supply energy to the boiler feed pump to compress the water to the boiler pressure p_1. In accordance with the discussion in Article 1·24, for horizontal flow through the pump without change in water velocity or specific volume, the work done by the pump on 1 lb of water, W_p, in foot-pound units, is

$$W_p = (p_1 - p_2)v_{f2} \tag{6·3}$$

where p_1 and p_2 are expressed in pounds per square foot absolute and v_{f2} is the specific volume of the saturated water supplied to the pump.

Since it is assumed that there is no heat transfer from the water to its surroundings in the pump, the energy supplied by the pump is stored in the high-pressure water, and the enthalpy of the boiler feedwater is

$$h_3 = h_{f2} + \frac{W_p}{J} \qquad (6\cdot4)$$

Also, since the energy supplied by the pump must come from the output of the prime mover, then the net output of the cycle per pound of fluid, W_{net}/J, is given by the equation

$$\frac{W_{net}}{J} = \frac{W_t - W_p}{J} = (h_1 - h_2) - \frac{W_p}{J} \qquad (6\cdot5)$$

The heat supplied in the steam-generating unit to produce 1 lb of steam, as discussed in Article 1·22, is

$$Q_{in} = h_1 - h_3 = h_1 - \left(h_{f2} + \frac{W_p}{J} \right) \qquad (6\cdot6)$$

Since the efficiency

$$= \frac{\text{heat equivalent of the net work done per lb of steam}}{\text{heat supplied to generate 1 lb of steam}}$$

then

$$\eta_t = \frac{(h_1 - h_2) - \dfrac{W_p}{J}}{h_1 - \left(h_{f2} + \dfrac{W_p}{J} \right)} \qquad (6\cdot7)$$

where η_t is the theoretical efficiency of the Rankine cycle.

Where the boiler pressure is under 400 psia and slide-rule calculations are used, the energy supplied to the pump may be neglected and Equation 6·7 reduces to the form

$$\eta_t = \frac{h_1 - h_2}{h_1 - h_{f2}} \qquad (6\cdot8)$$

Example 1. Compute the efficiency of the Rankine cycle if steam at 200 psia and 600 F is expanded to an exhaust pressure of 2 psia.

Solution: From the steam tables at 200 psia and 600 F, $h_1 = 1322$ and $s_1 = 1.6767$.

At the exhaust pressure of 2 psia and $s_2 = s_1 = 1.6767$, h_2 may be found from the Mollier chart to be 974 Btu per lb. Also, at 2 psia, $v_{f2} = 0.01623$ cu ft per lb, $h_{f2} = 94$, and $t_2 = 126$ F.

Then, the gross output of the prime mover,

$$\frac{W_t}{J} = h_1 - h_2 = 1322 - 974 = 348 \text{ Btu per lb}$$

The energy rejected to waste in the condenser is equal to

$$Q_{\text{out}} = h_2 - h_{f2} = 974 - 94 = 880 \text{ Btu per lb}$$

The energy input to the water from the boiler feed pump, W_p, is equal to

$$W_p = (p_1 - p_2)v_{f2} = 144(200 - 2)(0.01623) = 462 \text{ ft-lb per lb of fluid}$$

or $\dfrac{W_p}{J} = \dfrac{462}{778} = 0.594 \text{ Btu per lb}$

Then the enthalpy of the feedwater entering the boiler,

$$h_3 = h_{f2} + \frac{W_p}{J} = 94 + 0.6 = 94.6 \text{ Btu per lb}$$

The heat supplied in the boiler,

$$Q_{\text{in}} = h_1 - h_3 = h_1 - \left(h_{f2} + \frac{W_p}{J}\right) = 1322 - (94.0 + 0.6) = 1227.4 \text{ Btu per lb}$$

$$\eta_t = \frac{\text{output}}{\text{input}} = \frac{(h_1 - h_2) - \dfrac{W_p}{J}}{h_1 - \left(h_{f2} + \dfrac{W_p}{J}\right)} = \frac{(1322 - 974) - 0.6}{1322 - (94.0 + 0.6)} = 0.283 = 28.3\%$$

Neglecting the boiler feed pump,

$$\eta_t = \frac{\text{output}}{\text{input}} = \frac{h_1 - h_2}{h_1 - h_{f2}} = \frac{1322 - 974}{1322 - 94.0} = 0.283 = 28.3\%$$

It should be noted that for the boiler pressure of 200 psia used in the above example, the inaccuracies introduced by the use of the slide rule and the Mollier chart are such that the effect of the boiler feed pump may be neglected. However, at a high pressure such as 1000 psia, neglect of the pump would introduce an appreciable error.

The influence of initial pressure, superheat, and exhaust pressure upon the efficiency of the Rankine cycle is shown in Fig. 6·2. The improvement in efficiency with reduction in the exhaust pressure should be noted particularly. Also, the gain in efficiency for each 100 psi increase in initial pressure becomes less as the pressure increases. Since this cycle assumes frictionless adiabatic or ideal expansion of the steam in the prime mover, the Rankine-cycle efficiency is the best that is theoretically possible with the equipment arranged as in Fig. 6·1. Better theoretical efficiencies are possible by using more equipment in more complex cycles, but the discussion of such cycles is beyond the scope of this book.

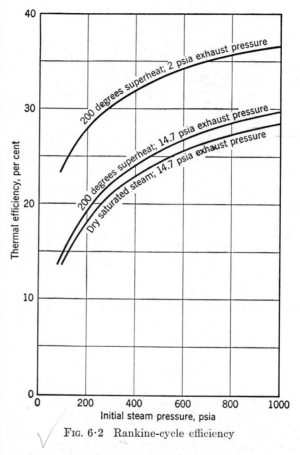

FIG. 6·2 Rankine-cycle efficiency

It should be noted from Fig. 6·2 and Example 1 that only a small part of the energy supplied in the boiler as heat is converted into work and the rest is lost in the condenser. In an actual cycle, using a real prime mover with its usual internal losses and with pressure drop and radiation losses from the piping system, the actual efficiency will be considerably less than the Rankine-cycle efficiency and the heat rejected to the condenser will be greater than for the Rankine cycle for the same initial and exhaust pressures. In many of the real cycles which are discussed in succeeding articles, the objective of the cycle arrangement is to reduce the exhaust loss or to utilize part or all of the energy in the exhaust steam for heating or manufacturing processes.

6·3 The simple noncondensing cycle. The simplest power-plant cycle is illustrated by the flow diagram of Fig. 6·3. Cold water, perhaps obtained from a stream or lake, is pumped into the boiler where it is converted into steam at boiler pressure by

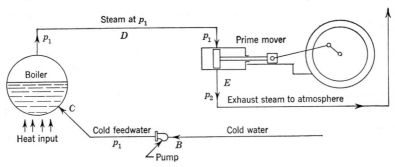

Fig. 6·3 Simple noncondensing power-plant cycle

the energy released through the combustion of fuel. The steam flows from the boiler to the prime mover in which it expands to atmospheric pressure. It is then discharged to the atmosphere. Some of the steam may find its way back to the water supply as rain, thus completing the cycle of operations. This cycle is called a *noncondensing* cycle since the prime mover is exhausting at a pressure equal to or above atmospheric pressure.

The actual efficiency of the cycle is based on the actual output of the prime mover as determined by test and may be defined as follows:

$$ n = \frac{\text{output}}{\text{input}} = \frac{\text{output of prime mover, Btu per hr}}{\text{input to boiler, Btu per hr}} $$

$$ n = \frac{\text{hp} \times 2545}{m_s(h_1 - h_c)} \tag{6·9} $$

where hp = horsepower output of the prime mover

m_s = steam passing through the prime mover, lb per hr

h_1 = enthalpy of steam leaving the boiler and entering the prime mover

h_c = enthalpy of feedwater at the entrance to the boiler

Equation 6·9 is based on the assumption that the heat loss by radiation, conduction, and convection from the piping system and equipment to the atmosphere is negligible and that the work required to operate the boiler feed pump may be neglected.

The horsepower output of the prime mover, if a steam engine, may be based upon the *indicated horsepower:* that is, the work done by the *steam on the piston of the engine.* The horsepower output of the prime mover may also be based upon the work done at the engine shaft or the *brake horsepower.* If a prime mover drives an electric generator, the output may be based upon the *kilowatt output* as determined by electric measuring instruments at the generator terminals, using the relationship 1 hp = 0.746 kw. In discussing efficiency, it is customary to specify that the efficiency is based upon the ihp, the bhp, or the kw output of the generator.

If the heat loss by radiation, conduction, and convection from the piping system and equipment to the atmosphere may be neglected, then, from the first law of thermodynamics, the heat rejected to the atmosphere in the exhaust steam equals the heat input to the cycle minus the heat converted into work, or

$$Q_r = Q_{in} - Q_w \qquad (6·10)$$

where Q_r = heat rejected to waste in the exhaust steam, Btu per hr

Q_{in} = input to the boiler, Btu per hr

Q_w = heat equivalent of the work done by the expanding *steam*, Btu per hr = ihp $\times$ 2545

The calculation of the cycle efficiency and the energy rejected in the exhaust steam may be illustrated by Example 2.

Example 2. Referring to Fig. 6·3, compute (*a*) the heat input in Btu per hr, (*b*) the cycle efficiency, and (*c*) the heat rejected to the atmosphere in Btu per hr for the following conditions:

Feed-water temperature at point B = 70 F

Boiler pressure, p_1 = 140 psia

Quality of steam at boiler outlet (point D) = 98.6%
Exhaust pressure, p_2 = 14.7 psia
Steam flow from boiler through engine = 2000 lb per hr
Ihp of engine = 80

Solution: The enthalpy of feedwater h_c at 70 F (if effect of compression is neglected) = 38.

The enthalpy of steam entering the prime mover at 140 psia and 98.6 per cent quality = $h_f + xh_{fg}$ = 324.82 + 0.986 × 868.2 = 1180.9.

(a)   Heat input to boiler = $m_s(h_1 - h_c)$

$$= 2000(1180.9 - 38)$$

$$= 2,286,000 \text{ Btu per hr}$$

(b)   Cycle efficiency (from Equation 6·9) = η

$$= \frac{80 \times 2545}{2,286,000} \times 100$$

$$= 8.9\%$$

(c) Heat rejected to waste (from Equation 6·10) = Q_r

$$= Q_{in} - Q_w$$

$$= (2,286,000) - (80 \times 2545)$$

$$= 2,082,000 \text{ Btu per hr or}$$

$$91.1\% \text{ of } Q_{in}$$

It should be noted in the preceding example that 8.9 per cent of the energy supplied to the boiler is converted into work in the prime mover while 91.1 per cent is wasted in the *exhaust steam discharged to the atmosphere.* This cycle is inefficient but has the advantages of simplicity and low cost of construction. It is used in applications where portability, simplicity, and low cost are important, as on construction jobs and the older types of steam locomotives.

6·4   The noncondensing cycle with direct-contact feed-water heater. The cycle shown in Fig. 6·4 is an improvement on the simple cycle of Fig. 6·3, because part of the waste energy in the hot exhaust steam is used to heat the cold water before it is pumped into the boiler. The cold water is supplied to a *direct-contact feed-water heater* through which the exhaust steam passes. At normal atmospheric pressure, the exhaust steam is at 212 F. The direct-contact heater is essentially a tank into which the water is sprayed and through which the exhaust steam from the engine flows to the atmosphere. The cold water is heated by direct contact with the hot steam, some of which condenses, and the hot water at 212 F is supplied to the boiler feed pump. Since this heat is recovered from the waste steam of the cycle shown in Fig. 6·3, it reduces the amount of fuel that must be burned to generate steam because of the higher temperature of the feed-

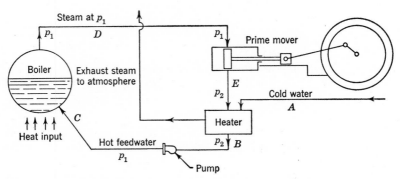

FIG. 6·4 Noncondensing power-plant cycle with direct-contact feed-water heater

water, and this cycle will be more efficient than the simple cycle of Fig. 6·3. A comparison of the results obtained in Example 3 with the results from Example 2 will show the savings effected by the use of the feed-water heater.

Example 3. Use the same data as in Example 2 except that the feedwater is heated in the direct-contact feed-water heater to the temperature of the exhaust steam, 212 F at 14.7 psia. Determine the same items as in Example 2.

Solution: The enthalpy of the feedwater h_c at 212 F (if the slight effect of compression of the water is neglected) = 180 Btu per lb.

(a) Heat input to boiler = $m_s(h_1 - h_c)$

$$= 2000(1180.9 - 180)$$

$$= 2,002,000 \text{ Btu per hr}$$

(b) Cycle efficiency $= \dfrac{\text{hp} \times 2545}{m_s(h_1 - h_c)}$

$$= \frac{80 \times 2545}{2,002,000} \times 100$$

$$= 10.15\%$$

(c) Energy rejected to waste $= Q_{in} - Q_w$

$$= 2,002,000 - (80 \times 2545)$$

$$= 1,798,000 \text{ Btu per hr or } 89.85\% \text{ of } Q_{in}$$

In Example 2, the cycle efficiency without the direct-contact feed-water heater was found to be 8.9 per cent. With the heater the cycle efficiency is 10.15 per cent or an increase in efficiency of 1.25 per cent. This will result in a fuel saving of 1.25/8.9 or 14 per cent of the fuel burned in the cycle shown in Fig. 6·3. Since the feed-water heater is a simple piece of equipment, modern locomotives and most small power plants are provided with heaters.

6·5 The noncondensing cycle with a heating or process load. In many industrial plants, in addition to the power load, it is necessary to supply heat for drying, cooking, heating of the

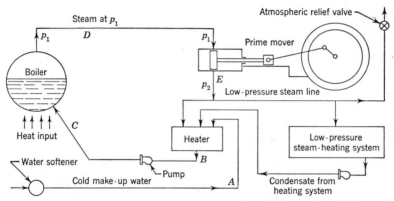

FIG. 6·5 Noncondensing power-plant cycle with direct-contact feed-water heater and low-pressure heating or process load

product being manufactured, or heating of buildings. Figure 6·5 shows an arrangement for *generating power and using the exhaust steam for a heating or process load.* The prime mover exhausts at a pressure near atmospheric pressure into the heating system. A relief valve permits the escape of surplus steam to the atmosphere if the heating system is unable to condense the steam. Exhaust steam from the prime mover is also supplied to a direct-contact heater which heats the warm *condensate* returned from the heating system as well as any cold *make-up* water which must be added to keep the system full. A water softener may be used to treat the make-up water and prevent scale formation in the boiler.

In Example 3, 89.85 per cent of the heat supplied in the boiler was discharged to waste in the exhaust steam. If all of this energy could be utilized in the heating system of the cycle shown in Fig. 6·5, then the waste energy is zero. If the heating system requires all of this energy, then, under the conditions of Example 3, 10.15 per cent of the cost of fuel should be charged to power and 89.85 per cent of the cost of fuel should be charged to the heating system which would have to be supplied with this energy even if power were purchased. The power generated in the cycle shown in Fig. 6·5 is often referred to as by-product power if the heating or process load can absorb all of the exhaust steam, and it can be generated at very low cost. In many instances, the heating system may require more steam during part of the year than can be passed through the engine, and some steam must be supplied to the heating system directly from the boiler. Under such conditions, the efficiency of the prime mover is of little importance.

6·6   The condensing cycle. Where the exhaust steam cannot be used for heating purposes and good efficiency is desired, the cycle shown in Fig. 6·6 may be employed. The prime mover, in this case a turbine, exhausts into a *condenser,* the function of which is to maintain a high vacuum at the turbine exhaust so as to permit the *expansion of the steam through a greater pressure range than would be the case with exhaust at atmospheric pressure.* For the Rankine or ideal cycle having isentropic expansion, the upper curves of Fig. 6·2 show the gain in efficiency due to a reduction in the back pressure from normal atmospheric pressure to 2 psia. In the actual prime mover which cannot attain an isentropic expansion, the actual efficiencies will be less than those shown on Fig. 6·2, but the gain due to the reduction in back pressure will be proportional to that shown in Fig. 6·2.

Cold circulating water is pumped through the tubes of the condenser which is an air-tight chamber attached to the turbine exhaust flange, and the condensed steam which collects on these cold tubes and falls to the bottom of the condenser is pumped out of the condenser and into the direct-contact heater. Small steam turbines or engines, driving such auxiliaries as pumps and fans, discharge to the heater and furnish the steam necessary to heat the cool condensate as well as any make-up water that must be supplied to overcome the loss of water in the system. Duplicate auxiliaries driven by electric motors may be operated in parallel with the steam-driven auxiliaries in order that the steam

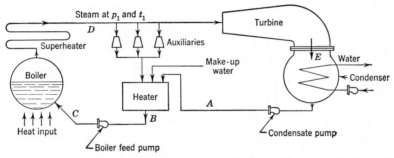

Fɪɢ. 6·6 Condensing power-plant cycle with steam-driven auxiliaries and direct-contact heater

supplied to the feed-water heater may not be in excess of that which the incoming water can condense. The make-up water may be treated chemically to remove scale-forming material from this water before introduction into the feed-water heater. In Fig. 6·6, the steam from the boiler flows through a superheater which is supplied with heat from the burning fuel. The rise in steam temperature in the superheater causes an increase in the volume of the steam with the result that a smaller weight of steam is required to do a given amount of work in the turbine, and the efficiency of the cycle is thereby increased.

6·7 The condensing cycle with an automatic-extraction turbine. An automatic-extraction turbine is a special type of turbine which is equipped with an automatic internal-control valve to allow the extraction from the turbine of a variable amount of steam at some constant pressure lower than the turbine-inlet pressure and higher than the exhaust pressure. In the cycle shown in Fig. 6·7, the steam may be extracted at some pressure slightly above atmospheric pressure and used in a heating system, for a process load, and for the direct-contact feed-water heater.

When there is no demand for heating or process steam, the steam supplied to the turbine may be expanded through the entire turbine to the vacuum at the condenser, and thus the maximum amount of work may be obtained from each pound of steam. When there is a demand for heating or process steam, the steam will be expanded from the turbine-inlet pressure to the

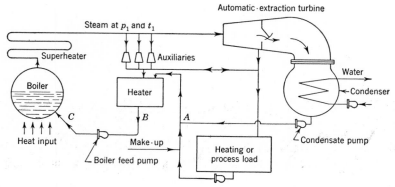

Fɪɢ. 6·7 Condensing power-plant cycle with automatic-extraction turbine, steam-driven auxiliaries, direct-contact feed-water heater, and heating or process steam load

extraction pressure with the production of a certain amount of power, after which the steam required for the heating or process load is removed from the turbine and the rest of the steam is expanded to the condenser pressure, thereby doing more work. With this arrangement, a quantity of steam varying from 0 to 95 per cent of the input may be bled from the turbine as needed, and the remainder of the steam may be expanded to the condenser pressure with maximum output of work per pound of steam. For seasonal and variable heating or process loads, the automatic-extraction turbine cycle is used extensively.

6·8   The regenerative power-plant cycle. Where power is the only useful output from a plant, modern power plants usually operate on the regenerative cycle, a simple flow diagram of which is shown in Fig. 6·8. Steam which enters the turbine at high pressure expands step by step in the turbine to the low exhaust pressure. Part of the steam is withdrawn from the turbine at intermediate pressures after it has done work by expansion from the initial pressure. This *extracted steam* is condensed in feed-water heaters, and the energy in this steam is thus returned to the boiler instead of being rejected to waste in the condenser cooling water. From three to six extraction heaters are normally connected to the turbine, depending upon the size of the unit and the initial steam pressure. As much as 25 per cent of the steam entering the turbine may be extracted in the heaters. This ex-

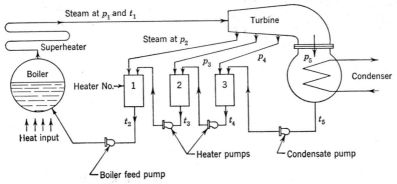

FIG. 6·8 Regenerative power-plant cycle

tracted steam is being used at an efficiency of 100 per cent since, if heat losses to the atmosphere from equipment are neglected, the energy in this steam as it enters the turbine is either con-verted into work or returned to the boiler. Thus the condenser loss of the cycle shown in Fig. 6·6 is reduced, and the overall efficiency is improved. Electrically driven auxiliaries are used with the regenerative cycle in order that all of the steam may be expanded in large, efficient turbines with the generation of the maximum possible amount of power instead of expansion through small and relatively inefficient units directly connected to auxil-iaries such as fans and pumps. Thermal efficiencies up to about 35 per cent are obtainable by the use of the regenerative cycle.

6·9 The reheating–regenerative power-plant cycle. In Article 5·17 it was stated that serious erosion of turbine blades and loss of turbine efficiency would occur if the quality of the exhaust steam became less than about 88 per cent and that high steam pressures required certain minimum steam temperatures to avoid such difficulties. Steam pressures higher than those recommended in Article 5·17 for a given steam temperature may be used by employing the reheating–regenerative cycle which is illustrated in Fig. 6·9. Steam is expanded through a high-pressure turbine to an intermediate pressure which is generally 25 to 40 per cent of the initial pressure. The exhaust steam from the

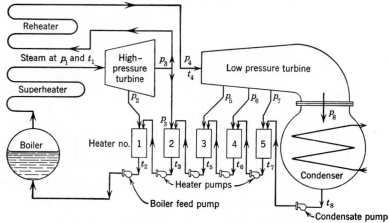

FIG. 6·9 Reheating–regenerative power-plant cycle

high-pressure turbine is then returned to a reheat superheater in the steam-generating unit. The steam is reheated at this intermediate pressure to a temperature equal to or not far below the initial steam temperature, after which it is piped to the low-pressure turbine in which the expansion is completed to the condenser pressure. Regenerative feed-water heaters are used as in the straight regenerative cycle for the purpose of reducing the condenser loss by heating the feedwater with steam which has done work in the turbine. In general, the reheating–regenerative cycle will produce a saving in fuel of 4 to 5 per cent as compared with the regenerative cycle for the same maximum steam temperature. Consequently, many large central-station plants located in regions of high-cost fuel are operating on this cycle in spite of its higher construction cost as compared with the straight regenerative cycle.

6·10   Overall steam power-plant performance. The function of a power plant is to produce high-grade energy, usually in the form of electric energy, from low-grade energy in the form of fuel. The preceding articles dealt with the conversion into work in a prime mover of the heat absorbed in a steam-generating unit in producing steam. In addition to the vapor-cycle efficiency, the overall performance of the power plant from fuel supplied to energy delivered depends upon several other factors such as:

1. As pointed out in Chapter 5, the efficiency of the steam-generating unit may be from 70 to 90 per cent, which means that 10 to 30 per cent of the energy in the fuel is not used in producing steam but is wasted.

2. Some of the steam is used to blow soot from the boiler surfaces and for other purposes not directly associated with power generation.

3. Owing to mechanical losses such as bearing friction and windage in the prime mover and generator and electrical losses in the generator, part of the energy converted into work by the expanding steam in the prime mover does not appear as electric energy at the generator terminals.

4. From 3 to 5 per cent of the generator output is required to operate electrically driven auxiliaries and lights in the plant itself and is not available for outside distribution.

5. Owing to variable loads and the need for maintaining equipment, energy is wasted in starting up cold units, shutting down hot units and operating units at uneconomical loads.

The overall performance of the plant from entering fuel to delivered energy is usually expressed in terms of the heating value of the fuel supplied to the plant per year and the net kilowatt-hours of electric energy delivered by the plant in the same period of time and is called the plant heat rate. Therefore,

Plant heat rate

$$= \frac{\text{lb of fuel burned per yr} \times \text{average heating value of fuel}}{\text{kw-hr of energy delivered per yr}}$$

Since 1 kw-hr = 3413 Btu, the overall thermal efficiency of the plant may be computed from the plant heat rate as follows:

$$\text{Overall thermal efficiency} = \frac{3413}{\text{plant heat rate}} \times 100\%$$

Example 4. The operating records of a power plant show that, over a period of 1 year, 1.24 lb of coal were burned per net kw-hr delivered by the plant. The average heating value of the fuel was 11,300 Btu per lb. Compute the plant heat rate and the overall plant efficiency.

Solution: (a) The plant heat rate = 1.24 lb of fuel per kw-hr $\times$ 11,300 Btu

per lb of fuel = 14,010 Btu per kw-hr

(b)   Overall efficiency = $\dfrac{3413 \text{ Btu per kw-hr}}{14,010 \text{ Btu per kw-hr}} \times 100 = 24.4\%$

Figure 6·10 illustrates the reduction in plant heat rate which has occurred during the past 50 years and the changes in maximum steam pressure and temperature which have been responsible for much of this improvement in performance. Some of the best central-station plants now in operation have a plant heat rate of about 9200 Btu per kw-hr.

PROBLEMS

1. Compute the efficiency of the Rankine cycle when steam is generated at 135 psig and 98 per cent quality with exhaust at atmospheric pressure, 14.7 psia. Neglect the effect of the boiler feed pump.

2. Compute the efficiency of the Rankine cycle when steam is generated at 240 psia and 600 F with exhaust at (a) atmospheric pressure, and (b) a vacuum of 28 in. of Hg. Barometric pressure is 30 in. of Hg. Neglect the boiler feed pump.

3. Compute the efficiency of a Rankine cycle when steam is generated at 1200 psia and 900 F with exhaust at a vacuum of 28 in. of Hg when the barometric pressure is 30 in. of Hg (a) neglecting the boiler feed pump, and (b) including the boiler feed pump.

4. A noncondensing power plant operating on the cycle shown in Fig. 6·3 generates steam at 120 psia and 98 per cent quality and exhausts at atmospheric pressure, 14.7 psia. Feedwater is available at 60 F. A total of 5000 lb of steam are generated per hr, and the ihp of the engine is 160. Draw a flow diagram similar to Fig. 6·3, and compute (a) the heat supplied in Btu per hr, (b) the efficiency of the cycle, and (c) the heat rejected to the atmosphere in Btu per hr.

5. If a direct-contact heater is added to the cycle of Problem 4 to produce the cycle shown on Fig. 6·4 and the feedwater is heated in the heater to 212 F, compute (a) the heat supplied in Btu per hr, (b) the efficiency of the cycle, (c) the heat rejected to the atmosphere in Btu per hr, and (d) the per cent improvement in efficiency over the efficiency of the cycle of Problem 4.

6. A simple noncondensing power plant operating on the cycle shown in Fig. 6·3 generates steam at 150 psig and 99 per cent quality and exhausts at atmospheric pressure, 14.7 psia. Feed-water temperature is 65 F, 4000 lb

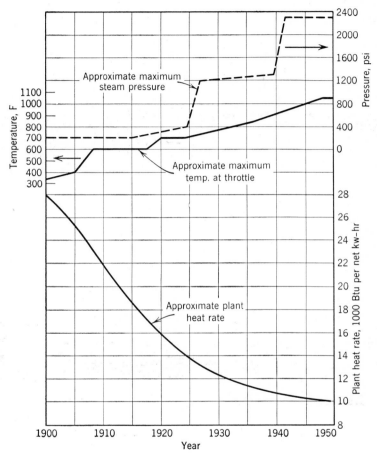

FIG. 6·10 Changes in steam conditions and plant economy

From Operating Experience with High-Pressure High-Temperature Steam Central Stations, by P. W. Thompson, Fourth World Power Conference, 1950

of steam are generated per hr, and the ihp of the engine is 150. Draw a flow diagram similar to Fig. 6·3, and compute (*a*) the heat supplied in Btu per hr, (*b*) the heat rejected to the atmosphere in Btu per hr, and (*c*) the efficiency of the cycle.

7. If a direct-contact feed-water heater is installed in the cycle of Problem 6 and the water is heated to the saturation temperature at the heater pressure, 14.7 psia, how much will the fuel consumption of the plant be reduced, in per cent?

8. In a condensing power-plant cycle as illustrated in Fig. 6·6, 50,000 lb of steam are generated per hr at 200 psia and 600 F. The feedwater is returned to the boiler from the heater at 210 F. The condenser pressure is 1.0 psia. The output of the generator which is driven by the turbine is 3,700 kw. Compute the efficiency of this cycle.

9. A power plant burned 1.41 lb of coal per net kw-hr delivered to the transmission line during 1951. The average heating value of the coal was 11,350 Btu per lb. Compute (*a*) the net plant heat rate, and (*b*) the overall thermal efficiency of the plant.

10. A power plant carried an average net load of 42,000 kw while operating continuously during the month of October and burned 20,500 tons of coal during this interval of time. The heating value of the coal was 12,400 Btu per lb. Compute (*a*) the net plant heat rate, and (*b*) the overall efficiency of the plant.

11. During the year 1951, an oil-fired steam power plant had an overall plant fuel rate of 0.8 lb of oil per kw-hr of energy delivered to the transmission line. The oil burned in this plant had an average gravity of 18 degrees API and an average heating value of 146,000 Btu per gal. Calculate (*a*) the net plant heat rate, and (*b*) the net overall efficiency.

12. A Diesel-engine-driven power plant is being considered for a particular installation. The engine manufacturer guarantees a brake thermal efficiency of 33 per cent at the point of most efficient operation of the engine when burning oil having a heating value of 19,000 Btu per lb. It is estimated that the average efficiency of the engine under variable load operation with allowance for losses in starting cold engines, idling, and shutting down hot engines, etc., will be 85 per cent of the maximum steady-load brake thermal efficiency. The average efficiency of the electric generator is estimated to be 89 per cent, and 94 per cent of the generator output is distributed from the plant over the transmission lines. Calculate the net plant heat rate and the specific fuel consumption in lb of oil per net kw-hr delivered.

7 · Steam Turbines

7·1 Introduction. The steam turbine is a prime mover in which a part of that form of energy of the steam evidenced by a high pressure and temperature is converted into kinetic energy of the steam and then into shaft work.

The concept of the steam turbine is not new, for about 120 B.C. Hero of Alexandria described a sphere which revolved owing to escaping steam, but its utilization was limited to a form of toy. An old sketch of Hero's turbine is shown in Fig. 7·1. Steam generated in a boiler passed through hollow trunnions into a hollow sphere. Mounted on the sphere were two outlets which were directed tangentially to the sphere and from which the steam issued in the form of a jet. The reactive force of the steam leaving the outlets turned the sphere about its axis.

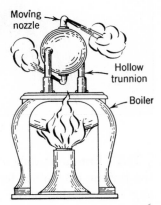

FIG. 7·1 Hero's reaction turbine principle

Some 20 centuries later, in 1882, a Swedish mechanical engineer, Dr. Carl DeLaval, constructed a steam turbine based upon the Hero reaction principle that was used for driving a cream separator. Later he developed the turbine shown in Fig. 7·2. Steam generated in a boiler passed through the stationary nozzle or nozzles where it acquired a high velocity. The high-velocity jet was then directed against a row of buckets or blades mounted on a wheel. The impulse force of the jet on the blades turned the wheel.

In 1884 an English inventor and shipbuilder, Sir Charles

Parsons, developed a steam turbine based on Hero's reaction principle which was later applied to practical maritime use. Many of the features of the modern turbine were introduced by DeLaval and Parsons.

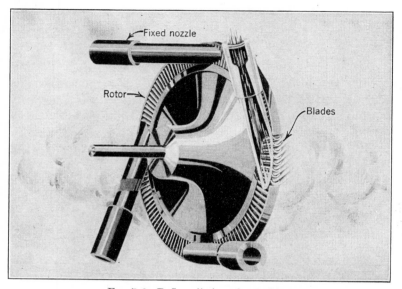

Fig. 7·2   DeLaval's impulse turbine

7·2   Fundamentals of the turbine.   The basic advantage of the turbine over other forms of prime movers is the absence of any reciprocating parts. With only rotating motion involved, high speeds are attainable. Since power is directly proportional to torque times speed, an increase in the rotative speed materially decreases the value of the torque required for a given power output. A decrease in the required torque permits a reduction in the size of the prime mover by reducing the length of the torque arm or the force acting on the torque arm. Also, with the absence of any reciprocating parts, vibration is greatly minimized. Owing to the high rotative speeds available with relatively little vibration, the size and cost of the driven machinery, of the building space, and of the foundations are greatly reduced. These advantages are most apparent in large prime movers and permit the steam turbine to be built in sizes ranging from a few horsepower to over 200,000 hp in single units.

Fundamentally, two types of turbines exist, based on the method by which the kinetic energy of the steam is converted into shaft work. They are the impulse turbine and the reaction turbine. The impulse turbine consists of two basic elements: a

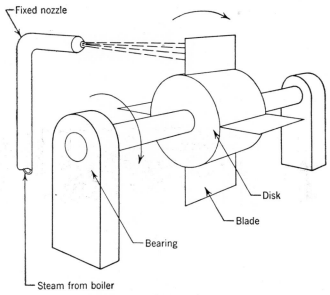

Fig. 7·3 A simple impulse turbine

fixed *nozzle* to convert the energy of the steam into kinetic energy, and a *rotor,* consisting of blades mounted on the periphery of a disk or wheel, to absorb the kinetic energy of the steam jet and to convert it into rotary motion. The reaction turbine has the same two basic parts but differs from the impulse turbine in that the blades of the impulse turbine are replaced by nozzles, mounted on the disk and rotating with it.

The principles underlying the two types of turbines are illustrated in Figs. 7·3 and 7·4. Only the essential parts are shown. Steam is produced in a boiler and piped to the turbine. Before reaching the nozzles, the steam has a very low velocity but is at a high pressure and temperature. On expanding to a lower pressure and temperature, the steam increases in velocity.

In the impulse turbine steam expands in fixed nozzles (see Fig. 7·3). The high-velocity steam jet is directed against the paddle wheel or rotor. An impulse or force is produced by the steam against the blades which, if sufficient to overcome friction, will cause the rotor to turn. Thus work is done on the rotor.

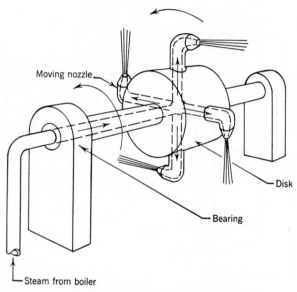

Fig. 7·4 A simple reaction turbine

In the reaction turbine (Fig. 7·4) steam expands in moving nozzles. Steam enters the hollow shaft and rotor and flows to the nozzles. When it expands through the nozzles from a high pressure to a low pressure, a reactive force is produced on nozzles, disk, and shaft. The reactive force will produce rotation opposite to the direction of the steam jet, and work will be done. An everyday application of this principle is the lawn sprinkler which rotates because of the reactive force of the water leaving the sprinkler nozzles.

In the actual turbine the nozzles do not resemble those shown in Fig. 7·3 or 7·4, but the principle of operation is the same.

Also, a *casing* is added to confine and direct the flow of steam. The disk, blades, nozzle, and casing are shown in the small turbine in Fig. 7·5. Steam enters from the left, passes through a valve controlled by a *governor* system, and enters the turbine proper. The governor automatically regulates the flow of steam to the nozzle to maintain constant speed. A *lubricating* system

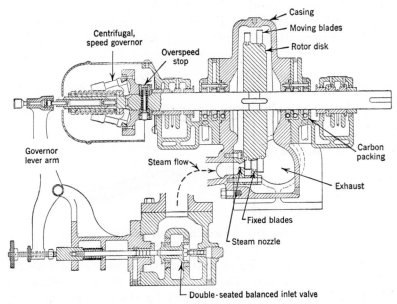

Fig. 7·5 Cross-sectional view of a small impulse turbine

supplies oil to the bearings on which the rotor shaft is mounted. Shaft packing is used to prevent steam leakage.

7·3 The turbine nozzle. The turbine nozzle performs two functions:

1. It transforms a portion of the energy of the steam, acquired in the steam-generating unit and evidenced by a high pressure and temperature, into kinetic energy.

2a. In the impulse turbine it directs the high-velocity steam jet against blades which are free to move in order to convert the kinetic energy into shaft work.

2b. In the reaction turbine the nozzles, which are free to move, discharge high-velocity steam. The reactive force of the steam against the nozzle produces motion, and work is done.

For the first funciton to be performed efficiently, the nozzle walls must be smooth, streamlined, and so proportioned as to satisfy the changing conditions of the steam flowing through the nozzle.

For the second function the nozzle should discharge steam at the correct angle with the direction of blade motion to allow a maximum conversion of kinetic energy into work.

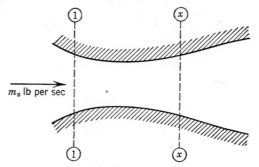

Fig. 7·6   An arbitrary flow passage

The main consideration in nozzle design is to provide a nozzle of proper wall contour. The contour of the walls depends upon the conditions of the steam required by the turbine and upon certain properties of the steam which are influenced by these established conditions. For nozzle design the engineer has at his disposal four fundamental *tools* or relations. They are:

1. The first law of thermodynamics.
2. The equation of continuity of flow.
3. The characteristic equation of state of the fluid.
4. The equation of the process.

The application of the first law of thermodynamics to nozzle flow has been discussed in Article 1·26. For a flow passage such as that shown in Fig. 7·6 the energy equation per pound of fluid (Equation 1·35) can be written as

$$\frac{V_1^2}{2gJ} + h_1 = \frac{V_x^2}{2gJ} + h_x \tag{7·1}$$

where V_1 = initial velocity, fps

h_1 = initial enthalpy, Btu per lb

V_x = velocity at any arbitrary point, x, downstream from the initial section, fps

h_x = downstream enthalpy, Btu per lb

From Article 1·26, it will be recalled that Equation 7·1 was developed on the assumption that no work is done between sections 1–1 and x–x and that the heat transferred and the change in potential energy are negligible. Furthermore, if it is assumed that the initial velocity, V_1, is small, then, Equation 7·1 reduces to

$$\frac{V_x^2}{2gJ} = h_1 - h_x \tag{7·2}$$

and
$$V_x = 223.8\sqrt{h_1 - h_x} \tag{7·3}$$

The equation of continuity of flow states that the mass rate of flow of the fluid is constant for all cross sections in the flow passage and is equal to the volume rate of flow divided by the specific volume of the fluid if the flow passage is completely filled with the fluid. Thus, for the passage shown in Fig. 7·6 the continuity equation can be written as

$$m_s = \frac{A_1 V_1}{v_1} = \frac{A_x V_x}{v_x} \tag{7·4}$$

where m_s = mass rate of flow, lb per sec

A = area at sections designated, sq ft

V = velocity at sections designated, fps

v = specific volume at sections designated, cu ft per lb

Note: In this chapter flow will be represented by m_s for pounds per second and m_m for pounds per minute.

The characteristic equation of state is the equation that relates the properties of the fluid. For a perfect gas it is $pv = RT$. For steam the equation is not so simple, and the steam tables or Mollier chart are used in place of an equation.

The equation of the process depends upon the flow conditions which the fluid undergoes. In actual flow processes the conditions may be quite complex. For this reason the simplifying assumption is often made that there is no friction. Thus, if there is no friction and no heat flow, the process becomes an isentropic process or one in which the entropy remains constant.

The application of these four basic tools to a nozzle can be illustrated best by an example.

Example 1. Steam enters a nozzle at 200 psia and 500 F with a rate of flow of 1 lb per sec. It expands without friction or heat flow to a pressure of 1 psia. If it is assumed that the initial velocity of the steam is negligible, find the proper areas of the nozzle at (a) 140 psia, and (b) 1 psia.

Solution: (a) The proper area of the nozzle is that area which will satisfy the continuity-flow equation at the point in question or $A_x = \dfrac{m_s v_x}{V_x}$. In this equation, the point x is reached by steam expanding from $p = 200$ psia and $t = 500$ F to $p_x = 140$ psia at constant entropy.

The process may be represented on the Mollier diagram as shown in Fig. 7·7. The point x for $p = 140$ psia is identified as point 4. Now, both the initial and final enthalpies may be obtained and are: $h_1 = 1269.4$ Btu per lb and $h_4 = 1234.7$ Btu per lb. From the general-energy equation, the velocity, V_4, can be calculated. Thus,

$$V_4 = 223.8\sqrt{h_1 - h_4}$$

$$= 223.8\sqrt{1269.4 - 1234.7}$$

$$= 1320 \text{ fps}$$

Also, the value of the specific volume of the steam, v_4, may be obtained from the steam tables at the point where $p = 140$ psia and $s = 1.6245$. From Table A·3, $v_4 = 3.584$ cu ft per lb.

Substituting these values in the continuity equation, gives

$$A_4 = \frac{m_s v_4}{V_4}$$

$$= \frac{1 \text{ lb per sec} \times 3.584 \text{ cu ft per lb}}{1320 \text{ fps}}$$

$$= 0.00271 \text{ sq ft}$$

(b) In a similar manner the area at the point x where $p = 1$ psia can be determined. If the point in the flow path where $p = 1$ psia and the entropy, $s = 1.6245$, is identified as point 11 (see Fig. 7·7) then the final enthalpy, $h_{11}, = 907.4$ Btu per lb. Also, the quality of the steam, x, at point 11 is approximately 80.8 per cent, as read on the Mollier chart.

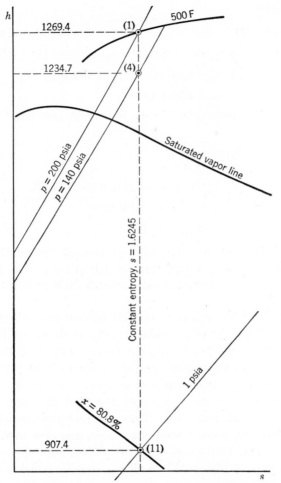

FIG. 7·7 Expansion process for steam in the nozzle of Example 1

From the general-energy equation, the velocity, V_{11}, can now be calculated. Thus,

$$V_{11} = 223.8\sqrt{h_1 - h_{11}}$$

$$= 223.8\sqrt{1269.4 - 907.4}$$

$$= 4240 \text{ fps}$$

At a pressure of 1 psia and a quality x of 80.8 per cent, the specific volume can be calculated by

$$v_{11} = v_f + xv_{fg}$$

where $v_f = 0.01614$ (Table A·2 at $p = 1$ psia)

$$v_{fg} = v_g - v_f = 333.6 - 0.01614 = v_g \text{ approximately} = 333.6$$

thus, $v_{11} = 0.808 \times 333.6$ approximately

or $v_{11} = 270$ cu ft per lb

Substituting these values in the continuity equation

$$A_{11} = \frac{m_s v_{11}}{V_{11}}$$

gives $$A_{11} = \frac{1 \text{ lb per sec} \times 270 \text{ cu ft per lb}}{4240 \text{ fps}}$$

$$= 0.0637 \text{ sq ft}$$

In a similar manner the required area of the nozzle at any other point in the flow path can be determined. The results of the calculations of areas for some intermediate points are shown in Table 7·1.

In Fig. 7·8A the values of specific volume and velocity of the steam and diameter of the tube section, as shown in Table 7·1, are plotted against pressure. The curves show that the specific volume and velocity increase with a decrease in pressure but that they do not increase at the same rate. The velocity increases more rapidly than the volume at the high pressures and less rapidly at the low pressures. Thus, the required diameter d will at first decrease, reach a minimum value, and then increase. By using the values of the diameters calculated, a nozzle can now be constructed (see Fig. 7·8B) having a contour which will give a constant pressure drop per unit of nozzle length, but which will not produce a well-defined jet.

A nozzle constructed to give a more concentrated jet is shown in Fig. 7·8D. The pressure, velocity, and diameter changes are shown in Fig. 7·8C. The point at which the diameter is a minimum is called the "throat." The section leading up to the "throat" is called the converging section, and the exit section is called the diverging section. A nozzle of this type is a converging–diverging nozzle. The nozzles shown in Fig. 7·8B and 7·8D

TABLE 7·1

NOZZLE AND STEAM VALUES

for

$m_s = 1$ Lb per Sec; $P_1 = 200$ Psia; $t_1 = 500$ F

(1) Point of Flow	(2) Pressure p, Psia	(3) Enthalpy, h, Btu per Lb	(4) Velocity V, Fps	(5) Specific Volume v, Cu Ft per Lb	(6) Area A, Sq Ft	(7) Diameter d, In.	(8) Remarks
1	200	1269.4	0	2.726	......	.....	Entrance
2	190	1263.4	546	2.830	0.00518	0.973	
3	170	1252.4	920	3.083	0.00335	0.793	
4	140	1234.7	1320	3.584	0.00271	0.703	
5	110	1213.0	1680	4.307	0.00256	0.683	
6	80	1186.2	2040	5.484	0.00268	0.699	Throat
7	50	1148.4	2450	8.26	0.00337	0.782	
8	20	1082.4	3050	18.6	0.00608	1.05	
9	15	1061.4	3220	24.3	0.00755	1.17	
10	7	1013.4	3560	47.0	0.0132	1.55	
11	1	907.4	4240	270	0.0637	3.42	Exit

would expand 1 lb of steam per sec from 200 psia and 500 F to 1 psia. As seen in Table 7·1 they would produce an exit velocity

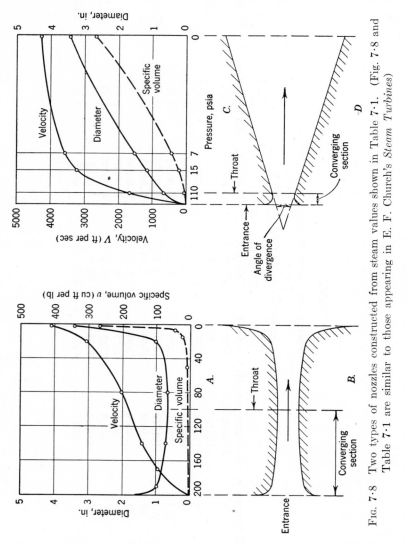

FIG. 7·8 Two types of nozzles constructed from steam values shown in Table 7·1. (Fig. 7·8 and Table 7·1 are similar to those appearing in E. F. Church's *Steam Turbines*)

of 4240 fps if no friction were encountered. If a nozzle is desired which will produce an exit velocity of 3050 fps under the same entrance conditions, it should be constructed as the ones previously designed but with only those sections up to section 8 included. Thus, the exit diameter of the new nozzle would only be 1.05 in. The exit pressure should then be maintained at 20 psia. A nozzle constructed as the originals but extending only to section 5, the throat section, would produce an exit velocity of 1680 fps under the same inlet conditions. The exit pressure should be maintained at 110 psia. A purely converging nozzle results. Thus, if a further reduction in velocity is desired, a nozzle of only converging shape is necessary.

In Table 7·1 the ratio of the pressure at the throat section to the pressure at inlet is equal to 110 ÷ 200 or 0.55. This ratio is called the "critical ratio," and the pressure at the throat is called the critical pressure. The "critical ratio" is constant for any particular gas, 0.55 for superheated steam, and 0.58 for wet steam. Thus, the throat pressure can be calculated readily if the initial pressure is known, and it can be shown experimentally that the flow of steam always reaches its maximum value when the exhaust pressure of a nozzle is equal to 0.55 of the initial pressure. Reduction in the exhaust pressure below 0.55 of the initial pressure will not increase the mass rate of flow of the steam.

The kinetic energy of the steam leaving the nozzles shown in Figs. 7·8B and 7·8D would be

$$\frac{V_1{}^2}{2 \times 32.2} = \frac{1}{64.4} (4240)^2 = 279,000 \text{ ft-lb per lb of steam}$$

If friction were encountered, as in the actual case, the exit velocity of the steam would be less than 4240 fps, and correspondingly the kinetic energy would be less. The efficiency of the actual nozzle would be the ratio of its kinetic energy to that of a nozzle operating under the same conditions but having no losses. The nozzle is designed to keep the losses, particularly the friction loss, small by the use of smooth streamlined walls and by proper adjustment of the length of the nozzle.

The length of the nozzles shown in Figs. 7·8B and 7·8D have been arbitrarily selected. Neither nozzle would perform efficiently under actual steam-flow conditions. Experimentally, it has been found that the converging section should be short and well rounded, as in Fig. 7·8D. The walls of the nozzle from the throat to exit are straight to simplify manufacture, and they are reamed or cast so that the angle of divergence between them (the total included angle) is about 10 degrees. The angle of divergence of the nozzle is selected through experience, and the length of the nozzle is thus fixed for a given throat and exit diameter or area.

The actual turbine nozzle is constructed to direct the jet at an

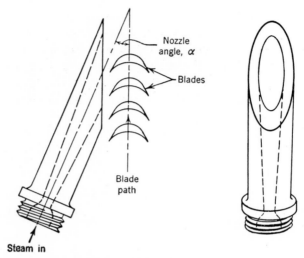

Fig. 7·9 An actual turbine nozzle and its position relative to the moving blades

angle with the direction of motion of the turbine blades as shown in Fig. 7·9. The angle subtended by the axis of the nozzle and the direction of motion of the blade is called the nozzle angle and is designated by α. The nozzle angle is made as small as satisfactory flow conditions permit in order that maximum thrust on the blade is obtained.

If more than one nozzle is necessary to handle a large steam volume, nozzles are generally manufactured in blocks. Two such sets of nozzle blocks are shown in Figs. 7·10A and 7·10B. The nozzles in Fig. 7·10A are converging–diverging nozzles, which operate at an exhaust pressure below the critical pressure. The nozzles in Fig. 7·10B are converging nozzles which exhaust to a pressure above the critical pressure.

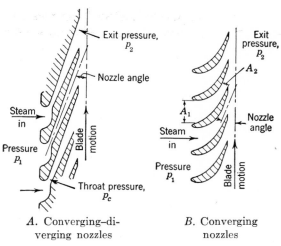

A. Converging–di-
verging nozzles

B. Converging
nozzles

Fig. 7·10   Nozzle blocks

7·4   Vector analysis.   To understand the principles underlying turbine-blade design, it is important to have a knowledge
of both vector quantities and scalar quantities.   Briefly, a scalar
quantity is one that has *magnitude* only, for example, the distance
a man walks measured in feet.   A vector quantity has both
magnitude and *direction,* for example, the displacement of a man
as he walks toward the northeast measured in feet but with the
direction specified as northeast.   The size of a scalar quantity is
designated by a number.   The size and direction of a vector are
usually represented by an arrow, its length to scale denoting
size and its head indicating the appropriate direction.   The addition and subtraction of two or more vector quantities can be
conveniently carried out graphically by proceeding as follows:

1. To perform vector addition, place the tail of one vector at
the head of the other.   The resultant vector is obtained by drawing the closing side to form a triangle and by placing the arrow-
head of the closing side nearest the second vector (Fig. 7·11A).

2. To perform vector subtraction reverse the direction of the
vector to be subtracted, and perform the same operation as in
vector addition, part 1 (Fig. 7·11B).

The velocity of an object is a vector quantity, and it is measured with respect to another object.   The velocity when measured

with respect to the earth will be called the *absolute* velocity. The velocity of an object when measured from another moving object (other than the earth) will be called the *relative* velocity. The absolute velocity of an object may be determined by the vector addition of its relative velocity with respect to a second object and the absolute velocity of the second object. The relative velocity of an object is determined by the vector subtraction of the absolute velocities of the two objects.

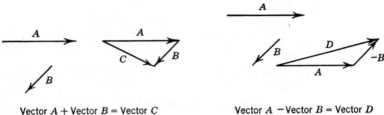

Vector A + Vector B = Vector C Vector A − Vector B = Vector D

A. Vector addition   *B*. Vector subtraction

Fig. 7·11   Vector arithmetic

From these fundamental concepts of vector arithmetic an equation defining relative velocity may be written. Thus,

$$V_a = V_b \;\leftrightarrow\; V_{ab} \tag{7·5}$$

or
$$V_{ab} = V_a \;\rightarrow\; V_b \tag{7·6}$$

where V_a = absolute velocity of object a
  V_b = absolute velocity of object b
and V_{ab} = relative velocity of object a with respect to object b

The symbols $\leftrightarrow$ and $\rightarrow$ represent vector addition and subtraction, respectively. **Caution:** The student must be careful never to add or subtract magnitudes only in solving vector equations.

As an example, assume that a train moves to the north at 20 miles per hr and that a man walks through the train at 5 miles per hr. The velocity of the train is an absolute velocity (measured with respect to the earth). The velocity of the man is a relative velocity (measured with respect to the train). If the man walks toward the front of the train, his absolute velocity is the vector sum of his relative velocity and the absolute velocity of the train or 25 miles per hr northward. If he walks to the rear of the train at 5 miles per hr, his absolute velocity is still the vector sum of the two velocities, but these now have opposite directions. Therefore, his absolute velocity becomes 15 miles per hr to the northward. Graphically, this example is solved as

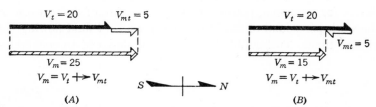

(A)   (B)

FIG. 7·12   Vector arithmetic of the first example of the train

shown in Figs. 7·12A and 7·12B where V_m is the absolute velocity of the man, V_t is the absolute velocity of the train, and V_{mt} is the relative velocity of the man with respect to the train.

In Fig. 7·13, the graphical solution is given for the case when the man walks eastward across the train aisle at 5 miles per hr as the train moves north at 20 miles per hr. His resultant absolute velocity can be measured directly from the length of the vector or calculated by trigonometry, for, in the right triangle,

$$V_m = \sqrt{(V_t)^2 + (V_{mt})^2}$$

or $V_m = \sqrt{(20)^2 + (5)^2} = 20.6$ miles per hr

The angle made by the resultant vector is 14° 2′ east of north. The vector equation for Fig. 7·13 is $V_m = V_t \leftrightarrow V_{mt}$.

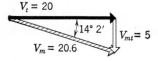

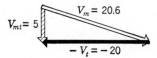

FIG. 7·13   Vector arithmetic for second example of train

FIG. 7·14   Vector arithmetic for third example of train

The relative velocity of the man could have been determined if the absolute velocity of the train, 20 miles per hr to the north, and the absolute velocity of the man, 20.6 miles per hr at an angle 14° 2′ east of north, were known. In Fig. 7·14, the solution is shown. Notice that the direction of the velocity vector V_t has been reversed and then added vectorially to V_m to solve for the relative velocity V_{mt}. The equation for Fig. 7·14 is $V_{mt} = V_m \rightarrow V_t$.

7·5   Impulse turbine blading.   Essentially, a turbine is a device for producing power. Power is the rate of doing work or the work per pound of fluid times the pounds of fluid flowing per unit of time. Turbine blading should be designed to convert as

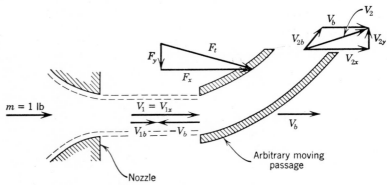

FIG. 7·15   Forces acting on an arbitrary passage

much of the kinetic energy of the steam leaving the nozzle into work as is practicable. In order to determine the proper blade shape for the production of maximum work, it is necessary to review certain fundamentals and to make certain simplifying assumptions in the application of these fundamentals.

Let is be assumed that a fluid, such as steam, is flowing through a curved passage and that the passage is capable of motion, as illustrated in Fig. 7·15. Further, let the symbols shown in Fig. 7·15, which will be used throughout the remainder of the chapter, represent the following:

(1) V_1 and V_2 are the initial and final absolute velocities of the steam, respectively.

(2) V_b is the absolute velocity of the passage.

(3) V_{1b} and V_{2b} are the initial and final relative velocities of the steam with respect to the passage.

(4) V_{1x} and V_{2x} are the components of V_1 and V_2 in the direction of motion of the passage.

(5) V_{1y} and V_{2y} are the components of V_1 and V_2 in a direction at right angles to the direction of motion of the passage.

(6) x represents the distance the passage moves in time θ.

Referring to the passage in Fig. 7·15, let the following be assumed:

1. The passage has a constant absolute velocity, $V_b = x/\theta$.
2. The absolute velocity V_1 has the same direction as V_b. Thus, its component in the x direction, $V_{1x} = V_1$.
3. There is no change in cross-sectional area of the passage.
4. The flow is frictionless.

The last two assumptions are made to eliminate the consideration of pressure drop in the passage and the resulting forces. From these two assumptions, it may also be concluded that the density of the steam remains constant in the passage and that V_{2b} will be equal to V_{1b} in magnitude.

It will be recalled that work is defined as the product of a force times the distance through which the force acts or

$$W = F_x x \qquad (7·7)$$

where W = work done by the fluid per lb of fluid

F_x = force exerted by the lb of fluid in the direction, x

x = distance traversed by the body on which the force acts in time, θ.

Newton's second law of motion states that the summation of the external forces acting on a body is equal to the time rate of change of momentum of the body. Mathematically, this statement may be written as

$$F_t = \frac{d(mV)}{d\theta} \qquad (7·8)$$

where F_t = the total or summation of all external forces acting on the body

mV = the momentum of the body having a mass, m, by definition

θ = the time at which the momentum is mV.

Generally, it is assumed that the mass of a body remains constant, and, further, it is convenient to write Equation 7·8 for

1 lb mass. In Article 1·4 1 lb_m is defined as 1/32.2 slugs. Thus, multiplying the right-hand side of Equation 7·8 by $\dfrac{1 \text{ slug}}{32.2 \text{ lb}_m}$ and letting $m = 1 \text{ lb}_m$, gives

$$F_t[\text{lb}_F] = \frac{1[\text{lb}_m][\text{slug}] \; dV \; [\text{fps}]}{32.2[\text{lb}_m] \; d\theta \quad [\text{sec}]} \qquad (7\cdot9)$$

Equation 7·9 is dimensionally correct since a 1-lb force is defined as 1 slug ft per sec².

Rearranging Equation 7·9 gives

$$F_t \, d\theta = \frac{1}{32.2} \, dV \qquad (7\cdot10)$$

and integrating between $\theta = 0$, $V = V_1$ and $\theta = \theta$, $V = V_2$ results in

$$F_t \int_0^\theta d\theta = \frac{1}{32.2} \int_{V_1}^{V_2} dV$$

or

$$F_t \theta = \frac{1}{32.2} \, (V_2 - V_1)$$

and

$$F_t = \frac{1}{32.2} \, (V_2 - V_1) \frac{1}{\theta} \qquad (7\cdot11)$$

The force, F_t, is the force of the passage on the fluid. An equal and opposite force is exerted by the fluid on the passage. Throughout the remainder of the chapter this opposite force will be designated by F_t, and its positive value will be determined by reversing the signs on the right-hand side of Equation 7·11. Thus, Equation 7·11 becomes, for the force of the fluid on the passage,

$$F_t = \frac{1}{32.2} \, (V_1 - V_2) \frac{1}{\theta} \qquad (7\cdot12)$$

Equation 7·12 is merely a statement of Newton's law and may be replaced by three force equations for the components of F_t in the x, y, and z directions. Thus, from Fig. 7·15 the horizontal and vertical components of the total force, F_t, are F_x and F_y, respectively, and are determined by the following equations:

$$F_x = \frac{1}{32.2}(V_{1x} - V_{2x})\frac{1}{\theta} \qquad (7\cdot13)$$

and

$$F_y = \frac{1}{32.2}(V_{1y} - V_{2y})\frac{1}{\theta} \qquad (7\cdot14)$$

where V_{1x} and V_{2x} are the horizontal components of the velocities and V_{1y} and V_{2y} are the vertical components of the velocities. For the passage in Fig. 7·15, F_x is that component of the force F_t which produces work on the passage since the passage is moving in the direction x. The force F_y produces no work but does produce a thrust. For a turbine blade the force F_y is the axial thrust, that thrust which is parallel to the turbine shaft. On substituting the expression for the force from Equation 7·13 into Equation 7·7, the work per lb of fluid becomes

$$W = \frac{1}{32.2}(V_{1x} - V_{2x})\frac{x}{\theta} \qquad (7\cdot15)$$

but x = the distance the blade moves through in the time θ, or

$$\frac{x}{\theta} = \text{the blade speed, } V_b$$

Thus, Equation 7·15 may be rewritten as

$$W = \frac{1}{32.2}(V_{1x} - V_{2x})V_b \text{ ft-lb per lb} \qquad (7\cdot16)$$

Power is the rate of doing work. Thus, if Equation 7·16 is multiplied by the mass rate of flow of the steam, m_s lb per sec,

$$\text{Power} = \frac{m_s}{32.2}(V_{1x} - V_{2x})V_b \text{ ft-lb per sec} \qquad (7\cdot17)$$

In Equations 7·16 and 7·17 the velocity components, V_{1x} and V_{2x}, may be positive or negative. It is customary to assign to them a positive value if they have the same direction of motion as the blade motion and a negative value if they have the opposite direction of motion.

Blade efficiency is defined as the ratio of work done on the blade to the energy supplied to the blade. For the passage shown in

Fig. 7·15 the only energy supplied per pound is the initial kinetic energy, $\dfrac{V_1^2}{2 \times 32.2}$. The blade efficiency, η, becomes

$$\eta = \frac{\dfrac{1}{32.2}(V_{1x} - V_{2x})V_b}{V_1^2/2 \times 32.2} \tag{7·18}$$

From Equation 7·16 it is apparent that the work done on the blade per pound of steam is a function of the blade velocity V_b and the change in velocity component of the steam, $V_{1x} - V_{2x}$. For any particular blade shape and initial velocity component V_{1x}, there is a definite blade velocity to give maximum work.

Two hypothetical blade shapes will now be considered and the proper blade velocity to give maximum work will be calculated for each.

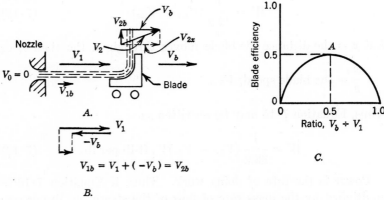

FIG. 7·16   Right-angle blade for Example 2

Example 2. Assume that a jet of fluid having an absolute velocity V_1 strikes a blade which has a right-angle turn as in Fig. 7·16A and which is free to move. Assume that the steady force of the jet causes the blade to move at an absolute velocity V_b and that the fluid leaves the blade with a relative velocity V_{2b} at right angles to V_b. Find the maximum blade work and the maximum blade efficiency.

Solution: The steam enters the blade with an absolute velocity V_1, and the blade has an absolute velocity V_b. Thus, the velocity of the steam relative to the blade is $V_{1b} = V_1 \rightarrow V_b$, as shown in Fig. 7·16B. The magnitude of the relative velocity of the steam is unchanged in the blade passage if there is no friction and no change in area for flow. Thus, the relative velocity of the steam leaving, V_{2b}, is equal to V_{1b} in magnitude but has a direction determined by the exit angle of the blade.

Since

$$V_2 = V_{2b} \nrightarrow V_b$$

then V_{2x}, the component of V_2 in the direction of V_b, is equal to V_b. The signs of V_1 and V_b are plus or to the right.

Substituting V_1 for V_{1x} and V_b for V_{2x} into Equation 7·16 gives

$$W = \frac{1}{32.2}(V_1 - V_b)V_b \text{ ft-lb per lb}$$

For a constant V_1 the work is a maximum when $dW/dV_b = 0$ or

$$\frac{d}{dV_b}\left[\frac{1}{32.2}(V_1 - V_b)V_b\right] = 0$$

Differentiating gives

$$\frac{1}{32.2}(V_1 - 2V_b) = 0$$

and

$$V_b = \frac{V_1}{2}$$

Thus, for maximum work, V_b should equal $V_1/2$. Substituting $V_b = V_1/2$ into the equation for work gives

$$W_{\max} = \frac{1}{32.2}\left(V_1 - \frac{V_1}{2}\right)\frac{V_1}{2} = \frac{1}{32.2}\left(\frac{V_1^2}{4}\right)$$

The maximum efficiency is $W_{\max} \div V_1^2/2 \times 32.2$ or

$$\eta_{\max} = \frac{2 \times 32.2}{32.2}\left(\frac{V_1^2}{4/V_1^2}\right) = \frac{1}{2} \text{ or } 50\% \quad \text{(see Point } A, \text{ Fig. } 7\cdot16C\text{)}$$

Example 3. Consider a blade shape as shown in Fig. 7·17A. Assume the velocities V_1 and V_b as shown. Find the blade work and the maximum blade efficiency.

Solution: The graphical solution for the initial relative velocity of the steam, V_{1b}, is shown in Fig. 7·17B. Again, if there is no friction or change in area for flow, V_{2b} has the same magnitude as V_{1b}. However, its direction is reversed. To obtain the absolute velocity of the steam leaving, add V_b vectorially to V_{2b}, or

$$V_2 = V_{2b} \nrightarrow V_b$$

From Equation 7·16,

$$W = \frac{1}{32.2}(V_{1x} - V_{2x})V_b$$

For this blade shape

$$V_{1x} = V_1 \quad \text{and} \quad V_{2x} = V_2$$

Thus,

$$W = \frac{1}{32.2}(V_1 - V_2)V_b \qquad\qquad\qquad \text{(a)}$$

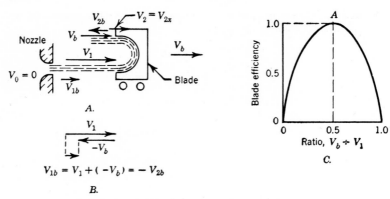

Fig. 7·17 Semi-circular blade for Example 3

but V_2 is equal in magnitude to $2V_b - V_1$ and is positive. Substituting $2V_b - V_1$ for V_2 gives

$$W = \frac{1}{32.2}(V_1 - 2V_b + V_1)V_b$$

$$= \frac{2}{32.2}(V_1 V_b - V_b^2) \qquad (b)$$

Differentiating the work with respect to V_b, setting equal to zero, and solving for V_b gives

$$V_b = \frac{V_1}{2}$$

The equation for maximum work is obtained by substituting $V_b = V_1/2$ into Equation b. Thus,

$$W = \frac{2}{32.2}\left(\frac{V_1^2}{2} - \frac{V_1^2}{4}\right) = \frac{V_1^2}{64.4}$$

Since $V_1^2/64.4$ is the amount of energy supplied, the maximum efficiency of the blade is 100 per cent (see Point A, Fig. 7·17C). An increase or decrease in the ratio of V_b/V_1 will reduce the blade efficiency.

The important conclusion to be drawn from Example 3 is that the ideal form for a turbine blade should be semi-circular. If frictionless flow and constant area are assumed, such a blade would have a theoretical maximum efficiency of 100 per cent. However, the blade cannot be utilized effectively in an actual turbine. The nozzle lies directly in the path of the moving blade and of the steam leaving the blade. Since each blade must be followed immediately by another to deliver work continuously, this ideal blade shape is impractical. Also, the losses due to friction increase as the ideal blade shape is approached.

In a turbine the nearest approach to the ideal condition is obtained by locating the nozzle at one side of the path of the blade and by directing the jet of steam into the blade at an angle. When this is done, the blade entrance angle must conform to the angle made by the relative velocity of the steam entering the blade. In Fig. 7·18 an actual nozzle and blade arrangement is shown. Also in Fig. 7·18 the vector diagram of the velocity of the steam entering and leaving the blade section is drawn.

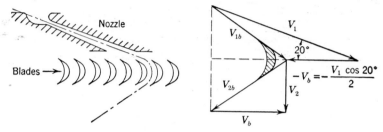

Fɪɢ. 7·18   Impulse blade conditions

The absolute velocity of the steam leaving the nozzle has a magnitude and direction represented by V_1. The angle α is the nozzle angle and is generally about 20 degrees. An angle much greater than 20 degrees would decrease the amount of work that could be done on the blade. If the angle is made smaller, the conditions approach the ideal conditions of the semi-circular blade, but the losses increase owing to the increase in the friction.

The steam strikes the blade at an angle β which is the angle that the relative velocity of the steam makes with the blade path. The relative velocity of the steam V_{1b} and its angle β are determined by the vector subtraction of the blade velocity V_b from the steam velocity V_1.

If no fluid friction occurs within the blade section and the flow area remains constant, the relative velocity of the steam leaving the blade V_{2b} will have a magnitude equal to that of V_{1b}, but its direction will be determined entirely by the blade exit angle γ. To give maximum efficiency, angle γ should be zero. However, as in the semi-circular blade shape this would be impractical. Generally, angle γ can be considered equal to angle β, and the blade shape is symmetrical.

7·6 Simple impulse turbine. The simple impulse turbine consists of a single row of nozzles and a single row of blades.

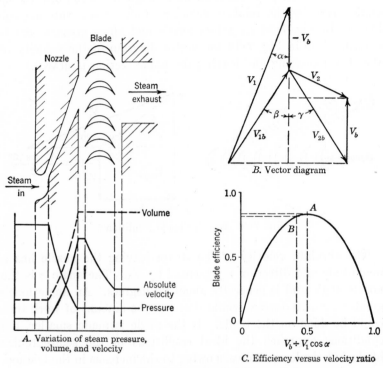

A. Variation of steam pressure, volume, and velocity

B. Vector diagram

C. Efficiency versus velocity ratio

Fig. 7·19   Simple impulse turbine analysis

The DeLaval turbine shown in Fig. 7·2 is a simple impulse turbine. A cut-away diagram (Fig. 7·19A) shows the nozzle and blade arrangement as viewed from the blade ends. Below the cut-away diagram the variations in pressure, volume, and velocity of the steam are plotted. The pressure decreases through the nozzle section only. The steam volume increases as the pressure decreases. The velocity increases in the nozzle section but decreases through the blade section as work is done.

In a simple impulse turbine where only a single row of blades is used, the blade velocity V_b should be made equal in magnitude to one-half the horizontal component of the absolute velocity of the entering steam V_1 or

$$V_b = \frac{V_1 \cos \alpha}{2} \quad \text{or} \quad \frac{V_b}{V_1 \cos \alpha} = \frac{1}{2} \quad \text{(see Fig. 7·18)}$$

This blade velocity V_b would give maximum efficiency for a symmetrical blade and for predetermined values of V_1 and angle α, as shown in Fig. 7·19C, point A. Figure 7·19B shows the vector diagram for a blade velocity V_b which is not made equal to $V_1 \cos \alpha \div 2$ and which results in a blade efficiency shown at point B, Fig. 7·19C. Therefore, if the absolute velocity of the steam V_1 is large, as is the case when steam expands in a single nozzle from a high pressure to a low pressure, the blade velocity should be correspondingly high.

However, it is customary to design turbines with mean blade velocities that will not exceed 1300 fps in order to avoid structural failure resulting from centrifugal force. Figure 7·20 shows a rear view of three typical, high-pressure, impulse turbine blades. Generally, they are made of a chrome–steel alloy, machined with key slots or dovetails at the root for fastening them to the rotor disk. A shroud band at the blade tips holds them together and prevents vibration.

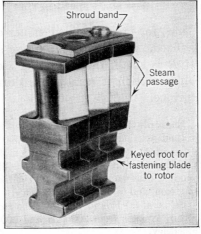

FIG. 7·20 Rear view of impulse turbine blades

The rotative speed of the turbine shaft is fixed by the design speed of the equipment being driven by the turbine. For a 60-cycle a-c two-pole generator the shaft speed must be 3600 rpm; for a four-pole generator, 1800 rpm. Auxiliary equipment such as fans and pumps have definite speed requirements for best efficiency. Speeds of such equipment seldom exceed 3600 rpm. If low speeds are desired, a gear reducer is placed between the turbine and the driven equipment.

The relation between blade velocity and shaft speed is given by the simple relation,

$$V_b = \frac{2\pi R n}{60} \quad \text{(see Fig. 7·21)} \quad (7·19)$$

where V_b = blade velocity, fps
R = blade radius, ft
n = shaft speed in rpm

Thus, for predetermined values of V_b and n the blade radius R is fixed. If R is large, the size and cost of the turbine is large. If R is small, the volume of steam that can pass through the blade section is small, thus decreasing the total output of the turbine.

Example 4. Assume that a simple impulse turbine is to expand steam without friction from 200 psia and 500 F to 1 psia, that the nozzle makes an angle of 20 degrees with the blade motion, that the blades are symmetrical, and that the turbine speed is to be 3600 rpm. Find (a) the blade velocity to produce maximum efficiency, (b) the blade radius R, (c) the work done per lb of steam, and (d) the blade efficiency.

Solution: (a) From Table 7·1, the steam velocity would be 4240 fps if the steam expands from 200 psia and 500 F to 1 psia. To produce maximum efficiency,

$$V_b = \frac{V_1 \cos \alpha}{2}$$

$$= \frac{4240 \cos 20}{2}$$

$$= 1990 \text{ fps} \qquad \text{(see Fig. 7·22)}$$

(b) From Equation 7·19,

$$V_b = \frac{2\pi R n}{60}$$

or

$$1990 = \frac{2\pi R 3600}{60}$$

or

$$R = 5.3 \text{ ft}$$

(*c*) From Equation 7·16,

$$\text{Work} = \frac{1}{32.2}(V_{1x} - V_{2x})V_b$$

$$= \frac{1}{32.2}(V_1 \cos \alpha - 0)V_1 \frac{\cos \alpha}{2}$$

$$= \frac{1}{32.2}(4240 \cos 20)1990$$

$$= 247,000 \text{ ft-lb per lb of steam}$$

(*d*) $\text{Blade efficiency} = \dfrac{247,000}{\dfrac{1}{2 \times 32.2}(4240)^2} \times 100 = 88.6\%$

where $\dfrac{(4240)^2}{64.4} = \text{initial kinetic energy}$

In the example the blade velocity is too high, since 1300 fps is considered the optimum practical blade velocity. It could be

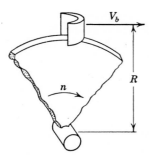

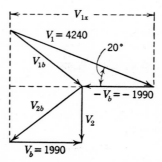

Fig. 7·21   Diagram for Equation 7·19

Fig. 7·22   Velocity diagram for Example 4

decreased by reducing the pressure drop originally assumed. If it were reduced without a corresponding reduction in pressure drop, the blade efficiency would then decrease, as shown in Example 5.

Example 5. Assume that the blade velocity is maintained at 1200 fps for the same steam and turbine conditions as in Example 4. Find the blade efficiency.

Solution:

$$V_1 = 4240 \text{ fps} \quad \text{(from Example 4)}$$

$$V_b = 1200 \text{ fps} \quad \text{assumed value} \quad \text{(see Fig. 7·23)}$$

$$\text{Work} = \frac{1}{32.2}(V_{1x} - V_{2x})V_b$$

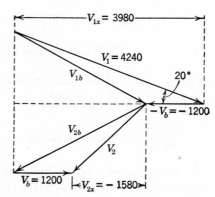

Fig. 7·23   Velocity diagram for Example 5

From the vector diagram $V_{1x} = 3980$ fps and $V_{2x} = -1580$ fps. Thus,

$$\text{Work} = \frac{1}{32.2}[3980 - (-1580)]1200$$

$$= 207,000 \text{ ft-lb per lb of steam}$$

and, since the initial kinetic energy is $(4240)^2/64.4 = 279,000$ ft-lb per lb steam, then,

$$\text{Blade efficiency} = \frac{207,000}{279,000} \times 100 = 74.0\%$$

Therefore, by keeping the blade velocity within a safe working limit without decreasing the pressure drop and thus decreasing the steam velocity, the blade efficiency was reduced from 88.6 per cent to 74.0 per cent.

7·7   Pressure staging.   For the impulse turbine two methods are employed to decrease the blade velocity and still maintain maximum blade efficiency for a given range of inlet and exhaust pressures. The first method is called pressure staging. If two or more simple impulse turbines are placed in series with their blades connected to a common shaft, the steam will expand from inlet pressure to exhaust pressure in stages. The number of stages or pressure reductions depends on the number of rows of nozzles through which the steam must pass. Each stage is called a Rateau stage. A cut-away section of three Rateau stages is

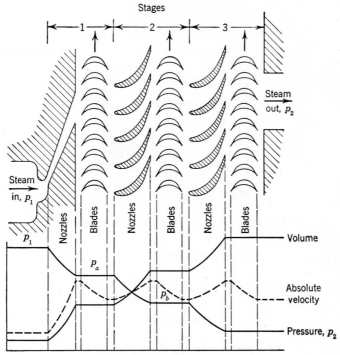

Fig. 7·24   Rateau or pressure staging

shown in Fig. 7·24. The changes in steam pressure, volume, and velocity are shown below the staging.

If pressures p_1 and p_2 are the same for the three Rateau stages as for the simple impulse turbine (Fig. 7·19), then the intermediate or stage pressures, p_a and p_b, shown in Fig. 7·24, could be fixed by the nozzle design to distribute the kinetic energy of the steam equally among the three stages.

Example 6. Assume the same conditions for three Rateau stages as were assumed in Example 4 for a simple impulse turbine. Also assume that the kinetic energy of the steam in Example 4, $(4240)^2/64.4$, is divided equally among the three Rateau stages by proper nozzle design. This will result in a steam velocity, V_1, of 2450 fps. Finally, assume that no energy which would be lost in a single stage is carried over from stage to stage. Find (a) the proper blade speed, (b) the blade radius, and (c) the work done in the three stages.

Solution: (a)

$$V_b = \frac{V_1 \cos \alpha}{2} = \frac{2450 \cos 20}{2}$$

$$= 1225 \times 0.94$$

$$= 1150 \text{ fps} \qquad \text{(see Fig. 7·25)}$$

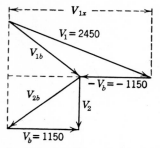

FIG. 7·25   Velocity diagram for Example 6

(b) From

$$V_b = 2\pi R \frac{n}{60}$$

$$R = \frac{1150 \times 60}{2\pi \times 3600}$$

$$R = 3.05 \text{ ft}$$

(c)   Work per stage $= \dfrac{1}{32.2}(V_{1x} - V_{2x})V_b$

$$= \frac{1}{32.2}(V_1 \cos \alpha - 0)\frac{V_1 \cos \alpha}{2}$$

$$= \frac{1}{32.2}(2450 \cos 20)\frac{2450 \cos 20}{2}$$

$$= \frac{1}{32.2}(2300)1150 = 82,400 \text{ ft-lb}$$

Work for 3 stages $= 3 \times 82,400 = 247,000$ ft-lb per lb steam

This is the same amount of work as was obtained in the single stage of Example 4.

Thus, by the use of three simple impulse turbines (three Rateau stages) acting in series between the same inlet and exhaust conditions as established for one simple turbine, the same work and efficiency can be maintained with a considerable decrease in blade velocity and blade radius.

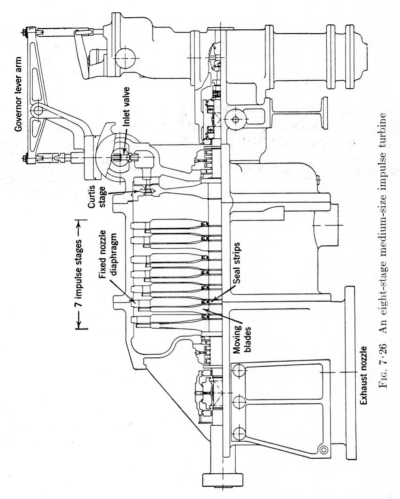

FIG. 7·26 An eight-stage medium-size impulse turbine

In practice, the use of a number of Rateau stages in place of a single simple impulse stage will result in better efficiency. Friction losses will be less for the lower steam velocities, and each stage will utilize some of the losses occurring in the preceding stage. Rateau stages are used in medium- and high-capacity turbines (see Fig. 7·26) where good efficiency is mandatory. The number of stages employed will be decided by the comparison of the increase in efficiency, the additional cost of the turbine, and the given capacity.

7·8   Velocity staging.   The second method employed in impulse-turbine design to decrease the blade velocity and still maintain maximum efficiency is called velocity staging.   Steam is permitted to expand through a stationary nozzle from inlet pressure to exhaust pressure as in the simple impulse turbine.   As the pressure drops in the nozzle, the kinetic energy of the steam increases by virtue of an increase in velocity.   A portion of the available kinetic energy is absorbed in a row of moving blades. After doing work on these blades, the steam enters a second row of blades which are stationary and merely act to redirect the flow of steam.   The steam after being redirected enters a second row of moving blades on which more work is done.

A cross section of such a stage and the change in steam pressure, volume, and velocity are shown in Fig. 7·27A.   The vector diagram for the steam entering and leaving each blade section is shown in Fig. 7·27B and represents the condition at which maximum blade efficiency will occur.   Unlike the simple impulse turbine or the pressure stage, the velocity stage utilizes more than one row of moving blades with a velocity decrease in each row.   Only one row of nozzles is necessary per stage.   The stationary blading does not change the magnitude of the velocity of the steam leaving the first row of blades V_2 (see Fig. 7·27B). It merely redirects the steam to give a velocity V_3, equal in magnitude to V_2, which enters the second row of moving blades.

To give maximum efficiency, the blade velocity V_b as shown by Fig. 7·27B becomes $V_1 \cos \alpha/2n$, where n = number of rows of moving blades.   Blade work is calculated for each row of moving blades in a manner similar to that used for a simple impulse turbine.   The total work of the stage is the sum of the work done by each row of moving blades.

Example 7.   Assume that the initial steam velocity V_1 is 4240 fps as in Examples 4 and 5 and that it makes an angle of 20 degrees with the direction of motion of the blade.   Assume frictionless flow.

Find (a) the blade velocity to give maximum work in two velocity stages as in Fig. 7·27, (b) the blade radius, and (c) the total work done on the blades.

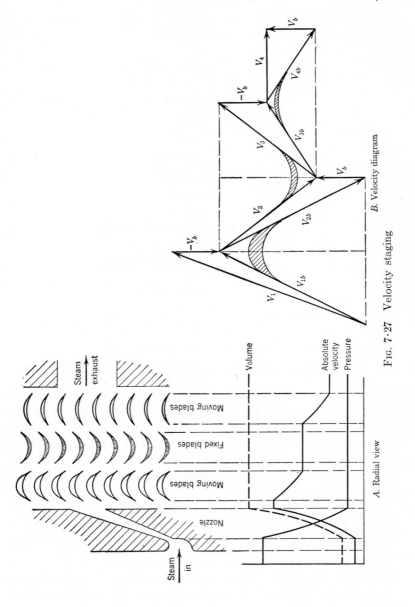

A. Radial view

B. Velocity diagram

Fig. 7·27 Velocity staging

Solution: (a)

$$V_b = \frac{V_1 \cos \alpha}{2n}$$

$$= \frac{4240 \cos 20}{4}$$

$$= 995 \text{ fps} \qquad \text{(see Fig. 7·28)}$$

(b) From
$$R = \frac{V_b 60}{2\pi n}$$

$$= \frac{60 \times 995}{2\pi 3600}$$

$$= 2.66 \text{ ft}$$

(c) Work for 1st row $= \dfrac{1}{32.2}(V_{1x} - V_{2x})V_b$

$$= \frac{1}{32.2}(3980 + 1990)$$

$$= 185{,}500 \text{ ft-lb}$$

Work for 2d row $= \dfrac{1}{32.2}(1990 - 0)995$

$$= 61{,}500 \text{ ft-lb}$$

Total work of the stage $= 247{,}000$ ft-lb per lb steam

Thus, it is evident that, theoretically by introducing a second row of moving blades (preceded by a fixed row of blades) to the simple impulse turbine, a lower blade velocity may be used with no sacrifice in work or efficiency. The blade radius is also less. In the actual machine using the velocity staging, the efficiency will be higher than a single-pressure stage turbine but lower than a group of pressure stages.

The velocity stage is used extensively in small turbines intended for driving auxiliary equipment. It is often called a Curtis stage after the name of the inventor. A small Curtis turbine is shown in Fig. 7·5. Note that the two rows of moving blades are connected to the same blade disk and turbine shaft. The row of stationary blades is fastened to the casing and lies between the two rows of moving blades. Typical blades are shown in Fig. 7·20.

There are two unique methods of applying the Curtis principle to small turbines without the necessity of adding a second row of blades. The turbines employing these methods are the re-entry turbine and the Terry turbine. The principles of operation of these turbines are shown in Fig. 7·29. The re-entry turbine

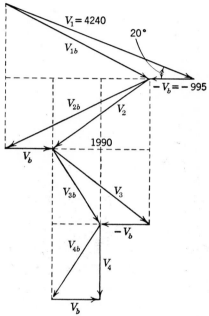

Fig. 7·28 Velocity diagram for Example 7

uses a re-entry chamber which replaces the fixed blades of the Curtis stage but which turns the steam through an angle sufficient to redirect the steam through the first row of moving blades. The Terry turbine has blades that are semi-circular in shape, approaching the ideal blade shape discussed in Example 3. The fixed blades are also semi-circular in shape, and the nozzle introduces steam parallel to the blade motion. A spiral path is taken by the steam as it enters and leaves the row of blades.

The Curtis or velocity stage is often used in large turbines to precede a series of pressure stages or reaction stages. Such use is to provide a cheaper turbine with little sacrifice in actual efficiency. The single Curtis stage replaces a number of pressure stages at the high-pressure end or inlet. At the low-pressure end, pressure stages have enough higher efficiency to warrant their use in place of velocity stages. A large turbine designed on these principles is shown in Fig. 7·26.

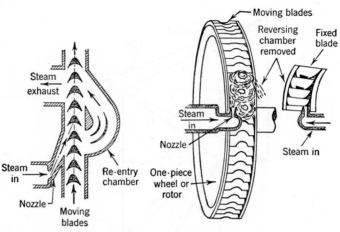

FIG. 7·29   Velocity compounding as illustrated by a re-entry turbine and a Terry turbine

7·9   The reaction turbine.   Theoretically, the reaction turbine differs from an impulse turbine using pressure stages only because the moving blades of the reaction turbine act as nozzles. As in the impulse turbine, fixed nozzles are provided between each two rows of moving blades. In order to insure a nozzle action in the moving blades, the blades are not built symmetrically but are constructed as the nozzle block shown in Fig. 7·10*B*. Thus, in a reaction turbine the fixed rows of nozzles and the moving rows of blades or nozzles are usually identical in form. A cross-sectional diagram of two reaction stages with the change in steam pressure, volume, and velocity is shown in Fig. 7·30*A*.

The steam pressure decreases continuously through the stages since both fixed and moving rows of blades act as nozzles. The steam volume increases continuously. The absolute steam velocity increases in the fixed rows of nozzles but decreases in the moving rows of blades. This is evident after an inspection of the velocity diagram (Fig. 7·30B). The absolute velocity of the steam V_1 decreases to a velocity V_2, but the relative velocity of the steam increases from V_{1b} to V_{2b}. The pressure drop for each row is small since a large number of stages are used between inlet

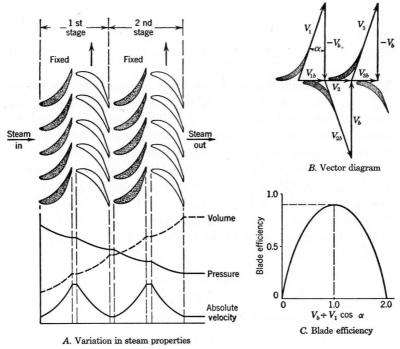

A. Variation in steam properties

B. Vector diagram

C. Blade efficiency

Fig. 7·30   Reaction turbine staging

and exhaust conditions. The small pressure drop in the nozzles results in a low steam velocity per stage. Thus, generally the velocity of reaction turbine blades is less than the velocity of impulse blades and may vary from 100 to 500 fps.

The velocity diagram of two reaction stages is shown in Fig. 7·30B. The blade shapes as drawn are called "symmetrical" because the two velocity diagrams are identical.

The work done by the steam on a reaction blade is calculated by the same method as was used to calculate the work done on an impulse blade. For example, the work per pound of steam for the symmetrical stage shown in Fig. 7·30B is given by

$$W = \frac{1}{32.2}(V_{1x} - V_{2x})V_b \text{ ft-lb}$$

where

$$V_{1x} = V_1 \cos \alpha$$

$$V_{2x} = 0$$

Thus,

$$W = \frac{1}{32.2}(V_1 \cos \alpha - 0)V_b \tag{7·20}$$

The blade velocity for maximum work is determined by differentiating the work with respect to blade velocity, equating the result to zero, and solving for V_b. The result shows that V_b should equal $V_1 \cos \alpha$. This is the condition established when the blade entrance angle is 90 degrees as shown in Fig. 7·30B.

The energy supplied to the reaction blade is equal to the initial kinetic energy, $V_1^2/64.4$, plus the energy transfer resulting from the steam expanding in the moving blade. In the case of the symmetrical reaction blade this energy is equal to $V_1^2/64.4$. Thus, the total energy supplied to the blade is $V_1^2/32.2$, and the blade efficiency becomes

$$\eta = \frac{W}{V_1^2/32.2} \tag{7·21}$$

Combining Equations 7·21 and 7·20 gives

$$\eta = \frac{V_b V_1 \cos \alpha}{V_1^2}$$

$$= V_b \frac{\cos \alpha}{V_1} \tag{7·22}$$

The maximum efficiency, when $V_b = V_1 \cos \alpha$, becomes

$$\eta_{\max} = \cos^2 \alpha \tag{7·23}$$

Example 8. A symmetrical reaction blade has an entrance angle of 90 degrees. Steam enters the blade with an absolute velocity of 500 fps. The fixed-nozzle angle, α, is equal to 20 degrees. Calculate (a) the proper blade velocity, and (b) the blade work in ft-lb per lb of steam.

Solution: (a) The relative velocity of the steam V_{1b} should have the same angle as the blade entrance angle; thus

$$V_b = V_1 \cos \alpha \qquad \text{(see Fig. } 7 \cdot 30B\text{).}$$

$$= 500 \cos 20$$

$$= 470 \text{ fps}$$

(b) From the general expression for blade work,

$$W = \frac{1}{32.2}(V_{1x} - V_{2x})V_b$$

but

$$V_{1x} = V_1 \cos \alpha = V_b$$

$$= 470 \text{ fps}$$

and

$$V_{2x} = 0$$

Thus,

$$W = \frac{1}{32.2}(470)(470)$$

$$= 6860 \text{ ft-lb per lb}$$

In the impulse turbine there is no drop in pressure through the moving blade sections. End thrust or axial thrust is produced entirely by the change in the components of the force of the steam jet which act at right angles to the direction of blade motion. The resulting thrust is quite small and can be absorbed in an especially designed thrust bearing. However, in the reaction turbine there is a pressure drop in each row of moving blades. This pressure drop or pressure differential is large when many stages are considered. Also, in the actual reaction turbine the rotor is cone-shaped (see Fig. $7 \cdot 31$) to provide for an increasing blade-ring area in order to accommodate the increasing steam volume. Pressure acting against the sloping sides of the rotor produce an added axial thrust. The total thrust cannot be absorbed in a bearing, and so dummy pistons are provided at the inlet end of the turbine against which the high inlet pressure is exerted. Proper design of the dummy piston sizes will counteract the axial thrust enough so that the thrust bearing can carry any excess.

Since there is a pressure differential across each row of moving blades in a reaction turbine, there is a tendency for steam to leak around the ends of the blades. This leakage tendency is

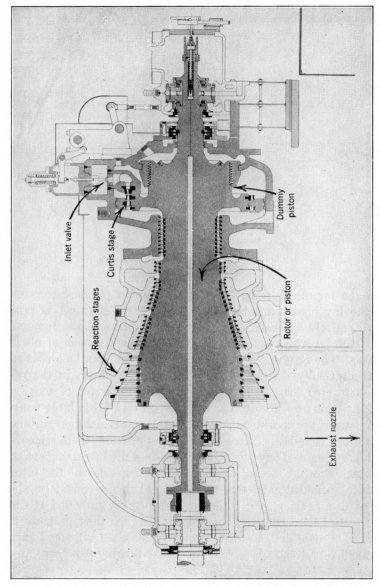

Fig. 7·31   A large reaction turbine with a Curtis stage at the inlet

not so pronounced in the impulse turbine. To prevent steam leakage seal strips are placed on the ends of the moving blades, as shown in Fig. 7·32. Seal strips on the fixed nozzle blocks at the point nearest the shaft are necessary in both the impulse and reaction turbines, as shown in Fig. 7·26. Seal strips and labyrinth arrangements are provided at the shaft on the high-pressure

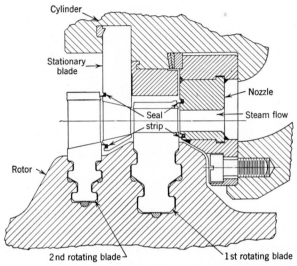

Fig. 7·32 Method of preventing steam leakage around blades by seal strips

end of the turbine to prevent steam leaking to the surroundings. These are shown in Fig. 7·33.

Seal strips are made thin to prevent excessive wear of the rotor or of the blades against which they may rub. Labyrinths are used to provide only the most circuitous path for the steam. The pressure drop resulting from the friction of the steam as it passes around the seal strips of the labyrinths keeps steam leakage at a minimum.

Generally, in reaction turbines the reaction staging is preceded by a Curtis impulse stage. The Curtis stage is placed at the high-pressure end of the turbine where it functions most efficiently, and its use is to reduce the total number of reaction stages necessary. Thus, the size of the reaction turbine is decreased with very little sacrifice in overall efficiency. The Curtis stage can be seen in Fig. 7·31. The rotor diameter decreases following the Curtis stage because steam enters the reaction blading throughout the reaction blade periphery, thus increasing the volume capacity, whereas steam flows through the Curtis stage through a relatively narrow arc of the blade periphery.

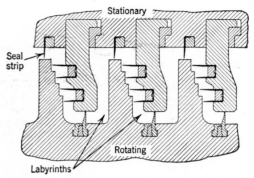

Fig. 7·33 Seal strips and labyrinths to prevent steam leakage at the shaft

7·10   Types of turbines. Many types of industrial turbines are in use today, depending upon the conditions under which they must operate. They are classified as high- or low-pressure turbines, according to the inlet pressure of the steam, and as superposed, condensing, and noncondensing turbines, according to the exhaust steam pressure. A superposed or high back-pressure turbine is one that exhausts to pressures well above atmospheric pressure, 100 to 600 psi. A superposed turbine operates in series with a medium-pressure turbine. The exhaust steam of the superposed turbine is used to drive the medium-pressure unit. The noncondensing turbine has lower exhaust pressures, but the steam still leaves at atmospheric pressure or above—15 to 50 psi. The exhaust steam may be used for drying or heating processes.

The condensing turbine operates at exhaust pressures below atmospheric pressure and requires the use of two auxiliaries: a condenser and pump. The condenser reduces the exhaust steam to water. As the steam is condensed and the water is removed by a pump, a partial vacuum is formed in the exhaust chamber of the turbine. This type of turbine is used chiefly for the low-cost electric power it produces.

If steam is required for processing, a turbine may be modified by extracting or bleeding the steam. Extraction takes place at one or more points between inlet and exhaust, depending upon the pressures needed for the processes. The extraction may be automatic or nonautomatic. Generally, factory processes require

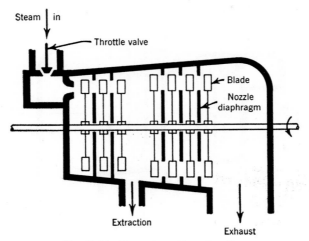

FIG. 7·34 Nonautomatic extraction

steam at a specific pressure; in this case, an automatic-extraction turbine is necessary. When steam is needed within the power plant itself for heating boiler feedwater, nonautomatic extraction is generally used. In Figs. 7·34 and 7·35 the two types of turbines are shown in simple form. In the automatic-extraction turbine, a diaphragm is inserted following the extraction point. A valve operates within the diaphragm to restrict the flow of steam toward the exhaust so as to maintain a constant pressure at the extraction point. A grid-type diaphragm valve is shown in Fig. 7·36. At the top of the valve is the control gear which adjusts the valve opening.

Turbines may be classified according to their speed and size. Small turbines, varying in size from a few horsepower to several thousand horsepower, are used to drive fans, pumps, and other auxiliary equipment directly. The speed of these units is adjusted to the speed of the driven machinery or is converted by a suitable gear arrangement. These turbines are used wherever steam is readily available at low cost or where exhaust steam is needed.

Turbines used for the production of electric power range in size from small units to those of over 150,000 kw, and the trend is

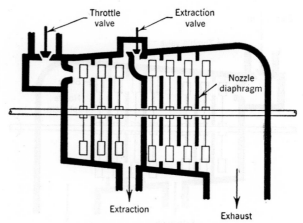

Fig. 7·35 Automatic extraction

toward even larger units. Since the United States has standardized on a frequency of 60 cycles per sec for a-c power, turbogenerator units are constructed to operate at 3600 or 1800 rpm. The selection of the speed depends almost entirely on the size of the turbogenerator desired. The speed of 3600 rpm is preferred whenever the size of the turbine permits. The turbine operating at the higher speed has the following advantages: lighter weight, more compactness, and greater suitability for high-pressure, high-temperature operation.

With a few exceptions turbines larger than 100,000 kw will operate at 1800 rpm. All turbines of smaller capacity will run at 3600 rpm. However, because of the advantages of the 3600-rpm unit and because of the greater efficiency of large units, turbine manufacturers will continue to raise the upper limit of speed and capacity.

Generally, turbogenerators on a single shaft and within a given speed range are constructed with either a single or a double casing. The double-casing arrangement is used for only the largest turbines falling within a given speed range. A double casing

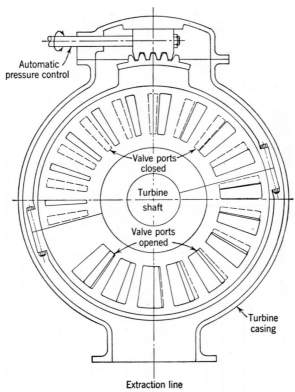

Fɪɢ. 7·36 A grid-type automatic-extraction valve

unit is called a tandem-compound turbine, and the flow is double-exhaust to accommodate the large volumes of steam occurring at the low-pressure end. Such a turbine is shown in Figs. 7·37 and 7·38.

In the turbine shown in Fig. 7·38, steam enters at the left and flows through the high-pressure element to the looping pipe at the top. The steam then passes to the low-pressure double-flow element and flows to the front and rear of the second element and

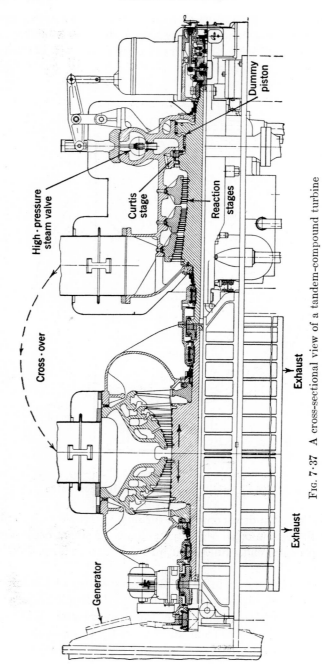

FIG. 7·37 A cross-sectional view of a tandem-compound turbine

Fig. 7·38 A tandem-compound steam turbogenerator

exhausts to a condenser below the floor. This provides twice the capacity of a single-flow turbine for a given speed. The generator, hydrogen-cooled, is the large cylindrical element in the center of the picture. The generator exciter is at the extreme right.

7·11 Turbine governors. Turbines are the most flexible prime movers in existence. They can supply power or steam and power for the widely varying demands of industry under exacting

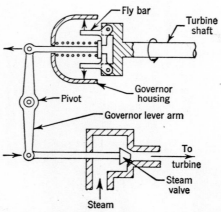

FIG. 7·39   A centrifugal "fly-bar" throttling governor

conditions. However, the ability to perform well under such conditions depends largely upon their automatic control as accomplished by regulators or governors. Although there are as many types of governors as there are variations in industrial requirements, only a few fundamental principles are involved. Usually the control depends upon the variation in the turbine speed. In turbines involving an extraction process, however, the control will also depend upon variations in steam pressure. These two types of governors will be discussed in some detail.

The speed governor maintains a nearly constant shaft speed in order that the generator can produce a constant electric frequency. Such a governor regulates the supply of steam to the turbine as variations in the load tend to increase or decrease its speed. The governor operates on the "fly-bar" principle as shown in Fig. 7·39. As the speed increases under a reduction in turbine load the fly bars move outward because of the increase in centrifugal force. The governor lever arm swings about a pivot and partially closes the inlet valve. The corresponding reduction in steam pressure brings the turbine speed back to normal. The governor operates in the reverse for increases in turbine load. This governor is called a throttling governor because the process is essentially a throttling process across the governor valve. This process was discussed in Article 1·27.

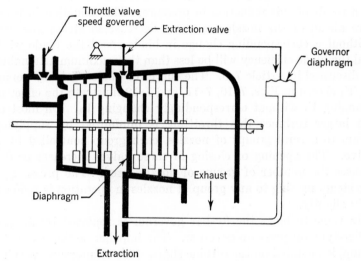

Fig. 7·40 An extraction governor, pressure-operated

The simple extraction governor as shown in Fig. 7·40 maintains a constant pressure in the extraction line for variations in the demand for process steam. The pressure in the extraction line actuates a diaphragm which opens or closes the extraction valve. A drop in pressure resulting from an increase in process steam demand causes the extraction valve to move downward. Less steam passes to the exhaust end of the turbine, and the pressure ahead of the extraction valve increases. Since the extraction governor does not control the turbine speed, a speed governor must also be included. The extraction valve shown in Fig. 7·36 acts as both diaphragm and valve. The grid opens or closes as the pressure varies in the extraction line. Although the governor in Fig. 7·40 is not in general use, the principles involved are applied to the more complicated types which operate in conjunction with the speed governor.

In larger turbines most of the mechanical system of relaying the motion of the fly-bar governor to the valve or valves is replaced by a hydraulic system using oil under pressure. This provides a more sensitive control.

The throttling governor shown in Fig. 7·39 reduces the pressure of the steam before it enters the first nozzles. A loss occurs as a result of this reduction in pressure. The reduction in pressure ahead of the nozzles causes a decrease in steam velocity. Without a corresponding change in blade speed the blade work and the blade efficiency will be less than the maximum attainable, as discussed in Article 7·5. The curves of blade efficiency versus V_b/V_1 shown in Figs. 7·16, 7·17, and 7·19 illustrate the effect of changing V_1 without correspondingly changing V_b. On most of the larger turbines this throttling is minimized by supplying steam to several groups of nozzles, each group controlled by a valve. The opening or closing of these valves increases or decreases the number of groups of nozzles used. The pressure of the steam passing to any group of nozzles in operation is reduced only slightly.

In some turbines the fly-bar governor is replaced by an impeller-type oil-pressure governor. The impeller, acting as an oil pump, is mounted on the turbine shaft. The oil pressure, varying as the square of the shaft speed, can be transmitted to the governing-valve mechanism. A decrease in shaft speed will produce a decrease in oil pressure. The decrease in oil pressure will cause the inlet valves to open, admitting more steam to the turbine.

All turbines are equipped with an overspeed governor or safety stop which will operate a quick-closing valve. The safety governor is usually adjusted to shut off the steam supplied to the turbine at overspeeds exceeding 10 per cent of the rated speed. Such a governor mechanism operates on the centrifugal principle, as shown in Fig. 7·41. A pin mounted in a recess drilled radially in the shaft is held flush with the shaft surface by a spring. If the overspeed exceeds 10 per cent of the rated speed, the pin will move outward far enough to release the trip lever. As the trip lever is released, the overspeed spring-operated valve will shut, and the supply of steam to the turbine will stop. The turbine will not operate until the valve and holding link are reset.

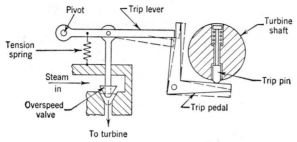

FIG. 7·41   Overspeed governor or safety stop

7·12   Turbine losses and performance. The performance of a steam turbine depends upon certain losses existing within the turbine and upon the external conditions under which it operates. Some of the losses to be found in any turbine are as follows:

1. Steam friction losses in nozzle and blade passages.
2. Steam leakage losses.
3. Losses in the exhaust steam.
4. Rotational losses due to friction in the bearings and fanning action of the blades.
5. Radiation of heat to the surroundings.

The loss in the exhaust steam is inherent in all steam-driven prime movers and is similar to the exhaust loss of internal-combustion engines. It will average about 60 per cent of the total input to the turbine. It can be reduced by decreasing the pressure at which the turbine exhausts, but the minimum exhaust pressure that can be attained is 1 to 2 in. of Hg absolute. To obtain such a low pressure, it is necessary to condense the steam and to pump the water against atmospheric pressure to discharge it from the condenser. If a turbine exhausts at pressures above atmospheric pressure, the steam may be used for heating. Thus, the loss occurring in the turbine is a gain in the heating system.

Steam leakage occurs mainly around the ends of reaction-turbine blades, around the nozzle diaphragms of impulse and reaction turbines, and between the turbine shaft and its bearings. These losses are reduced by the use of seal strips or carbon packing.

The steam friction loss can be reduced by decreasing the velocity of the steam as it passes from stage to stage. The multi-stage turbines are constructed for this purpose. Friction in the bearings is small and is held to a minimum by a proper lubricating system. To reduce the heat lost to the surroundings, most turbines are heavily insulated. Losses other than the exhaust losses will amount to about 10 per cent of the total input.

Some of the external conditions that have a marked effect on the turbine performance are:

1. Inlet pressure and temperature of the steam.
2. Exhaust pressure of the steam.
3. Turbine speed.
4. Load carried by the turbine.

One of the most common measures of the relative performance of turbines is called *steam rate,* and its units are pounds per kilowatt-hour.

A turbine has an ideal steam rate and an actual steam rate. The ideal steam rate may be defined as the amount of steam in pounds per hour that would be necessary to produce 1 kw if the isentropic enthalpy change for the turbine is completely converted into work. Thus,

$$\text{Ideal steam rate} = \frac{3413 \text{ Btu per kw-hr}}{(h_1 - h_2)_s \text{ Btu per lb}} \qquad (7 \cdot 24)$$

where $(h_1 - h_2)_s$ = isentropic enthalpy drop between inlet conditions and the exhaust pressure

The actual steam rate is defined as the amount of steam in pounds per hour actually used by the turbine divided by the power produced in kilowatts or the

$$\text{Actual steam rate} = \frac{\text{steam used (lb per hr)}}{\text{power produced (kw)}} \qquad (7 \cdot 25)$$

Example 9. A turbine produces 1000 kw on test and consumes 16,000 lb of steam per hr. Steam enters the turbine at 200 psia and 540 F and leaves at 3 in. Hg absolute. Calculate the ideal steam rate and the actual steam rate.

Solution: (*a*) From the Mollier chart the isentropic enthalpy drop from inlet to exhaust is $(h_1 - h_2)_s = 1290 - 940 = 350$ (see accompanying Fig. 7·42)

Thus,   Ideal steam rate $= \dfrac{3413 \text{ Btu per kw-hr}}{350 \text{ Btu per lb}}$

$$= 9.75 \text{ lb per kw-hr}$$

(*b*) Actual steam rate as determined from the test data $= \dfrac{16{,}000 \text{ lb per hr}}{1000 \text{ kw}}$

$$= 16 \text{ lb per kw-hr}$$

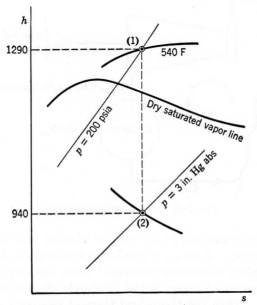

Fig. 7·42   Mollier diagram for Example 9

In comparing the performance of steam turbines, it is customary to determine (*a*) the theoretical or highest possible thermal efficiency, (*b*) the actual thermal efficiency, and (*c*) the ratio of actual to theoretical efficiency, generally known as the engine efficiency.

Thermal efficiency is defined as the ratio of the work done in the prime mover to the heat supplied to the prime mover. For a steam turbine the ASME Power Test Codes arbitrarily defines the heat supplied to the turbine as the amount of energy required to convert saturated water at the turbine exhaust pressure to steam at the throttle pressure and temperature. Thus, for the turbine shown in Fig. 7·43 the heat supplied per pound of steam is defined as $h_1 - h_{f2}$. This definition is restricted to straight, condensing turbines and should not be applied to extraction turbines.

The theoretical thermal efficiency is based on the assumption

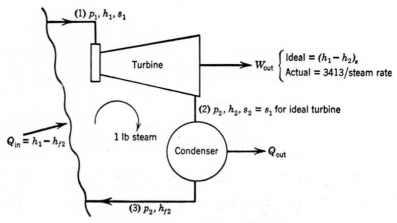

FIG. 7·43 Simple condensing cycle

that the steam expands in the turbine without heat transfer and without friction. Such an expansion is discussed in Article 1·23 and takes place at constant entropy. Thus, the theoretical work done per pound of steam is the isentropic change in enthalpy, $(h_1 - h_2)_s$. Then the *theoretical thermal efficiency*, η_t, may be computed as follows:

$$\eta_t = \frac{\text{theoretical work (Btu per lb steam)}}{\text{heat supplied (Btu per lb steam)}} = \frac{(h_1 - h_2)_s}{h_1 - h_{f2}} \quad (7\cdot26)$$

In the real turbine, friction of the steam in flowing at high velocities through the nozzles and blades, windage losses in spinning disks and blades at high speeds in the steam atmosphere, leakage, heat transfer to the surroundings, and other factors prevent the attainment of a constant entropy expansion. In computing the actual or real thermal efficiency, the work done is determined by test, but the heat supplied is still arbitrarily defined as $h_1 - h_{f2}$ Btu per lb steam. The actual work done per pound of steam is computed by dividing 3413 Btu per kw-hr by the actual steam rate in pounds per kilowatt-hour. Then the actual thermal efficiency, η_a, may be computed as follows:

$$\eta_a = \frac{\text{actual work (Btu per lb steam)}}{\text{heat supplied (Btu per lb steam)}} = \frac{3413/\text{actual steam rate}}{h_1 - h_{f2}}$$

$$(7 \cdot 27)$$

Because of the second law of thermodynamics as discussed briefly in Article 1·28, it is impossible for any turbine to attain a high thermal efficiency, and the very best of turbines operating on the highest steam pressures and temperatures and the lowest possible exhaust pressures are still incapable of producing a thermal efficiency of 50 per cent. Since heat energy is low-grade energy which is difficult to convert into work and then only with low efficiency, the true measure of performance of the turbine is the extent to which the actual thermal efficiency as given by Equation 7·27 approaches the theoretical efficiency as given by Equation 7·26. The ratio of the actual to ideal thermal efficiency is known as the *engine efficiency, η_e.*

Therefore,

$$\text{Engine efficiency, } \eta_e = \frac{\eta_a}{\eta_t} = \frac{3413/\text{actual steam rate}}{(h_1 - h_2)_s} \qquad (7 \cdot 28)$$

Example 10. For the turbine in Example 9 calculate (a) the ideal thermal efficiency, (b) the actual thermal efficiency, and (c) the engine efficiency.

Solution: (a)

$$\eta_t = \frac{(h_1 - h_2)_s}{(h_1 - h_{f2})}$$

but, from Example 9,

$$(h_1 - h_2)_s = 1290 - 940 = 350 \text{ Btu per lb}$$

$$h_1 = 1290 \text{ Btu per lb}$$

and

$$h_{f2} = 83 \text{ Btu per lb } (h_f \text{ at 3 in. of Hg abs})$$

Thus,
$$= \frac{1290 - 940}{1290 - 83}$$

$$= \frac{350}{1207}$$

$$= 0.29 \text{ or } 29\%$$

(*b*) The actual thermal efficiency is

$$= \frac{1000 \times 3413 \text{ Btu per hr}}{16,000(1290 - 83) \text{ Btu per hr}}$$

$$= 0.177 \text{ or } 17.7\%$$

(*c*) $$\eta_e = \frac{\eta_a}{\eta_t}$$

but $\eta_a = 17.7\%$ from Example 9

and $\eta_t = 29.0\%$ from above

Thus, $$\eta_e = \frac{17.7}{29.0}$$

$$= 0.61 \text{ or } 61\%$$

The approximate full-load steam rates of actual turbines ranging in size from 500 to 7500 kw are shown in Fig. 7·44. The steam rate decreases with an increase in turbine size, turbine load, and turbine pressure. Also, the steam rate decreases with an increase in inlet steam temperature and with a decrease in exhaust pressure. The steam rate will increase with a decrease in load.

Engine efficiencies for units rated at 100,000 kw or higher will be as high as 85 per cent. The engine efficiency decreases rapidly from 75 per cent for a 10,000-kw turbine to 50 per cent for units under 500 kw. The same factors that tend to increase the actual steam rate will decrease the engine efficiency.

PROBLEMS

1. A gas enters a nozzle with a velocity of 20 fps and an enthalpy of 100 Btu per lb and exhausts from the nozzle with an enthalpy of 50 Btu per lb. If no heat is transferred to or from the gas, calculate the velocity of the gas leaving the nozzle.

2. What per cent error is made in calculating the final velocity of the gas for Problem 1 if it is assumed that the initial velocity is zero?

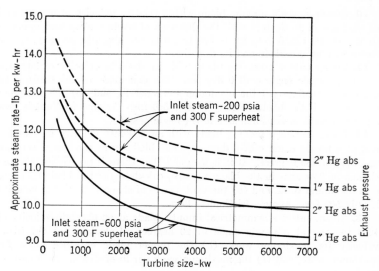

Fig. 7·44 Actual steam rates for small turbines

3. Calculate the exit area of a converging nozzle in which 1 lb of steam per sec expands isentropically from 100 psia and 460 F to 70 psia.

4. Calculate the exit velocity of the steam and the exit area of the converging–diverging nozzle in which 1 lb of steam per sec expands isentropically from 100 psia and 500 F to 14.7 psia.

5. One pound of steam expands isentropically from 200 psia and 500 F to 2 psia. Calculate (*a*) the throat velocity, (*b*) the throat area, (*c*) the exit velocity, and (*d*) the exit area.

6. If the divergence angle for the nozzle in Problem **5** is to be 10 degrees, calculate the length of the nozzle from throat to exit: i.e., the length of the diverging section.

7. What is the proper exhaust pressure for a nozzle which is to expand steam isentropically from 200 psia and 400 F and which will produce a jet velocity of 2500 fps? Assume that the initial velocity is negligible. What nozzle contour should be used?

8. Steam leaves a nozzle and enters a moving blade with an absolute velocity of 1000 fps. If the nozzle angle α is 18 degrees and the blade velocity is 500 fps, find the relative velocity of the steam with respect to the blade. What angle does the relative velocity of the steam make with the blade direction?

9. It is desired to have the steam enter a blade without shock or turbulence; i.e., the relative velocity should be tangent to the blade entrance angle. If the absolute velocity of the blade is 600 fps and the nozzle angle α is 20 degrees, calculate the required absolute velocity of the steam entering the blade if the blade entrance angle is 45 degrees.

10. Steam leaves a moving blade with a relative velocity of 500 fps and at an angle of 45 degrees with the direction of blade motion and opposite to it. If the blade velocity is 500 fps, find the absolute velocity of the steam leaving the blade and its direction.

11. Steam enters a moving blade with an absolute velocity of 2000 fps and at a nozzle angle α of 0 degrees. The exit angle of the blade is 90 degrees. Calculate (*a*) the maximum work per lb, and (*b*) the work per lb of steam if the blade velocity is only 500 fps. Assume frictionless flow and constant cross-sectional area in the blade passage.

12. Steam enters a moving blade with an absolute velocity of 2000 fps and at a nozzle angle α of 0 degrees. The blade turns the steam through an angle of 180 degrees. If it is assumed that there is no friction and no change in flow area in the blade passage, calculate (*a*) the blade speed to give maximum work, and (*b*) the work per lb of steam if the blade velocity is only 500 fps. Assume frictionless flow.

13. Steam enters a symmetrical impulse blade at an absolute velocity of 1200 fps and at a nozzle angle of 20 degrees. Calculate (*a*) the blade velocity for maximum work, (*b*) the proper blade entrance angle for maximum work, and (*c*) the maximum work per lb of steam. Assume frictionless flow.

14. A symmetrical impulse blade has a velocity of 500 fps. Steam enters at a nozzle angle of 23 degrees and an absolute velocity of 1000 fps. Calculate (*a*) the proper blade entrance angle for shockless flow, (*b*) the blade work per lb of steam, and (*c*) the blade efficiency for frictionless flow.

15. Steam enters the nozzle of an intermediate, Rateau, impulse stage with a velocity of 500 fps. The nozzle has an angle α of 20 degrees. The blades are symmetrical, and their velocity is 1000 fps. Calculate (*a*) the proper enthalpy drop in the nozzle to give maximum blade work, and (*b*) the maximum blade work.

16. A Curtis stage consists of two rows of moving blades. The steam enters with an absolute velocity of 2000 fps and at a nozzle angle of 20 degrees. Calculate (*a*) the blade speed to give maximum work, and (*b*) the maximum work per lb of steam.

17. Steam enters a "symmetrical" reaction blade with an absolute velocity of 600 fps and at a nozzle angle of 20 degrees. The blade entrance angle is 90 degrees. What is the proper blade velocity for shockless entrance? Calculate the blade work per lb of steam for this condition.

18. A straight, condensing turbine delivering 20,000 kw has a steam rate of 7.75 lb per kw-hr at full load. The steam enters at 800 psia and 900 F and leaves at 1.0 psia. Calculate (*a*) the theoretical steam rate, (*b*) the enthalpy of the steam leaving the turbine if it is assumed that the heat flow is zero, (*c*) the quality of the exhaust steam, and (*d*) the specific volume of the exhaust steam.

19. Calculate (*a*) the theoretical turbine thermal efficiency, (*b*) the actual turbine thermal efficiency, and (c) the engine efficiency of the turbine in Problem 18.

20. A condensing turbine delivers 2500 kw and uses 50,000 lb of steam per hr. The steam enters the turbine at 200 psia and 500 F and exhaust at 2 psia. Calculate (a) the steam rate, (b) the engine efficiency, and (c) the enthalpy of the steam in the exhaust if no heat is transferred.

8 · *Steam Engines*

8·1   Introduction. Although the internal-combustion engine and the steam turbine have replaced the steam engine in many applications, the steam engine is still preferred for certain purposes. The internal-combustion engine is a compact lightweight efficient unit burning expensive fuel and is particularly adapted to the transportation field. The steam turbine, which has been built in sizes of more than 200,000 hp in a single unit, is a high-capacity high-speed prime mover. The steam engine is used extensively where a small- or medium-capacity slow-speed prime mover is desired. It is suited to variable-speed operation and to applications requiring high starting torque and reversibility, such as the steam locomotive. In capacities up to at least 1000 hp, it is more efficient than a steam turbine when exhausting at a back pressure equal to or higher than atmospheric pressure and is, therefore, used extensively in plants requiring both power and low-pressure steam for heating and process loads.

8·2   The D-valve engine. One of the simplest and commonest forms of steam engines is the D-slide-valve engine illustrated in Fig. 8·1. The engine is *double-acting* since the crank end of the cylinder is closed by a cylinder head having a stuffing box through which the piston rod extends to a *crosshead* operating in a straight line in crosshead guides. The crosshead is connected to the crankshaft by a connecting rod, crankpin, and crank which converts the reciprocating motion of the piston to rotary motion of the crankshaft.

Steam is admitted through a hand-operated *throttle valve* and an automatic *governor valve* to the *steam chest* of the engine. The *D valve* in the steam chest is given a reciprocating motion from an *eccentric, eccentric rod,* and *valve stem.* This valve admits high-pressure steam alternately to the head end and crank end of the cylinder at the correct piston positions and also allows the expanded steam to flow from the cylinder into the exhaust pipe after it has done work on the moving piston.

The *shaft* of the engine is supported in a *main bearing* and an *outer bearing*. A *flywheel* is keyed to the shaft and, because of the inertia of its heavy rim, tends to keep the engine rotating at

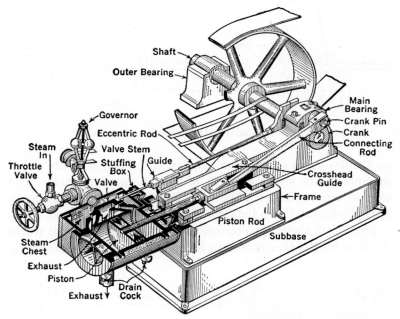

FIG. 8·1 Throttle-governed simple D-slide-valve engine

a uniform speed as the force of the steam on the piston varies during each revolution of the engine.

8·3 Operation of the D-valve engine. The valve of the engine illustrated in Fig. 8·1 is operated from an eccentric which is clamped to the shaft and may be rotated about the shaft to time the valve motion with respect to the movement of the piston. The eccentric, as shown in Fig. 8·2, is in effect a crankpin which has been enlarged to surround the shaft. As the shaft rotates, the center of the eccentric travels in a circle about the shaft at a radius r from the shaft and gives the valve a reciprocating motion equal to $2r$.

The D valve receives its name from the shape of a longitudinal section through the valve which is shown in Fig. 8·3. Cored passages in the cylinder casting connect slots or ports in the valve seating surface to each end of the cylinder. The valve is held

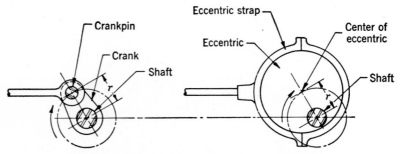

FIG. 8·2 Similarity between crank and eccentric

on the flat valve seat by the unbalanced force due to the steam pressure in the steam chest in which the valve operates. The exhaust opening beneath the valve is connected by a passage in the cylinder casting to the exhaust pipe.

Figure 8·3 shows the position of the piston at the point where the D valve has been moved to the right from its mid-position by

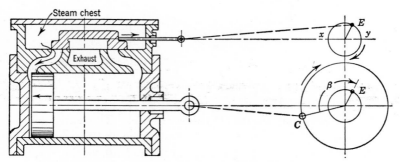

FIG. 8·3 Position of piston and valve at head-end admission

an amount just sufficient to begin to open the steam port and allow the high-pressure steam to flow from the steam chest to the cylinder on the head end. This is known as the position of *admission*. The crankpin is at the position *C*, the shaft is rotating in a clockwise direction, and the eccentric is in position E ahead of the crank by an angle β which is more than 90 degrees. The angle β is determined by the position in which the eccentric is clamped to the shaft and is adjusted so that steam may enter the cylinder a few degrees of crankshaft rotation before the crankpin is in the dead-center position. This will allow the steam pressure to build up in the cylinder to the pressure in the steam chest before the piston starts to move on its power stroke.

As the crankpin travels in a clockwise direction from position

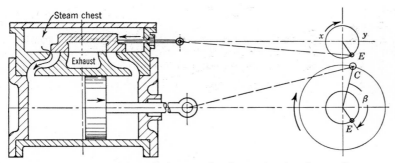

Fɪɢ. 8·4   Position of piston and valve at head-end cut-off

C indicated in Fig. 8·3, the valve is moved to the right until the eccentric reaches y, at which point the valve is at its position of maximum travel to the right. Further rotation of the engine shaft reverses the direction of motion of the valve until in Fig. 8·4 it is on the point of closing the port and stopping the flow of steam to the cylinder. This is called the point of *cut-off*. As the piston travels from the position shown in Fig. 8·3 to the position shown in Fig. 8·4, the port is open, and steam from the steam chest flows through the port to maintain the steam pressure on the piston.

As the crankpin rotates from the position shown in Fig. 8·4 to the position shown in Fig. 8·5, the piston is traveling to the right, the port is closed by the valve, and the steam in the cylinder is expanding. At the point shown in Fig. 8·5, the valve has been displaced to the left until the port is being uncovered by the exhaust edge of the valve, and the steam in the cylinder is on the point of being discharged from the cylinder to the exhaust space. This is known as the point of *release*.

As the crankpin travels from the position shown in Fig. 8·5 to the crank-end dead-center position, the piston continues to move to the right, the port opening increases, and the steam escapes from the head end of the cylinder to the exhaust pipe until the cylinder pressure falls to the exhaust pressure. Further rotation

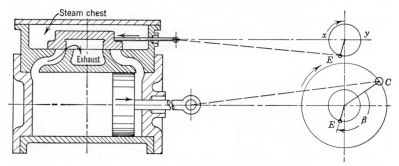

FIG. 8·5   Position of piston and valve at head-end release

of the engine brings the eccentric position to the point x where the valve reaches its maximum travel to the left. The piston returns toward the head end with the exhaust port open until the valve reaches the position shown in Fig. 8·6 where the valve is on the point of closing the exhaust port. This is called the point of *compression*.

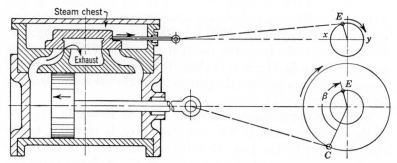

FIG. 8·6   Position of piston and valve at head-end compression

While the crankpin travels from the position shown in Fig. 8·6 to the original position shown in Fig. 8·3, the port is closed and the steam trapped in the cylinder is compressed, thus cushioning the piston and bringing it to a stop on head-end dead center without shock or knocking in the bearings.

Figures 8·3 to 8·6, inclusive, show the action of the valve in admitting and exhausting steam at the head end of the cylinder. The same actions occur on the crank end in the same relative piston positions.

Figure 8·7 shows an indicator card from a steam engine. The four *events of the stroke* are indicated on the diagram. Steam enters the cylinder from the point of admission to the point of

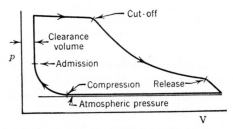

FIG. 8·7   Indicator diagram showing events of the stroke

cut-off. Steam leaves the cylinder from the point of release to the point of compression. Between cut-off and release, the steam in the cylinder expands while the steam is compressed between the points of compression and admission.

Where the steam pressure exceeds 100 psig, the unbalanced force due to the steam pressure on the D valve creates considerable friction between the valve and the valve seat. Also, the use of superheated steam makes it difficult to lubricate the rubbing surfaces properly. Consequently, for higher steam pressures and for superheated steam, as in the locomotive, a piston valve is used in preference to the D valve. The piston valve as illustrated in Fig. 8·8 is in effect a flat D valve rolled into a cylinder. A replaceable liner is pressed into the cylinder casting to take the wear from the valve. The valve is provided with four piston rings to form seals and reduce leakage. The high-pressure steam is admitted to the central space around the valve while the exhaust steam is discharged from each end of the valve. Figure 8·8 shows the valve in position to admit steam on the head end with the exhaust port open on the crank end.

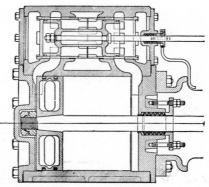

FIG. 8·8   Cylinder with piston valve

8·4   The four-valve (Corliss) engine.   The Corliss valve gear was invented by George H. Corliss in 1846 and for many years was the standard type of valve gear in use on large heavy-duty engines where good efficiency rather than low first cost was of importance.   The arrangement of the cylinder and valves is shown in Fig. 8·9.   One inlet valve is located at the top of each

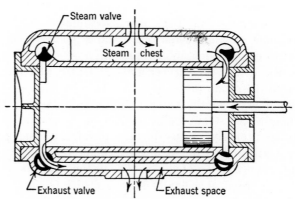

FIG. 8·9   Valve arrangement of Corliss engine

end of the cylinder, and one exhaust valve is located at the bottom of each end of the cylinder.   The valve seats extend across the cylinder casting and are bored to a cylindrical shape.   Oscillating valves are given a semi-rotary motion through a suitable linkage actuated by one or more eccentrics on the shaft of the engine.

Large engines often have one eccentric to operate the exhaust valves and another eccentric to operate the steam valves. The time of opening and closing of the exhaust valves and the time of opening of the inlet valves can be adjusted by the position of the eccentrics on the shaft and the lengths of the adjustable links which impart oscillating motion to the valves. The time of closing of the inlet valve is under the control of the governor and is varied with the load on the engine so as to maintain the desired engine speed. Short ports, large and unrestricted valve opening, and separate and adjustable valves make for better steam distribution and higher efficiency than is obtainable from single-valve engines.

8·5   The unaflow engine. The characteristic features of a unaflow engine are (1) separate steam-inlet valves for the head and crank ends of the cylinder, (2) a central exhaust passage extending around the cylinder and connected to the interior of the cylinder by a belt of holes or ports in the cylinder wall, and (3) a piston which serves as the exhaust valve. Figure 8·10 is a sectional view of a large single-cylinder heavy-duty unaflow engine. Steam enters each end of the cylinder through a *balanced poppet valve* located in the upper part of the cylinder-head castings. A row of central exhaust ports extends around the middle of the cylinder casting. The exhaust steam is discharged through these ports when they are uncovered by the piston as it approaches its dead-center positions.

The piston must be long enough so that, on dead center, one face of the piston is close to the cylinder head in order to reduce the clearance to the desired amount, and the other face of the piston has completely uncovered the centrally located exhaust ports. Since the length of the exhaust ports is about 10 per cent of the stroke, the length of the piston is about 90 per cent of the stroke. This results in a long piston and a cylinder about 60 per cent longer than the cylinder of a Corliss engine for the same stroke. In the engine illustrated in Fig. 8·10, the piston rod extends through the piston and head-end cylinder head to form a tail rod which is supported on a crosshead. The weight of the large piston is thus transferred to the external crossheads, and cylinder wear is greatly reduced.

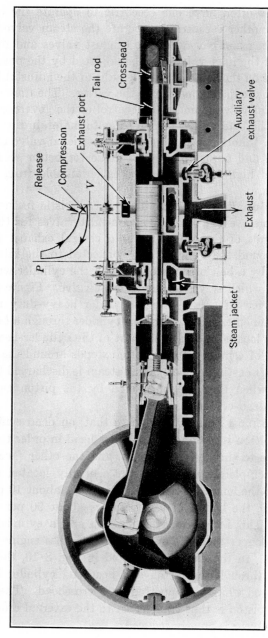

Fig. 8·10 Sectional view of large unaflow engine with auxiliary exhaust valves

A typical indicator diagram is illustrated in Fig. 8·10 above the crank end of the cylinder. The steam is admitted through the poppet valve just before the piston reaches dead center. After the valve has been closed on the power stroke, the steam expands until the piston uncovers the central exhaust ports and permits the steam to escape through the central exhaust opening. On the return stroke, compression begins when the piston covers the exhaust ports.

High-pressure steam flows from the inlet pipe through hollow spaces or steam jackets in the cylinder heads to the inlet valves, thus keeping the cylinder heads as hot as possible.

Figure 8·11 shows a section through the double-seat balanced poppet valve which is used on most unaflow engines and on many four-valve engines where high steam temperatures would cause leakage due to valve and seat distortion and lubrication troubles with sliding surfaces. The illustration shows the valve in the open position. In the closed position, the rigid valve body which is secured to the valve stem rests on the lower valve seat while the spring loaded upper disk is free to adjust itself to any distortion caused by differential expansion of the two valve seats. The upper valve seat is slightly larger than the lower one so that the valve may be removed vertically through the upper valve-seat opening. Since the high-pressure steam acts upon both the upper and lower surfaces of the valve, it is in balance except for the area represented by the differences between the two valve seats and the cross-sectional area of the valve stem. Consequently, the valve can be opened by exerting a much smaller force than would be required to open a single-seat valve, such as the conventional automobile-engine valve, with the high-pressure steam holding the valve closed. The valve illustrated in Fig. 8·11 when properly fitted to its seats will remain steam-tight for a long period of time.

Figure 8·12 shows three types of unaflow cylinders with the piston on head-end dead-center positions in each case and with typical indicator diagrams for both head and crank ends. In Fig. 8·12*A*, the engine is designed to exhaust at a back pressure of about 2 psia. The clearance is such that the steam trapped in the cylinder at the point of compression will be compressed to the initial or line pressure when the piston reaches dead center. In

Fig. 8·12*B*, the cylinder is designed for exhaust at atmospheric pressure. For the same cylinder volume as in the preceding case, about 6.5 times as much steam by weight will be present in the cylinder at the point of compression because of the higher pressure, and a larger clearance volume (10 to 20 per cent) will be required to prevent the compression pressure from exceeding the initial steam pressure.

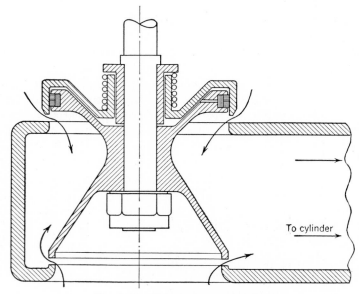

To cylinder

FIG. 8·11   Balanced poppet valve

Should it become necessary to operate the engine of Fig. 8·12*A* at atmospheric exhaust pressure, the small clearance volume and the greater weight of steam in the cylinder at the point of compression would result in excessive compression pressure. To permit operation of this engine at atmospheric exhaust pressure, it is necessary to provide for either (1) an increased clearance volume in the cylinder heads, controlled by automatic or hand-operated shut-off valves, or (2) auxiliary exhaust valves to delay the point of compression. Figures 8·12*C* and 8·10 show cylinders provided with auxiliary exhaust valves which are held open on the compression stroke of the piston to delay the point of compression when exhausting at atmospheric pressure. They are inoperative when exhausting at a vacuum. Thus the same engine may be operated either condensing or noncondensing.

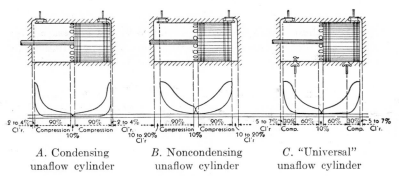

A. Condensing
unaflow cylinder

B. Noncondensing
unaflow cylinder

C. "Universal"
unaflow cylinder

FIG. 8·12   Effect of exhaust pressure upon the clearance required in unaflow engines

8·6   Cylinder arrangement of engines. Practically all steam engines are double acting; that is, the crank end of the cylinder is closed by a cylinder head, and steam is admitted to both sides of the piston. The single-cylinder engine which receives steam at line pressure and exhausts at exhaust pressure is often called a *simple* engine and is represented diagrammatically in Fig. 8·13A. This engine cannot start when on dead center. If frequent starting under load is necessary, two simple engines may be connected to the same crankshaft with their cranks at right angles. Then one piston is near its mid-position when the other one is on dead center, and the engine is always in a position in which it can be started under load. This is called a *twin* engine and is shown in Fig. 8·13B. The steam locomotive has a twin engine which is capable of slipping the driving wheels on the rails with the locomotive stationary or operating at low speeds. Where space limitations are important, three or four simple cylinders may be assembled into a multicylinder vertical engine having many of the constructional features of a large multicylinder Diesel engine.

When it is desirable to build an engine for high economy and to expand the steam through a greater pressure range than is justified in a simple engine, a *compound engine* may be used. The compound engine consists of two cylinders operating in series.

The steam is expanded from the initial pressure to some intermediate pressure in a high-pressure cylinder from which it exhausts into a receiver or reservoir. Steam from the receiver at
the intermediate pressure is then expanded in a low-pressure
cylinder to the exhaust pressure. Because of the increased volume of steam at the lower pressure, the low-pressure cylinder has
a piston displacement several times the piston displacement of the

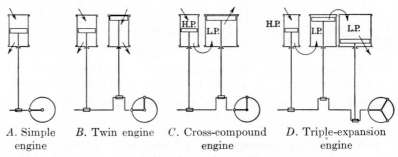

A. Simple   *B.* Twin engine   *C.* Cross-compound   *D.* Triple-expansion
    engine   engine   engine

Fig. 8·13   Cylinder arrangement of steam engines

high-pressure cylinder. A *cross-compound* engine is illustrated in
Fig. 8·13*C*. The high- and low-pressure cylinders are connected
to a common shaft by cranks which are set at right angles. High-
pressure steam may be admitted to the low-pressure cylinder for
starting if the high-pressure piston is not in a starting position.
It is customary to use the same stroke for both cylinders so that
the diameter of the low-pressure cylinder is generally 1.5 to 2.2
times the diameter of the high-pressure cylinder.

Expansion of steam through a still greater pressure range may
be carried out in a *triple-expansion engine,* as illustrated in Fig.
8·13*D*. This engine consists of a high-pressure cylinder, an intermediate-pressure cylinder, and a low-pressure cylinder with the
cranks set at angles of 120 degrees. The steam passes through
the three cylinders in series, and the volumes of the several cylinders are proportionate to the steam volumes which they handle.
In some large engines two low-pressure cylinders of moderate
size have been used in parallel instead of one large low-pressure
cylinder.

It is customary in describing engines to specify the diameter of
the cylinder and the stroke of the piston in inches and to state

the stroke *last.* Thus a 10 × 14 engine would be a single cylinder or simple engine having a 10-in.-diameter cylinder and a 14-in. stroke. A 12 × 24 × 20 engine would be a compound engine having a 12-in. high-pressure cylinder diameter, a 24-in. low-pressure cylinder diameter, and a 20-in. stroke in each cylinder. A 12 × 24 × 36 × 26 engine would be a triple-expansion engine having cylinder diameters of 12, 24, and 36 in., and a 26-in. stroke in each cylinder.

8·7 Governing of steam engines. A *governor* is a device for maintaining a reasonably constant speed on an engine operating on a variable load. If the load is increased, the speed of the engine will decrease unless arrangements are made to admit more steam. Conversely, the engine will speed up if the load is decreased and may wreck itself through overspeeding if the steam input is not decreased.

Engines may be governed by *throttling* the steam supply, or by *varying the point of cut-off* of the steam-inlet valve.

The throttle governor is illustrated in Fig. 8·1. A set of three balls are mounted on flat springs and are rotated about a vertical shaft by means of bevel gears and a belt drive from the engine shaft. The speed of rotation of the governor shaft is therefore proportional to the shaft speed of the engine. If the engine speed increases above normal, the centrifugal force of the rotating fly balls causes them to move outward against the resistance of the flat springs. As the flat springs bend outward, the height of the governor is decreased, and the governor valve is partially closed, thus reducing the steam flow to the engine. The partial closing of the governor valve has the effect of reducing the steam pressure on which the engine is operating. Figure 8·14*A* shows on the same co-ordinates three indicator cards taken at successively lower loads on a throttle-governed engine. The positions of the various events of the stroke remain unchanged, but the area of the indicator cards and the mean effective pressures change, owing to reduction in the pressure in the steam chest as the load decreases.

The throttle governor has the advantage of simplicity and low cost. Since it reduces the pressure in the steam chest of the engine, the engine does not have the advantage of the full pressure except on full load. Consequently, the efficiency at part-load operation is poor. The variable cut-off governor is designed to permit operation of the engine on full steam pressure at all loads and should therefore give better economy on part-load operation.

Figure 8·15 illustrates one type of flywheel governor which will vary the amount of steam admitted to the cylinder through change in the point of cut-off. The eccentric is mounted on a pivot or

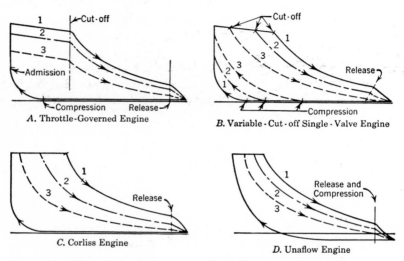

FIG. 8·14 Effect of load changes on the indicator cards of various types of engines

eccentric bearing attached to the hub of the flywheel. When the engine comes up to rated speed, a weight swings outward under the influence of centrifugal force against a leaf spring which is mounted in the flywheel. The weight is connected to an arm of the eccentric by means of a link and rotates the eccentric about the eccentric pivot. In Fig. 8·15, the position of the crank and the position of the center of the eccentric with respect to the center of the shaft are shown in the starting or full-load position. When the engine comes up to full speed, the movement of the governor weight swings the eccentric about the pivot in such a manner as to bring the center of the eccentric nearer to the center of the shaft, thus decreasing the valve movement and causing the valve to close sooner.

The effect of this governor upon the shape of the indicator card is shown in Fig. 8·14B for three different loads on the engine. As the load decreases, the point of cut-off occurs earlier, but the engine continues to operate on full steam pressure. In a single-valve engine, since all of the events of the stroke are controlled

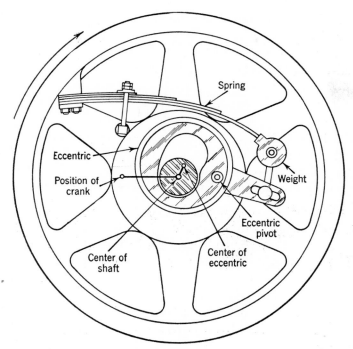

Fig. 8·15 Armstrong centrifugal flywheel governor

by one valve, the effect is also to make release and compression occur earlier as the load decreases.

In the Corliss or four-valve engine, the operation of the exhaust valve and the opening of the inlet valve are controlled from a fixed eccentric on the shaft. The governor controls only the point at which the inlet valve closes. Figure 8·14C shows an indicator card from a Corliss engine for three different loads. All events are fixed except the point of cut-off which changes with load.

In the unaflow engine, the piston is the exhaust valve; release and compression are therefore independent of the load. The governor and valve gear are designed to open the inlet valve at a fixed point and to close it at a variable position which depends upon the speed of the engine. Figure 8·14D shows unaflow engine indicator cards for three loads. Only the point of cut-off changes with load.

8·8 Indicated and brake horsepower. The brake horsepower of a steam engine may be determined by the use of a prony brake, as discussed in Article 3·12 in connection with the internal-combustion engine, using the equation,

$$\text{Bhp} = \frac{2\pi rFn}{33,000} \tag{8·1}$$

The indicated horsepower of a steam engine may be determined from the areas of the indicator cards and data on the engine performance, as discussed in Article 3·11, except that the following differences exist between steam and internal combustion engines:

1. Steam engines are usually double acting, and it is necessary to determine the indicated horsepower of the head end and crank end separately and add them to get the total ihp. On the crank end, the net area upon which the steam acts is the area of the piston minus the cross-sectional area of the piston rod.

2. The number of power strokes per minute on each side of the piston is equal to the *revolutions per minute.* Therefore,

$$\text{Head-end ihp} = \frac{P_{ih}LA_{h}n}{33,000} \tag{8·2}$$

$$\text{Crank-end ihp} = \frac{P_{ic}LA_{c}n}{33,000} \tag{8·3}$$

where P_{ih} = average mep of head-end indicator cards
P_{ic} = average mep of crank-end indicator cards
L = length of stroke, ft
A_{h} = net area of head end of piston, sq in.
A_{c} = net area of crank end of piston, sq in.
n = rpm

As in the case of the internal-combustion engine, the fhp = total

ihp − bhp, and the mechanical efficiency = $\dfrac{\text{bhp}}{\text{total ihp}}$.

The calculation of indicated horsepower, brake horsepower, friction horsepower, and mechanical efficiency may be illustrated by Example 1.

Example 1. Calculate the ihp, bhp, fhp, and mechanical efficiency of a 12 × 15 simple engine with 2½-in.-diameter piston rod, running at 250 rpm under the following conditions: mean area of head-end indicator cards, 2.7 sq in.; mean area of crank-end indicator cards, 2.75 sq in.; average length of indicator cards, 3.4 in.; scale of indicator spring, 60 psi; net brake load, 600 lb; radius of brake arm, 3.0 ft; initial steam pressure, 100 psig; quality of steam, 98 per cent; barometric pressure, 29.5 in. of Hg; atmospheric exhaust; steam consumption, 3000 lb per hr.

Solution:

Head-end mep, $P_{ih} = \dfrac{\text{area of indicator card}}{\text{length of indicator card}} \times \text{scale of spring}$

$$P_{ih} = \frac{2.7}{3.4} \times 60 = 47.7 \text{ psi}$$

Crank-end mep, $P_{ic} = \dfrac{2.75}{3.4} \times 60 = 48.6 \text{ psi}$

Head-end ihp $= \dfrac{P_{ih}LA_h n}{33{,}000} = \dfrac{47.7 \times \dfrac{15}{12} \times \left(12^2 \times \dfrac{\pi}{4}\right) \times 250}{33{,}000}$

$\qquad = 51.2 \text{ ihp}$

Crank-end ihp $= \dfrac{P_{ic}LA_c n}{33{,}000} = \dfrac{48.6 \times \dfrac{15}{12} \times (12^2 - 2.5^2)\dfrac{\pi}{4} \times 250}{33{,}000}$

$\qquad = 49.9 \text{ ihp}$

Total ihp $= 51.2 + 49.9 = 101.1 \text{ ihp}$

Bhp $= \dfrac{2\pi r F n}{33{,}000} = \dfrac{2\pi \times 3 \times 600 \times 250}{33{,}000} = 85.7 \text{ bhp}$

Fhp $= \text{total ihp} - \text{bhp} = 101.1 - 85.7 = 15.4 \text{ fhp}$

Mechanical efficiency $= \dfrac{\text{bhp}}{\text{total ihp}} = \dfrac{85.7}{101.1} \times 100 = 84.7\%$

As illustrated in Fig. 8·16, the friction horsepower of an engine at zero brake horsepower is equal to the indicated horsepower at that load and is almost constant, regardless of load. There-

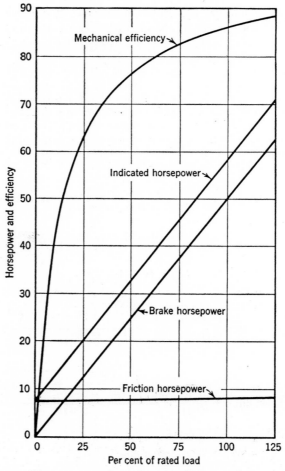

FIG. 8·16 Horsepower and mechanical efficiency of steam engine

fore, the difference between the indicated and brake horsepower is about constant at all loads. The mechanical efficiency is zero at zero brake horsepower and increases with load to values of 85 to 92 per cent at full load, depending upon the size and type of engine.

8·9   Losses due to initial condensation and incomplete expansion.   During the exhaust stroke of the engine, the steam which is normally wet is discharged at a saturation temperature that depends upon the exhaust pressure.   At standard atmospheric pressure this temperature is 212 F; at a back pressure of 2 psia the temperature is 126 F.   The cold wet exhaust steam chills the cylinder walls during exhaust with the result that a substantial part of the high-pressure steam admitted to the cylinder is condensed on the cylinder walls and does no work, thereby resulting in a loss which is normally referred to as the *initial condensation* loss.

Many of the improvements to steam engines have been made in an effort to reduce the initial condensation loss.   Figure 8·17

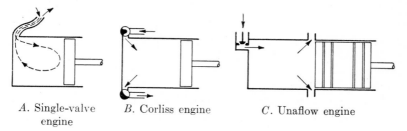

 A. Single-valve *B*. Corliss engine *C*. Unaflow engine
   engine

Fig. 8·17   Path of steam through engine cylinders

shows the path of the steam as it flows through three common types of engine cylinders.   In the simple D-valve engine, the cold exhaust steam sweeps across the cylinder head and flows through the long steam passage on the exhaust stroke of the engine.   Then the hot high-pressure steam flows through the same long steam passage and into the cylinder where it comes in contact with the cold cylinder head and piston.   The large amount of cold metal surface in contact with the incoming steam causes as much as 60 per cent of this steam to condense.

In the four-valve or Corliss engine, the steam and exhaust ports are separate, are short, and present much less surface for condensation.   Consequently, initial condensation is much less than in the single-valve engine.

In the unaflow cylinder illustrated in Fig. 8·17, the wet exhaust steam is discharged through the central exhaust belt at the end of the stroke, and the steam trapped in the cylinder at compression is practically dry.   During the long compression stroke (90 per cent of the stroke of the engine), the work of compression superheats the steam in the cylinder which in turn heats the cylinder walls, so that the steam-jacketed cylinder head, the piston, and the small amount of surface in the clearance space are hot before the high-pressure steam is admitted. Consequently, initial condensation is much less than in the single-valve or four-valve engines.

Initial condensation can be reduced by using a compound or triple-expansion engine since expansion in series through two or more cylinders reduces the pressure range and therefore the temperature difference between the exhaust and incoming steam in each cylinder. In recent years, the unaflow engine has largely replaced the compound engine except for constant-load operation, since the primary reason for compounding, that is, reduction in initial condensation, can be realized in the single-cylinder unaflow engine.

As indicated in Fig. 8·14, the effect of an increased load on an engine is a higher steam pressure at release. When the exhaust valve opens and steam at a pressure considerably above the exhaust pressure is allowed to discharge through the exhaust valve, the further work that could have been done by expansion of that steam is lost. This loss is negligible on light loads but may become quite serious at heavy loads. On the other hand, the initial condensation loss is most serious at light loads because of the lower mean steam pressure and temperature in the cylinder and the fact that a given amount of condensation is a larger percentage of the total steam flow on light loads than on heavy loads. Consequently, the average engine loses in efficiency at light loads owing to initial condensation and loses at heavy loads owing to incomplete expansion. It is therefore customary to rate an engine at such an output that minimum steam consumption per horsepower-hour occurs at about 75 per cent of rated capacity. Then the engine will operate from 50 per cent of rated capacity to rated capacity with good performance.

The *steam rate* of an engine is determined by dividing the steam flow in pounds per hour by the indicated or brake horsepower of the engine. The steam rate is therefore the pounds of steam used per indicated horsepower-hour or brake horsepower-hour. Typical steam-rate curves for common types of engines are shown in Fig. 8·18 when operating noncondensing and also at a back pressure of 2 psia. Attention should be directed to the following points:

1. The reduction in the steam rate due to the lower exhaust pressure when operating condensing.

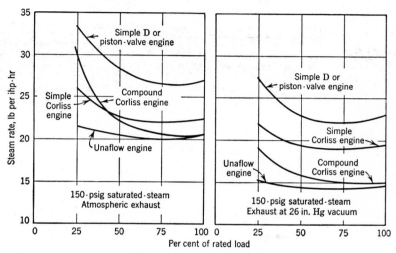

FIG. 8·18 Steam rates of typical engines of about 200 hp capacity

2. The comparative performance of the different types of engines.
3. The rapidly increasing steam rates at loads below 50 per cent of rated capacity, due to initial condensation.
4. The increasing steam rates at full load due to incomplete expansion of the steam.
5. The excellent performance of the unaflow engine over a wide range of loads.

8·10   Thermal efficiency of steam engines.   The Rankine cycle was discussed in Article 6·2, and the thermal efficiency of the steam turbines was discussed in Article 7·12. The thermal efficiency of the steam engine is computed in the same way as the thermal efficiency of the steam turbine except that the steam rates and efficiencies may be expressed in terms of indicated horsepower, brake horsepower, or kilowatt output of an electric generator.

It is *assumed* that the engine is connected into a circuit as shown in Fig. 8·19 under the following conditions:

1. There is no heat transfer or pressure drop in the piping system.
2. The condensed steam (condensate) leaves the condenser as saturated water at the condenser pressure.

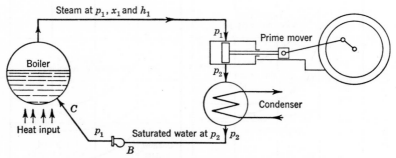

Fig. 8·19   Flow diagram for computing thermal efficiency

Then, the *actual* thermal efficiency η_a may be computed as follows:

$$\eta_a = \frac{\text{output, Btu per hr}}{\text{input, Btu per hr}} = \frac{\text{hp} \times 2545}{m(h_1 - h_{f2})} \qquad (8\cdot4)$$

where hp = ihp or bhp of the engine

   m = lb of steam supplied per hr

   h_1 = enthalpy of steam supplied to the prime mover

   h_{f2} = enthalpy of saturated water at the exhaust pressure p_2

   η_a = actual thermal efficiency based upon either the ihp or bhp

If the engine is driving an electric generator, the efficiency may be based upon the output of the generator by substituting the product (kw × 3413) for (hp × 2545) in the numerator of Equation 8·4.

The theoretical or ideal efficiency of the steam engine may be computed by the methods outlined in Article 7·12 by assuming that the expansion of the steam in the engine occurs without friction or heat transfer to the surroundings, that is, at constant entropy.   Then, the theoretical thermal efficiency,

$$\eta_t = \frac{\text{theoretical output per lb of steam}}{\text{input per lb of steam}} = \frac{(h_1 - h_2)_s}{h_1 - h_{f2}} \quad (8 \cdot 5)$$

where $(h_1 - h_2)_s$ is the change in enthalpy when steam which is supplied to the engine with an enthalpy of h_1 is expanded at constant entropy to the exhaust pressure.

As discussed in Article 7·12, the real measure of performance of a steam engine is the extent to which the actual efficiency approaches the ideal or theoretical Rankine-cycle efficiency. The engine efficiency is defined as follows:

$$\text{Engine efficiency} = \frac{\text{actual thermal efficiency}}{\text{theoretical thermal efficiency}} = \frac{\eta_a}{\eta_t} \quad (8 \cdot 6)$$

Engine efficiencies of more than 80 per cent are obtainable with high-grade engines.

It is often necessary to determine the enthalpy of the exhaust steam leaving an engine. In Article 1·23, the first law of thermodynamics was applied to the prime mover, and the following equation was developed:

$$\frac{W}{J} = (h_1 - h_2) - Q \quad (1 \cdot 31)$$

in which W = work done in the engine, ft-lb per lb of steam

h_1 = enthalpy of steam supplied to the engine

h_2 = actual enthalpy of exhaust steam leaving the engine

Q = heat transferred from the steam to the surroundings, Btu per lb of steam

Rearranging Equation 1·31 gives

$$h_2 = h_1 - \left(\frac{W}{J} + Q \right) \quad (8 \cdot 7)$$

Also,

$$\frac{W}{J} = \frac{2545}{\text{steam rate based upon ihp}}$$

The heat transferred to the surroundings, Q, may be estimated on the basis of experience and in a well-insulated engine may generally be neglected.

The method of computing the thermal performance of an engine may be illustrated by the following example:

Example 2. Using the data and results from Example 1, compute the actual thermal efficiency, the ideal or theoretical thermal efficiency, the engine efficiency, the steam rate, and the enthalpy of the exhaust steam.

Solution:

$$p_1 = 100 \text{ psig} + 29.5 \text{ in. Hg} = 100 + 0.491 \times 29.5 = 114.5 \text{ psia}$$

$$h_1 \text{ at } 114.5 \text{ psia and } 98\% \text{ quality} = 309 + 0.98\,(880) = 1172 \text{ Btu per lb}$$

$$h_{f2} = h_f \text{ at } 14.5 \text{ psia} = 180 \text{ Btu per lb}$$

h_2 after *isentropic* expansion from 114.5 psia and 98 per cent quality to 14.5 psia can be determined from the Mollier chart (Fig. A·1) and is found to be 1025 Btu per lb.

$$\text{Ihp} = 101.1$$

$$\text{Bhp} = 85.7$$

Then, the actual efficiency,

$$\eta_a, \text{ based upon ihp} = \frac{101.1 \times 2545}{3000(1172 - 180)} \times 100 = 8.65\%$$

$$\eta_a, \text{ based upon bhp} = \frac{85.7 \times 2545}{3000(1172 - 180)} \times 100 = 7.3\%$$

The ideal or theoretical efficiency,

$$\eta_t = \frac{1172 - 1025}{1172 - 180} \times 100 = 14.85\%$$

The engine efficiency, based upon the ihp,

$$= \frac{\eta_a}{\eta_t} = \frac{8.65}{14.85} \times 100 = 58.2\%$$

$$\text{The steam rate, based upon the ihp} = \frac{3000 \text{ lb of steam per hr}}{101.1 \text{ ihp}}$$

$$= 29.65 \text{ lb per ihp-hr}$$

$$\text{The steam rate, based upon the bhp} = \frac{3000 \text{ lb of steam per hr}}{85.7 \text{ bhp}}$$

$$= 35.0 \text{ lb per bhp-hr}$$

The actual enthalpy of the exhaust steam, neglecting heat transfer to the surroundings,

$$= h_2 = h_1 - \frac{W}{J} = 1172 - \frac{2545 \text{ Btu per hp-hr}}{29.65 \text{ lb of steam per ihp-hr}} = 1172 - 86$$

$$= 1086 \text{ Btu per lb of steam}$$

The thermal efficiency of steam engines varies from 5 to 25 per cent, depending upon the kind of engine, the load on the engine, the initial pressure and temperature of the steam, and the exhaust pressure.

PROBLEMS

Calculate (*a*) the ihp, (*b*) the bhp, (*c*) the fhp, (*d*) the mechanical efficiency, (*e*) the thermal efficiency based upon the ihp, (*f*) the thermal efficiency based upon the bhp, (*g*) the steam rate based upon the ihp, (*h*) the steam rate based upon the bhp, (*i*) the ideal or theoretical efficiency, (*j*) the engine efficiency based upon the ihp, and (*k*) the enthalpy of the exhaust steam leaving the engine, neglecting heat transfer to the surroundings, for the following sets of data:

Item Type of Engine	Engine 1 D Valve	Engine 2 Piston Valve	Engine 3 Corliss	Engine 4 Unaflow	Engine 5 Unaflow
Diameter × stroke, in.	10 × 15	12 × 16	16 × 24	16 × 18	30 × 36
Diameter of piston rod, in.	2.0	2.5	3.0	2.75	5.0
Mean area of head-end indicator cards, sq in.	1.70	1.63	1.57	1.20	1.12
Mean area of crank-end indicator cards, sq in.	1.73	1.61	1.62	1.23	1.17
Mean length of indicator cards, in.	2.5	2.7	2.6	2.9	2.8
Scale of indicator spring, lb	60	60	80	80	80
Speed of engine, rpm	300	280	120	250	200
Length of prony-brake arm, ft	3.0	4.0	5.0	5.0	10.0
Net brake load, lb	350	370	1710	570	2200
Initial steam pressure, psig	105	165	165	145	165
Initial quality of steam, %	98.5	99.1	99.3		
Initial steam temperature, F				400	500
Exhaust pressure, psia	14.7	14.7	4.0	3.0	2.0
Atmospheric pressure, psia	14.7	14.7	14.7	14.7	14.7
Steam consumption, lb per hr	2060	2350	4400	2240	12,500

9 . *Pumps*

9·1   Introduction.   One of the most important problems of the engineer is the efficient and controlled transfer of fluids from one point to another.   This transfer may be opposed by gravitational force, by some other external force, or by friction.   Under certain conditions the gravitational force and other forces may act to aid the transfer, but friction always exists as a force opposing motion.   The engineer attempts to reduce the effect of friction and at the same time takes advantage of useful forces to produce a motion of the fluids under conditions that can be controlled.

As previously defined, a fluid is a substance in a liquid, gaseous, or vapor state which offers little resistance to deformation.   Common examples of the three states of a fluid are water as a liquid, air as a gas, and steam as a vapor.   All of these types of fluids have a tendency to move because of natural forces acting on them.   A city may be supplied with water flowing by gravity from high ground.   Air may circulate in an auditorium because of its own temperature difference.   Steam rises through the water in a boiler owing to the difference in density or specific weight of the steam and water.   In many cases, however, the circulation is inadequate, and mechanical equipment must be built to supplement the natural circulation.   Often mechanical circulation is the only means of obtaining the desired fluid flow.   The equipment for producing this fluid flow is divided into two major classes: *pumps* for handling liquids, and *fans, blowers,* and *compressors* for handling gases or vapors.

Both classes of equipment in various forms may be found in the modern stationary power plant or in small mobile power plants such as the aircraft engine, Diesel locomotive, or automobile engine.   Thus, in the field of heat power most mechanical methods of producing flow are utilized, and the fundamentals

470

covered here are applicable in other fields of engineering. Before the general design and application of flow equipment are discussed, a brief survey will be made of the fundamentals of fluid properties and fluid-flow measurements.

9·2 Pressure-measuring instruments. Pressure is defined as a force per unit area, and in engineering applications its units are commonly lb per sq in., psi, or lb per sq ft, psf. However, it is often convenient to represent a given pressure by the height of a column of fluid that will produce at its base the given pressure. The height of the column is called pressure head or just head. For example, at ordinary elevations on the earth's surface

TABLE 9·1

SPECIFIC GRAVITY AND SPECIFIC WEIGHT OF SOME LIQUIDS

Liquid	Temperature, F	Specific Gravity	Specific Weight (Lb per Cu Ft)
Ethyl alcohol	32	0.79	49.4
Methyl alcohol	32	0.81	50.5
Draft gage oil	32	0.84	52.4
Water	39	1.00	62.4
Sea water	59	1.02	64.0
Mercury	32	13.596	848.0

mercury weighs approximately 848 lb per cu ft (see Table 9·1). If a cube of mercury 1 ft on a side is placed on a surface, it will exert a force of 848 lb, a pressure of 848 psf, or a pressure of (848 ÷ 144) psi over the contact surface (see Fig. 9·1). If three

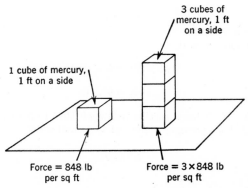

FIG. 9·1 Variation of force at the bottom of a column of material

such cubes are placed on top of each other, they will produce a force of 2544 lb, a pressure of 2544 psf, or a pressure of (2544 ÷ 144) psi. Thus, a pressure of 848 psf is equivalent to a head of 1 ft of mercury and a pressure of 2544 psf is equivalent to a head of 3 ft of mercury. A 1-in. head or column of mercury is equivalent to 0.491 psi.

The pressure or force per unit area exerted by a column of material depends on the height of the column and its average specific weight, or

$$p = h\gamma \tag{9·1}$$

where p = pressure, psf
$\quad h$ = height of column, ft
$\quad \gamma$ = specific weight, lb per cu ft

The use of Equation 9·1 is illustrated by several examples.

Example 1. What is the pressure in psi exerted on a diver 200 ft below the surface of the ocean? Assume an average specific weight of sea water as 64 lb per cu ft.
Solution:

$$p = h\gamma$$

where h = 200 ft
$\quad \gamma$ = 64 lb per cu ft

thus, $p = 200 \times 64 = 12{,}800$ psf

or $p = 88.9$ psi

Example 2. A pressure of 20 psi would support a column of river water how many ft high?
Solution:

$$p = h\gamma$$

where p = 20 × 144 psf
$\quad \gamma$ = 62.4 lb per cu ft

thus, $144 \times 20 = h \times 62.4$

$$h = 46.1 \text{ ft}$$

Example 3. If air has a specific weight of 0.075 lb per cu ft, how many ft of air would give a pressure equivalent to 3 in. of water?
Solution:

$$p = h\gamma$$

where $h = \frac{3}{12}$ ft
$\quad \gamma$ = 62.4 lb per cu ft

thus, $$p = \frac{3}{12} \text{ ft} \times 62.4 \frac{\text{lb}}{\text{cu ft}} = 15.6 \text{ psf}$$

or $$p = \frac{\frac{3}{12} \times 62.4}{144} = 0.108 \text{ psi}$$

This pressure is converted to feet of air by

$$p = h\gamma$$

where $p = 15.6$ psf
$\gamma = 0.075$ lb per cu ft

thus, $$15.6 = h \times 0.075$$

$$h = 208 \text{ ft of air}$$

Fluid pressure is the force per unit area resulting from the bombardment of the molecules of a fluid against a confining surface. The force per unit area produced by the random motion of the molecules is called static pressure, and it is that pressure which tends to burst the walls confining the fluid. At a given point and time, a fluid, whether stationary or in motion, exerts an equal static pressure in all directions.

In a moving fluid the force per unit area produced by the ordered motion (motion in a definite direction) of a mass or group of molecules is called velocity pressure, and it is that pressure which is only exerted in the direction of motion of the fluid. Velocity pressure is the force per unit area that will result from the complete conversion of the kinetic energy of a moving fluid to mechanical potential energy. Velocity head is the vertical distance a fluid will rise if its kinetic energy is completely converted to mechanical potential energy.

Velocity pressure and velocity head may be explained by a simple experiment. A large tank, as shown in Fig. 9·2, is filled with a liquid to a height h ft above an orifice A located at the horizontal surface S–S. The specific weight of the liquid is γ lb per cu ft. The velocity of the liquid at the orifice A is V fps, and all particles of fluid are directed vertically upward. If the flow in the tank, in the orifice, and in the free jet leaving the orifice is frictionless, then the following deductions can be made:

1. The liquid at the surface of the large tank has a mechanical potential energy with respect to surface S–S per pound of fluid of h ft-lb.

2. The kinetic energy of the liquid leaving the orifice per pound of fluid is equal to the original mechanical potential energy or $V^2/2g = h$.

3. The liquid at the orifice has sufficient kinetic energy in the direction of flow to produce a jet h ft high.

From these deductions it can be stated that the velocity head of the liquid at the orifice and in the direction of flow is $V^2/2g = h_v$, expressed in feet of the fluid flowing. Also, since the liquid at

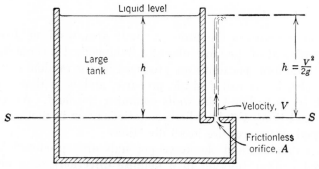

Fig. 9·2 Example of velocity head

the orifice has only a vertical velocity component, its velocity head in any other direction is zero. The velocity pressure at the orifice is $\gamma V^2/2g = p_v$, psf.

The sum of the static pressure and the velocity pressure measured at the same point in the fluid is called total pressure.

In order to measure static, velocity, or total pressure, some method must be used to "pick up" the force resulting from the pressure and to transmit this force to a force-measuring instrument or pressure gage. For pressures that are not pulsating rapidly, the most common pressure "pickup" is a small tube or pipe. One end is exposed to the fluid under test; consequently, the tube is generally filled with this fluid. In some cases, however, this is not true, and these cases will be discussed later. The other end of the tube is connected by a pipe or hose to the pressure gage. The pressure to be measured is transmitted through the stationary fluid in the tube to the gage.

Static pressure or total pressure can be picked up by a single tube. Velocity-pressure measurements require the use of two tubes: one tube to transmit the total-pressure effect and the other tube to transmit the static-pressure effect. The velocity pressure is obtained by subtracting the static pressure from the total pressure. In Fig. 9·3 the method of locating the "pick-up" tubes for measuring the three pressures is shown.

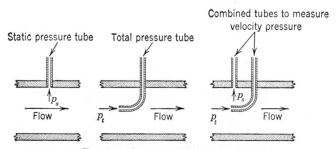

FIG. 9·3   Pressure "pick-up" tubes

The static tube must be placed at right angles to the direction of flow to avoid picking up any velocity pressure or impact effect of the fluid. The total pressure tube must be turned directly into the flow stream in order that the full impact or velocity-pressure effect of the moving fluid may be transmitted to the pressure gage in addition to the static-pressure effect. The total-pressure tube is often called an impact tube or Pitot tube (named after Henri Pitot).

For convenience the double-tube arrangement used to measure velocity pressure is combined into a single unit, as shown in Fig. 9·4. One tube is placed inside another. The outer tube with openings in the sides is the static-pressure tube. The inner tube, open at the end, is the total-pressure tube. The difference in pressures, $p_t - p_s$, as measured by some form of pressure gage, is the velocity pressure p_v.

Instruments or *gages* used to measure pressures that do not vary rapidly may be divided into two classes: mechanical and fluid-type instruments. The Bourdon gage discussed in Article 1·9 is a common type of mechanical gage. It is generally used to measure static pressures where precision of the instrument is not to be closer than a few pounds per square inch. Two other types of mechanical gages are shown in Fig. 9·5A and 9·5B. They are the inverted-bell gage (Fig. 9·5A) and the diaphragm gage (Fig. 9·5B). Both are commonly used to measure pressures or pressure differences of small magnitude. A variation in pressure on the underside of the bell or diaphragm will cause it to move up or down, and this movement is amplified by the lever arm connected to the gage pointer. Movement of the pointer depends on the

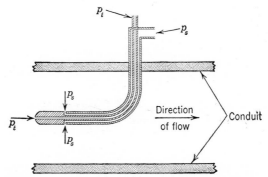

FIG. 9·4 A Pitot tube for measuring velocity pressure

difference in pressure between the atmosphere and the point of measurement. Thus, the pressure indicated, as in most gages, is a pressure difference, absolute pressure minus atmospheric pressure, called gage pressure.

The fluid-type gage is generally called a manometer and is essentially a U tube filled with a liquid such as mercury, water, or alcohol. The Greek prefix "mano," meaning thin or rare, infers that this gage is used to measure small pressures or small pressure differences. Three types of manometers are shown in Figs. 9·6A, 9·6B, and 9·6C. These operate in the same manner as the barometer described in Article 1·9, but they differ in that they register differences in pressure (in other words, both legs of the U are exposed and thus are under pressure). Usually, one leg of the U is at atmospheric pressure. However, in Fig. 9·6B, the manometer may have both legs attached to pressure pickups at pressures other than atmospheric pressure. Its use in measuring velocity pressure from the static- and total-pressure pick-up tubes is shown in Fig. 9·7, and the necessary calculations, with a

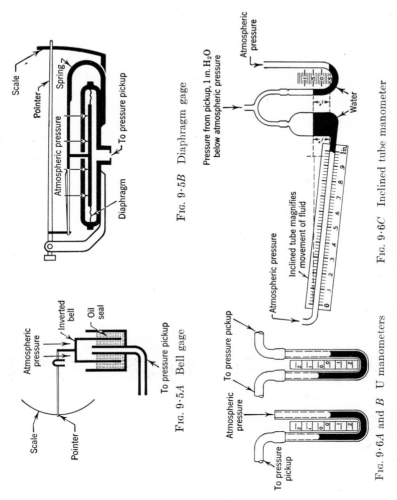

Fig. 9·5B Diaphragm gage

Fig. 9·6C Inclined tube manometer

Fig. 9·5A Bell gage

Fig. 9·6A and B U manometers

proper consideration for corrections, are shown by the following examples:

Example 4. Assume that water flows through the pipe shown in Fig. 9·7 and that the manometer fluid is Hg. If the difference in level of the Hg is 4 in., calculate (*a*) the velocity pressure in psi, and (*b*) the velocity head in ft of water.

Pumps

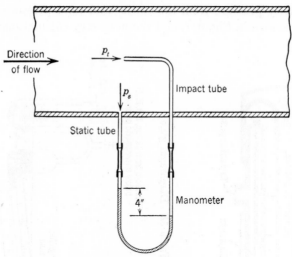

Fig. 9·7   Figure for Examples 4 and 5

Solution: (*a*) Assume that each tube is filled with water up to the manometer fluid (shaded).   Then, the pressure on the left leg of the manometer, $p_s + 4$ in. Hg, just balances the pressure on the right leg of the manometer, $p_t + 4$ in. H_2O (4 in. H_2O displaces the 4 in. Hg), or

$$p_t + 4 \text{ in. } H_2O = p_s + 4 \text{ in. Hg}$$

and rearranging

$$p_t - p_s = 4 \text{ in. Hg} - 4 \text{ in. } H_2O$$

but $p_t - p_s = p_v$, the velocity pressure

thus, $p_v = 4 \text{ in. Hg} - 4 \text{ in. } H_2O$

$$= 4 \text{ in. Hg} \times \frac{1 \text{ ft}}{12 \text{ in.}} \times \frac{13.6 \times 62.4 \text{ lb}}{\text{ft}^3} \times \frac{1 \text{ ft}^2}{144 \text{ in.}^2}$$

$$- 4 \text{ in. } H_2O \times \frac{1 \text{ ft}}{12 \text{ in.}} \times \frac{62.4 \text{ lb}}{\text{ft}^3} \times \frac{1 \text{ ft}^2}{144 \text{ in.}^2}$$

$$= 4 \text{ in. Hg} \times \frac{0.491 \text{ psi}}{\text{in. Hg}} - 4 \text{ in. } H_2O \times \frac{0.0361 \text{ psi}}{\text{in. } H_2O}$$

$$= 1.964 - 0.144$$

$$= 1.82 \text{ psi}$$

(b) **From** part *a*,

$$p_v = 1.82 \times 144 \text{ psf}$$

thus,

$$h_v = \frac{1.82 \times 144 \text{ lb}}{\text{ft}^2} \times \frac{1 \text{ ft}^3}{62.4 \text{ lb}}$$

$$= 4.2 \text{ ft of water}$$

Example 5. Assume that air having a specific weight of 0.08 lb per cu ft flows through the pipe shown in Fig. 9·7 and that the manometer fluid is water. If the difference in level of the water is 4 in., calculate (a) the velocity pressure in psi, and (b) the velocity head in ft of air.

Solution: (a) The 4 in. of air in the right leg of the manometer which displaces the 4 in. of water may be neglected because of its low specific weight.

Thus, $\qquad p_t = p_s + 4 \text{ in. H}_2\text{O}$

or $\qquad p_t - p_s = 4 \text{ in. H}_2\text{O}$

and $\qquad p_v = 4 \text{ in. H}_2\text{O}$

$$= 4 \text{ in. H}_2\text{O} \times \frac{1 \text{ ft}}{12 \text{ in.}} \times \frac{62.4 \text{ lb}}{\text{ft}^3} \times \frac{1 \text{ ft}^2}{144 \text{ in.}^2}$$

$$= 4 \text{ in. H}_2\text{O} \times \frac{0.036 \text{ psi}}{1 \text{ in. H}_2\text{O}}$$

$$= 0.144 \text{ psi}$$

(b) From part *a*,

$$p_v = 0.144 \times 144 \text{ psf}$$

thus,

$$h_v = \frac{0.144 \times 144 \text{ lb}}{\text{ft}^2} \times \frac{1 \text{ ft}^3}{0.08 \text{ lb}}$$

$$= 259 \text{ ft of air}$$

The manometer shown in Fig. 9·6C is used to increase the precision of the U-tube manometer by inclining one leg of the U. The inclined tube on the left amplifies the movement of the liquid in the manometer. The tube on the right is the ordinary U tube, shown for comparison. Both gages read a pressure of 1.0 in. of water less than atmospheric pressure.

The type of liquid used in a manometer depends upon the magnitude of the pressures involved and the desired precision of the instrument. A liquid having the larger specific weight or specific gravity is used in manometers to measure the highest pressures. Table 9·1 gives the specific weight and specific gravity of a number of liquids at standard temperatures and ordinary elevations.

The lines connecting the pressure pick-up elements or tubes and the pressure gages must be installed and operated in a manner such that they are filled at all times with only one known fluid; otherwise, unpredictable errors will arise. For example, when measurements of the pressure of a gas or vapor are being

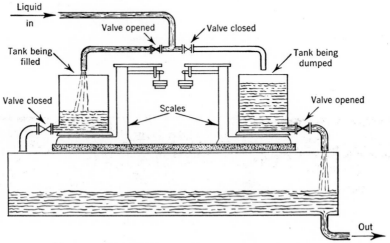

Fig. 9·8 Weighing a liquid without interrupting flow

taken, the connecting lines should be kept free of pockets of liquids, such as condensed water vapor, or the connecting lines should be completely filled with water. When measurements of the pressure of liquids are being taken, the connecting lines should be kept free of gas or air pockets.

9·3 Measurements of fluid flow. In most processes where flow occurs, the engineer is interested in having a continuous record of the quantity of fluid flowing or a means of measuring, from time to time, the quantity. The most accurate method is calibrated weighing. Weighing immobile material involves no serious problem, but weighing continuously moving fluids introduces complications. Generally, flow cannot be interrupted. To prevent such an interruption more than one container is provided, with inlets to both as shown in Fig. 9·8. While one container is being filled, the other is being weighed and emptied. By alternating the process, flow can be maintained.

The greatest disadvantage of the weighing process is that often the quantities involved are large and require bulky tanks and scales. In such cases, weighing is considered impractical and is only used for test and calibration purposes.

Another common method of measuring flow is by means of the weir. A weir is a dam built in the path of flow in which a V notch or rectangular notch is cut and through which the fluid passes. From accurate measurement of the height of the water crest above the bottom of the notch the quantity of flow can be calculated by empirical formulas. The weir is used mainly in open channels, as shown in Fig. 9·9. The weir is also used in

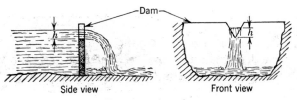

FIG. 9·9 A weir

closed conduits and tanks where the vessel is not completely filled with the fluid being measured.

In closed conduits completely filled with the fluid, a convenient method of measuring the quantity of fluid flowing is to utilize the Pitot tube to measure velocity head, to convert this head into fluid velocity, and then to calculate the quantity flowing by the law of continuity of flow.

Let us assume that a fluid flows through a pipe having a cross-sectional area, A, with a flow of m_s lb per sec as shown in Fig. 9·10. If the fluid completely fills the area A and has a specific volume of v cu ft per lb then, by the law of continuity of flow, as discussed in Article 7·3,

$$m_s = \frac{AV}{v} \tag{9·2}$$

Further, if the velocity head, h_v, is measured by means of static and total pressure tubes or by a Pitot tube, then the velocity can be calculated by

$$\frac{V^2}{2g} = h_v, \text{ ft of fluid flowing}$$

or $$V = \sqrt{2gh_v}$$ (9·3)

Combining Equations 9·2 and 9·3 gives

$$m_s = \frac{A}{v}\sqrt{2gh_v}$$ (9·4)

Thus, by measuring A and h_v and determining v for the conditions of the fluid, an indirect measure of m_s is obtained.

If the velocity varies across the pipe diameter, it is necessary to find the mean velocity of the fluid by obtaining a number of readings of the velocity pressure at different points in the cross section. This is called traversing the area.

The method of obtaining the velocity of a fluid by velocity-pressure measurement is illustrated by the following example:

Example 6. Find the velocity of a gas having a specific weight of 0.07 lb per cu ft if a water manometer connected as shown in Fig. 9·10 registers 3.0 in. of water.

Solution:

$$p = h_w \gamma_w = h_g \gamma_g$$

where $h_w = \frac{3}{12}$ ft of water
      γ_w = specific weight of water
         = 62.4 lb per cu ft
      h_g = velocity head, ft of the gas
      γ_g = specific weight of the gas
         = 0.07 lb per cu ft

Thus, $$p = \tfrac{3}{12} \times 62.4 = h_g \times 0.07$$

and $$h_g = 223 \text{ ft}$$

But $$V = \sqrt{2gh_v}$$

where $h_v = h_g = 223$ ft
      $g = 32.2$ ft per sec^2

Thus, $$V = \sqrt{2 \times 32.2 \times 223}$$

$$= 119.5 \text{ fps}$$

The Pitot tube with a manometer, as a means of determining the rate of flow, has certain disadvantages. It cannot, in many cases, be a permanent installation and cannot be traversed in a conduit through which a fluid flows under pressure without great difficulty. The Pitot tube is used, however, to measure the flow of air or other gases when under slight pressures.

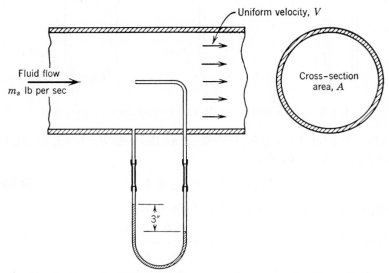

FIG. 9·10   Measurement of flow by pressure pick-up (see Example 6)

In most permanent installations some form of flow meter such as shown in Figs. 9·11A, B, C is used. These metering devices are carefully designed obstructions placed in the flow path to produce a measurable decrease in static pressure and a corresponding increase in velocity pressure. A theoretical analysis based on the flow conditions existing at the constrictions will disclose how the flow rate may be calculated. Let it be assumed that the flow through any of the devices shown in Fig. 9·11 is such that

1. The flow is frictionless between points 1 and 2, where the areas are A_1 and A_2.
2. The potential energy change between points 1 and 2 is negligible.

484   *Pumps*

3. The fluid completely fills the areas A_1 and A_2, and the static pressure taps are located at the areas A_1 and A_2.

On the basis of the first two assumptions it may be concluded that the total head at point 2 is equal to the total head at point 1.

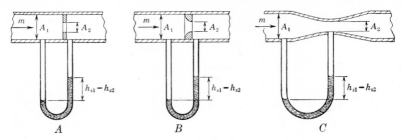

Fig. 9·11   The orifice, nozzle, and Venturi for measuring flow

Since the total head, h_t, is defined as the velocity head, h_v, plus the static head, h_s, then

$$h_{v1} + h_{s1} = h_{v2} + h_{s2} \qquad (9 \cdot 5)$$

or, rearranging, $h_{s1} - h_{s2} = h_{v2} - h_{v1}$

but

$$h_{v2} - h_{v1} = \frac{V_2{}^2}{2g} - \frac{V_1{}^2}{2g}$$

thus

$$h_{s1} - h_{s2} = \frac{V_2{}^2}{2g} - \frac{V_1{}^2}{2g} \qquad (9 \cdot 6)$$

As shown in Fig. 9·11, the manometers indicate the differential static head, $h_{s1} - h_{s2}$.

On the basic of the third assumption the equation of continuity of flow may be applied thus,

$$m_s = \frac{A_1 V_1}{v_1} = \frac{A_2 V_2}{v_2} \qquad (9 \cdot 7)$$

From Equation 9·7,

$$V_1 = \frac{A_2 V_2 v_1}{A_1 v_2} \qquad (9 \cdot 8)$$

Combining Equations 9·8 and 9·6, eliminating V_1, rearranging, and solving for V_2 gives

$$V_2 = \sqrt{2g(h_{s1} - h_{s2})\left[\cfrac{1}{1 - \left(\cfrac{A_2 v_1}{A_1 v_2}\right)^2}\right]} \qquad (9\cdot 9)$$

and, from Equation 9·7,

$$m_s = \frac{A_2}{v_2}\sqrt{2g(h_{s1} - h_{s2})\left[\cfrac{1}{1 - \left(\cfrac{A_2 v_1}{A_1 v_2}\right)^2}\right]} \qquad (9\cdot 10)$$

In Equation 9·10 the areas, A_1 and A_2, and the change in static head, $h_{s1} - h_{s2}$, are measurable. The specific volumes are known or can be calculated for the fluid flowing. Thus, the mass rate of flow, m_s, can be determined.

Since the original assumptions are not true for actual flow conditions, the rate of flow, m_s, as calculated from Equation 9·10, should be multiplied by one or more correction factors. These correction factors are determined experimentally and differ with each type of meter. The Venturi meter will produce results that most nearly approach the values obtained by the foregoing assumptions. The results obtained from an orifice require the greatest correction. Although the Venturi meter approaches the theoretically correct type of flow meter, its added bulk and weight restrict its use.

An application of the Venturi meter is illustrated in the following example:

Example 7. Assume that the rate of flow of cold water is to be measured with a Venturi meter of the dimensions shown in Fig. 9·12. Assume that a mercury manometer indicates a difference in level of 4 in. Find the cu ft of water flowing per sec for frictionless flow.

Solution:

$$h_{s1} - h_{s2} = 4 \text{ in. of Hg} - 4 \text{ in. of } H_2O$$

$$= 4 \times 13.6 \text{ in. of } H_2O - 4 \text{ in. of } H_2O$$

or

$$h_{s1} - h_{s2} = \frac{4 \times 12.6}{12} \text{ ft of } H_2O$$

$$= 4.2 \text{ ft of } H_2O$$

Thus,

$$\frac{V_2{}^2}{2g} - \frac{V_1{}^2}{2g} = 4.2 \text{ ft of water}$$

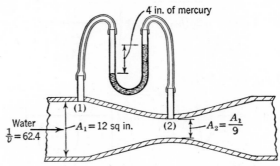

FIG. 9·12   Figure for Example 7

Also, since $v_1 = v_2$ for a liquid,

$$A_1 V_1 = A_2 V_2$$

where A_1 = area at point 1 or $\frac{12}{144}$ sq ft

$$A_2 = \text{area at point 2 or } \frac{12}{144 \times 9} \text{ sq ft}$$

Thus, $$\frac{12}{144} V_1 = \frac{12}{9 \times 144} V_2$$

or $$V_1 = \frac{V_2}{9}$$

Substituting the value of V_1 in the preceding equation, we get

$$\frac{V_2^2}{2g} - \frac{(V_2^2)}{2g(9)^2} = 4.2$$

or $$\frac{V_2^2}{64.4} - \frac{V_2^2}{81 \times 64.4} = 4.2$$

or $$V_2^2 = \frac{64.4 \times 4.2 \times 81}{80}$$

$$V_2 = 16.6 \text{ fps}$$

and $$m_s = \frac{A_2 V_2}{v_2} = \frac{12 \times 16.6 \times 62.4}{9 \times 144}$$

or $$m_s = 9.6 \text{ lb per sec}$$

9·4   Pump testing.   In the selection or testing of a pump the first thing to be considered is its capacity in gallons per minute. Some methods of measuring flow have been discussed in Article

9·3. In pump testing, the most accepted and convenient method of measuring capacity is by means of the orifice, nozzle, or Venturi.

The next consideration is the total dynamic head against which the pump operates. The total dynamic head may be defined as the sum of the changes in elevation, static head, and velocity head of the fluid from intake to discharge of the pump. Thus, as shown in Fig. 9·13, the total dynamic head, h_t, is given by the equation

$$h_t = (y_2 - y_1) + \left(\frac{V_2^2}{2g} - \frac{V_1^2}{2g}\right) + \left(\frac{p_2 - p_1}{\gamma}\right) \quad (9·11)$$

in which $y_2 - y_1$ = change in elevation between pick-up tube locations, ft of fluid flowing

$\dfrac{V_2^2}{2g} - \dfrac{V_1^2}{2g}$ = change in velocity head between pick-up tube locations, ft of fluid flowing

$\dfrac{p_2 - p_1}{\gamma}$ = change in static head between pick-up tube locations, ft of fluid flowing

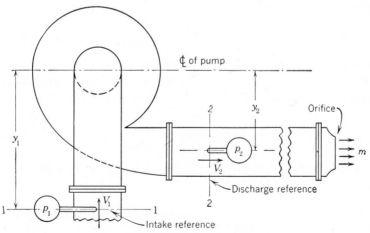

Fig. 9·13 Pump test arrangement

In Equation 9·11 and as illustrated in Fig. 9·13, the elevations y_1 and y_2 are measured with respect to the pump center line. This is in accordance with test code practices. However, it is evident that $y_2 - y_1$ is constant, regardless of the datum from which y_1 and y_2 are measured.

When Equation 9·11 is multiplied by 1 lb of fluid flowing per min, it becomes identical with Equation 1·34, derived in Article 1·24. Thus, the work done by the pump on the fluid in foot-pounds per pound is

$$W = 1 \times h_t = 1 \times \left[(y_2 - y_1) + \left(\frac{V_2^2}{2g} - \frac{V_1^2}{2g} \right) + \left(\frac{p_2 - p_1}{\gamma} \right) \right]$$

and the work done on the fluid in foot-pounds per minute is

$$W = m_m h_t = m_m \left[(y_2 - y_1) + \left(\frac{V_2^2}{2g} - \frac{V_1^2}{2g} \right) + \left(\frac{p_2 - p_1}{\gamma} \right) \right]$$

$$(9·12)$$

where m_m = lb of fluid flowing per min

h_t = total dynamic head, ft of fluid flowing

The horsepower delivered to the fluid is called hydraulic horsepower and is equal to

$$\text{Hydraulic hp} = \frac{h_t m_m}{33,000} \qquad (9·13)$$

The pump horsepower is the sum of the power required to overcome the pump losses and hydraulic power, and is equal to the hydraulic horsepower divided by the pump efficiency, η, or

$$\text{Pump hp} = \frac{h_t m_m}{\eta 33,000} \qquad (9·14)$$

The following example will be used to illustrate the calculations for a pump test assembly:

Example 8. Assume that the following data are obtained for the pump shown in Fig. 9·13: The rate of flow of water as measured by the orifice is 8000 lb per min; the intake static gage is located 4 ft below the pump center line and reads 10 psig; the discharge static gage is 2 ft below the pump center line and reads 50 psig. The gages are located as close to the pump as possible. The area of the intake and discharge pipes are 1 sq ft and ¾ sq ft, respectively. The pump efficiency is 70 per cent. Assume that γ is numerically equal to $1/v$ since 1 lb mass will weigh approximately 1 lb at the earth's surface.

Calculate: (a) capacity of the pump, gpm; (b) total dynamic head, ft; (c) hydraulic hp, (d) pump hp.

Solution: (a)

$$\text{Capacity, gpm} = \frac{8000 \text{ lb per min}}{8.33 \text{ lb } H_2O \text{ per gal } H_2O}$$

$$= 965 \text{ gpm}$$

(b)
$$h_t = (y_2 - y_1) + \left(\frac{V_2^2 - V_1^2}{2g}\right) + \left(\frac{p_2 - p_1}{\gamma}\right)$$

where $y_2 = -2$ ft
$y_1 = -4$ ft

and
$$p_2 = 50 \times 144 \text{ psf}$$

$$p_1 = 10 \times 144 \text{ psf}$$

$$\gamma = 62.4 \text{ lb per cu ft}$$

From the continuity-flow equation,

$$V_1 = \frac{m_m v_1}{A_1} = \frac{8000}{1 \times 62.4}$$

$$= 128.2 \text{ fpm}$$

$$= 2.14 \text{ fps}$$

and
$$V_2 = \frac{m_m v_2}{A_2} = \frac{8000}{\frac{3}{4} \times 62.4}$$

$$= 170.8 \text{ fpm}$$

$$= 2.84 \text{ fps}$$

Thus,
$$h_t = [-2 - (-4)] + \left[\frac{(2.84)^2 - (2.14)^2}{2g}\right] + \left[\frac{144}{62.4}(50 - 10)\right]$$

$$= 2 + 0.1 + 92.4 = 94.5 \text{ ft}$$

(c)
$$\text{Hydraulic hp} = \frac{m_m h_t}{33,000}$$

$$= \frac{8000 \times 94.5}{33,000}$$

$$= 22.9$$

(d)
$$\text{Pump hp} = \frac{\text{hydraulic hp}}{\text{pump efficiency}}$$

$$= \frac{22.9}{0.7}$$

$$= 32.7$$

In referring to Equation 9·12 and Fig. 9·13 it should be emphasized that the static-pressure gages must be located at the reference planes shown by y_1 and y_2. If for practical reasons the gages cannot be so located, it will be necessary to correct the gage readings to those values which the gages would read if they were to be moved to the reference planes. Some rules may be stated for these gage corrections.

1. No gage correction is necessary if the pick-up tube from the reference plane to the gage is filled with air. Normally, this will occur when the gage reading is a vacuum and the gage is above its connection point. Because of the low specific weight of the air in the connection tube, the correction is assumed to be zero.

2. If the pick-up tube is filled with the liquid flowing and the gage is located below the reference plane, the gage will read high by the difference in elevation between the plane of reference and the gage.

3. If the pick-up tube is filled with the liquid flowing and the gage is located above the plane of reference, the gage will read low by the difference in elevation between the plane of reference and the gage.

4. If a manometer is used in which the liquid in the manometer differs from the liquid being pumped a manometer correction should be made. This type of correction is shown in Examples 4 and 7 in this chapter.

Example 9. Assume that the following data are obtained for the pump shown in Fig. 9·14: The pump delivers oil, specific gravity of 0.8, at the rate of 10,000 lb per min; the intake static gage is located 10 ft above the intake reference point and reads 10 in. of Hg vac; the discharge-pressure gage is located 12 ft above the discharge reference plane and reads 100 psig. The areas of intake and discharge pipes are equal, and the reference planes are at the same elevation. Calculate (a) the total dynamic head, (b) the hydraulic hp.

Solution: (a) The total dynamic head is

$$h_t = (y_2 - y_1) + \left(\frac{V_2^2}{2g} - \frac{V_1^2}{2g}\right) + \left(\frac{p_2}{\gamma_2} - \frac{p_1}{\gamma_1}\right)$$

where $\qquad\qquad y_2 - y_1 = 0 \quad$ given

and $\qquad\qquad \dfrac{V_2^2}{2g} - \dfrac{V_1^2}{2g} = 0 \quad$ since $\quad A_1 = A_2$

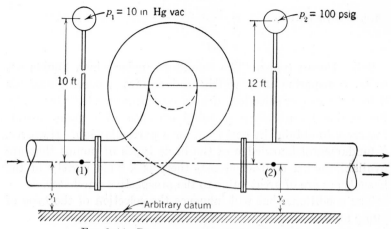

FIG. 9·14 Pump arrangement for Example 9

The discharge gage reads low by 12 ft of the fluid flowing; thus, the static discharge head is actually greater by 12 ft, or

$$\frac{p_2}{\gamma_2} = \frac{100 \times 144}{62.4 \times 0.8} + 12$$

where $\gamma_2 = 62.4 \times 0.8$ = specific weight of the oil, lb per cu ft

thus,
$$\frac{p_2}{\gamma_2} = 288 + 12 = 300 \text{ ft of oil}$$

The intake gage reads a vacuum; thus, the pressure at point 1 is not sufficient to sustain a column of oil. The pick-up tube will be filled with air, and no correction is necessary because of the low specific weight of air. The intake head is

$$\frac{p_1}{\gamma_1} = \frac{-10 \times 0.491 \times 144}{62.4 \times 0.8} \qquad (\gamma_1 = \gamma_2 = 62.4 \times 0.8)$$

$$= -14.2 \text{ ft of oil}$$

The total head becomes $h_t = 300 - (-14.2)$

$$= 314.2 \text{ ft of oil}$$

(b) The hydraulic hp is

$$\text{Hydraulic hp} = \frac{m_m h_t}{33,000}$$

where $h_t = 314.2$ ft
$m_m = 10,000$ lb per min

Thus, the hydraulic hp $\quad = \dfrac{10,000 \times 314.2}{33,000}$

$$= 95.2$$

9·5 Pump types. The conditions under which liquids are to be transported vary widely and require a careful analysis before the proper selection of a pump can be made. Generally, the engineer purchasing a pump consults with pump manu- facturers to obtain the best type for a particular job. However, a fundamental knowledge of the basic types of pumps that are available and a realization that there is a wide variety of the basic types are of great value to the prospective purchaser.

The conditions that will influence the selection of the type of pump are:

1. The type of liquid to be handled: that is, its viscosity, clean- liness, temperature, and so on.
2. The amount of liquid to be handled.
3. The total pressure against which the liquid is to be moved.
4. The type of power to be used to drive the pump.

Pumps may be divided into four major classifications:

1. Piston pumps or reciprocating pumps driven by steam en- gines or electric motors.
2. Centrifugal pumps driven by steam turbines or electric motors.
3. Rotary pumps driven by steam turbines or electric motors.
4. Fluid-impellent pumps which are not mechanically operated but are fluid-pressure-operated.

9·6 Reciprocating pumps. The most simple, reliable, flex- ible, and inexpensive pump is the single direct-acting steam pump, commonly called a simplex pump. Essentially it consists of a steam cylinder and piston in line with a water cylinder and piston. The two pistons have a common piston rod, as shown in Fig. 9·15.

Steam under a pressure p acts against a piston-face area A, to produce a force, $F = pA$. If the piston stroke is of length L, the work per stroke is FL or pAL. If no losses are considered, the work of the steam piston is transferred to the water piston and in turn is transferred to the water, thus,

$$pAL = p_1A_1L$$

or $$pA = p_1A_1$$

Therefore, $$p_1 = \frac{pA}{A_1}$$

By varying the steam pressure p, or each of the areas A or A_1, any reasonable water pressure can be obtained. If a high water

FIG. 9·15 Simplex pump

pressure is demanded, such as in the case when water must be supplied at 1500 psia without a correspondingly high steam pressure, the area A_1 must be made quite small or the product pA made large.

If the water pressure is to be maintained, the steam pressure must also be maintained. Thus, the steam is not permitted to expand but is introduced throughout the full length of the stroke. A slide-D valve or piston valve is used on the steam cylinder and opens or closes only at the beginning or end of the stroke. The water valves are generally the spring-loaded disk type, similar to the one shown in Fig. 9·16. If the pressure acting on the underside of the flexible-valve disk becomes great enough to overcome the spring force and the pressure acting on the upper side of the disk, the valve disk will lift from its seat. As the pressure drops, it is returned to the closed position by the spring.

The simplex pump owing to its reciprocating motion produces a pulsating flow. The pulsations can be reduced by operating two simplex pumps in parallel but out of phase with each other. If the two pumps are installed as a unit, the unit is called a

duplex pump. A side view of the duplex pump is shown in Fig.
9·17.

In Fig. 9·17 the D-slide valve on the steam cylinder is shown
in mid-position for a mid-position of the steam piston. The pump
will not operate under these conditions. The valve linkage will
have to be set so that steam exhausts from one end of the cylinder while steam is entering the other end. That is, for operation
the valve should be near the end of its stroke for a mid-position

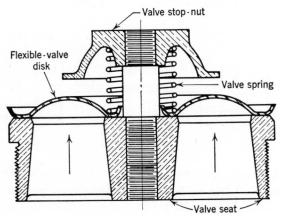

FIG. 9·16 A spring-loaded disk-type water valve

of the steam piston. Also, during operation the water-discharge
valve for one end of the water cylinder and the water-intake
valve for the opposite end of the cylinder will open simultaneously.

Under heavy duty and severe service or where gritty or dirty
liquids are pumped, the piston-type pump is generally replaced
by a plunger-type reciprocating pump (see Fig. 9·18). The
plungers are connected by side rods located outside the cylinder.
The plungers have separate cylinders. In Fig. 9·18, if the
plungers move to the left, water will flow in the directions indicated. The wearing surfaces of the plungers are clearly visible,
and packing can be replaced with a minimum down time.

Both the piston and plunger pumps may be motor-driven
rather than steam-driven. A belt drive reduces the speed of
the motor, and a flywheel provides sufficient inertia to carry the

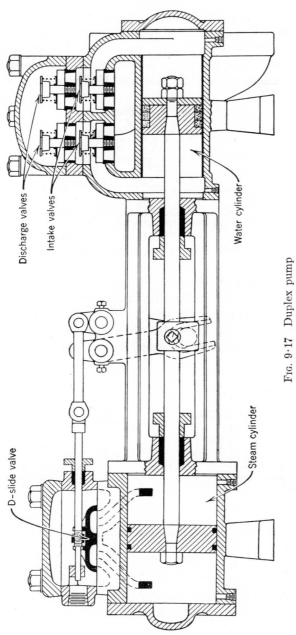

Fig. 9·17 Duplex pump

pump past the end of the strokes. A relief valve must be placed on the pump-discharge line to prevent overloading the motor in case the liquid pressure becomes excessive. The relief valve is not necessary when the pump is steam-driven, since the steam piston will stop without being damaged if overloaded.

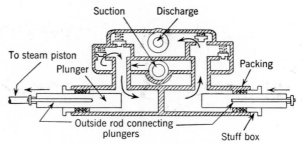

Fig. 9·18 Plunger-type reciprocating pump

9·7 Centrifugal pumps. In the reciprocating pump, the pressure head is produced by the transverse motion of a piston. In the centrifugal pump, the head is produced by the centrifugal force imparted to the liquid from the rotary motion of an impeller. An illustration of the principle involved is shown in Fig.

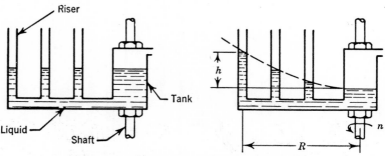

Fig. 9·19 A pressure head produced by centrifugal force.

9·19. A tank is filled with a liquid. Risers are attached to a tube extending from the tank. The assembly is keyed to a vertical shaft and is free to rotate. If the assembly is stationary, the liquid level is the same in the risers and tank. If the assembly is rotated, the liquid will rise in the risers and will drop in the tank, as shown in Fig. 9·19. The difference in liquid level or pressure head h produced at a distance R from the center of rotation is due to the centrifugal force imparted to the liquid. The equation for the head is

$$h = \frac{V^2}{2g}$$

where h = head, ft of the liquid

$V = \dfrac{2\pi Rn}{60}$ = linear velocity at the distance R from the center of rotation, fps

g = acceleration of gravity

This is the mechanical potential energy of the liquid. The fluid also has a mechanical kinetic energy due to the motion of the assembly. The kinetic energy $V^2/2g$ is called the velocity head of the liquid. The total head of the liquid is the sum of the pressure head and velocity head, or V^2/g. Since $V = 2\pi Rn/60$, then the total head is equal to $(2\pi Rn)^2/3600\,g$.

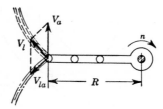

Fig. 9·20 Plan view of assembly in Figure 9·19

If water is supplied to the tank in Fig. 9·19 and if the pressure head produced by rotation is sufficient to cause water to spill over the end riser, a crude centrifugal pump would result. To a motionless observer looking down on the assembly, the water leaving the riser would appear to trace a spiral and move in the same direction as the direction of motion of the assembly. To an observer located on the moving assembly, the water would appear to leave in a direction opposite to the direction of motion of the assembly (see Fig. 9·20). The motions of the liquid and of the assembly are shown by the velocity vectors. V_a is the absolute velocity of the assembly. V_l is the absolute velocity of the liquid, and the vector difference between them gives the relative velocity of the liquid with respect to the assembly.

The centrifugal pump, which utilizes these principles, consists of an impeller or rotating section to produce the flow and a casing to enclose the liquid and to direct the liquid properly as it leaves the impeller. The liquid enters the impeller at its center or "eye" and parallel to the shaft. By centrifugal force the liquid passes to the impeller rim through the space between the backward curved blades, as shown in Fig. 9·21. As shown in Fig. 9·20, the velocity of the liquid with respect to the impeller is V_{la}, which is in a direction opposite to the impeller motion. The impeller blades are curved backward to permit the liquid to flow to the rim of the impeller with a minimum of friction. As the liquid leaves the impeller, it is thrown in a spiral motion forward with a velocity, V_l.

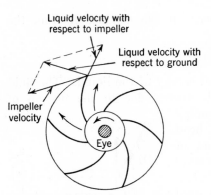

FIG. 9·21   Velocities of liquid and impeller at impeller outlet

The water is guided away from the impeller by two basic types of casings: the volute, and the turbine or diffuser. A simple volute pump is shown in Fig. 9·22A to E. Liquid enters the impeller at the "eye," is thrown to the outside, and leaves the pump through the expanding spiral or volute casing. The casing has the volute shape to permit flow with a minimum of friction and to convert a part of the velocity head into static head. The static head is the head that overcomes resistance to flow.

The turbine or diffuser pump has the same type of impeller as the volute pump. The casing has a circular shape, and within the casing is a diffuser ring on which are placed vanes (see Fig. 9·23A and B). The vanes direct the flow of liquid and a decrease in the velocity of the liquid occurs because of an increase in the area through which the liquid flows. Thus, part of the velocity head is converted into static head as in the volute pump. For a multistage pump, the diffuser pump has a more compact casing than the volute pump. The diffuser pump design is adaptable to differences in flow conditions since the same casing can be used with various arrangements of diffuser vanes. In the volute pump a variation in the requirements of the volute casing demands

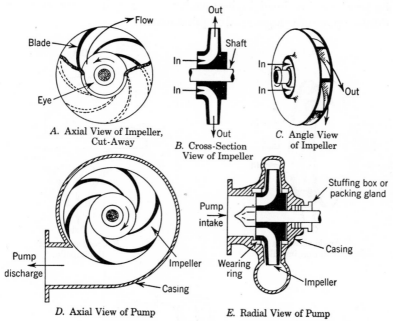

A. Axial View of Impeller, Cut-Away

B. Cross-Section View of Impeller

C. Angle View of Impeller

D. Axial View of Pump

E. Radial View of Pump

FIG. 9·22 A single-suction enclosed-impeller volute centrifugal pump

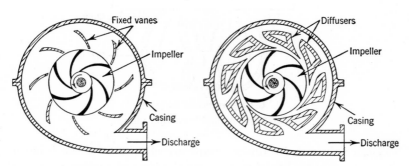

FIG. 9·23 Two types of diffuser vane centrifugal pumps

alterations in the casing itself. Generally, the volute pump will be used for low-head high-capacity flow requirements and the diffuser pump for high-head requirements.

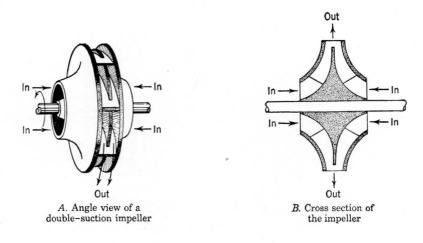

A. Angle view of a
double-suction impeller

B. Cross section of
the impeller

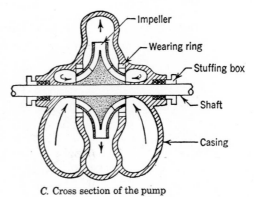

C. Cross section of the pump

FIG. 9·24   A double-suction pump

Both volute and diffuser pumps are classified by the type of impeller, the number of stages, and the type of suction or intake used. A pump similar to the one shown in Fig. 9·22 but having two "eyes" on the impeller is called a double-suction pump. The use of the double suction, one "eye" located on each side of the impeller, permits forces acting on the impeller to be balanced, thus reducing the axial thrust on the shaft. Also, the double-suction pump is used for handling hot water where there is danger of water flashing into steam at points of low pressure. The double suction offers little resistance to flow; thus, low-pressure

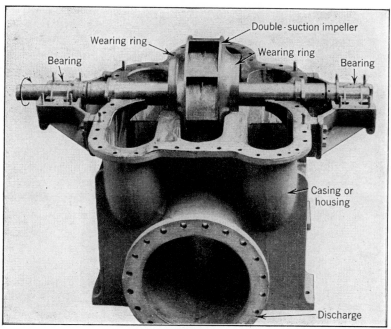

Fig. 9·25 Lower housing of a double-suction volute centrifugal pump

areas are less apt to occur. The double-suction pump is used also for large capacities. A double-suction pump is shown in Figs. 9·24*A*, *B*, *C* and 9·25.

When two or more impellers are mounted on the same shaft and act in series, the pump is called a multistage pump, the number of stages corresponding to the number of impellers used. The lower casing of a six-stage pump is shown in Fig. 9·26. This is a boiler-feed pump capable of delivering 415,000 lb of water per hr against a pressure of 1500 psi. Multistaging produces better performance, higher pump efficiency, and smaller impeller diam-

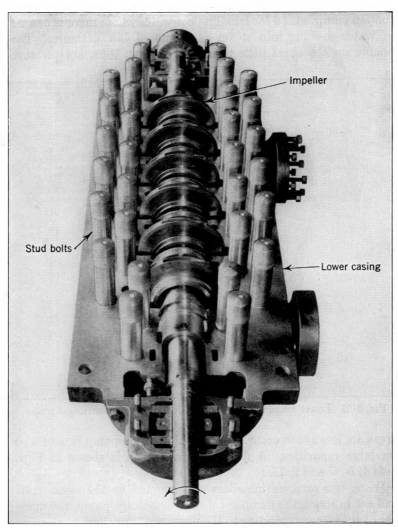

FIG. 9·26 A multistage diffuser-vane centrifugal pump

eters for high-pressure heads. Usually each stage produces the same head, and the total head developed would be the number of stages times the head produced per stage.

The types of impellers installed in centrifugal pumps are as numerous as the uses to which the pumps are put. Classification, however, can be made by designating the direction of flow

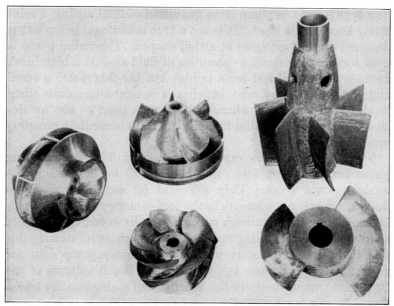

A. Closed impeller,   *B.* Open impellers,   *C.* Axial-flow
    double suction   mixed flow   impellers

Fig. 9·27 Several impeller designs

of the fluid leaving the impeller. All pumps have the intake parallel to the impeller shaft. The discharge, however, may be radial, partially radial and axial, or axial. In the radial-type impeller the suction and discharge are at right angles. The radial impeller may be of the closed or the open type. The term closed or open refers to the fluid passage within the impeller. The open impeller has one side of the flow path open to the pump casing or housing. The closed impeller has both sides of the flow path enclosed by the sides of the impeller as in Fig. 9·27*A*.

The partially radial impeller discharges at an angle greater

than 90 degrees with intake and is of the open-impeller design
(see Fig. 9·27*B*).

The axial-flow impeller discharges at an angle of approximately 180 degrees with the intake and is generally of the propeller type. Two types of axial-flow impellers are shown in
Fig. 9·27*C*.

Each of the impeller types has a specific purpose. The axial-
flow type is used to pump large quantities of fluid against a relatively small static head. It is not a true centrifugal pump but is
designed on the principles of airfoil shapes. The radial pump is
used for handling smaller quantities of fluid against a high head,
because the centrifugal force is high but the flow path is small
and restrictive. The open impeller is designed to handle dirty
liquids such as sewage, where the flow path must be less restrictive. The partially radial impeller covers intermediate pumping
conditions.

9·8 Miscellaneous types of pumps. The reciprocating
pump and the centrifugal pump have many applications in the
modern power plant. They are used for supplying water to
boilers, returning condensate to the feed-water system, and circulating cooling water through condensers. However, they are not
so adaptable for handling viscous liquids such as lubricating oils
and fuel oils as are rotary pumps. The rotary pump does not
rely on centrifugal force to produce flow. Small volumes of the
liquid are trapped between the impeller and casing and are transferred from a low-pressure intake to a higher-pressure discharge.
The rotary pump is classed as a positive-displacement pump.

The rotary pump shown in Fig. 9·28 is used for pumping oils
against pressures as high as 3000 psi. Liquid enters the inlet,
divides, and flows to the ends of the rotors. It then enters the
openings between the rotor teeth and is enclosed and propelled
to the discharge pipe at the center. No valves are necessary,
and axial and radial thrust on the shaft is eliminated.

To handle very viscous liquids such as hot tars, greases, and
rosins, a rotary pump similar to the one shown in Fig. 9·29 may
be used. Two helical gears in mesh enclose the liquid between
the teeth and the pump casing and transfer the liquid to the
discharge. A steam jacket surrounding the pump reduces the
viscosity of the liquid by increasing its temperature.

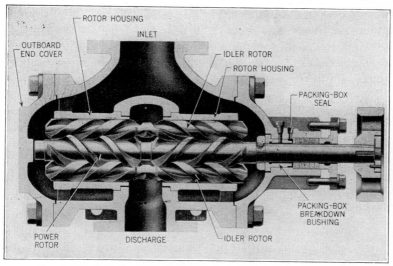

FIG. 9·28 Section through Imo rotary pump for pumping oils

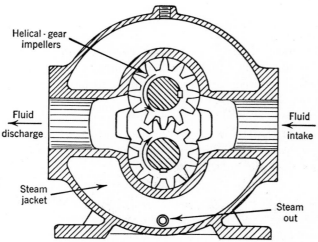

FIG. 9·29 A spur-gear rotary pump for handling viscous liquids

One type of pump is sometimes found in stationary power plants and is used extensively in locomotives as a boiler-feed pump that does not utilize a mechanical drive. The pump is called a steam-jet injector. A simple injector is shown in Fig. 9·30. Steam enters at the left and passes through the nozzle, thus acquiring a high velocity. Owing to the high velocity at the nozzle exit, the pressure is reduced. Atmospheric pressure will force water into the section surrounding the nozzle opening. The water will then be entrained by the steam jet and carried

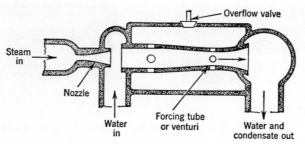

FIG. 9·30 Steam-jet injector

into the forcing tube. In the forcing tube the steam will condense, and the water will increase in velocity. As the Venturi section increases in area, the velocity head of the water developed in the forcing tube will be converted into pressure head. The water can be raised to a pressure equal to or greater than the original steam pressure.

The injector is mechanically an inefficient pump, but the condensation of the steam raises the temperature of the feedwater. The injector cannot be used for pumping feedwater that is at a temperature higher than 100 to 120 F.

The same principles may be applied to the pumping of air or gas as shown in Fig. 9·31. The steam-jet air ejector is actually a thermocompressor and is used to remove air from regions at low pressures to atmospheric pressure. The ejector is an important auxiliary of the steam condenser discussed in Chapter 11.

9·9 Pump performance. Most pump manufacturers test their pumps and can furnish data on the performance of each type and size. Generally the performance characteristics of a pump are represented by characteristic curves similar to those shown in Fig. 9·32. The head, horsepower, and capacity are expressed in per cent of their values at the maximum efficiency of

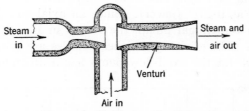

Fig. 9·31 Steam-jet air ejector

the pump. The curves show the usual trend of the characteristics for most centrifugal pumps when operated at the pump speed to give maximum efficiency. If possible a pump should operate at

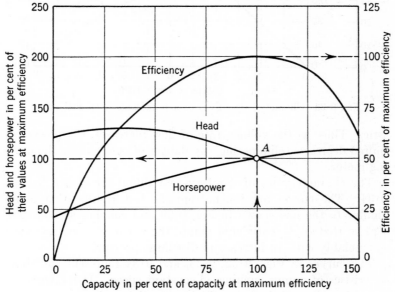

Fig. 9·32 Typical characteristic curves of a pump

the point where the efficiency is 100 per cent of the maximum efficiency, or at point *A* in Fig. 9·32.

In characteristic curves, the head, capacity, and power may

be expressed in terms of the actual values obtained rather than in per cent of the values at maximum efficiency. Such a characteristic curve is shown in Fig. 9·33 for an axial-flow deep-well pump having 16 stages and using an impeller similar to the one shown in Fig. 9·27C (lower). Since an axial-flow pump is not basically a centrifugal pump, the curves in Fig. 9·32 and Fig. 9·33 differ. The efficiency and head curves are similar, but the power curve for the axial-flow pump has a drooping character-

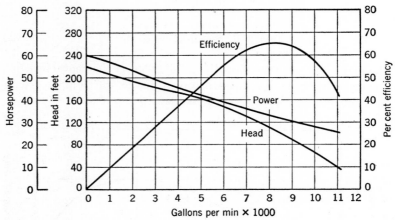

Fig. 9·33 Characteristic curves of a multistage deep-well pump

istic. Thus, as the volume rate of flow increases, the power required decreases, eliminating any danger of overloading the driving motor.

The characteristics of a rotary-gear pump are shown in Fig. 9·34. The curves are taken from the test results of a pump similar to the one shown in Fig. 9·29 and running at 600 rpm. Unlike that of a centrifugal pump, the capacity does not vary appreciably with an increase in discharge pressure.

The curves in Figs. 9·32, 9·33, and 9·34 represent the characteristics of pumps running at constant speed. If the speed of any pump is varied, there will be a variation in the operation of the pump with a corresponding change in the characteristic curves. Under certain conditions if the speed of a centrifugal pump is varied, the variations in the pump head, capacity, and power are predictable. The predictions are based on the basic

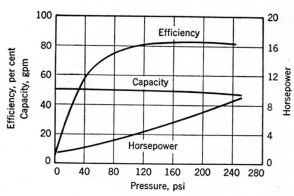

Fɪɢ. 9·34 Characteristic curves of a gear-type rotary pump

principles of operation of the centrifugal pump, and the principles are often called the pump laws. The laws are stated as follows:

1. The volume rate of flow is proportional to the speed, or

$$m_m v \propto n$$

2. The pressure or head is proportional to the speed squared, or

$$h \propto n^2$$

3. The power is proportional to the speed cubed, or

$$hp \propto n^3$$

These laws are exact when the fluid is incompressible, when the fluid always leaves the pump impeller tangentially to the blades, and when the pump is operated at the point of maximum efficiency. If we assume that these criteria are true, the volume rate of flow of the liquid $m_m v$ is equal to the product of the radial velocity of the liquid leaving the pump V_R and the area between impeller blades A. Thus,

$$m_m v = V_R A \quad \text{from the law of continuity of flow}$$

but the velocity V_R is proportional to the speed, or

$$V_R \propto n$$

Since the area A is constant, then

$$m_m v \propto n$$

The head against which a pump operates is equal to a factor f times $V^2/2g$ or

$$h = f \frac{V^2}{2g}$$

Based on the preceding criteria, the factor f will not change, and

$$h \propto V^2$$

but $$V \propto n$$

thus, $$h \propto n^2$$

The power is equal to the product of a constant, the head h, and the quantity $m_m v$; thus,

$$\text{hp} \propto h m_m v$$

or $$\text{hp} \propto n \times n^2 \propto n^3$$

Example 10. If the speed of a centrifugal pump is doubled, how will the head, capacity, and power vary?

Solution: (a)

$$\frac{h_2}{h_1} = \frac{n_2{}^2}{n_1{}^2} \qquad \text{But} \quad n_2 = 2n_1$$

or $$h_2 = h_1 \frac{(2n_1)^2}{n_1{}^2}$$

$$= 4h_1 \text{ or 4 times the original head}$$

(b) The capacity will double.

(c) $$\frac{\text{hp}_2}{\text{hp}_1} = \frac{n_2{}^3}{n_1{}^3}$$

$$\text{hp}_2 = \text{hp}_1 \frac{(2n_1)^3}{n_1{}^3}$$

$$\text{hp}_2 = 8 \text{ hp}_1 \text{ or 8 times the original power}$$

From Example 10 it can be seen that caution should be used before the speed of a pump is increased to increase its capacity. The power unit driving the pump may be heavily overloaded and severely damaged.

PROBLEMS

1. Convert the following pressures into equivalent heads in in. of Hg: 10 psi, 1000 psf, 20 in. of water, and 200 ft of air at 200 F and 14.7 psia.

2. What are the equivalent heads in ft of water of the following pressures: 15 psi, 20 in. of Hg, 15 ft of oil with a specific gravity of 0.85?

3. A gage is located 30 ft below the steam drum of a boiler. If the tube to the gage is filled with condensed steam and the gage reads 100 psi, what is the pressure in the boiler drum in psia?

4. A gage located 15 ft above a water main reads 60 psi. What is the water pressure in the main in psia? If another gage is located 10 ft below the water main and is connected at a point close to the connection of the first gage, what will the second gage read?

5. A Pitot tube is placed in an air duct to measure the velocity pressure or velocity head of the air. A manometer connected to the static tube reads 3 in. of water, and a manometer connected to the total pressure or impact tube reads 3.5 in. of water. If the air in the duct has a specific weight of 0.075 lb per cu ft, find (*a*) the total, static, and velocity heads in ft of air, (*b*) the velocity of the air in the duct, (*c*) the flow of air in lb per sec if the duct area is 9 sq ft.

6. Water flows in a 6-in. pipe at the rate of 100 gpm. If the specific weight of the water is 62.4 lb per cu ft, what is the water velocity in fps? What is the velocity head in ft of water? What would be the velocity of the water if the 6-in. pipe were reduced to a 3-in. pipe?

7. Assume that the rate of flow of water in a 4-in. pipe is to be measured with a Venturi meter having a throat diameter of 2 in. The difference in the level of a mercury manometer connected to the static tubes at inlet and throat of the Venturi is 3 in. of Hg. If ideal flow conditions are assumed, what is the flow of the water in lb per hr?

8. Water enters a Venturi meter at the rate of 250,000 lb per hr. If the pressure at the entrance to the meter is 30 psig and the diameters at entrance and throat of the meter are 7 in. and 3.5 in., respectively, calculate the gage pressure at the throat of the meter. Assume ideal flow conditions in the meter.

9. An orifice is used to measure the steam flow in a pipe. The pipe area is 0.8 sq ft, and the area at the orifice throat is 0.6 sq ft. The static-pressure differential across the orifice is 1 in. of Hg. If the specific volume of the steam is 2 cu ft per lb, calculate the flow of the steam in lb per hr. Assume ideal flow conditions in the orifice.

10. A pump delivers 30,000 gal of water per hr against a total head of 25 psi. If the specific weight of water is 62.4 lb per cu ft, calculate the hydraulic hp.

11. A pump delivers 1000 lb of sludge per min against a total head of 50 psi. If the sludge has a specific gravity of 1.3, calculate the hydraulic hp or hp output of the pump.

12. A pump delivers 50 cu ft of water per min. If static gages located at the pump intake and discharge read 15 psi and 100 psi, respectively, and require no correction for elevation, find the hydraulic hp of the pump. The intake and discharge pipes are of equal diameter.

13. If the discharge gage of Problem 12 is located 10 ft below the pump center line and the intake gage is located 5 ft above the pump center line, find the hydraulic hp of the pump. Assume all other values remain the same as in Problem 12.

14. An oil has a specific gravity of 40 degrees API. The oil is pumped at the rate of 100 gpm from an oil reservoir to a heat exchanger. The center line of the pump is level with the oil in the reservoir. Assume that there is no friction in the intake pipe to the pump. The discharge gage, located 5 ft below the pump center line, reads 25 psig. The intake and discharge pipes are 4 in. in diameter. Calculate the input to the pump in kw if the pump efficiency is 65 per cent.

15. The measured input to a pump delivering water is 7.5 hp. A gage, located 2 ft above the pump center line on the intake line, reads 1.0 psig. A gage at the discharge, 8.5 ft above the pump center line, reads 80 psig. If the pump efficiency is estimated to be 75 per cent and the change in velocity head is zero, calculate the flow rate in lb per hr.

16. A pump delivers water at the rate of 2000 gpm. The intake pipe has an inside area of 115 sq in. The discharge pipe has an inside area of 58 sq in. The static gage at pump intake indicates a pressure of 10 in. of Hg vac and is located 3 ft above the pipe and pump center lines. The static gage at pump discharge indicates a pressure of 20 psig and is located at the pump center line. If the pump efficiency is 70 per cent, calculate (a) the velocity head change across the pump, (b) the hydraulic hp, (c) the pump hp.

17. The static-pressure gage on the intake side of a pump reads 8 in. of Hg vac and is 5 ft above the pump center line. The static-pressure gage at the discharge reads 40 psig and is 5 ft above the pump center line. The area of the suction pipe is 1 sq ft, and the discharge-pipe area is 0.8 sq ft. A mercury manometer attached to a Venturi meter located in the discharge line indicates a differential static pressure of 10 in. of Hg. The area at the throat of the Venturi is 0.2 sq ft. If the fluid being pumped has a specific gravity of 1.1 and the pump has an efficiency of 70 per cent, calculate the hp required to drive the pump.

18. When running at 2000 rpm a centrifugal pump delivers 500 lb of water per min against a total head of 50 psi. Assuming that the pump laws hold, find the total head, capacity, and power of the same pump if its speed is increased to 3000 rpm.

10 · Draft, Fans, Blowers, and Compressors

10·1 Introduction. In nearly every phase of modern life there can be found a need for supplying or removing gases or vapors to or from a space. The transfer of the gases or vapors is achieved by natural or mechanical circulation, and the problems encountered are similar to those found in the movement of liquids.

Natural circulation will occur wherever there is a temperature differential within a given volume of gas or vapor. Many homes are heated by warm-air systems which operate by natural circulation. The difference in density or specific weight of the warm and cold air within the building is sufficient to produce flow. If unobstructed, the warm air will rise from the furnace to the rooms, and the cool air will return by gravity to the furnace room.

Forced or mechanical circulation is accomplished by using fans, blowers, or compressors. Fans are used where relatively low-pressure heads, a few inches of water to 1 psi, are encountered. Blowers are used for pressure heads ranging from a few psi to medium heads of 35 to 50 psi. Compressors are used to cover the range of pressure heads above 35 psi. However, there is no sharp dividing line between the ranges covered by the three classes of equipment.

10·2 Natural draft. Air can be supplied to a furnace by natural circulation. The pressure differential which is necessary for the natural circulation is called natural draft. If the hot gases produced in a furnace are discharged directly to the atmosphere, the draft or pressure differential between the points of air intake and gas exhaust is small. Consequently, to make available a greater draft, the hot exhaust or flue gases are discharged to the atmosphere through a stack or chimney. For example, assume that the hot flue gases are discharged through a stack which is H ft high, as shown in Fig. 10·1, and that the flow of gases and air through the furnace is stopped momentarily by placing a diaphragm at point A.

Then, the pressure differential at point A will be

$$\Delta p = (H\gamma_a + p_b) - (H\gamma_g + p_b)$$

$$= H\gamma_a - H\gamma_g \qquad (10·1)$$

where Δp = pressure differential, psf
$\quad\quad H$ = stack height, ft
$\quad\quad \gamma_a$ = specific weight of the air, lb per cu ft
$\quad\quad \gamma_g$ = specific weight of the hot gases, lb per cu ft
$\quad\quad p_b$ = the atmospheric pressure acting on the column of air and gases, psf

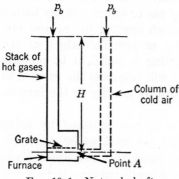

FIG. 10·1   Natural draft

The differential pressure Δp is called the theoretical draft of the stack. This theoretical draft is never attainable in practice but represents the maximum draft that could be attained if there were no friction in the stack.

Since the air and hot gases follow the laws of perfect gases closely, the density of each can be calculated by the relation

$$p_b V = mRT$$

or

$$p_b = \rho RT$$

where $\rho = m/V$ = density of the gases or air, lb per cu ft
$\quad\quad p_b$ = barometric pressure, psf
$\quad\quad T$ = the absolute temperature of the gases or air, deg R
$\quad\quad R$ = the gas constant of the air or gases, ft-lb per lb per deg R

The value of R for the air is known and is 53.3. The value of R for the flue gases can be found if the analysis of the flue gases is known. For most practical purposes it can be assumed that the gas constant for the flue gases is the same as for air since both consist mainly of the same element, nitrogen.

On the earth's surface and using ordinary instrumentation and slide-rule calculations, the engineer may substitute the numerical value of the density of the air and gases for the value of γ_a and γ_g, respectively. The error in assuming that 1 lb mass weighs 1 lb is not appreciable.

Example 1. A stack 300 ft high will produce what theoretical draft if the average gas temperature is 540 F and the air temperature is 40 F? Assume a barometer reading of 29 in. of Hg.
Solution:

$$\rho_a = \frac{p_b}{R_a T_a}$$

where $p_b = 29 \times 0.491 \times 144$
$R_a = 53.3$
$T_a = 460 + 40 = 500$ R

Thus,
$$\rho_a = \frac{29 \times 0.491 \times 144}{53.3 \times 500}$$

$$= 0.077 \text{ lb per cu ft}$$

Also,
$$\rho_g = \frac{p_b}{R_g T_g}$$

where $p_b = 29 \times 0.491 \times 144$ psf
$R_g = R_a = 53.3$ approximately
$T_g = 540 \times 460 = 1000$ R

Thus,
$$\rho_g = \frac{29 \times 0.491 \times 144}{53.3 \times 1000}$$

$$= 0.038 \text{ lb per cu ft}$$

and since, numerically, $\rho_a = \gamma_a$ and $\rho_g = \gamma_g$ then,

$$\Delta p = H(\gamma_a - \gamma_g)$$

$$= 300(0.077 - 0.038)$$

$$= 11.4 \text{ psf}$$

Generally, pressure differences as small as those that occur in chimney calculations are expressed in inches of water rather than in pounds per square inch. Thus, the theoretical draft for Example 1 expressed in feet of water is

$$D = \frac{\Delta p}{\gamma_w} = \frac{11.4 \text{ lb per sq ft}}{62.4 \text{ lb per cu ft}} = 0.18 \text{ ft H}_2\text{O}$$

or
$$D = \frac{11.4}{62.4} \times 12 = 2.19 \text{ in. of water}$$

Because of the friction losses resulting from the flow of the gases through the various passes of the furnace and through the stack, the actual draft obtained from a given stack is as much as 15 per cent less than the theoretical draft.

The cross-sectional area A of a stack can be determined from the continuity-flow equation,

$$m_s = \frac{AV}{v}$$

where m_s = gas flowing, lb per sec
v = specific volume of the gas, cu ft per lb
A = area of stack, sq ft
V = gas velocity, fps

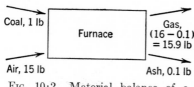

FIG. 10·2   Material balance of a furnace

The rate of flow of the gas m_s can be calculated by making a material balance of the constituents entering and leaving the furnace, as shown in Fig. 10·2. The air–fuel ratio, 15 to 1 in Fig. 10·2, will depend upon the type of coal burned, the air required for theoretical combustion, and the amount of excess air that will be necessary for complete combustion under the fuel and furnace conditions at maximum load. The amount of ash that will be produced can be estimated closely. The velocity of the gas should be kept low to keep friction losses at a minimum but not so low as to require an uneconomical stack area.

Example 2. Assume that a furnace uses 3600 lb of coal per hr and that the maximum air necessary for combustion is 15 lb per lb coal. If the anticipated gas temperature is 540 F, and the most economical velocity of the gases is 25 fps, find the stack area required. Assume an ash loss of 10 per cent of the coal fired and a barometer reading of 29 in. of Hg.

Solution:

$$m = 1 + 15 - 0.1 = 15.9 \text{ lb gas per lb coal}$$

$$m_s = \frac{15.9 \times 3600}{3600} \text{ lb gas per sec}$$

$$= 15.9$$

$$\rho_g = \frac{29 \times 0.491 \times 144}{53.3 \times (540 + 460)} = \frac{1}{v}$$

$$= 0.038 \text{ lb per cu ft}$$

But,

$$m_s = \frac{AV}{v}$$

or

$$A = \frac{m_s v}{V}$$

$$= \frac{15.9 \text{ lb of gas per sec}}{0.038 \text{ lb of gas per cu ft} \times 25 \text{ fps}}$$

$$= 16.7 \text{ sq ft}$$

In addition to producing sufficient draft for small-power-plant operation, a stack is inexpensive to maintain, and it aids in dispersing smoke and fly ash. It has definite disadvantages which are as follows: (1) There is not adequate control of the draft, (2) there is a definite limitation to the maximum draft attainable, and (3) there is a definite hazard to aircraft.

10·3 Mechanical draft. In power-plant engineering the fan plays an important part. Generally, in small furnace installations a stack can produce a draft sufficiently high to supply air adequately to the fuel bed and to remove the flue gases. But the present-day capacities of boilers and furnaces require mechanical draft to supplement the natural draft produced by the stack. Mechanical draft is divided into two systems: forced draft and induced draft. In the forced-draft system the fan is located on the air-intake side of the furnace. A positive pressure, a pressure above atmospheric pressure, is produced under the fuel bed and acts to force air through the bed. The forced-draft system is necessary in installations where the pressure drop in the intake system and fuel bed is high. The pressure drop will be high in installations employing air preheaters and/or underfeed stokers.

The underfeed stoker has an inherently deep fuel bed and a correspondingly high resistance to air flow.

Generally, the pressure in a furnace should be slightly less than atmospheric pressure. If it is too high, there will be leakage of asphyxiating gases into the boiler room and the tendency for blowback when furnace inspection doors are opened. If the pressure in the furnace is too low, there will be air leakage to the furnace with a corresponding reduction in the furnace temperature. Because of these restrictions on the desirable pressure within the furnace, the forced-draft system is generally accompanied by a natural-draft system, in order that the removal of the flue gases may be accomplished. However, if the stack draft is inadequate owing to the high resistance created by the furnace passes, economizers, and air preheaters, an induced-draft system is generally added to supplement the stack draft. In the induced-draft system a fan is placed in the duct leading to the stack. The relative positions of the forced- and induced-draft fans are shown in Fig. 10·3.

When a forced- and an induced-draft fan are used in combination, the system is called balanced draft. The variation in pressure for such a draft system is shown in Fig. 10·3. The forced-draft fan produces a positive pressure which decreases slightly through the duct work and sharply through the air preheater and fuel bed. If the system is properly controlled, a pressure of a few hundredths of an inch of water less than atmospheric pressure is maintained in the furnace proper. The pressure continues to drop through the boiler passes, economizer, and air preheater until it is raised by the induced-draft fan and by the stack to atmospheric pressure.

The present trend is to construct more furnaces with gas-tight casings in order that they may be operated under pressures well above atmospheric pressure. Combustion efficiency is improved at elevated pressures, and the induced-draft fan with its high maintenance cost can be eliminated completely. A number of furnaces using the cyclone burner are now designed to operate at pressures as high as 80 in. of water above atmospheric pressure.

10·4   Fans. Fans are used extensively in the heating and ventilating industry and in most power plants. Their basic design principles fall into two classes: axial-flow fans and centrifugal- or radial-flow fans. Axial-flow fans are basically rotating airfoil sections similar to the propeller of an airplane. An analysis of their design is beyond the scope of this book. It is im-

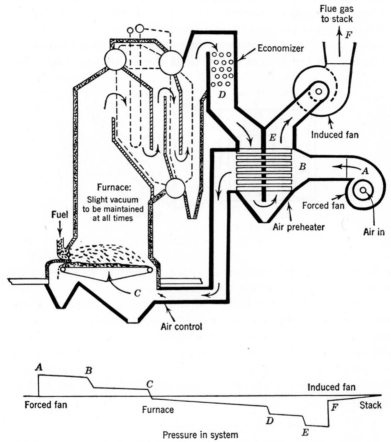

FIG. 10·3 A balanced draft system and its corresponding pressure variation

portant to realize, however, that the movement of the gases created by the axial-flow fan is not due to centrifugal force.

The simplest axial-flow fan is the small electric fan used for circulating air in rooms against very little resistance. Axial-flow fans used for industrial purposes are the two-blade or multiblade propeller type, and the multiblade airfoil type similar to the one shown in Figs. 10·4 and 10·5. Air enters the fan suction from the left and flows over the rotor with a minimum of turbulence owing to the streamline form of the rotor and drive mechanism. The airstream is straightened by guide vanes located on the discharge side, thus decreasing the rotational energy of the air by converting it to energy of translation.

The axial-flow fan operates best under conditions where the resistance of the system is low, as in the ventilating field. The

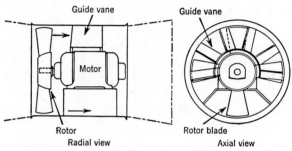

Fig. 10·4   An axial-flow fan

axial-flow fan occupies a small space, is light in weight, is easy to install, and handles large volumes of air.

Centrifugal fans may be divided into two major classes: (1) the long-blade or plate-type fan, and (2) the short-blade multiblade fan. The blades of either type may be pitched toward the direction of motion of the fan, radially, or away from the direction of motion of the fan. The velocity diagrams for the various blade shapes are shown in Fig. 10·6. The velocities are based on three assumptions:

1. The blade velocity V_b is the same for each type of fan.

2. The relative velocity of the air with respect to the blade V_{ab} has a direction parallel to the angle of the blade tip; in other words, the air follows exactly the path of the blade shape.

3. The relative velocity V_{ab} is the same for the three types of fans.

Although the assumptions do not hold exactly, certain principles of fan operation may be developed from the velocity diagrams.

The backward-curved blade produces the lowest air velocity V_a. The velocity head, $V_a^2/2g$, will be correspondingly low, and

FIG. 10·5 Intake of an axial-flow fan

more of the energy of the fan will be converted into static head. The forward-curved fan will produce the lowest static head, but, because of the higher air velocity produced, it is more adaptable

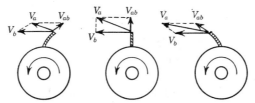

FIG. 10·6 Velocity diagrams for the backward-, radial-, and forward-curved blade fan

for handling large air volumes, provided the resistance of the system is low. The radial blade has operating characteristics that lie between the extreme forward- and backward-curved blades.

A plate-type radial-blade rotor with double inlet is shown in Fig. 10·7. It is best suited for handling dirty gases, since there are no pockets in the blades to catch and collect the dirt. The rotor has wearing strips welded to the blades to increase their

Wearing strip with welded beading

FIG. 10·7 A plate-type radial-blade fan rotor, double suction

life. The fan is designed for induced-draft service. The housing of such a fan may have catch plates in the scroll face to collect the fly ash.

The rotor in Fig. 10·8 has the backward-curved plate-type blades with a single suction or inlet. Its characteristics are high speed, nearly constant capacity for various pressure conditions, and a nonoverloading power requirement for its complete range of head and capacity. The fan with backward-curved blades is used for forced draft.

One of the best centrifugal fans for ventilating requirements is the multiblade fan shown in Figs. 10·9 and 10·10. It operates at low wheel-tip speeds, and the air turbulence is low, thus reducing noise generation. With the large inlet possible for a given-diameter wheel, the volume capacity of the fan is high for

Fig. 10·8   Plate-type backward-curved blade fan rotor, single inlet

its size. This type of fan is used extensively to circulate air in schools, office buildings, and public buildings.

10·5   Fan testing. A fan test generally includes the measurement of the static, velocity, and total heads against which the fan operates; the determination of the volume rate of flow of air or gas; and the calculation of the air horsepower delivered by the fan. The measurement of the heads can be made conveniently by a Pitot tube, as discussed in Chapter 9. The volume rate of flow is calculated from the measured value of the velocity

Fig. 10·9   Sirocco multiblade forward-curved-blade fan rotor

head. The air horsepower is determined for a fan in the same way that hydraulic horsepower is determined for a pump. Thus,

$$\text{Air hp} = \frac{h_t m_m}{33,000} \qquad (10\cdot2)$$

where h_t = total head against which the fan operates expressed in ft of air

m_m = flow of air, lb per min

Throughout the remainder of the chapter m_m will represent flow in pounds per minute and m_s flow in pounds per second.

The total head of the fan, h_t, is equal to the work required of the fan per pound of air moved. Thus, by applying the first law of thermodynamics to the fan in the same manner as was done for the pump in Article 1·24, the work per pound of air and the head become

$$W = h_t \times 1 = (y_2 - y_1) + \left(\frac{V_2{}^2}{2g} - \frac{V_1{}^2}{2g}\right) + \left(\frac{p_2}{\gamma_2} - \frac{p_1}{\gamma_1}\right) \qquad (10\cdot3)$$

where the subscripts 2 and 1 represent discharge and intake, respectively. The head resulting from a difference in elevation

Fig. 10·10 A Sirocco multiblade fan

from intake to discharge, $y_2 - y_1$, is negligible. The use of an average specific weight, γ, to replace γ_2 and γ_1 will not introduce an appreciable error in calculating the static head of a fan; therefore, the Equation 10·3 reduces to

$$h_\iota = \frac{V_2{}^2 - V_1{}^2}{2g} + \frac{p_2 - p_1}{\gamma} \qquad (10·4)$$

where $\dfrac{V_2{}^2 - V_1{}^2}{2g}$ = velocity head against which the fan operates, ft of air

$\dfrac{p_2 - p_1}{\gamma}$ = static head against which the fan operates, ft of air

The power required to drive the fan is equal to the air horsepower divided by the fan efficiency. Thus,

$$\text{Fan hp} = \frac{\text{air hp}}{\eta} \qquad (10 \cdot 5)$$

where η = fan efficiency

In many fan installations air enters the fan from a large space and is discharged through a duct. In this case the static and velocity heads at inlet are approximately zero. Thus, the total head against which the fan operates will be the head produced in the discharge duct near the fan. An example of the calculations made on such an installation follows:

Example 3. Assume that air enters a fan at a temperature of 70 F and an atmospheric pressure of 29 in. of Hg from a large room and is discharged to a duct having an area of 9 sq ft. Pick-up tubes or Pitot tubes are used to measure the static and total heads on the discharge duct. If water manometers connected to the static-pressure tube and total-pressure tube read 3.0 in. and 3.5 in., respectively, as illustrated in Fig. 10·11, find (a) the static, velocity, and total heads in ft of air in the duct; (b) the velocity of the air in the duct, (c) the volume and mass rate of flow, (d) the air hp.

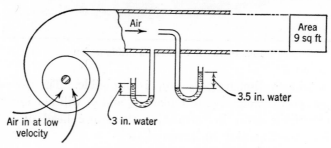

Fig. 10·11   Figure for Example 3

Solution: (a) The heads in in. of water can be converted to ft of air by the relation,

$$h_w \gamma_w = p_2 = h_a \gamma_a$$

where h_w = head, ft of water
γ_w = specific weight of water, lb per cu ft
h_a = head, ft of air
γ_a = specific weight of air, lb per cu ft
p_2 = static pressure, psf

For engineering calculations it may be assumed without introducing an appreciable error that the specific weight of the air, γ_a, is numerically equal to the value of the density of air, ρ_a. But the density of the air can be calculated by use of the perfect gas law.

$$p = \rho_a RT$$

or

$$\rho_a = \frac{p}{RT}$$

where p = atmospheric pressure = $144 \times 29 \times 0.491$ psf
$R = 53.3$ for air
$T = 70 + 460 = 530$ R

thus,

$$\rho_a = \gamma_a \quad \text{numerically}$$

$$= \frac{144 \times 29 \times 0.491}{53.3 \times 530}$$

$$= 0.073 \text{ lb per cu ft}$$

The static head in the duct in ft of air is

$$\frac{p_2}{\gamma_a} = h_s = \frac{h_w \gamma_w}{\gamma_a} = \frac{\dfrac{3.0 \text{ in. water}}{12 \text{ in. per ft}} \times 62.4 \text{ lb water per cu ft}}{0.073 \text{ lb air per cu ft}} = 214 \text{ ft of air}$$

The total head in ft of air is

$$h_t = \frac{h_w \gamma_w}{\gamma_a} = \frac{\dfrac{3.5}{12} \times 62.4}{0.073} = 249 \text{ ft of air}$$

Thus, the velocity head in ft of air is

$$h_v = h_t - h_s = 249 - 214 = 35 \text{ ft of air}$$

(b) The velocity head $h_v = V^2/2g$. Then,

$$V = \sqrt{2gh_v}$$

$$= \sqrt{2 \times 32.2 \times 35}$$

$$= 47.5 \text{ fps}$$

(c) From the law of continuity of flow, the volume rate of flow,

$$m_s v = AV$$

where A = area of the duct, sq ft
V = velocity of the air at area A, fps

then,

$$m_s v = 9 \times 47.5 = 428 \text{ cu ft per sec}$$

or $m_m v = 25,700$ cfm

The mass rate of flow,

$$m_m = AV \frac{1}{v}$$

$$= 25,700 \times 0.073$$

or $m_m = 1880$ lb per min

(d)   Air hp $= \dfrac{h_t m_m}{33,000}$

$$= \frac{249 \times 1880}{33,000} = 14.2$$

Sometimes a fan has an inlet as well as a discharge duct. If the ducts are of equal area, the velocity of the air will be the same at inlet and discharge, and the velocity head against which the fan operates will be zero. Thus, the total head against which the fan operates will be the difference between the discharge and inlet static heads. If the ducts are of unequal area, the fan will operate against a head equal to the difference in the total heads at discharge and inlet.

Example 4. Assume that air enters a fan through a duct 16 sq ft in area. The inlet static pressure is 1 in. of water less than atmospheric pressure. The air leaves the fan through a duct 9 sq ft in area, and the discharge static pressure is 3.0 in. of water above atmospheric pressure. If the specific weight of the air is 0.075 lb per cu ft, and the fan delivers 20,000 cfm, find (a) the total head against which the fan operates, (b) the air hp, (c) the fan efficiency if the power input to the fan is 17 hp at the coupling.

Solution: (a) The total head against which the fan operates is given by

$$h_t = \frac{p_2 - p_1}{\gamma} + \frac{V_2{}^2 - V_1{}^2}{2g}$$

where $p_2 = \dfrac{3 \text{ in.}}{12 \text{ in./ft}} \times 62.4 \dfrac{\text{lb}}{\text{cu ft}} = 15.6$ psf

$$p_1 = -\frac{1 \text{ in.}}{12 \text{ in./ft}} \times 62.4 \frac{\text{lb}}{\text{cu ft}} = -5.2 \text{ psf}$$

Also, $V_2 = (m_s v) \dfrac{1}{A_2}$

$$= \left(\frac{20,000}{60}\right) \times \frac{1}{9}$$

$$= 37.0 \text{ fps}$$

and $$V_1 = (m_s v)\frac{1}{A_1}$$

$$= \left(\frac{20,000}{60}\right) \times \frac{1}{16}$$

$$= 20.8 \text{ fps}$$

Thus, substituting these values into the equation for total head gives

$$h_t = \left[\frac{15.6 - (-5.2)}{0.075}\right] + \left[\frac{(37)^2}{64.4} - \frac{(20.8)^2}{64.4}\right]$$

$$= 277.5 + 14.5$$

$$= 292.0 \text{ ft of air}$$

(b) $$\text{Air hp} = \frac{h_t m_m}{33,000}$$

where $h_t = 292$ ft of air
$m_m = 20,000 \times 0.075$ lb per min

Thus, $$\text{Air hp} = \frac{292 \times 20,000 \times 0.075}{33\,000}$$

$$= 13.3$$

(c) $$\eta = \frac{\text{air hp}}{\text{input hp}}$$

$$= \frac{13.3}{17.0} \times 100$$

$$= 78.2\%$$

10·6 Fan performance. Fans are tested by the manufacturers, and usually the results of the operation of the fans are presented in tables or in characteristic curves. The curves may include the variations in head, capacity, power, and efficiency for a constant speed or may be a family of curves for a series of constant speeds. By careful survey of the various types of fans and their characteristics, the fan purchasers can select the type and size of fan best fitted to perform a given function.

Within a given class or type of fan there are certain general characteristics that are common to the many different designs. The curves in Fig. 10·12 show the variation in pressure and power for differing capacities for an axial-flow fan similar to the one in Fig. 10·4 and operating at constant speed. The fairly constant power output over a wide range of capacities is common to most axial-flow fans. Thus, there will be little tendency to overload the driving motor, regardless of the change in conditions

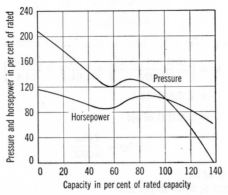

FIG. 10·12   Characteristic curves of the axial-flow fan

under which the fan operates. This is called a nonoverloading characteristic. The capacity decreases more or less at a constant rate for an increase in resistance or pressure. The efficiency

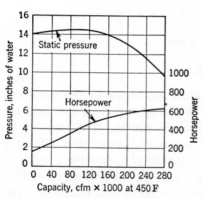

FIG. 10·13   Characteristics of a radial-blade fan

of such a fan is generally somewhat lower than the efficiency of centrifugal fans except at low pressures. By varying such things as the pitch diameter or width of the blades, the point of maximum efficiency can be varied to cover a wide range of conditions.

The characteristics of a radial-blade centrifugal fan (Fig. 10·7) are shown in Fig. 10·13. The power increases with a decrease in pressure and in increase in capacity, but the increase is not sharp enough to overload the driving motor if proper selection of the motor is made. Generally, the characteristics of the radial-blade centrifugal fan will be a compromise of the characteristics of the backward-curved-blade and forward-curved-blade fans.

The backward-curved-blade centrifugal fan of Fig. 10·8 will have characteristics as shown in Fig. 10·14. Best efficiencies are obtained with rotors having backward-curved blades and the power curve for these rotors shows a nonoverloading character-

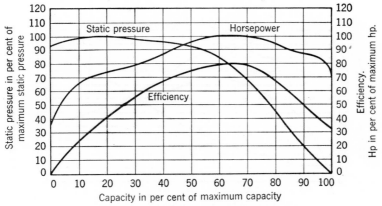

FIG. 10·14 Characteristic curves of a backward-curved blade fan

istic over the complete range of pressures and capacities. The point of maximum efficiency occurs at the point of maximum power. Above 50 per cent of the maximum capacity a decrease in capacity will increase the pressure sharply. This fan is excellent for forced-draft service, for, as the fuel bed of a furnace closes and restricts the flow of air from the fan, the fan pressure will rise sharply. The increase in fan pressure will tend to open the fuel bed to admit more air to the furnace.

The forward-curved-blade fan of Fig. 10·9 has an overloading power characteristic as shown in Fig. 10·15. If reasonable care is exercised in figuring the conditions under which the fan will operate, a motor can be selected to prevent its overloading. The point of maximum efficiency occurs near the point of maximum pressure.

Centrifugal fans have the same general laws governing their

speed characteristics as the centrifugal pumps and for the same reasons (see Article 9·9). Restated, these laws for a given fan are as follows:

1. Capacity is proportional to the fan speed.
2. Pressure or head is proportional to the fan speed squared.
3. Power is proportional to the fan speed cubed.

These laws apply only to a constant specific weight of air.

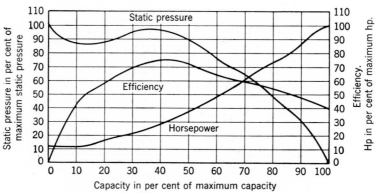

Fɪɢ. 10·15   Characteristic curves of a forward-curved blade fan

Example 5. A fan delivers 10,000 cfm at a static pressure of 2 in. of water when operating at a speed of 400 rpm. The power input required is 4 hp. Find (a) the speed, (b) pressure, and (c) power of the same fan and installation if 15,000 cfm are desired.

Solution: (a)

$$mv \propto n$$

or
$$\frac{n_2}{n_1} = \frac{m_2v_2}{m_1v_1} \quad \text{or} \quad n_2 = n_1 \frac{m_2v_2}{m_1v_1}$$

where $n_1 = 400$, $m_2v_2 = 15,000$, $m_1v_1 = 10,000$

thus,
$$n_2 = \frac{15,000}{10,000} \times 400 = 600 \text{ rpm}$$

(b)
$$h \propto n^2$$

or
$$\frac{h_2}{h_1} = \frac{n_2^2}{n_1^2} \quad \text{or} \quad h_2 = h_1 \frac{n_2^2}{n_1^2}$$

where $n_2 = 600$, $n_1 = 400$, $h_1 = 2$

thus,
$$h_2 = \frac{(600)^2}{(400)^2} \times 2 = 4.5 \text{ in.}$$

(c)
$$hp \propto n^3$$

or
$$\frac{hp_2}{hp_1} = \frac{(n_2)^3}{(n_1)^3} \quad \text{or} \quad hp_2 = \frac{(n_2)^3}{(n_1)^3} \times hp_1$$

where $n_2 = 600$, $n_1 = 400$, $hp_1 = 4$

thus,
$$hp_2 = \frac{(600)^3}{(400)^3} \times 4 = 13.5$$

10·7 Blowers. Blowers may be divided into two types: (1) rotary blowers, and (2) centrifugal blowers. A common type of rotary blower is the Roots two-lobe blower shown in Fig. 10·16.

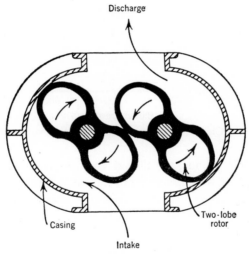

Fig. 10·16 A Roots two-lobe blower

Two double-lobe impellers mounted on parallel shafts connected by gears rotate in opposite directions and at the same speed. The impellers are machined to afford only a small clearance between them and between the casing and impellers. As the lobes revolve, air is drawn into the space between the impellers and the casing, where it is trapped, pushed toward the discharge, and expelled. The air is trapped and discharged in volumes equal to the space between the impellers and casing, and the operation is repeated four times for each rotation of the shaft.

In order to change the volume rate of flow or volume capacity of the blower, the blower speed is changed. The pressure developed by the blower will be whatever is necessary to force the air through the piping system. The volume of air delivered by the blower will not change appreciably with variations in re-

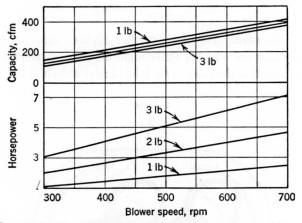

FIG. 10·17   Characteristic curves of a two-lobe rotary blower

sistance to flow. Thus, the blower is called a positive-displacement blower. The characteristics of the blower are shown in Fig. 10·17 for various speeds. Note that at a speed of 600 rpm an increase in pressure from 2 to 3 psi increases the power required by 1.5 times, but the capacity remains fairly constant. Care should be taken in operating any positive-displacement blower. A safety valve or limit valve should be placed on the discharge line to prevent the discharge pressure becoming excessive in case the outlet is fully closed. The limit valve will prevent overloading the discharge line and the driving motor. The advantages of the rotary blower are:

1. Simple construction.
2. Positive air movement.
3. Economy of operation and low maintenance.

Centrifugal blowers and compressors operate on the same principles as centrifugal pumps and resemble to a marked degree the closed-impeller centrifugal pumps described in Chapter 9. A sectional view of a single-stage single-suction blower is shown in Fig. 10·18. It is capable of delivering 15,000 cfm against a

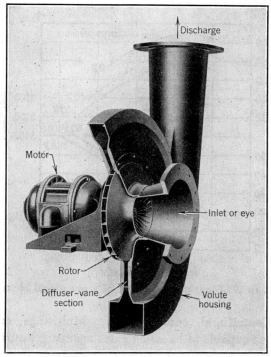

Fig. 10·18 Single-stage, single-suction, centrifugal blower

pressure of 3 psi. The casing or housing is constructed of heavy steel plate, and the impeller is an aluminum-alloy casting. Typical performance curves for this type blower are shown in Fig. 10·19. If care is taken in providing the proper drive motor, the overload characteristics of the centrifugal blower will cause no trouble. The blower shown in Fig. 10·18 uses a motor with a 15 per cent overload factor. Note the effect of inlet temperature of the air on pressure and power. This is a result of the change in specific weight of air with temperature.

For volumes greater than those that can be handled by the single-stage single-suction blower, a single-stage double-suction blower is used, as illustrated in Figs. 10·20 and 10·21. The impeller is shown in Fig. 10·22. This blower is capable of supplying 26,000 cfm of air at 60 F and atmospheric pressure against a 54 in. water column or 2 psi.

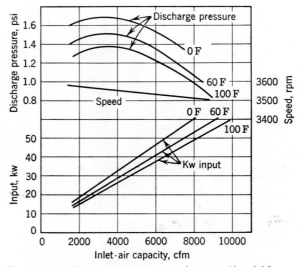

FIG. 10·19   Characteristic curves of a centrifugal blower

10·8   Centrifugal compressors.   Multistage centrifugal blowers when capable of handling gases against pressures greater than 35 psig are generally classed as compressors. They resemble multistage centrifugal pumps, and many of the problems encountered in their design are similar to those encountered in pump design. A complete centrifugal compressor unit with turbine drive is shown in Fig. 10·23. The impellers are of the single-suction type, and passages lead the air or gas from the discharge of one impeller to the suction side of the next impeller.

Because of an increase in temperature of the gas or air as the pressure is increased, cooling is generally necessary. If the pressures are not high, cooling water circulated in labyrinths between impellers may be sufficient. When high pressures are encountered, the gas may be cooled in interstage coolers. The reason for maintaining the gas at a low temperature is to permit an increase in the mass rate of flow with a corresponding reduction in size and horsepower. A pressure–volume diagram (Fig. 10·24) of the air as it is compressed will show more clearly the reason for intercooling between stages.

Fig. 10·20 A double-suction centrifugal blower with cover removed

Assume that 1 lb of air is introduced to a compressor at a low pressure p_0 and that the volume of the 1 lb of air is represented by volume v_1. As work is done on the air by the compressor rotor, the air pressure will rise and the volume will decrease. The rise in pressure may follow any one of a number of paths such as 1–2, 1–3, or 1–4. The paths taken by the air will depend upon the conditions under which the air is compressed. If no heat is lost or gained by the air in the compression process, the air will be compressed to the pressure p_5 by path 1–2. This is called adiabatic compression. If the air is maintained at a constant temperature throughout the compression process, the air will be compressed to the pressure p_5 by path 1–4. This is called isothermal compression.

FIG. 10·21   Single-stage double-suction blower (rated at 26,200 cfm of air
and 14.3 psi against 54 in. water column)

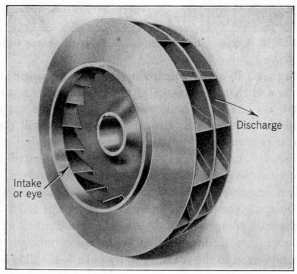

FIG. 10·22   Impeller of the blower shown in Fig. 10·21

The work done on the air is represented by the areas lying within the dotted lines and the path taken by the air in the compression process. The work done for adiabatic compression is the area 0–1–2–5. The area for isothermal compression is

FIG. 10·23 A four-stage centrifugal blower with turbine drive

0–1–4–5. Thus, we may conclude that the work required for compressing air that is maintained at constant temperature is less than that required for the adiabatic compression.

The actual compression process for the multistage compressor using interstage cooling is some path 1–3 which approaches the path 1–4. More cooling would decrease the work of compression but would increase the size and cost of the cooling system.

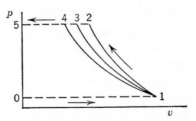

FIG. 10·24 The pressure–volume diagram for a compressor

Axial-flow compressors are designed on the principles of the airfoil section, and the blade shapes will be similar to the axial-flow fan shown in Fig. 10·4. A multistage axial-flow compressor is shown in Fig. 12·1. The compressor is an essential part of the gas-turbine cycle. The gas is not cooled between stages, because a portion of the additional work necessary to compress the gas adiabatically over the work necessary to compress it isothermally will be recovered in the gas turbine.

The advantages of centrifugal and axial-flow blowers and compressors are:

1. Nonpulsating discharge of the gas.
2. No possibility of building up excessive discharge pressures.
3. A minimum of parts subject to mechanical wear.
4. No valves necessary.
5. A minimum of vibration and noise.
6. High speed, low cost, and size for high capacity.

10·9   Reciprocating compressors.   The reciprocating compressor is a positive-displacement machine which operates in a manner similar to a reciprocating pump. It may be driven by a steam or gas engine or by a motor. A flywheel is used to carry the compressor piston over its dead-center positions. The cylinder walls are either air- or water-cooled. Air cooling is used where freezing temperatures may be encountered and for most small or portable compressors. For air-cooled cylinders fins are used to increase the area for transferring heat.

Single-stage compressors are used when the requirements are for:

1. Compactness at some sacrifice in efficiency of operation.
2. Moderate discharge pressures.
3. Moderate air capacities.

A single-stage compressor consists of a single cylinder and piston which is generally double acting. Gas is alternately drawn into and discharged from each end of the cylinder. An ideal compressor would take in a volume of air equal to the cylinder volume, compress it to the discharge pressure at constant temperature, and discharge the total final volume of air. None of these requirements is fulfilled in the actual compressor. Clearance must be provided for valve operation and between piston and cylinder heads. Also, the air temperature will rise during compression. The pressure–volume diagram of the air during the complete cycle is illustrated in Fig. 10·25.

Assume that the piston is at the extreme right and that the volume of the air in the head-end position of the cylinder is equal to V_2. As the piston moves toward the left, the air is compressed along line 2–3 to the final pressure p_3. (Isothermal compression would follow the dotted line 2–3′.) At point 3 the discharge valve opens, and a volume of air equal to $V_3 - V_4$ is discharged. The discharge valve will close at point 4. Air remaining in the clearance space will expand along line 4–1 as the piston moves to the right. At point 1 the intake valve opens, and air is drawn in equal in volume to $V_2 - V_1$.

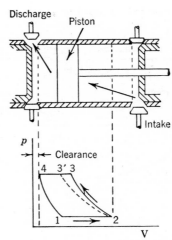

FIG. 10·25 Pressure–volume diagram for an actual compressor

If the clearance volume is large, less air can be drawn into the cylinder, and the compressor capacity is reduced with no effect on discharge pressure. This fact is utilized in controlling the output of constant-speed compressors for loads from zero to the maximum. Clearance at maximum loads is held to the minimum requirements compatible with good design. At low loads additional clearance is provided by the manual or automatic opening of valves to clearance pockets. Indicator diagrams are shown in Fig. 10·26 for a clearance-controlled compressor operating at various loads.

To compress large volumes of air the compressors are constructed to perform the process in steps or stages. A multistage compressor has as many stages as cylinders. The cylinders may be in line, in which case a single-drive mechanism can be used for as many as three pistons, or they may be placed side by side in a tandem arrangement.

A motor-driven two-stage air compressor is shown in Fig. 10·27. Air is drawn into the cylinder, located nearest to the reader, and is compressed alternately in the head end and crank end of the cylinder and discharged to the intercooler located above the cylinders. The cooled air then passes to the high-pressure second stage and is further compressed and discharged to the air system. A section through the high-pressure stage is shown in Fig. 10·28. On leaving the intercooler (Fig. 10·29) the air flows through pockets, which catch the moisture carried in the air, and enters the high-pressure cylinder. The cylinder and head are completely water-jacketed, and the piston is lubricated from a feed at the top of the cylinder. An end view of the cylinder is shown in Fig. 10·30. The intake and discharge valves consist of concentric disks operating over annular ports in a valve seat, Fig. 10·31. The valve disks are held in the closed position by springs until the pressure differential across the disks becomes great enough to compress the springs. The valve action is quick and affords a maximum valve diameter. The valves are guided by rods or keepers located 120 degrees apart. Disk valves of similar design, using flat springs which operate over rectangular openings, provide similar quick valve action over a large effective area.

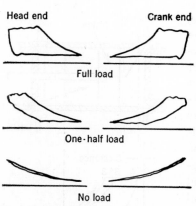

Head end   Crank end

Full load

One-half load

No load

FIG. 10·26   Effect of clearance control on an indicator diagram for a compressor

Intercoolers are provided in multistage reciprocating compressors as in centrifugal compressors to reduce the amount of work required to compress a given weight of gas from a low pressure to a high pressure. The pressure–volume diagrams or indicator cards for a two-stage compressor using intercooling are illustrated in Fig. 10·32 with the high-pressure card superposed on the low-pressure card. The shaded area represents the work saved by cooling the air from point 3 to point 4. The dotted line is the line of constant temperature compression.

For most compressed-air systems the auxiliaries of the reciprocating compressor are:

1. An aftercooler.
2. A receiver.
3. An air-intake filter.

Air-intake filters prevent dirt from entering the cylinders and increasing the wear of the walls and pistons. Since reciprocating machines produce pulsating flow, a receiver or tank to which the air is discharged is employed to absorb the pulsations. The receiver also acts as a reservoir to maintain constant air pressure under varying loads. The aftercooler cools the air and reduces

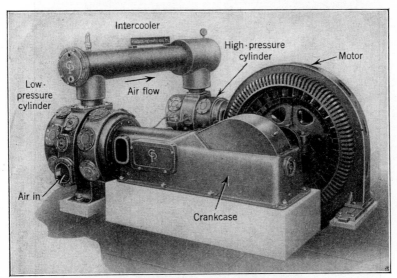

Fig. 10·27 A two-stage reciprocating air compressor with intercooler

the specific volume of the air. Thus less receiver volume and smaller piping can be used for a given weight rate of flow of air.

10·10 Application of the first law of thermodynamics to compressors. Compressors are used to move gases and vapors under conditions such that the specific weight of the fluid cannot be assumed constant. The following assumptions are made in developing the energy equation for a compressor:

1. One pound of fluid leaves the compressor for each pound that enters.

2. The areas at entrance and exit sections are such that the kinetic energy of the fluid is negligible or of the same order of magnitude so that the change in kinetic energy in the compressor may be neglected.

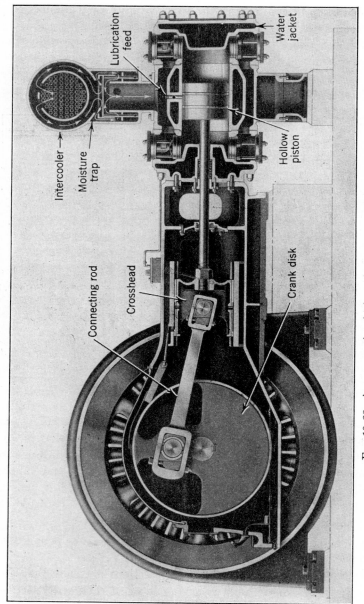

FIG. 10·28   A cross-sectional view of a two-stage compressor

3. The change in mechanical potential energy due to a difference in elevation between entrance and exit sections may be neglected.

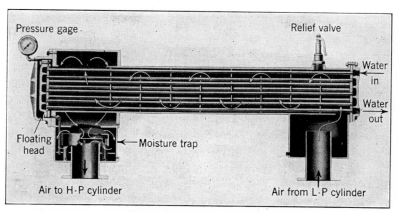

Fig. 10·29 An intercooler

On the basis of the above assumptions, the general energy equation for a compressor may be written as follows, with the negligible terms canceled:

$$\cancel{\frac{V_1}{J}} + \cancel{\frac{V_1^2}{2gJ}} + u_1 + \frac{p_1v_1}{J} + \frac{W}{J} = \cancel{\frac{V_2}{J}} + \cancel{\frac{V_2^2}{2gJ}} + u_2 + \frac{p_2v_2}{J} + \dot{Q} \qquad (10\cdot6)$$

Since, by definition, $h = u + pv/J$, Equation 10·6 may be rewritten as

$$h_1 + \frac{W}{J} = h_2 + Q \qquad (10\cdot7)$$

where h_1 and h_2 are the enthalpies of the gas at entrance and exit in Btu per pound, W is the work done by the compressor on the gas in foot-pounds per pound, and Q is the heat lost by the gas in Btu per pound.

Generally, the heat transferred to the surroundings from the gas is appreciable. However, it is sometimes assumed that the heat dissipated, Q, is small or negligible. A compression process with no heat transfer is called an adiabatic compression, and the energy equation for the adiabatic compressor becomes

$$\frac{W}{J} = h_2 - h_1 \qquad (10\cdot8)$$

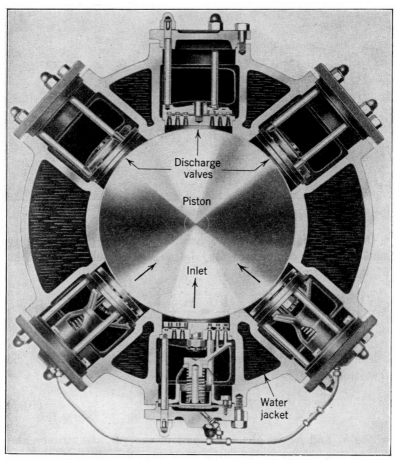

Fig. 10·30   End view of a compressor cylinder showing valves

Example 6.   Assume that 100,000 lb of steam per hr are to be compressed from 1 psia and 80 per cent quality to 14.7 psia and 300 F without heat transfer.   Calculate the power required to compress the steam.

Solution: Since $Q = 0$ by assumption,

$$\frac{W}{J} = h_2 - h_1$$

where $\qquad$ $h_2 = 1192.8$ Btu per lb $\qquad$ (Table A·3)

$h_1 = h_f + xh_{fg}$ at 1 psia and $x = 0.8$

$= 69.7 + 0.8 \times 1036.3$ $\qquad$ (Table A·2)

$= 898.7$ Btu per lb

Thus, $\qquad$ $\dfrac{W}{J} = 1192.8 - 898.7$

$= 294.1$ Btu per lb

and $\qquad$ Power $= 100,000 \times 294.1$

$= 29,410,000$ Btu per hr

The hp required to compress the steam is

$$\text{hp} = \frac{29,410,000}{2545}$$

$= 11,550$

The above example should help to show why exhaust steam from a turbine is condensed before it is returned to the boiler. The amount of power required to compress water from 1 to 14.7 psia would be a small fraction of the amount required to compress steam.

Equation 10·7 may be used to calculate the work required to compress air or any other fluid if the change in enthalpy of the

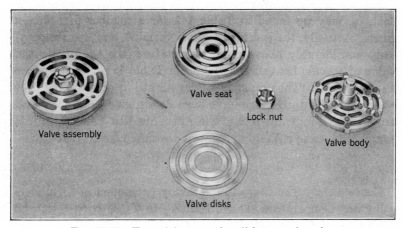

Fig. 10·31 Essential parts of a disk-type air valve

air between the inlet and exit sections can be determined. In Article 1·21, it was stated that, for a perfect gas,

$$h_1 - h_2 = c_p(t_1 - t_2)$$

where c_p = constant-pressure specific heat
  · t_1 = temperature of fluid at entrance to apparatus
   t_2 = temperature of fluid at exit from apparatus

NOTE: The temperature difference $t_1 - t_2$ in degrees Fahrenheit is equal to $T_1 - T_2$ degrees Rankine.

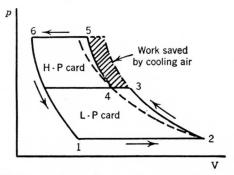

FIG. 10·32 Pressure–volume diagram for a two-stage reciprocating compressor

For temperatures near normal room temperatures, the specific heat, c_p, may be found in Table 1·1 for a number of common gases. Actually, the specific heat is a variable, and, for temperatures considerably above room temperature, the use of a mean value of specific heat such as found in Table 1·1 may introduce a serious error. The properties of dry air at low pressure but over a large temperature range have been determined accurately and are presented in Table A·4 of the Appendix. In Table A·4, it is assumed that the enthalpy is zero at absolute zero so that

$$h = c_p T \tag{10·9}$$

Consequently, the change in enthalpy per pound of air undergoing any temperature change from T_1 to T_2 or t_1 to t_2 can be determined by taking the difference of the tabular values of the enthalpy at the initial and final temperatures as given in Table A·4.

Example 7. An air compressor compresses air from 14.7 psia and 60 F to 60 psia and 440 F. If the compression process is without heat loss, calculate the power required to compress 10 lb of air per sec.

Solution: The energy equation for the compressor is given by

$$\frac{W}{J} = h_2 - h_1$$

where

$$h_2 = 216.3 \text{ Btu per lb} \qquad \text{(Table A·4)}$$

$$h_1 = 124.3 \text{ Btu per lb}$$

Thus,

$$\frac{W}{J} = 216.3 - 124.3$$

$$= 92.0 \text{ Btu per lb}$$

and

$$\text{The power} = 92 \times 10 \text{ Btu per sec}$$

The hp delivered by the compressor to the air is

$$\text{Power} = \frac{92 \times 10 \times 3600}{2545}$$

$$= 1300 \text{ hp}$$

Alternate Solution: Using the mean value of the constant-pressure specific heat of air from Table 1·1, $c_p = 0.237$,

$$\frac{W}{J} = h_2 - h_1 = c_p(t_2 - t_1)$$

$$= 0.237(440 - 60)$$

$$= 90.1 \text{ Btu per lb}$$

The alternate solution assuming constant specific heat introduces an error of $1.9 \div 92$ or approximately 2 per cent. This error will be greater at elevated temperatures. It should be noted that the difference in temperature is the same whether Fahrenheit or Rankine temperatures are used.

PROBLEMS

1. Calculate the height of a stack to produce a theoretical draft of 2 in. of water if the air temperature is 100 F and the average flue-gas temperature is 400 F. Assume that the barometer reads 29.96 in. of Hg and that the flue gases have a molecular weight of 30.

2. If the actual draft required for a furnace is 2.5 in. of water and the frictional losses in the stack are 15 per cent of the theoretical draft, calculate the required stack height. Assume that the flue gases have an average temperature of 300 F and a molecular weight of 30. Assume an air temperature of 50 F.

3. A stack 270 ft high has frictional losses that are 20 per cent of the theoretical draft. If the gases are at an average temperature of 450 F and the air temperature is 70 F, calculate the actual draft produced by the stack.

4. Calculate the hp required to drive a fan that takes 10,000 cfm of air from a room at 100 F and delivers it through a duct 12 sq ft in area. Static discharge pressure is 3 in. of water. The barometer reads 29.5 in. of Hg, and the overall efficiency of the fan is 60 per cent.

5. An induced-draft fan operates against a static head of 2 in. of water. The velocity of the hot gases is approximately the same from intake to discharge. If the gases have a specific volume of 25 cu ft per lb and are flowing at the rate of 10,000 cfm, calculate the hp required to drive the fan. The fan efficiency is 60 per cent.

6. A forced-draft fan delivers air to a furnace from the boiler room at a static pressure of 3 in. of water. Furnace conditions require 15 lb air per lb coal, and 40,000 lb of coal are burned per hr. Air velocity in the duct is 40 fps. What hp must be delivered by the fan?

7. A gas enters a compressor with an enthalpy of 100 Btu per lb and leaves with an enthalpy of 200 Btu per lb. Heat transferred to the surroundings is 20 Btu per lb of gas. What is the power required of the compressor if the flow of the gas is 10 lb per sec?

8. Air is compressed without heat transfer from 100 F and 14.7 psia to 420 F and 60 psia. Calculate the work done on the air per lb of air, assuming (a) constant specific heat, and (b) variable specific heat.

9. What hp is required to drive a compressor that compresses 600 lb of air per min without heat transfer from 70 F and 14.7 psia to 450 F and 75 psia? The compressor operates with a mechanical efficiency of 98 per cent. What is the volume rate of flow of the air at intake in cfm?

10. Calculate the work required to compress without heat transfer 1 lb of oxygen from 70 F and 14.7 psia to 60 psia and 350 F. Use the specific-heat values shown in Table 1·1.

11. Work Problem 10, assuming the same conditions for hydrogen.

11 · Feed-Water Heaters and Condensers

11:1 Introduction. In all power-plant cycles there are the following basic types of equipment:

1. Prime movers for producing work.
2. Stacks, fans, pumps, compressors, or similar equipment for producing fluid flow.
3. Heat exchangers for transmitting heat from one fluid to another.

The power plants used in the transportation field operate on simple cycles at some sacrifice in efficiency in order to reduce the space occupied by and the weight of the equipment. Stationary power plants, in which the weight and space factors are less important, may operate on complicated cycles in order to maintain high efficiencies. Thus, in the stationary steam power-plant cycle there are units that are not entirely essential to power generation but are necessary for good economy of operation. Some of these units, such as the economizer and air preheater, have been discussed in Chapter 5. The steam-generating unit, including the economizer and air preheater, is essentially a heat exchanger.

Two other types of heat exchangers that are common in stationary power plants are the condenser and the feed-water heater. They are distinct and separate pieces of equipment, and their relative positions and primary functions in the cycle have been discussed briefly in Chapter 6.

The design of feed-water heaters and condensers is based on certain fundamental principles of heat transfer, and these principles apply to the design of other types of heat exchangers. Heat is transferred from one point to another by radiation, conduction, and convection. In most industrial and power-plant processes involving the transfer of heat, at least two of the three means of transfer are employed. Thus, in a steam generator, heat is transferred to the boiler tubes by radiation and convection and through the boiler tubes to the water by conduction. In the feed-water heater and condenser, the heat is transferred mainly by convection and conduction. The net transfer by radiation is negligible. The two types of heaters or condensers that are employed to transfer heat from one fluid to another are:

1. Direct-contact or open heaters or condensers.
2. Surface heaters or condensers.

11·2   Direct-contact feed-water heaters.   The primary function of the feed-water heater is to increase the overall efficiency of the cycle. The increase in efficiency is accomplished by heating the water with exhaust steam which would otherwise be wasted or with steam extracted from the turbine. With the feedwater entering at high temperatures the boiler is relieved of a part of its load, and the temperature stresses within the boiler are reduced.

Either the direct-contact or surface type, feed-water heater may be used. The direct-contact heater is often called an open heater, although it may operate at pressures above atmospheric pressure. A typical direct-contact heater is illustrated in Fig. 11·1. It consists mainly of an outer shell in which are placed trays or pans. Water enters at the top of the shell. It feeds by gravity over rows of staggered trays which break up the solid stream of water. Steam entering near the center of the shell intimately mingles with the water and condenses. In condensing, the steam gives up heat to the water. The heated water and condensate mixture is collected at the bottom of the shell and is removed by a boiler feed pump. A float control operating the inlet water valve maintains a constant level in the feed-water tank. A vent at the top removes the excess steam and the noncondensable gases. In the larger heaters where the vented steam is appreciable, a vent condenser may be employed. Water, before it enters the tray section of the feed-water heater, is passed through coils in the vent condenser. Heat is transferred from the vented steam to the water as the steam is condensed. The condensate from the vent condenser is returned to the heater. Noncondensable gases are expelled to the atmosphere.

Because of the stress limitations of the heater shell, the steam pressure is limited to a few pounds per square inch above atmospheric pressure, although pressures to 70 psia have been used.

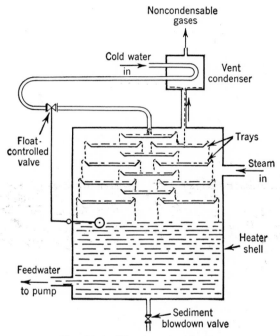

FIG. 11·1 Direct-contact heater

Consequently, the feedwater is rarely heated above 220 F. If direct-contact heaters are used in series, a feed-water pump must be installed ahead of each heater. The advantages of the direct-contact feed-water heater are:

1. Complete conversion of the steam to water is accomplished.
2. Noncondensable corrosive gases are removed from the feedwater.
3. The removal of impurities in the water is possible.
4. The water is brought to the temperature of the steam.
5. The heater acts as a small reservoir.

Even with a lack of knowledge of the events that take place within a direct-contact feed-water heater, one can analyze the performance of a heater by writing an energy balance for it. Assume that water enters the heater shown in Fig. 11·2 from more than one source and that all of the steam introduced to the heater is condensed. If no heat is gained or lost through the heater walls, and if the potential and kinetic energies of steam and water do not change appreciably within the heater, the energy balance of the unit can be written as follows:

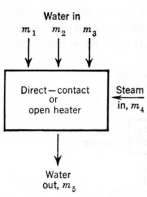

Fig. 11·2 Flow diagram for a direct-contact heater

$$\text{Energy out} = \text{energy in}$$

or
$$m_5 h_5 = m_1 h_1 + m_2 h_2 + m_3 h_3 + m_4 h_4 \qquad (11 \cdot 1)$$

where m_5 = quantity of water out, lb, = $m_1 + m_2 + m_3 + m_4$
   h_5 = enthalpy of the water out, Btu per lb
m_1, m_2, m_3 = quantities of water in at the points 1, 2, 3, respectively, lb
h_1, h_2, h_3 = enthalpies of the water in at the points 1, 2, 3, respectively, Btu per lb
   m_4 = steam in, lb
   h_4 = enthalpy of steam in, Btu per lb

If the pressure effect is neglected, the enthalpy of the water entering the heater is equal to the enthalpy of the saturated water, h_f, at the inlet temperature. It is customary to assume, unless otherwise known, that the water leaving the heater is saturated water at the heater pressure.

Example 1. Saturated steam at a pressure of 20 psia enters the feed-water heater shown in Fig. 11.2. Water enters from three sources at temperatures, $t_1 = 70$ F, $t_2 = 100$ F, and $t_3 = 150$ F and in amounts, $m_1 = 1000$ lb per hr, $m_2 = 5000$ lb per hr, and $m_3 = 3000$ lb per hr. If the water leaves at the saturation temperature corresponding to 20 psia, find the pounds of steam entering the heater.
Solution: Since
$$m_5 h_5 = m_1 h_1 + m_2 h_2 + m_3 h_3 + m_4 h_4$$

where $m_1 = 1000$, $m_2 = 5000$, $m_3 = 3000$

$$m_5 = m_1 + m_2 + m_3 + m_4 = 9000 + m_4$$

Also, $h_5 = h_f$ at 20 psia = 196.16 Btu per lb

and $h_1 = 38.04$, $h_2 = 67.97$, $h_3 = 117.89$

and $h_4 = h_g$ at 20 psia = 1156.3 Btu per lb

Then,

$(9000 + m_4)196.16$

$$= 1000 \times 38.04 + 5000 \times 67.97 + 3000 \times 117.89 + m_4 \times 1156.3$$

and $$960m_4 = 1,034,000$$

$$m_4 = 1080 \text{ lb per hr}$$

It should be recognized that the maximum temperature to which the water can be heated in a direct-contact heater is the saturation temperature corresponding to the pressure of the steam if sufficient steam is available. In Example 1 it was assumed that the water left at the maximum temperature.

11·3   Closed feed-water heaters. Closed heaters or surface-type feed-water heaters are of the shell and tube design. Generally, the water is introduced to the heater through tubes around which the steam circulates. Closed heaters may be classified as single or multipass and straight tube or bent tube. In a single-pass heater the water flows in only one direction. In a multipass heater the water reverses direction as many times as there are passes. A two-pass straight-tube type of closed feed-water heater is illustrated in Fig. 11·3. Water enters at the bottom of one end of the heater and flows through the lower bank of tubes to the opposite end where its direction is reversed. The water returns through the upper bank of tubes to the outlet at the top. Steam enters the shell at the top and flows toward each end, and condensate leaves the shell at the bottom.

A floating head is provided to permit the tubes to expand. Vents at the top are provided to remove gases trapped in the shell. The heater shown in Fig. 11·3 is designed for a water pressure of 1100 psi. Closed heaters placed in series require only

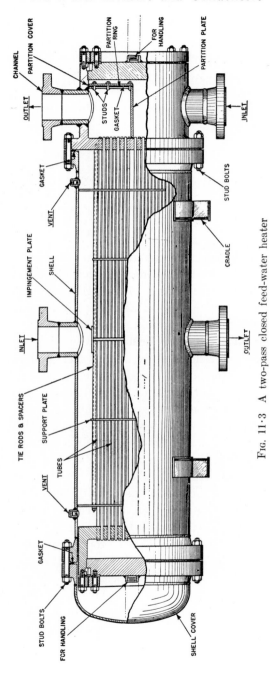

Fig. 11·3 A two-pass closed feed-water heater

one feed-water pump unless the pressure drop through the heaters is high. If bent tubes are used in place of the straight tubes, as shown in Fig. 11·4, no floating head is necessary. However, the bent tubes may be difficult to clean.

In closed heaters the feedwater can never be heated to the temperature of the steam, but generally the temperature difference at the outlet is not greater than 15 F. To maintain a high overall

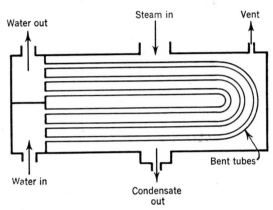

Fig. 11·4 A bent-tube closed feed-water heater

heat transfer for the heater the water velocity should be high, but pumping costs will limit the velocity. A balance between pumping costs and the amount of heat transferred will result in water velocities of 3 to 8 fps. Generally, the heaters are rated in terms of the square feet of heat-transfer surface and of the quantity of heat transferred.

An energy balance can be written for the closed feed-water heater as for the direct-contact feed-water heater, or it may be written in the form

Total heat transferred = heat given up by the steam

= heat absorbed by the water

or, as in Fig. 11·5,

$$Q = m_1(h_1 - h_2) = m_3(h_3 - h_4) \qquad (11·2)$$

where Q = total heat transferred, Btu

$\quad m_1$ = steam circulated, lb

$\quad h_1$ = enthalpy of the steam in, Btu per lb

$\quad h_2$ = enthalpy of the condensate out, Btu per lb

$\quad m_3$ = feedwater circulated, lb

$\quad h_3$ = enthalpy of the feedwater out, Btu per lb

$\quad h_4$ = enthalpy of the feedwater in, Btu per lb

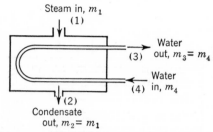

Fɪɢ. 11·5   Flow diagram for a surface heater

Example 2.   Steam enters the heater in Fig. 11·5 at 100 psia and 400 F and is condensed. The condensate leaves as saturated liquid. Water enters at 70 F and leaves at a temperature of 17.8 F less than the steam temperature. Find the lb of steam required per lb of feedwater.

Solution: From Equation 11·2,

$$m_1(h_1 - h_2) = m_3(h_3 - h_4)$$

where $h_1 = h_s$ at 100 psia and 400 F = 1227.6 Btu per lb

$\quad h_2 = h_f$ at 100 psia = 298.4 Btu per lb

$\quad h_3 = h_f$ at (327.8 F − 17.8 F) = 279.9 Btu per lb

$\quad h_4 = h_f$ at 70 F = 38.04 Btu per lb

$\quad m_3$ = 1 lb H_2O

Thus, $\qquad\qquad m_1 = \dfrac{279.9 - 38.04}{1227.6 - 298.4}$

$$= 0.26 \text{ lb steam per lb water}$$

11·4   Condensers.   The primary function of a condenser is to reduce the exhaust pressure of the prime mover. A reduction in the exhaust pressure will increase the pressure and temperature drop through the prime mover and will result in a corresponding increase in efficiency and output. Secondary functions of the condenser are:

1. To reduce the amount of make-up boiler feedwater by condensing the steam in order that it can be returned to the boiler.

2. To remove air or other noncondensable gases which are corrosive.

As in the case of feed-water heaters, condensers are classed as direct-contact or surface types.

The direct-contact type condenser is a jet condenser consisting of water nozzles, a steam-and-water-mixing chamber, and a Venturi section or a tailpipe. It operates in a manner similar to the jet pump discussed in Chapter 9. The jet condenser may be used where it is not necessary to reclaim the condensate. Although it requires more cooling water than a surface condenser, the jet condenser has the following advantages:

1. Construction and operation are simple.
2. No vacuum pump is required to remove noncondensable gases from the steam.

The jet condenser is used mainly for small prime mover installations in industry.

The conventional surface condenser is of a shell and tube construction. Cooling water passes through the tubes, and steam circulates around the tubes and is condensed and removed. At no time do the steam and condensate come into contact with the cooling water. Condensers, like feed-water heaters, are classified as single or multipass and straight or bent tube. Generally, condensers used with prime movers are the straight-tube single- or two-pass type.

A cut-away view of a single-pass surface condenser is shown in Fig. 11·6. Water enters from the bottom left, passes through the tubes, and leaves at the upper right. Steam enters the condenser shell from above, circulates around the nest of tubes, and then flows toward the center or core which is the zone of lowest pressure. Air and noncondensable gases are removed from one end of the core at the vents. The condensed steam or condensate flows by gravity to the condensate well or hot well. The condensate is then removed from the well by a pump. An end view and a side view of the condenser are shown in Fig. 11·7.

Because cooling water is usually corrosive in nature, condenser tubes are often made of special alloys of copper or aluminum. Among these are Admiralty metal, Muntz metal, arsenical copper, and aluminum brass, to name a few.

The tubes may be rolled into each end plate. In this case, expansion is taken care of by bowing the tubes. The tubes of some condensers are rolled into and keyed to one end plate and

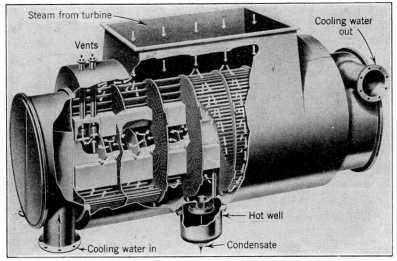

Fig. 11·6   A cut-away view of a single-pass surface condenser

are free to move in the other end plate. Leakage between the tube and end plate is prevented by packing, as illustrated in Fig. 11·8. Expansion and contraction of the condenser shell may be taken care of by providing an expansion joint in the shell wall at one end, as shown in Fig. 11·9.

Owing to the expansion and contraction of the exhaust line or nozzle leading from the turbine to the condenser, all condensers are either rigidly suspended from the turbine or connected to the turbine by an expansion joint. In the former case, the condenser may be placed on spring supports. The spring supports permit the condenser to rise or fall without overloading the turbine exhaust line. In the latter case, the condenser will be rigidly

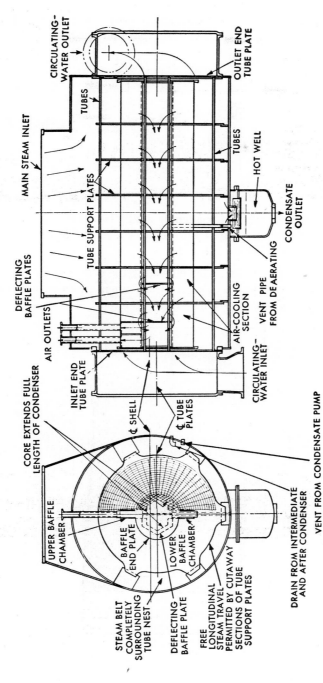

CIRCULATING-WATER OUTLET

OUTLET END TUBE PLATE

TUBES

MAIN STEAM INLET

TUBES

TUBE SUPPORT PLATES

HOT WELL

DEFLECTING BAFFLE PLATES

CONDENSATE OUTLET

AIR-COOLING SECTION

VENT PIPE FROM DEAERATING

AIR OUTLETS

INLET END TUBE PLATE

CIRCULATING-WATER INLET

CORE EXTENDS FULL LENGTH OF CONDENSER

℄ SHELL

℄ TUBE PLATES

VENT FROM CONDENSATE PUMP

UPPER BAFFLE CHAMBER

BAFFLE END PLATE

LOWER BAFFLE CHAMBER

DRAIN FROM INTERMEDIATE AND AFTER CONDENSER

STEAM BELT COMPLETELY SURROUNDING TUBE NEST

DEFLECTING BAFFLE PLATE

FREE LONGITUDINAL STEAM TRAVEL PERMITTED BY CUTAWAY SECTIONS OF TUBE SUPPORT PLATES

FIG. 11·7   End and side views of the radial-flow condenser shown in Fig. 11·6

anchored to the floor. All expansion or contraction in the turbine exhaust line will be taken up in the expansion joint.

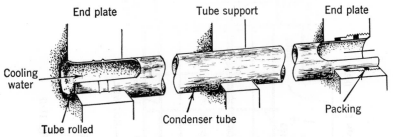

Fig. 11·8 Method of installing tubes in a condenser

There are a number of condenser auxiliaries that are essential to the proper functioning of the condenser. They are illustrated in Fig. 11·10 and are as follows:

1. A condensate hot well for collecting the condensate.

2. A condensate pump to return the condensate to a surge tank where it can be reused as boiler feedwater.

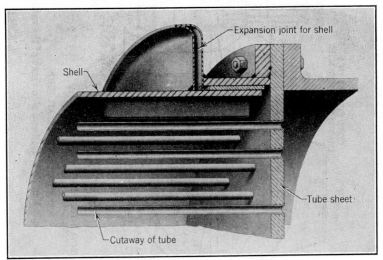

Fig. 11·9 Expansion joint for condenser shell

3. A circulating pump for circulating the cooling water.

4. An atmospheric relief valve for relieving the pressure in the

condenser in case the condenser or auxiliaries do not function properly.

5. An air ejector or a vacuum pump for removing the noncondensable gases from the condenser.

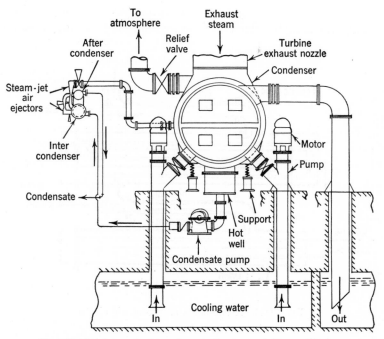

Fig. 11·10 An end view of a condenser and its auxiliaries

The condensate pump and circulating-water pump are generally of the centrifugal type. If the source of the cooling water is a lake or river, there is no need for water conservation. However, in many localities, the water supply may be low. In such a case, the cooling water, after passing through the condenser, is pumped to a cooling pond or cooling tower where it is cooled by contact with air and then is recirculated through the condenser.

If noncondensable gases are permitted to collect in the condenser, the vacuum in the condenser will decrease. A decrease in the vacuum will result in a decrease in the pressure drop through the turbine and will affect adversely the turbine efficiency. Also, the noncondensable gases are highly corrosive. Thus, their removal in the condenser is essential. They may be removed by a vacuum pump or by a steam-jet air ejector as described in Chapter 9 (see Fig. 9·31). A diagrammatic sketch of a two-stage air ejector is shown in Fig. 11·11.

Steam enters the first and second stages through nozzles where it acquires a high velocity. The air and some vapor from the

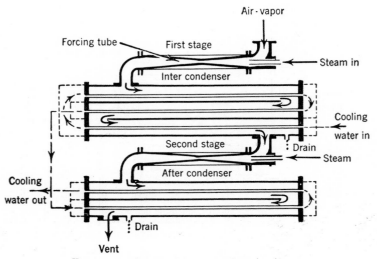

Fig. 11·11   A two-stage steam-jet air ejector

main condenser is entrained by the high-velocity steam and is compressed in the first stage, forcing tube. The forcing tube is the Venturi-shaped section shown in Fig. 11·11. The steam and vapor are condensed in the intercondenser and drained to the hot well of the main condenser.

Air in the intercondenser is then entrained by high-velocity steam leaving the second-stage nozzles, is compressed further in the second stage, forcing tube. Steam is condensed in the after-condenser and is drained to the main condenser. The air is vented to the atmosphere. Normally, condensate from the turbine condenser is used as cooling water to condense the steam in the ejector. Both the condensate and cooling water will then be returned to a surge tank.

Characteristic curves for typical ejectors are shown in Fig. 11·12. For a given capacity the multistage air ejector produces lower pressures than the single-stage ejector.

The design and performance of a condenser depends upon many factors involving a knowledge of the fundamentals of thermodynamics and of heat transfer. The efforts of the engineer are directed toward increasing the amount of heat that can be transferred from the exhaust steam to the cooling water and toward

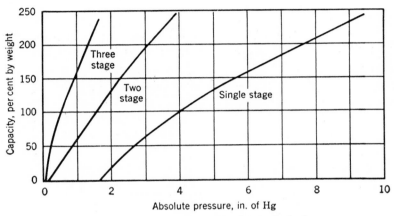

FIG. 11·12 Characteristic curves for typical ejectors

increasing the heat-transfer rate to reduce the size of the condenser. The amount of heat that can be transferred for a given heat-transfer area is affected by (1) the flow paths of the water and steam, (2) the velocities of the steam and water, and (3) the various resistances to heat flow produced by layers of gas, steam vapor, dirt, and scale. Normally, for each square foot of condensing surface and for each degree temperature difference between the steam and water, the heat-transfer rate will vary from 500 to 700 Btu per hr.

11·5 Surface-condenser calculations. As in the case of feed-water heaters, the first law of thermodynamics can be applied to a condenser without a knowledge of events occurring within the condenser. It is customary to assume that the changes in kinetic and potential energies are negligible and that the heat lost to the surroundings is negligible. Thus, as developed in

Article 1·22, the equation for the heat released by the steam in the condenser, shown in Fig. 11·13, is

$$Q = m_4(h_1 - h_4) \qquad (11 \cdot 3)$$

The heat gained by the cooling water is given by the equation

$$Q = m_3(h_2 - h_3) \qquad (11 \cdot 4)$$

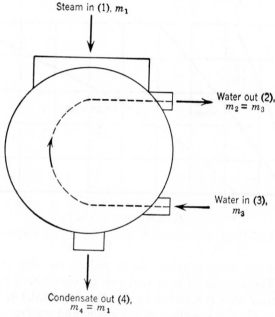

Steam in (1), m_1

Water out (2), $m_2 = m_3$

Water in (3), m_3

Condensate out (4), $m_4 = m_1$

FIG. 11·13   Flow diagram for a surface condenser

Since the heat released by the steam is equal to the heat gained by the cooling water, then Equations 11·3 and 11·4 may be combined to give

$$Q = m_4(h_1 - h_4) = m_3(h_2 - h_3) \qquad (11 \cdot 5)$$

Since the specific heat of the cooling water is approximately one, Equation 11·5 may be rewritten as

$$Q = m_4(h_1 - h_4) = m_3(t_2 - t_3) \qquad (11 \cdot 6)$$

where Q = heat transferred from the steam to water, Btu per hr
  m_4 = steam leaving the turbine, lb per hr
  h_1 = enthalpy of the steam leaving the turbine, Btu per lb
  h_4 = enthalpy of the condensate, Btu per lb
  m_3 = cooling water circulated, lb per hr
  t_2 = temperature of the cooling water leaving the condenser
  t_3 = temperature of cooling water entering the condenser

In Equation 11·6 the terms that are known with close approximation are m_4, h_4, and t_3. Usually, h_4 is equal to or within 5 Btu per lb of the enthalpy of saturated liquid at the condenser pressure. If it is necessary to know accurately the value of the enthalpy of the steam leaving the turbine, h_1, it must be calculated.

Referring to Equation 1·32, which was derived by applying the first law of thermodynamics to a turbine, it is evident that

$$h_1 = h_0 - \frac{W}{J} \qquad (11 \cdot 7)$$

where h_0 = enthalpy of steam at the turbine throttle
  $\dfrac{W}{J}$ = work of the turbine in Btu per lb
  h_1 = enthalpy of the exhaust steam entering the condenser, Btu per lb

In Equation 11·7 the value of W/J is equal to 3413 ÷ steam rate of the turbine. Thus, Equation 11·7 becomes

$$h_1 = h_0 - \frac{3413}{m_{sr}} \qquad (11 \cdot 8)$$

where h_1 = enthalpy of the exhaust steam, Btu per lb
  h_0 = enthalpy of the steam at the throttle, Btu per lb
  m_{sr} = steam rate of the turbine, lb per kw-hr

Example 3. The enthalpy of steam at the throttle of a turbine is 1260 Btu per lb. The turbine steam rate is 15 lb per kw-hr. Condenser cooling water enters at 60 F and leaves at 80 F. Condensate leaves at 90 F. Calculate (a) the enthalpy of the steam entering the condenser, and (b) the amount of cooling water per kw delivered by the turbine.

Solution: (a)

$$h_1 = h_0 - \frac{3413}{m_{sr}}$$

$$= 1260 - \frac{3413}{15}$$

$$= 1032 \text{ Btu per lb}$$

(b) The energy balance on the condenser is given by Equation 11·6, or

$$m_4(h_1 - h_4) = m_3(t_2 - t_3)$$

where m_4 = 15 lb per hr per kw
        h_1 = 1032 Btu per lb
        $h_4 = h_f$ at 90 F
          = 58 Btu per lb
  $t_2 - t_3$ = 80 - 60
        = 20

Thus, $m_3 = 15 \dfrac{(1032 - 58)}{20}$

$$= 729 \text{ lb per hr per kw}$$

In order to approximate the amount of cooling water, m_3, required to condense m_4 lb of steam per hr, it is customary to assume that $h_1 - h_4$ is 950 Btu per lb. The temperature difference, $t_2 - t_3$, will vary with conditions but normally will be between 10 and 20 degrees. Thus, the value of m_3/m_4 for most condensers is between 950/10 and 950/20, or 95 to 47.5 lb of cooling water required per lb of steam condensed. As stated in Chapter 5, approximately 8 lb of steam are generated for every pound of coal burned in a power plant. Thus, between 95 × 8 and 47.5 × 8 lb of cooling water are required for every pound of coal burned or on the average; 500 tons of cooling water are needed for every ton of coal used.

Since the amount of cooling water required for large power plants is often as much as that required for the populace of a city, these plants must be located close to lakes, the sea, or large rivers.

Example 4. Assume that a large power plant has a maximum capacity of 1,000,000 kw and requires 8 lb steam per hr per kw. If the cooling water increases in temperature 12 degrees through the condensers, estimate the amount of cooling water required in gpm.
Solution:

$$m_3(t_2 - t_3) = m_4(h_1 - h_4)$$

where $t_2 - t_3 = 12$

$\qquad h_1 - h_4 = 950$ (estimate)

$\qquad m_4 = 1,000,000 \times 8$

Thus, $\qquad m_3 = \dfrac{1,000,000 \times 8 \times 950}{12}$

$$= 633 \times 10^6 \text{ lb per hr}$$

$$= 1,270,000 \text{ gpm}$$

PROBLEMS

1. Water enters a direct-contact feed-water heater at 80 F. Steam is introduced at 10 psig and 98 per cent quality. If the water leaves as saturated liquid at the steam pressure, find the lb of water heated per lb of steam. Assume atmospheric pressure equal to 15 psi.

2. Water enters a direct-contact feed-water heater from two sources: (*a*) 60,000 lb per hr at 70 F, (*b*) 5000 lb per hr at 200 F. If the steam enters as dry saturated steam at 30 psia and the water leaves at a temperature 5 F below the saturation temperature corresponding to 30 psia, how much steam is used?

3. Steam enters a closed heater at 100 psia and 360 F, and the condensate leaves at the saturation temperature. Water is heated from 100 F to within 15 F of the saturation temperature corresponding to the steam pressure. Find the lb of water heated per lb of steam.

4. A closed heater operates in series with a direct-contact heater in a regenerative cycle. Steam bled from the turbine at 50 psia and dry, saturated enters the closed heater, is condensed, and leaves the heater as saturated water. It then is trapped back to the direct-contact heater without any change in enthalpy. Steam at 20 psia and 95 per cent quality is bled from the same turbine and enters the direct-contact heater. Water enters the direct-contact heater from the turbine condenser at 100 F, and leaves the heater at 225 F. It is then pumped to the closed heater without change in enthalpy. The feedwater leaves the closed heater at 265 F. Sketch the system and, for each lb of feedwater that leaves the closed heater, calculate (*a*) the amount of steam used in the closed heater, and (*b*) the steam used in the direct-contact heater. Assume that one lb of steam enters the turbine for each lb of water that leaves the closed heater.

5. Steam enters a condenser at 1 psia and an enthalpy of 1050 Btu per lb. Condensate leaves the condenser at the saturated temperature corresponding to the steam pressure. How much cooling water is required per lb of steam if the water enters at 70 F and leaves at 88 F?

6. A turbine delivering 2000 kw consumes 60,000 lb of steam per hr. Steam enters the turbine at 200 psia and 540 F and exhausts to a condenser at 1 psia. Calculate the enthalpy of the exhaust steam if the turbine has a 100 per cent mechanical efficiency and no heat is lost through the turbine casing.

7. A condenser is used for the turbine in Problem 6. Cooling water enters the condenser at 75 F and leaves at 93 F. Condensate from the condenser leaves at 100 F. How much cooling water is required in lb per hr?

8. A turbine delivers 25,000 kw at a steam rate of 9.0 lb per kw-hr based on the flow at the turbine throttle. A total of 56,000 lb of steam per hr is bled from the turbine for four feed-water heaters. Steam exhausts from the turbine at 1 psia and 88 per cent quality. Cooling water for the condenser enters at 80 F and leaves at 90 F. The condensate is saturated. Calculate the cooling water required in gpm.

12 · *The Gas-Turbine Power Plant*

12·1   Introduction.   In 1791, John Barber obtained a patent in England on a gas turbine which had most of the essential elements of a modern gas turbine. The fundamental principle of the gas turbine is therefore not new. Early in the 20th century, serious attention was given to the development of the gas turbine as a prime mover. Dr. A. J. Buchi of Sulzer Bros. in Switzerland and Dr. S. A. Moss of the General Electric Company, respectively, pioneered the development of the exhaust-gas-turbine-driven supercharger for Diesel and aircraft engines. World War II greatly accelerated the development of the exhaust-gas-turbine-driven supercharger for the aircraft piston engine and also produced the gas turbine for use in high-speed jet-propelled fighter aircraft.

The development of the gas turbine had been retarded by the low efficiency of compressors and the inability of available metals to operate at the required high temperatures without failure. During the past decade, highly efficient air compressors have been built. Advances in high-temperature metallurgy are making alloys available which can be operated for reasonable periods of time at temperatures of 1500 to 1600 F. The simple gas-turbine power plant combined with the jet-propulsion principle has become the standard propulsion unit for high-speed military aircraft. As the efficiency of the gas-turbine power plant is improved through the use of higher temperatures and better turbines and compressors, it is probable that the gas-turbine geared to a propeller may come into general use in large airplanes requiring power units of 5000 hp or more. Several gas-turbine-driven electric locomotives are currently operating on American and foreign railroads. A number of units in capacities of 3000 to 5000 kw are driving electric generators in stationary power plants. Intensive research is being directed toward the burning of pulverized coal in the gas-turbine power plant since coal is cheaper than oil in many sections of the country.   In the size range of 2000 to 10,000 hp and perhaps larger, the gas turbine is becoming a very important type of power plant.

The simple gas-turbine power plant has the advantages of high rotative speed, light weight, small space requirements, few auxiliaries, simplicity, and ability to operate without cooling water.   The efficiency can be increased substantially by the addition of heat exchangers at the sacrifice of simplicity, space, weight, and cost.

12·2   The simple gas-turbine power plant.   The simple gas-turbine power plant consists of three major elements: (1) the

Fig. 12·1   Gas-turbine axial-flow compressor unit with top half of casing removed

air compressor, (2) a combustion chamber or combustor, and (3) the turbine.   To these pieces of equipment must be added a starting motor, a generator or driven equipment, a governing system, and a lubrication system.   Figure 12·1 is a shop view of a gas turbine and axial-flow compressor with the top casing removed.   The six-stage reaction turbine in the foreground is quite similar in essential details to a steam turbine. The turbine is directly connected to an axial-flow compressor which is similar to a reaction turbine driven backward.

Figure 12·2 shows a diagrammatic arrangement of the gas-turbine power plant. Air at atmospheric pressure is compressed in the axial-flow compressor *B* to a discharge pressure of 40 to

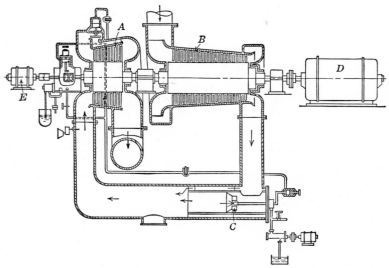

Fig. 12·2 Schematic diagram of arrangement of simple gas-turbine power plant

90 psig. The compressed air flows to the combustor *C* where liquid fuel is injected continuously and burned at such a rate as to result in a gas temperature at the combustor outlet of 1300 F or more. The hot gas is then expanded through the turbine *A* to atmospheric pressure. From 65 to 80 per cent of the output of the turbine is required to operate the compressor; the rest of the turbine output may be used to drive an electric generator *D*, the propeller of a ship, or the propeller of an airplane. A starting motor is necessary to rotate the compressor and turbine and start a flow of gas through the system.

Figure 12·3 illustrates the changes in the volume and pressure of the air and products of combustion during the cycle. Air is drawn into the compressor at atmospheric pressure p_1, is compressed to the discharge pressure p_2, and is discharged from the compressor at pressure p_2. The cross-hatched area $ABCD$ represents the work done by the compressor in compressing the air from p_1 to p_2. The point C represents the pressure and volume of the air leaving the compressor. As the compressed air flows through the combustor, the combustion of the injected fuel raises the temperature of the gas. If the effect of friction is neglected, the pressure remains constant, and point E of Fig. 12·3 represents

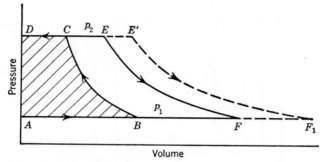

FIG. 12·3 Pressure–volume diagram of the gas-turbine cycle

the volume of the gas entering the turbine at 1000 F. In the turbine, the gas expands along the curve EF of Fig. 12·3 and is then discharged to the atmosphere at pressure p_1. The area $DEFA$ represents the work done by the hot gas in expanding in the turbine. Since the area $ABCD$ represents the work required to compress the air, the difference between these areas or the area $CEFB$ represents the net work available for overcoming friction and driving a generator.

If the gas could be heated in the combustor to 1500 F, the volume of gas entering the turbine would be represented by point E' on Fig. 12·3, expansion in the turbine would follow curve $E'F'$, the output of the turbine would be represented by area $DE'F'A$, and the net output would be represented by area $CE'F'B$. The increased net output due to an increase in the gas temperature at the turbine inlet from 1000 to 1500 F is represented by the area $EE'F'F$. Maximum output requires, therefore, that the gas be supplied to the turbine at a temperature as high as can be utilized without damage to the metals exposed to the high-temperature gas.

In the actual gas-turbine power plant, 65 to 80 per cent of the turbine output is required to drive the compressor. In the steam-turbine power plant, the working fluid is condensed with a very large reduction in volume so that less than 1 per cent of the turbine output is required to operate the boiler feed pump which

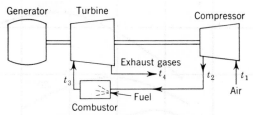

Fig. 12·4   The simple gas-turbine power-plant cycle

corresponds to the air compressor of the gas-turbine power plant. Consequently, for the same net plant output, the gas turbine must produce three to four times as much power as a steam turbine. Such heat-transfer equipment as boilers, economizers, superheaters, condensers, feed-water heaters, forced- and induced-draft fans, and an extensive piping system, all of which are necessary in an efficient steam power plant, are eliminated in the simple gas-turbine power plant. However, if maximum efficiency is desired in the gas-turbine power plant, large heat exchangers, water-circulating pumps, and piping are necessary, and the gas-turbine plant loses much of its simplicity.

The thermal efficiency of a gas-turbine power plant may be defined as follows:

$$\eta = \frac{\text{hp} \times 2545}{m Q_H} \tag{12·1}$$

where hp = net output, hp

m = fuel burned per hr, lb

Q_H = higher heating value of fuel, Btu per lb

The efficiency of a simple gas-turbine power plant, such as the one illustrated in Fig. 12·4, depends upon the temperature of the gas supplied to the turbine and upon the pressure ratio, p_2/p_1. For a constant-air temperature at the inlet to the compressor, the influence of pressure ratio and turbine-inlet temperature upon the thermal efficiency is illustrated in Fig. 12·5. For a given turbine-inlet temperature, there is a particular pressure ratio

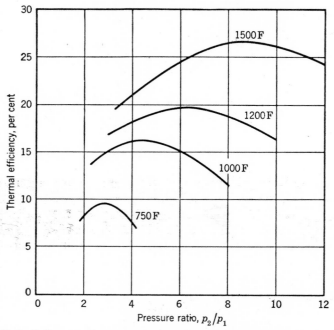

Fig. 12·5   Influence of pressure ratio and turbine-inlet temperature upon thermal efficiency

which gives maximum efficiency, and this optimum pressure ratio increases with inlet temperature. The marked increase in efficiency with increase in inlet temperature should be noted. As the high-temperature characteristics of metals are improved and inlet temperatures higher than 1500 F become practical, the field of the gas turbine as an economical prime mover will expand rapidly.

In Article 1·23, the application of the first law of thermodynamics to the prime mover was discussed, and the following equation was developed:

$$\frac{W}{J} = (h_1 - h_2) - Q \qquad (1 \cdot 31)$$

where h_1 = enthalpy of 1 lb of fluid entering the prime mover

h_2 = enthalpy of 1 lb of fluid leaving the prime mover

Q = heat transferred to the surroundings per lb of fluid flowing through the prime mover

W = work done per lb of fluid in ft-lb units

In the gas turbine, the flow rate is so high that the heat-transfer term may be neglected, and the equation reduces to the form

$$\frac{W}{J} = h_1 - h_2 \qquad (12 \cdot 2)$$

In Article 1·21, it was pointed out that, for a perfect gas,

$$h_1 - h_2 = c_p(T_1 - T_2) \qquad (12 \cdot 3)$$

where c_p is the specific heat at constant pressure.

The numerical value of c_p varies with temperature. For moderate changes in temperature, mean values may be used. For the temperature range used in the gas-turbine power plant, accurate analysis requires consideration of the variation in the specific heat with temperature. The properties of air at high temperatures including the effect of variable specific heat have been computed and tabulated and are reproduced in short form in Table A·4 of the Appendix. It is assumed that the enthalpy of 1 lb of dry air is zero at absolute zero. Therefore, for any temperature, T, expressed in degrees Rankine, $h = c_p T$. Consequently, the change in enthalpy per pound of air flowing through the turbine can be determined by taking the difference in the values of enthalpy in Table A·4 for the air at the temperatures at which it enters and leaves the turbine.

The same type of analysis can be applied to the compressor, and to the combustor and any heat exchangers that may be used in the gas-turbine power-plant cycle.

Example 1. In the simple gas-turbine cycle illustrated in Fig. 12·4, $t_1 = 80$ F, $t_2 = 460$ F, $t_3 = 1300$ F, $t_4 = 780$ F. For a flow of 1 lb of fluid, compute (a) the work done in compressing the fluid in the compressor, (b) the heat supplied in the combustor, (c) the work done in the turbine, and (d) the efficiency of the cycle.

Solution: The enthalpy of 1 lb of air entering and leaving the compressor and turbine may be obtained from Table A·4 of the Appendix for the given temperatures and will be found to be as follows:

$$t_1 = 80\ F \text{ at compressor inlet;} \qquad h_1 = 129.1$$

$$t_2 = 460\ F \text{ at compressor outlet;} \qquad h_2 = 221.2$$

$$t_3 = 1300\ F \text{ at turbine inlet;} \qquad h_3 = 438.8$$

$$t_4 = 780\ F \text{ at turbine outlet;} \qquad h_4 = 301.5$$

(a) For the compressor, $\dfrac{W}{J} = h_2 - h_1 = 221.2 - 129.1 = 92.1$ Btu input as work per lb of air compressed

(b) For the combustor, $Q = h_3 - h_2 = 438.8 - 221.2 = 217.6$ Btu supplied per lb of air

(c) For the turbine, $\dfrac{W}{J} = h_3 - h_4 = 438.8 - 301.5 = 137.3$ Btu output as work per lb of air

(d) The cycle efficiency, $\eta = \dfrac{\text{net output as work}}{\text{heat input}}$

$$= \frac{\text{turbine output} - \text{input to compressor}}{\text{heat supplied}}$$

$$= \frac{137.3 - 92.1}{217.6} \times 100 = 20.8\%$$

The actual efficiency of the gas-turbine power plant will be less than the result obtained in Example 1 because of incomplete combustion of fuel in the combustor, radiation losses from the piping and machinery, bearing and windage losses, generator losses, etc. Also, this analysis neglects the weight of fuel introduced into the combustor and the change in the chemical constituents flowing through the apparatus as a result of the combustion processes. The errors so introduced are small and do not justify a more complex analysis in a brief discussion of the subject.

12·3   The gas-turbine power plant with regenerator.   In the simple cycle illustrated in Fig. 12·4, the exhaust gases are discharged to waste from the turbine at a temperature of 600 to 900 F, depending upon the turbine-inlet temperature. Part of this waste energy can be recovered by utilizing the hot waste gas to preheat the compressed air in a regenerator or heat exchanger ahead of the combustor, as shown in Fig. 12·6. It is evident from Figs. 12·4 and 12·6 that the heat transferred from the exhaust gases to the air in the regenerator results in a sub-

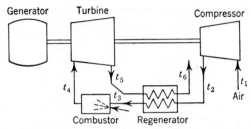

FIG. 12·6 The gas-turbine power-plant cycle with regenerator

stantial reduction in the amount of fuel required to produce the desired turbine-inlet temperature.

Example 2. A regenerator is added to the gas-turbine cycle shown in Fig. 12·4 under such conditions that the temperatures entering and leaving the compressor and turbine of Example 1 remain unchanged, but the air is heated in the regenerator to 700 F. Compute the heat supplied per lb of air flowing through the combustor and the cycle efficiency.

Solution: Since it is assumed that the temperatures entering and leaving the compressor and turbine are unchanged by the addition of the regenerator, the net output of the cycle remains unchanged at $137.3 - 92.1 = 45.2$ Btu of work per lb of air as determined in Example 1.

In Example 1, the air was heated from 460 to 1300 F in the combustor by the addition of 217.6 Btu per lb of air. By using the regenerator, air is heated in the combustor from 700 to 1300 F. At 700 F,

$$h = 281.1 \text{ Btu per lb of air}$$

Then, $\quad Q = 438.8 - 281.1 = 157.7$ Btu per lb of air

The cycle efficiency, $\eta = \dfrac{45.2 \text{ Btu converted into net work}}{157.7 \text{ Btu supplied}} \times 100$

$$= 28.7\%$$

In Fig. 12·7, thermal efficiency at optimum pressure ratio is plotted against turbine-inlet temperature for several gas-turbine power-plant cycles. The lowest curve labeled "simple cycle" refers to the cycle shown in Fig. 12·4, whereas the curve labeled "75 per cent regeneration" applies to the cycle shown in Fig. 12·6 when a regenerator of sufficient size is used to recover 75 per cent of the heat that could be recovered if the air were heated to the exhaust-gas temperature. The substantial gain in efficiency due to the use of the regenerator is clearly indicated in Fig. 12·7.

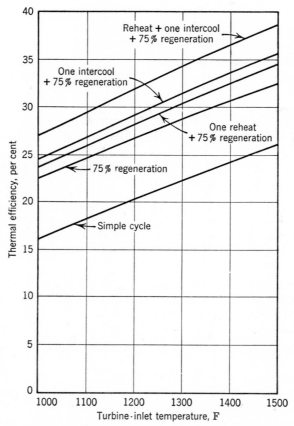

Fig. 12·7   Effect of regeneration, intercooling, and reheating upon thermal efficiency

12·4   The gas-turbine power plant with intercooler and/or reheater. When air is compressed rapidly, the work done on the air produces an increase in temperature with the result that the volume of the compressed air is greater than it would be if the increase in temperature had not occurred. Since the work required to compress air to a given pressure depends upon the volume, the power required to operate the compressor would be reduced if the air could be cooled during compression. Figure 12·8 illustrates a cycle in which a two-stage compressor with intercooler is used. The air is compressed to an intermediate pressure in the low-pressure compressor, is cooled in an intercooler or heat exchanger supplied with cooling water, and is then compressed to the final pressure in the high-pressure compressor. As a result of cooling, the high-pressure compressor can be made smaller and the power consumption will be reduced. In Fig. 12·7,

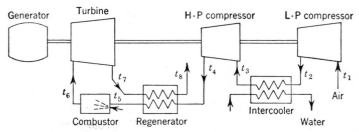

FIG. 12·8   The gas-turbine power-plant cycle with regenerator and two-stage compression with intercooling

the curve labeled "one intercool + 75 per cent regeneration" shows the efficiency obtainable with this cycle, and, by comparison with the curve labeled "75 per cent regeneration," illustrates the gain due to the use of two-stage compression.

Another method of improving efficiency is illustrated in Fig. 12·9. The expansion of the gas takes place in a high-pressure and a low-pressure turbine in series, and a second combustor is located between the turbines. Since the turbine-inlet temperature is limited by the life of the metals in contact with the hot gas, the fuel combines with only a small part of the oxygen in the high-pressure combustor, and an ample supply of oxygen is available for the combustion of more fuel in the low-pressure combustor. The cycle shown in Fig. 12·9 is called a reheating cycle. If the temperature of the gases at the inlet to the low-pressure turbine is raised to a temperature equal to the inlet temperature at the high-pressure turbine, the temperature level through the machine is increased. The exhaust-gas temperature will be higher, but this extra energy can be recovered in the regenerator. A comparison of the curves marked "75 per cent regeneration" and "one reheat + 75 per cent regeneration" on Fig. 12·7 will show the improvement in efficiency due to reheating.

A further gain in efficiency will result from combining the

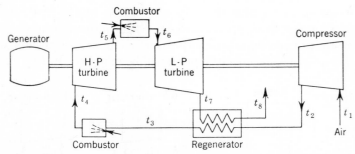

Fig. 12·9   The gas-turbine power-plant cycle with regenerator and reheater

regenerator, intercooler, and reheater into the cycle shown in Fig. 12·10. The thermal efficiency of this cycle is shown by the highest curve in Fig. 12·7.

Large modern steam power plants will operate at efficiencies of 30 to 37 per cent. Diesel engines will operate at an efficiency of

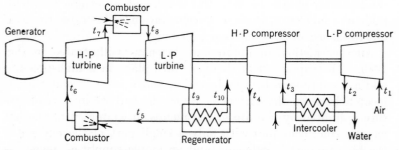

Fig. 12·10   The gas-turbine power-plant cycle with regenerator, reheater, and two-stage compression with intercooling

about 30 per cent and steam power plants of capacities comparable to the capacity of the gas-turbine power plant will give an efficiency of about 25 per cent. It is evident from an inspection of Fig. 12·7 that, at a turbine-inlet temperature of 1500 F which is now considered practical, the gas-turbine power plant can be built to produce comparable efficiencies by the use of a regenerator, two-stage compression with an intercooler, and possibly one reheat.

12·5   The aircraft gas-turbine power plant.   Because of space and weight limitations, the aircraft gas turbine cannot be equipped with a regenerator or intercooler and consequently operates on the simple cycle illustrated in Fig. 12·4. In the turbo-prop engine, illustrated in Fig. 12·11, the excess power developed

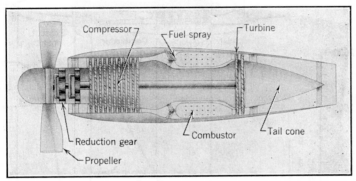

Fig. 12·11   Aircraft gas-turbine power plant with geared propeller

by the turbine over that required to drive the compressor is used to drive a propeller through speed-reducer gearing. The ability to build such units in capacities in excess of that obtainable from a piston engine plus the reduction in weight and frontal area as compared to that of the piston engine makes such a unit attractive in spite of its higher fuel consumption.

Aircraft that are designed for operation at speeds above 500 miles per hr are now powered almost exclusively by the jet-propulsion type of gas-turbine unit. Figure 12·12 illustrates diagrammatically a section through such a unit and shows the changes in pressure, temperature, and velocity as the gases flow through it. Because of the high speed of the airplane, the air enters an inlet section which is designed as a diffuser to slow down the velocity and convert part of the kinetic energy of the high-velocity air stream into pressure. The air is then compressed in a compressor, and fuel is supplied in a combustor as in the conventional gas-turbine power plant. However, in the turbojet

engine, the turbine is designed to produce only enough power to
drive the compressor. As shown in the pressure curve in Fig.
12·12, the gases leave the turbine at a back pressure that is considerably in excess of atmospheric pressure and are then expanded
in a nozzle to atmospheric pressure. The increase in velocity as

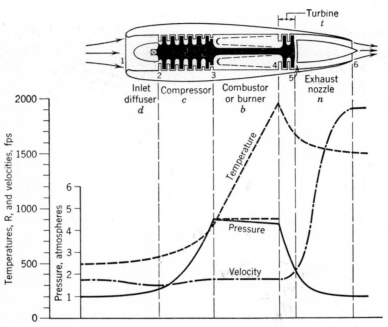

FIG. 12·12   Pressure, temperature, and velocity changes in the aircraft jet-
propulsion unit

the gases expand in the nozzle is shown in Fig. 12·12. Since the
gases leave the unit at a very much higher velocity than they had
at entrance, the increase in velocity or momentum of the gases in
flowing through the unit creates a reaction or thrust in the opposite direction that propels the airplane.

The thrust can be increased at a sacrifice in fuel economy by
installing a second combustor between the turbine and the exhaust nozzle. The amount of fuel that can be burned in the main
combustor is limited by the safe operating temperature of the
metal in the turbine with the result that the gases which leave the

turbine are still rich in oxygen and can support combustion if fuel is sprayed into the air stream. The higher temperature and enthalpy of the gases that result from the burning of fuel immediately ahead of the exhaust nozzle increase the velocity of the gases leaving the nozzle and therefore increase the reaction or thrust produced by the unit. The increased thrust that can be obtained by designing the unit for "after-burning" or fuel injection between the turbine and the exhaust nozzle is particularly effective during take-off or combat conditions where, for short periods of time, reduced efficiency is of less importance than increased thrust.

PROBLEMS

1. The following temperatures apply to the simple gas-turbine power plant cycle shown in Fig. 12·4: $t_1 = 100$ F; $t_2 = 440$ F; $t_3 = 1200$ F; $t_4 = 780$ F. Compute for a flow of 1 lb of air the following quantities, using (1) enthalpy values from Table A·4, and (2) constant specific-heat values from Table 1·1: (a) work input to compressor, (b) work output of turbine, (c) net cycle output, (d) heat supplied, (e) cycle efficiency.

2. A regenerator is added to the cycle used in Problem 1, and all conditions remain the same as in Problem 1 except that the air leaves the regenerator at 700 F. Compute the same items as in Problem 1.

3. A gas-turbine power plant operates on the cycle illustrated in Fig. 12·8. Temperatures are as follows: $t_1 = 80$ F; $t_2 = 320$ F; $t_3 = 100$ F; $t_4 = 360$ F; $t_5 = 680$ F; $t_6 = 1500$ F; $t_7 = 800$ F. Flow is 70 lb of air per sec. Compute (a) hp input to the compressors, (b) hp output of the turbine, (c) net hp output of the cycle, (d) heat input to the air in the combustor, (e) cycle efficiency.

4. In Problem 3, cooling water is supplied to the intercooler at 70 F and leaves at 100 F. How many gal of water must be circulated per min?

5. In Problem 3, the fuel oil burned in the combustor has a heating value of 19,000 Btu per lb. If the combustion efficiency is 98 per cent, how much oil is burned per hr?

6. In Problems 3 and 5, 93 per cent of the net output of the cycle appears as electric energy at the generator terminals. Calculate (a) the overall efficiency of the plant, and (b) the plant heat rate in Btu per kw-hr delivered by the generator.

13 · Mechanical Refrigeration

13·1 Introduction. Previous chapters have dealt with the equipment and methods used to produce power by the conversion of low-grade energy into shaft work. Refrigeration is the process of removing heat from some product or substance in order to freeze it or to maintain its temperature below that of the atmosphere.

Refrigeration is generally produced in one of three ways: (1) by the melting of a solid, (2) by the sublimation of a solid, and (3) by the evaporation of a liquid. Ice melts at 32 F and, in so doing, absorbs its latent heat of fusion which is 144 Btu per lb. Temperatures lower than 32 F may be obtained by using a mixture of ice and salt. Solid carbon dioxide or Dry Ice passes directly from a solid to a gaseous state at −109.3 F and has about twice as much refrigerating capacity as the same weight of ice. It is used extensively when perishable materials are shipped under conditions where weight or salt water are objectionable. Most of the commercial refrigeration is produced by the evaporation of a liquid which is called a *refrigerant*. The evaporation of water under normal atmospheric conditions is used in dry climates for the cooling of residences and business houses. *Mechanical refrigeration* depends upon the evaporation of a liquid refrigerant that, because of its cost, must be used over and over again in a closed circuit. This circuit includes the following essential equipment:

1. An *evaporator* or heat exchanger in which a liquid refrigerant may evaporate at a low temperature and pressure, thus absorbing heat from the surroundings.

2. A *compressor* in the compression system (or other apparatus in the absorption system) for removing the low-pressure vapor from the evaporator and delivering it at a higher pressure to the

condenser. The compressor is driven by a motor or engine, and the energy represented by the work done in compressing the fluid is absorbed by the refrigerant that leaves the compressor as a superheated vapor.

3. A *condenser* or heat exchanger in which the high-pressure refrigerant is cooled and condensed by rejection of heat to a coolant, either water or air.

4. An *expansion valve* or other device for regulating the rate of flow of the high-pressure liquid refrigerant from the condenser to the evaporator in which a low pressure is maintained by the compressor.

The refrigerant during this cycle accomplishes two major purposes without destroying itself: viz., it removes heat from the substance to be refrigerated, and it rejects this heat at a higher-temperature level to some other substance such as normal atmospheric air or well water.

Mechanical refrigeration is used mainly for (1) the preservation of food and other perishable products during storage and transportation, (2) the manufacture of ice and solid carbon dioxide, and (3) the control of air temperature and humidity in air-conditioning systems.

13·2   Refrigeration by evaporation of a liquid. Let Fig. 13·1 represent an insulated box containing hot air and an evaporator or boiler. Assume that the evaporator has a free vent to the atmosphere and contains water at 212 F. If the air in the box is at a temperature above 212 F, heat will flow from the air to the water in the boiler, steam will be generated at 212 F with the absorption of the latent heat of evaporation, and the steam will escape to the atmosphere through the vent, thus removing the latent heat of evaporation from the box. Unless heat is supplied to the air in the box, the temperature of the air will decrease until it approaches the vaporization temperature of the water in the boiler.

A refrigerant may be substituted for the water in the evaporator or boiler of Fig. 13·1. A refrigerant is a liquid that will boil at a temperature low enough to maintain the desired temperature in the refrigerated space. The boiling points or saturation temperatures at standard atmospheric pressure of a number of common refrigerants are as follows:

Ammonia (NH₃)	-28 F
Freon 12 (CCl₂F)	-22 F
Methyl chloride (CH₃Cl)	-11 F
Sulphur dioxide (SO₂)	$+14$ F

If liquid ammonia at atmospheric pressure should be placed in the evaporator of Fig. 13·1, it would boil at -28 F, would

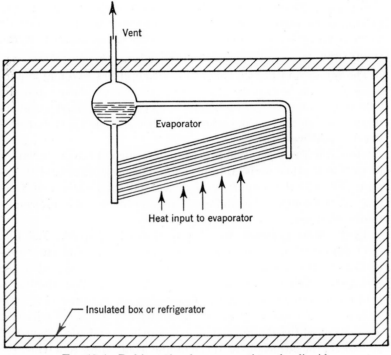

Fig. 13·1   Refrigeration by evaporation of a liquid

absorb its latent heat of evaporation from the contents of the box or refrigerator, and would deliver this latent heat to the outside atmosphere via the ammonia vapor escaping through the vent. If the refrigerator were well insulated and the evaporator contained enough liquid ammonia, the contents of the refrigerator would be cooled to a temperature approaching -28 F.

If ammonia were cheap and plentiful and the escaping gases were not obnoxious, refrigeration could be produced continuously by supplying liquid ammonia to the evaporator as needed and allowing the vapor to escape to the atmosphere. However, re-frigerants are expensive, and it is necessary to condense the vapor leaving the evaporator and return it to the evaporator again in a closed system. In the *compression system of refrigeration* which will be discussed in subsequent articles, it is the function of the compressor, condenser, and expansion valve to bring about con-densation of the vapor that leaves the evaporator and to return it to the evaporator as a liquid.

The relation between the saturation temperature and the satu-ration pressure of some common refrigerants is shown in Fig. 13·2. An ideal refrigerant is one that will evaporate at a pressure slightly above atmospheric pressure and at a temperature low enough to maintain the desired refrigerator temperature. It should condense at a moderate pressure at the temperature exist-ing in a condenser supplied with surface or well water or normal atmospheric air as the cooling medium. Tables of the thermal properties of refrigerants will be found in textbooks on refrigera-tion. These tables are similar in arrangement to the tables of the properties of steam except that the zero of enthalpy is the en-thalpy of saturated liquid at -40 F.

The unit of capacity of a refrigeration system is the *ton of refrigeration* or the ton of ice melting. A refrigeration machine is said to have a capacity of 1 ton of refrigeration for each 288,000 Btu absorbed by the refrigerant in the evaporator while operating continuously 24 hr per day. This is equal to the quantity of heat required to melt 1 ton (2000 lb) of 32 F ice, allowing 144 Btu for each pound of ice melted. This heat absorption is at the rate of 12,000 Btu per hr or 200 Btu per min. One ton of refrigeration is therefore defined as the absorption of heat in the evaporator by the refrigerant at the rate of 200 Btu per min.

13·3   The compression system of refrigeration. The flow diagram of the compression system of refrigeration is shown in Fig. 13·3. Liquid refrigerant is vaporized in the evaporator at an evaporator pressure, p_e. The vapor is compressed in a com-pressor to a discharge pressure, p_c, and is delivered to a water- or air-cooled condenser in which the vapor is condensed at the con-denser pressure p_c to form a liquid. The liquid refrigerant is collected in a receiver from which it flows through the expansion valve in which the pressure is reduced to the evaporator pressure p_e. A low pressure p_e exists from the discharge side of the

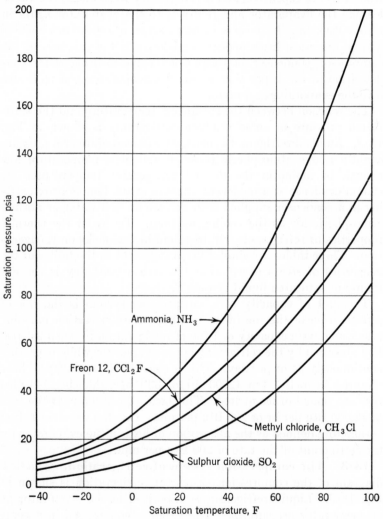

Fɪɢ. 13·2 Saturation pressure and temperature of some common refrigerants

expansion valve through the evaporator to the compressor. A high pressure p_c exists from the discharge side of the compressor through the condenser to the expansion valve.

The required pressure in the evaporator depends upon the temperature to be maintained in the evaporator, the refrigeration capacity of the system, and the amount of surface in the evaporator, since the heat must flow from the refrigerator through the evaporator surface to the refrigerant. The required pressure in

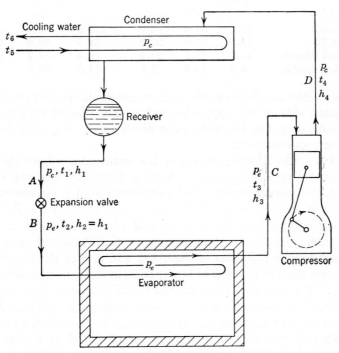

Fig. 13·3   Flow diagram of the compression refrigeration cycle

the condenser depends upon the temperature of the cooling water or air to which the heat is being rejected, the amount of surface through which the heat is being transferred, and the amount of heat to be rejected. Table 13·1 shows the evaporator and condenser pressures that will exist at several saturation temperatures for some of the common refrigerants. For minimum power input to the compressor, the evaporator pressure should be as high as possible, and the condenser pressure should be as low as possible.

Owing to frictional resistance to flow, a pressure drop occurs between the discharge side of the expansion valve and the com-

TABLE 13·1

EVAPORATOR AND CONDENSER PRESSURES FOR VARIOUS SATURATION
TEMPERATURES

Refrigerant	Evaporator Pressure (p_e), Psia			Condenser Pressure (p_c), Psia		
	−20 F	0 F	+20 F	70 F	80 F	90 F
Ammonia	18.3	30.4	48.2	128.8	153.0	180.6
Freon 12	15.3	23.9	35.8	84.8	98.8	114.3
Methyl chloride	11.7	18.9	29.2	73.4	86.3	100.6
Sulphur dioxide	5.9	10.4	17.2	49.6	59.7	71.3

pressor inlet and between the compressor discharge and the high-pressure side of the expansion valve. By careful design, this pressure drop can be made quite small and is neglected in the subsequent discussion.

13·4   The Mollier diagram for ammonia. Since the refrigeration cycle may be considered as involving only two pressures, the evaporator and condenser pressures, it is convenient to represent the properties of refrigerants graphically on a diagram having enthalpy as the abscissa and absolute pressure as the ordinate. Such a diagram, known as the Mollier diagram, is reproduced for ammonia in Figs. A·2 and A·3 of the Appendix. Pressure from 10 to 300 psia is plotted as ordinate to a logarithmic scale. The enthalpy of saturated liquid ammonia at −40 F is assumed to be zero. In order to conserve space through the elimination of those areas of the diagram that are not needed for the solution of problems, only those areas of the chart having enthalpy values from −26 to +200 Btu per lb are plotted on Fig. A·2; Fig. A·3 is plotted for enthalpy values from 500 to 830 Btu per lb.

A plot of enthalpy versus pressure of saturated liquid ammonia gives the saturated liquid line which extends diagonally across Fig. A·2. The region to the left of this line is the compressed liquid region. In this region, dotted lines which are approximately vertical are plotted to show the enthalpy of 1 lb of compressed liquid ammonia at 10-degree increments of temperature. The area to the right of the saturated liquid line is the wet vapor region in which the enthalpy, quality, and specific volume of wet ammonia vapor of low quality are shown. Roughly parallel and to the right of the saturated liquid line is a set of curves of constant quality which are plotted for increments of 5 per cent of quality from zero to 30 per cent. Lines of specific volume of the wet ammonia vapor are also plotted in this region for specific volumes from 0.1 to 8 cu ft per lb. That part of the complete Mollier diagram for ammonia which is represented by Fig. A·2 is used for the solution of problems involving the condition of the ammonia as it leaves the condenser and as it is supplied to and discharged from the expansion valve.

Figure A·3 shows the properties of superheated ammonia and wet ammonia vapor of high quality and is used in determining the properties of ammonia leaving the evaporator, entering and leaving the compressor, and entering the condenser. A curve labeled "saturated vapor" is obtained by plotting the enthalpy of dry saturated ammonia against pressure and divides the area of this chart into a superheat region to the right of this curve and a wet vapor region to the left of it. In the wet region, lines of constant quality are roughly parallel to the saturated vapor line and are plotted for increments of 5 per cent of quality, starting with 75 per cent. To the right of the saturated vapor line, in the superheat region, lines of constant temperature are plotted in 10-degree increments as dotted lines. When the pressure and temperature of superheated ammonia are known, a point representing the state of the ammonia can be located on the chart, and the enthalpy and other properties can be read directly from the appropriate scales. Curves of specific volume and constant entropy appear on the chart as diagonal lines.

Example 1. Determine (*a*) the enthalpy of liquid ammonia at 20 F and 200 psia, (*b*) the enthalpy, and specific volume of wet vapor at 30 psia and 10 per cent quality, (*c*) the enthalpy, specific volume, and entropy of wet vapor at 30 psia and 95 per cent quality, and (*d*) the enthalpy, specific volume, and entropy of ammonia at 40 psia and 200 F.

Solution: (*a*) The intersection of the 200-psia line with the 20 F compressed liquid line on Fig. A·2 gives a value of 65 Btu per lb for enthalpy.

(*b*) The intersection of the 30-psia line and the line of 10 per cent quality in the wet vapor region of Fig. A·2 gives an enthalpy of 99 Btu per lb and a specific volume of 0.93 cu ft per lb.

(*c*) The intersection of the 30-psia line with the line of 95 per cent quality in the wet vapor region of Fig. A·3 gives an enthalpy of 583 Btu per lb, a specific volume of 8.8 cu ft per lb, and an entropy of 1.275.

(*d*) The intersection of the 40-psia line and the 200 F line in the superheat region of Fig. A·3 gives an enthalpy of 720 Btu per lb, a specific volume of 10.4 cu ft per lb and an entropy of 1.50.

Figure 13·4 shows a compression refrigeration cycle on the pressure–enthalpy or Mollier diagram. The points *A*, *B*, *C*, and *D* of Fig. 13·4 correspond to the points having the same symbols on the flow diagram (Fig. 13·3). Point *A* represents the condition of the liquid ahead of the expansion valve. Point *B* repre-

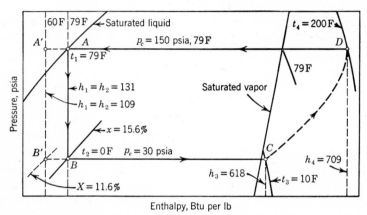

FIG. 13·4   Compression refrigeration cycle on the Mollier diagram

sents the condition of the refrigerant after it has passed through the expansion valve and is at the evaporator pressure. Points *C* and *D* represent the state of the refrigerant at entrance to and exit from the compressor. The enthalpy values which appear on Fig. 13·4 were obtained from the Mollier diagram (Figs. A·2 and A·3).

The changes in enthalpy, the heat absorbed or rejected, and the work done on the refrigerant as it passes through the throttle valve, evaporator, compressor, and condenser are discussed in the subsequent articles of this chapter.

13·5   The expansion valve.   The expansion valve usually consists of a valve stem having a conical point that can be screwed in or out of an opening in the valve seat, thus permitting close regulation of the area through which the refrigerant flows from the condenser pressure to the evaporator pressure. If the expansion valve is well insulated to prevent heat transfer from the surroundings to the refrigerant, then, since no work is done in the valve and the kinetic energy of the fluid on each side of the valve is small, the enthalpy of the refrigerant remains constant, and the process is a throttling process as discussed in Article 1·27. Therefore,

$$h_1 = h_2 \qquad (13 \cdot 1)$$

where h_1 = enthalpy of the refrigerant ahead of the expansion valve

h_2 = enthalpy of the refrigerant beyond the expansion valve

If the refrigerant is saturated ammonia at a condenser pressure of 150 psia ahead of the expansion valve, the state of the refrigerant is represented by point A on Fig. 13·4, the temperature is 79 F, and the enthalpy is 131 Btu per lb. Below the expansion valve, for an evaporator pressure of 30 psia, the temperature is 0 F (see Fig. 13·2 or the saturation line of Fig. A·2), the enthalpy is 131 Btu per lb, and the quality is 15.6 per cent. The throttling process in the expansion valve is represented on the Mollier diagram by a vertical or constant-enthalpy line drawn from point A on the saturated liquid line to point B on the line representing the evaporator pressure. A total of 15.6 per cent of the liquid is converted into vapor since the enthalpy of saturated liquid ammonia at 150 psia is more than the enthalpy of saturated liquid ammonia at 30 psia, and the excess enthalpy results in vaporization of part of the liquid at the lower pressure.

If the liquid ammonia at 150 psia condenser pressure had been cooled below the saturation temperature (79 F) to a final temperature of 60 F ahead of the expansion valve, the state of the subcooled liquid would be represented by point A' on Fig. 13·4, and the enthalpy would be 109 Btu per lb. Upon throttling to 30 psia, the quality would be 11.6 per cent at an enthalpy of 109 Btu.

13·6   The evaporator. The heat absorbed in the evaporator per pound of refrigerant is equal to the increase in enthalpy of the refrigerant as it passes through the evaporator as discussed in Article 1·22, or

$$Q_e = m_r(h_3 - h_2) \qquad (13 \cdot 2)$$

or $$Q_e = m_r(h_3 - h_1) \qquad (13\cdot3)$$

where Q_e = heat absorbed in evaporator, Btu per min

m_r = refrigerant circulated, lb per min

h_3 = enthalpy of refrigerant leaving the evaporator, Btu per lb

h_2 = enthalpy of refrigerant leaving the expansion valve and entering the evaporator, Btu per lb

h_1 = enthalpy of refrigerant ahead of the expansion valve, Btu per lb

The expansion valve is usually adjusted to produce a few degrees of superheat in the refrigerant entering the compressor. If it is assumed that the pipe connecting the evaporator and the compressor is well insulated, the enthalpy of the superheated vapor leaving the evaporator and entering the compressor can be obtained by locating the point C in the superheated region of the Mollier chart at the pressure and temperature of the vapor. For ammonia at 30 psia and 10 F, the enthalpy is 618 Btu per lb, and the point C is shown on Fig. 13·4.

Since 1 ton of commercial refrigeration is equal to the absorption of 200 Btu per min, then

$$\text{Refrigeration capacity in tons} = \frac{Q_e}{200} = \frac{m_r(h_3 - h_1)}{200} \qquad (13\cdot4)$$

For the conditions represented in Fig. 13·4 and with 3.0 lb of ammonia circulated per min,

$$Q_e = m_r(h_3 - h_1) = 3.0(618 - 131) = 1461 \text{ Btu per min}$$

$$\text{Refrigeration capacity} = \tfrac{1461}{200} = 7.30 \text{ tons}$$

If the liquid ammonia had been subcooled at 150 psia to 60 F, as indicated by point A' on Fig. 13·4, then $Q_e = m_r(618 - 109) = 1527$ Btu per min or 7.63 tons. It is desirable, therefore, that the liquid refrigerant be cooled to as low a temperature as possible ahead of the expansion valve, provided that this cooling is done by water or air.

13·7 The compressor. The compressors that are used in refrigerating systems are similar in principle to compressors used for compressing other fluids such as air and may be classified as follows: (1) single- or double-acting reciprocating piston, (2) rotary, (3) gear, and (4) multistage centrifugal.

A reciprocating single-acting two-cylinder piston type of ammonia compressor is illustrated in Fig. 13·5. The piston is provided with an extension head containing the inlet valve. The refrigerant is admitted to the cylinder above the piston but below the extension head in which the inlet valve is located. The discharge valves are built into the cylinder head. By using the entire

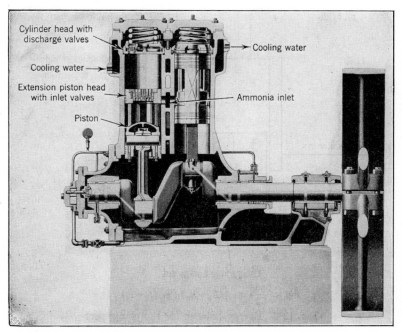

Cylinder head with discharge valves

Cooling water

Cooling water

Extension piston head with inlet valves

Ammonia inlet

Piston

Fig. 13·5 Two-cylinder vertical single-acting ammonia compressor

area of the cylinder head and extension piston head for discharge and suction valves, the piston can be operated at fairly high speeds without producing excessive pressure drop through the valves. The cylinder head is held on a seat by a coil spring and is free to move vertically if a slug of liquid ammonia should enter the cylinder and be compressed against the cylinder head. The cylinders are water-jacketed to reduce the power consumption and improve cylinder-wall lubrication.

In the Diesel engine, the temperature of the air increases during compression to about 1000 F as a result of the work done on the air during compression. In the refrigerating compressor, the temperature of the refrigerant likewise increases during compression because of the work done on it. Because of the pressure drop through the valves and the heat exchange between the refrigerant and the cylinder walls, it is very difficult to determine the exact behavior of the refrigerant during a complete revolution

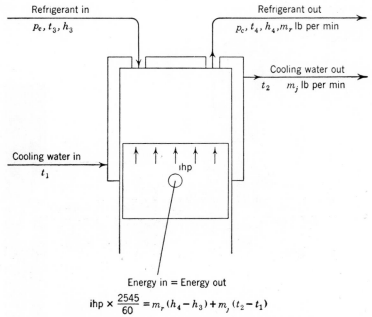

$$\text{ihp} \times \frac{2545}{60} = m_r\,(h_4 - h_3) + m_j\,(t_2 - t_1)$$

FIG. 13·6   Energy balance for the compressor

of the compressor. However, the pressure and temperature of the refrigerant can be measured at entrance to and exit from the compressor. The points C and D have been located in Fig. 13·4 from such readings of pressure and temperature, and a dotted line has been drawn between them to indicate that the actual change of pressure and temperature of the refrigerant at intermediate pressures during the compression process is unknown. The increase in enthalpy during compression is due to the work done on the refrigerant by the piston of the compressor.

The energy balance for the compressor is illustrated in Fig. 13·6. From the first law of thermodynamics, energy in = energy out. Neglecting any heat transfer which may take place between the compressor and the air, the energy is supplied as indicated horsepower or work done by the piston on the refrigerant and may be computed as follows:

$$\text{Energy in} = \text{ihp} \times \frac{2545}{60} \text{ Btu per min} \qquad (13\cdot5)$$

Energy is removed from the compressor by the refrigerant and by cooling water. Therefore,

$$\text{Energy out} = m_r(h_4 - h_3) + m_j(t_2 - t_1) \qquad (13\cdot6)$$

where m_r = refrigerant delivered by the compressor, lb per min

m_j = cooling water circulated through the jacket of the compressor, lb per min

h_3 = enthalpy of refrigerant entering the compressor, Btu per lb

h_4 = enthalpy of refrigerant leaving the compressor, Btu per lb

t_1 = temperature of cooling water entering compressor, F

t_2 = temperature of cooling water leaving compressor, F

Then, from the first law of thermodynamics,

$$\text{Ihp} \times \frac{2545}{60} = m_r(h_4 - h_3) + m_j(t_2 - t_1) \qquad (13\cdot7)$$

The calculation of the energy balance on the compressor may be illustrated by Example 2.

Example 2. A total of 3.0 lb of ammonia is compressed per min. The ammonia enters the compressor at 30 psia and 10 F and leaves at 150 psia and 200 F, as shown on Fig. 13·4. A total of 5.0 lb of cooling water enters the compressor jacket per min at 60 F and leaves at 67 F. The ihp is found to be 7.25. Check the energy balance.

Solution:

$$\text{Energy in} = \text{ihp} \times \frac{2545}{60} = 7.25 \times \frac{2545}{60} = 308 \text{ Btu per min}$$

$$\text{Energy out} = m_r(h_4 - h_3) + m_j(t_2 - t_1)$$

$$= 3.0(709 - 618) + 5.0(67 - 60)$$

$$= 308 \text{ Btu per min}$$

13·8   The condenser. Except in small units such as household refrigerators which have air-cooled condensers, the condenser is water-cooled and operates on the same principle as the

steam condenser of the power plant. The pipe between the compressor and the condenser is not insulated, since any heat lost to
the atmosphere from this pipe reduces the heat to be removed
in the condenser. The superheated ammonia entering the condenser is cooled to the saturation temperature, condensed at the
saturation temperature corresponding to the condenser pressure,
and perhaps subcooled to a temperature below the saturation
temperature. An ample supply of cold cooling water reduces
the pressure required to effect condensation of the refrigerant and
thereby reduces the power required to operate the compressor.

Neglecting the heat transferred to the surrounding air and
referring to Fig. 13·3 and Fig. 13·4, the energy balance for the
condenser may be written as follows:

Energy given up by refrigerant = energy absorbed by cooling water

or $$Q_c = m_r(h_4 - h_1) = m_c(t_6 - t_5) \qquad (13\cdot8)$$

where Q_c = heat rejected to condenser, Btu per min
m_r = refrigerant circulated, lb per min
m_c = condenser cooling water, lb per min
h_4 = enthalpy of refrigerant leaving the compressor
h_1 = enthalpy of refrigerant leaving the condenser
t_5 = temperature of cooling water entering condenser
t_6 = temperature of cooling water leaving condenser

**13·9   Energy balance for the compression refrigerating
cycle.** Energy is supplied to the system as heat in the evaporator and as work in the compressor. If heat transfer from the
piping system is neglected, energy is removed as heat in the
cylinder jacket and condenser circulating water. Consequently,
from the first law of thermodynamics, the following energy balance may be written:

$$Q_e + \text{ihp} \times \tfrac{2545}{60} = Q_c + Q_j \qquad (13\cdot9)$$

where Q_e = heat absorbed in the evaporator, Btu per min
Q_c = heat rejected in the condenser, Btu per min
Q_j = heat rejected to compressor jacket water, Btu per
min, or $m_j(t_2 - t_1)$, from Equation 13·7

Where complete test data are available for calculation of all items
in Equation 13·9, failure of the calculated quantities to balance

in accordance with Equation 13·9 may be due to heat transfer from the piping or errors in the data.

Since, from Equation 13·7,

$$\text{Ihp} \times \tfrac{2545}{60} - Q_j = m_r(h_4 - h_3)$$

Equation 13·9 may also be written thus:

$$Q_e + m_r(h_4 - h_3) = Q_c \qquad (13 \cdot 10)$$

For a flow of 1.0 lb of ammonia per min and with reference to Fig. 13·4,

$$Q_e = h_3 - h_2 = h_3 - h_1 = 618 - 131 = 487 \text{ Btu}$$

$$h_4 - h_3 = 709 - 618 = 91 \text{ Btu}$$

$$Q_c = h_4 - h_1 = 709 - 131 = 578 \text{ Btu}$$

$$Q_e + (h_4 - h_3) = 487 + 91 = 578 = Q_c$$

It may therefore be stated that the energy rejected to cooling water in the condenser equals the heat absorbed by the refrigerant in the evaporator plus the increase in enthalpy of the refrigerant due to work done on it in the compressor if no heat transfer occurs in the piping system or to cooling water in the compressor.

13·10 Coefficient of performance. The performance of heat-power machinery such as engines and turbines is expressed in terms of thermal efficiency where thermal efficiency is defined as the ratio of the energy converted into work to the energy supplied to the machine. The objective is the performance of maximum work from the energy supplied. In the refrigeration cycle, the objective is the removal of heat from a refrigerated substance or space with the least possible input of work to operate the compressor. The performance of a refrigeration system is expressed by a term known as the *coefficient of performance*, which is defined as the ratio of the heat absorbed by the refrigerant while passing through the evaporator to the work input required to compress the refrigerant in the compressor, both terms being expressed in consistent units. The input required to compress the refrigerant may be taken as the theoretical amount of work required for isentropic compression, the actual indicated horsepower of the compressor, the horsepower input at the crankshaft of the compressor, or the electric input to the motor that drives the compressor. The basis upon which the input is measured must be specified if the term coefficient of performance is to have any significance.

Example 3. Three pounds of ammonia are circulated per minute under the conditions shown in Fig. 13·4. The input to the shaft of the compressor is 10 hp. Compute the coefficient of performance based upon the input to the compressor.

Solution: The heat absorbed in the evaporator by the refrigerant,

$$Q_e = m_r(h_3 - h_1) = 3.0(618 - 131) = 1461 \text{ Btu per min}$$

$$\text{The shaft work} = \frac{10 \text{ hp} \times 2545 \text{ Btu per hp-hr}}{60 \text{ min per hr}} = 424 \text{ Btu per min}$$

$$\text{Coefficient of performance} = \frac{1461 \text{ Btu per min absorbed in refrigerator}}{424 \text{ Btu per min input to compressor as work}}$$

$$= 3.45$$

This coefficient of performance of 3.45 means that 3.45 Btu are absorbed by the refrigerant in the evaporator for each Btu of work required to operate the compressor. Obviously, the coefficient of performance should be as great as possible. Anything that decreases the evaporator pressure or increases the condenser pressure reduces the coefficient of performance through increase in the work required to compress 1 lb of refrigerant.

13·11 The heat pump. There are many areas of the country where it is desirable to cool office and residential buildings during the hot summer months and necessary to heat them during the winter months. This can be done by a refrigerating system for cooling and a conventional heating plant for heating. However, both functions can be combined into a single set of apparatus called the heat pump which is illustrated in Fig. 13·7.

During the hot summer months, the cooling cycle operates as a conventional refrigerating machine with the room air being cooled by blowing it across the coils of an evaporator. The heat absorbed in the evaporator plus the work input to the compressor is discharged to the atmosphere in an air-cooled condenser.

During the heating season, the path of the refrigerant is reversed by suitable valves so that the coil that is used as an evaporator during the summer months becomes the condenser during the heating season and the coil that is used as a condenser during

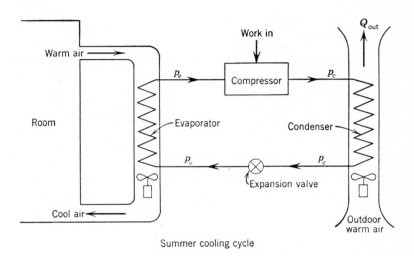

Summer cooling cycle

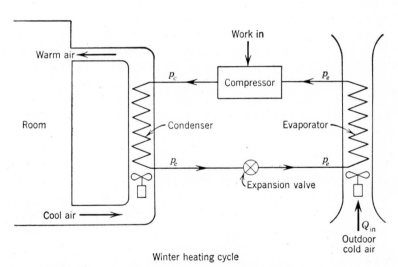

Winter heating cycle

Fig. 13·7   Heating and cooling cycles of the heat pump

the cooling season becomes the evaporator during the heating season. Then heat is absorbed from the outdoor atmosphere by the refrigerant in the evaporator. The heat so absorbed plus the work input to the compressor is delivered by the condenser to the air that is being circulated in the office or home. Figure 13·7 shows the atmosphere as the sink into which the heat is rejected during the summer cooling cycle and the source of the heat in the winter heating cycle. Water or the ground around the building may be used instead of the atmosphere as the sink and source for the heat. Well water or the soil are subject to less temperature variations during the year but may require more expensive installations than heat-transfer coils installed in the air.

Since the heat delivered to the building during the heating season comes from the heat absorbed at low temperature from the air, water, or ground, plus the work input required to compress the refrigerant, the heating load may be several times the amount of electric energy purchased. However, electric energy is high-grade expensive energy which probably is generated in a power plant burning fuel with an efficiency that is *relatively low* in accordance with the second law of thermodynamics. Moreover, transmission and distribution losses still further reduce the percentage of energy in the original fuel that appears as electric energy at the location of the heat pump. Consequently, the heat delivered to the building by the heat pump is less than the energy in the fuel that was burned to produce the electric energy used to operate the heat pump.

In regions having low-cost electric energy, fairly long and heavy cooling requirements, and moderate heating loads, the ability of the heat pump to use the same equipment for both heating and cooling may make the installation an attractive one.

For a more complete discussion of the compression system of refrigeration and a discussion of the absorption system, the properties of refrigerants, the thermodynamics of the refrigeration cycle, and the applications of refrigeration to cooling, to the production of ice and solid carbon-dioxide, and to air conditioning, the reader is referred to the references at the end of this chapter.

PROBLEMS

The following data apply to compression refrigerating systems as illustrated in Fig. 13·3:

Item	Test Number				
	1	2	3	4	5
1. Condenser pressure, psia	140	160	150	180	170
2. Evaporator pressure, psia	25	20	30	15	20
3. Temperature of liquid ammonia before expansion valve, F	75	83	74	85	84
4. Temperature of ammonia leaving evaporator, F	0	−10	+20	−20	0
5. Temperature of ammonia leaving compressor, F	235	240	220	250	245
6. Temperature of cooling water supplied to condenser and compressor jacket, F	60	63	60	72	70
7. Temperature of cooling water leaving condenser, F	70	78	68	84	81
8. Temperature of cooling water leaving compressor jacket, F	67	....	65	76	76
9. Ammonia circulated per min, lb	5	7	4	6	9
10. Cooling water circulated per min through condenser, lb	350	....	346	....	.....
11. Cooling water circulated per min through compressor jacket, lb	25	0	30	25	40
12. Ihp of compressor	17.8	....	14.1	....	30.9

Draw for each set of data, a flow diagram similar to Fig. 13·3, and place on this diagram the following results to be obtained from the Mollier diagram: (a) enthalpy of the ammonia ahead of the expansion valve, (b) enthalpy and quality of ammonia beyond the expansion valve, (c) enthalpy of ammonia leaving the evaporator, and (d) enthalpy of ammonia leaving the compressor.

Assume no heat transfer from the piping system and compute:

1. The heat absorbed in the evaporator in Btu per min.
2. The capacity of the system in tons of commercial refrigeration.
3. The heat rejected to the condenser in Btu per min.
4. The condenser cooling water required per min (where the weight of cooling water is given, check the data).
5. The heat removed by the compressor jacket water in Btu per min.
6. The ihp of the compressor, by use of the energy balance (Equation 13·9). Where the ihp is given, check the data by the energy balance.
7. Where the ihp is given, compute the coefficient of performance.

REFERENCES

B. F. Raber and F. W. Hutchinson, *Theory of Mechanical Refrigeration*, John Wiley & Sons.

H. G. Venemann, *Refrigeration Theory and Applications*, Nickerson & Collins Company.

N. R. Sparks, *Theory of Mechanical Refrigeration*, McGraw-Hill Book Company.

H. J. Macintire and F. W. Hutchinson, *Refrigeration Engineering*, John Wiley & Sons.

Refrigerating Data Book, Volumes I and II, American Society of Refrigerating Engineers.

R. C. Jordan and G. B. Priester, *Refrigeration and Air Conditioning*, Prentice-Hall.

Appendix

TABLE A·1
DRY SATURATED STEAM: TEMPERATURE TABLE*

Temp., F	Abs Press, Lb Sq In.	Specific Volume			Enthalpy			Entropy			Temp., F
t	p	Sat. Liquid v_f	Evap. v_{fg}	Sat. Vapor v_g	Sat. Liquid h_f	Evap. h_{fg}	Sat. Vapor h_g	Sat. Liquid s_f	Evap s_{fg}	Sat. Vapor s_g	t
32	0.08854	0.01602	3306	3306	0.00	1075.8	1075.8	0.0000	2.1877	2.1877	32
35	0.09995	0.01602	2947	2947	3.02	1074.1	1077.1	0.0061	2.1709	2.1770	35
40	0.12170	0.01602	2444	2444	8.05	1071.3	1079.3	0.0162	2.1435	2.1597	40
45	0.14752	0.01602	2036.4	2036.4	13.06	1068.4	1081.5	0.0262	2.1167	2.1429	45
50	0.17811	0.01603	1703.2	1703.2	18.07	1065.6	1083.7	0.0361	2.0903	2.1264	50
60	0.2563	0.01604	1206.6	1206.7	28.06	1059.9	1088.0	0.0555	2.0393	2.0948	60
70	0.3631	0.01606	867.8	867.9	38.04	1054.3	1092.3	0.0745	1.9902	2.0647	70
80	0.5069	0.01608	633.1	633.1	48.02	1048.6	1096.6	0.0932	1.9428	2.0360	80
90	0.6982	0.01610	468.0	468.0	57.99	1042.9	1100.9	0.1115	1.8972	2.0087	90
100	0.9492	0.01613	350.3	350.4	67.97	1037.2	1105.2	0.1295	1.8531	1.9826	100
110	1.2748	0.01617	265.3	265.4	77.94	1031.6	1109.5	0.1471	1.8106	1.9577	110
120	1.6924	0.01620	203.25	203.27	87.92	1025.8	1113.7	0.1645	1.7694	1.9339	120
130	2.2225	0.01625	157.32	157.34	97.90	1020.0	1117.9	0.1816	1.7296	1.9112	130
140	2.8886	0.01629	122.99	123.01	107.89	1014.1	1122.0	0.1984	1.6910	1.8894	140
150	3.718	0.01634	97.06	97.07	117.89	1008.2	1126.1	0.2149	1.6537	1.8685	150
160	4.741	0.01639	77.27	77.29	127.89	1002.3	1130.2	0.2311	1.6174	1.8485	160
170	5.992	0.01645	62.04	62.06	137.90	996.3	1134.2	0.2472	1.5822	1.8293	170
180	7.510	0.01651	50.21	50.23	147.92	990.2	1138.1	0.2630	1.5480	1.8109	180
190	9.339	0.01657	40.94	40.96	157.95	984.1	1142.0	0.2785	1.5147	1.7932	190
200	11.526	0.01663	33.62	33.64	167.99	977.9	1145.9	0.2938	1.4824	1.7762	200
210	14.123	0.01670	27.80	27.82	178.05	971.6	1149.7	0.3090	1.4508	1.7598	210
212	14.696	0.01672	26.78	26.80	180.07	970.3	1150.4	0.3120	1.4446	1.7566	212
220	17.186	0.01677	23.13	23.15	188.13	965.2	1153.4	0.3239	1.4201	1.7440	220
230	20.780	0.01684	19.365	19.382	198.23	958.8	1157.0	0.3387	1.3901	1.7288	230
240	24.969	0.01692	16.306	16.323	208.34	952.2	1160.5	0.3531	1.3609	1.7140	240
250	29.825	0.01700	13.804	13.821	216.48	945.5	1164.0	0.3675	1.3323	1.6998	250
260	35.429	0.01709	11.746	11.763	228.64	938.7	1167.3	0.3817	1.3043	1.6860	260
270	41.858	0.01717	10.044	10.061	238.84	931.8	1170.6	0.3958	1.2769	1.6727	270
280	49.203	0.01726	8.628	8.645	249.06	924.7	1173.8	0.4096	1.2501	1.6597	280
290	57.556	0.01735	7.444	7.461	259.31	917.5	1176.8	0.4234	1.2238	1.6472	290

Temp (°F)	Abs. Press.	v_f	v_{fg}	v_g	h_f	h_{fg}	h_g	s_f	s_{fg}	s_g
300	67.013	0.01745	6.449	6.466	269.59	910.1	1179.7	0.4369	1.1980	1.6350
310	77.68	0.01755	5.609	5.626	279.92	902.6	1182.5	0.4504	1.1727	1.6231
320	89.66	0.01765	4.896	4.914	290.28	894.9	1185.2	0.4637	1.1478	1.6115
330	103.06	0.01776	4.289	4.307	300.68	887.0	1187.7	0.4769	1.1233	1.6002
340	118.01	0.01787	3.770	3.788	311.13	879.0	1190.1	0.4900	1.0992	1.5891
350	134.63	0.01799	3.324	3.342	321.63	870.7	1192.3	0.5029	1.0754	1.5783
360	153.04	0.01811	2.939	2.957	332.18	862.2	1194.4	0.5158	1.0519	1.5677
370	173.77	0.01823	2.606	2.625	342.79	853.5	1196.3	0.5286	1.0287	1.5573
380	195.77	0.01836	2.317	2.335	353.45	844.6	1198.1	0.5413	1.0059	1.5471
390	220.37	0.01850	2.0651	2.0836	364.17	835.4	1199.6	0.5539	0.9832	1.5371
400	247.31	0.01864	1.8447	1.8633	374.97	826.0	1201.0	0.5664	0.9608	1.5272
410	276.75	0.01878	1.6512	1.6700	385.83	816.3	1202.1	0.5788	0.9336	1.5174
420	308.83	0.01894	1.4811	1.5000	396.77	806.3	1203.1	0.5912	0.9166	1.5078
430	343.72	0.01910	1.3308	1.3499	407.79	796.0	1203.8	0.6035	0.8947	1.4982
440	381.59	0.01926	1.1979	1.2171	418.90	785.4	1204.3	0.6158	0.8730	1.4887
450	422.6	0.0194	1.0799	1.0993	430.1	774.5	1204.6	0.6280	0.8513	1.4793
460	466.9	0.0196	0.9748	0.9944	441.4	763.2	1204.6	0.6402	0.8298	1.4700
470	514.7	0.0198	0.8811	0.9009	452.8	751.5	1204.3	0.6523	0.8083	1.4606
480	566.1	0.0200	0.7972	0.8172	464.4	739.4	1203.7	0.6645	0.7868	1.4513
490	621.4	0.0202	0.7221	0.7423	476.0	726.8	1202.8	0.6766	0.7653	1.4419
500	680.8	0.0204	0.6545	0.6749	487.8	713.9	1201.7	0.6887	0.7438	1.4325
520	812.4	0.0209	0.5385	0.5594	511.9	686.4	1198.2	0.7130	0.7006	1.4136
540	962.5	0.0215	0.4434	0.4649	536.6	656.6	1193.2	0.7374	0.6568	1.3942
560	1133.1	0.0221	0.3647	0.3868	562.2	624.2	1186.4	0.7621	0.6121	1.3742
580	1325.8	0.0228	0.2989	0.3217	588.9	588.4	1177.3	0.7872	0.5659	1.3532
600	1542.9	0.0236	0.2432	0.2668	617.0	548.5	1165.5	0.8131	0.5176	1.3307
620	1786.6	0.0247	0.1955	0.2201	646.7	503.6	1150.3	0.8398	0.4664	1.3062
640	2059.7	0.0260	0.1538	0.1798	678.6	452.0	1130.5	0.8679	0.4110	1.2789
660	2365.4	0.0278	0.1165	0.1442	714.2	390.2	1104.4	0.8987	0.3485	1.2472
680	2708.1	0.0305	0.0810	0.1115	757.3	309.9	1067.2	0.9351	0.2719	1.2071
700	3093.7	0.0369	0.0392	0.0761	823.3	172.1	995.4	0.9905	0.1484	1.1389
705.4	3206.2	0.0503	0	0.0503	902.7	0	902.7	1.0580	0	1.0580

* Abridged from *Thermodynamic Properties of Steam* by Joseph H. Keenan and Frederick G. Keyes. Copyright, 1937, by Joseph H. Keenan and Frederick G. Keyes. Published by John Wiley & Sons, New York.

TABLE A·2

DRY SATURATED STEAM: PRESSURE TABLE*

Abs Press., Lb Sq In. p	Temp., F t	Specific Volume		Enthalpy			Entropy			Internal Energy		Abs Press., Lb Sq In. p
		Sat. Liquid vf	Sat. Vapor vg	Sat. Liquid hf	Evap hfg	Sat. Vapor hg	Sat. Liquid sf	Evap sfg	Sat. Vapor sg	Sat. Liquid uf	Sat. Vapor ug	
1.0	101.74	0.01614	333.6	69.70	1036.3	1106.0	0.1326	1.8456	1.9782	69.70	1044.3	1.0
2.0	126.08	0.01623	173.73	93.99	1022.2	1116.2	0.1749	1.7451	1.9200	93.98	1051.9	2.0
3.0	141.48	0.01630	118.71	109.37	1013.2	1122.6	0.2008	1.6855	1.8863	109.36	1056.7	3.0
4.0	152.97	0.01636	90.63	120.86	1006.4	1127.3	0.2198	1.6427	1.8625	120.85	1060.2	4.0
5.0	162.24	0.01640	73.52	130.13	1001.0	1131.1	0.2347	1.6094	1.8441	130.12	1063.1	5.0
6.0	170.06	0.01645	61.98	137.96	996.2	1134.2	0.2472	1.5820	1.8292	137.94	1065.4	6.0
7.0	176.85	0.01649	53.64	144.76	992.1	1136.9	0.2581	1.5586	1.8167	144.74	1067.4	7.0
8.0	182.86	0.01653	47.34	150.79	988.5	1139.3	0.2674	1.5383	1.8057	150.77	1069.2	8.0
9.0	188.28	0.01656	42.40	156.22	985.2	1141.4	0.2759	1.5203	1.7962	156.19	1070.8	9.0
10	193.21	0.01659	38.42	161.17	982.1	1143.3	0.2835	1.5041	1.7876	161.14	1072.2	10
14.696	212.00	0.01672	26.80	180.07	970.3	1150.4	0.3120	1.4446	1.7566	180.02	1077.5	14.696
15	213.03	0.01672	26.29	181.11	969.7	1150.8	0.3135	1.4415	1.7549	181.06	1077.8	15
20	227.96	0.01683	20.089	196.16	960.1	1156.3	0.3356	1.3962	1.7319	196.10	1081.9	20
25	240.07	0.01692	16.303	208.42	952.1	1160.6	0.3533	1.3606	1.7139	208.34	1085.1	25
30	250.33	0.01701	13.746	218.82	945.3	1164.1	0.3680	1.3313	1.6993	218.73	1087.8	30
35	259.28	0.01708	11.898	227.91	939.2	1167.1	0.3807	1.3063	1.6870	227.80	1090.1	35
40	267.25	0.01715	10.498	236.03	933.7	1169.7	0.3919	1.2844	1.6763	235.90	1092.0	40
45	274.44	0.01721	9.401	243.36	928.6	1172.0	0.4019	1.2650	1.6669	243.22	1093.7	45
50	281.01	0.01727	8.515	250.09	924.0	1174.1	0.4110	1.2474	1.6585	249.93	1095.3	50
55	287.07	0.01732	7.787	256.30	919.6	1175.9	0.4193	1.2316	1.6509	256.12	1096.7	55
60	292.71	0.01738	7.175	262.09	915.5	1177.6	0.4270	1.2168	1.6438	261.90	1097.9	60
65	297.97	0.01743	6.655	267.50	911.6	1179.1	0.4342	1.2032	1.6374	267.29	1099.1	65
70	302.92	0.01748	6.206	272.61	907.9	1180.6	0.4409	1.1906	1.6315	272.38	1100.2	70
75	307.60	0.01753	5.816	277.43	904.5	1181.9	0.4472	1.1787	1.6259	277.19	1101.2	75
80	312.03	0.01757	5.472	282.02	901.1	1183.1	0.4531	1.1676	1.6207	281.76	1102.1	80
85	316.25	0.01761	5.168	286.39	897.8	1184.2	0.4587	1.1571	1.6158	286.11	1102.9	85
90	320.27	0.01766	4.896	290.56	894.7	1185.3	0.4641	1.1471	1.6112	290.27	1103.7	90
95	324.12	0.01770	4.652	294.56	891.7	1186.2	0.4692	1.1376	1.6068	294.25	1104.5	95
100	327.81	0.01774	4.432	298.40	888.8	1187.2	0.4740	1.1286	1.6026	298.08	1105.2	100
110	334.77	0.01782	4.049	305.66	883.2	1188.9	0.4832	1.1117	1.5948	305.30	1106.5	110

Abs Press P	Temp t	v_f	v_g	h_f	h_{fg}	h_g	s_f	s_{fg}	s_g	u_f	u_g
120	341.25	0.01789	3.728	312.44	877.9	1190.4	0.4916	1.0962	1.5878	312.05	1107.6
130	347.32	0.01796	3.455	318.81	872.9	1191.7	0.4995	1.0817	1.5812	318.38	1108.6
140	353.02	0.01802	3.220	324.82	868.2	1193.0	0.5069	1.0682	1.5751	324.35	1109.6
150	358.42	0.01809	3.015	330.51	863.6	1194.1	0.5138	1.0556	1.5694	330.01	1110.5
160	363.53	0.01815	2.834	335.93	859.2	1195.1	0.5204	1.0436	1.5640	335.39	1111.2
170	368.41	0.01822	2.675	341.09	854.9	1196.0	0.5266	1.0324	1.5590	340.52	1111.9
180	373.06	0.01827	2.532	346.03	850.8	1196.9	0.5325	1.0217	1.5542	345.42	1112.5
190	377.51	0.01833	2.404	350.79	846.8	1197.6	0.5381	1.0116	1.5497	350.15	1113.1
200	381.79	0.01839	2.288	355.36	843.0	1198.4	0.5435	1.0018	1.5453	354.68	1113.7
250	400.95	0.01865	1.8438	376.00	825.1	1201.1	0.5675	0.9588	1.5263	375.14	1115.8
300	417.33	0.01890	1.5433	393.84	809.0	1202.8	0.5879	0.9225	1.5104	392.79	1117.1
350	431.72	0.01913	1.3260	409.69	794.2	1203.9	0.6056	0.8910	1.4966	408.45	1118.0
400	444.59	0.0193	1.1613	424.0	780.5	1204.5	0.6214	0.8630	1.4844	422.6	1118.5
450	456.28	0.0195	1.0320	437.2	767.4	1204.6	0.6356	0.8378	1.4734	435.5	1118.7
500	467.01	0.0197	0.9278	449.4	755.0	1204.4	0.6487	0.8147	1.4634	447.6	1118.6
550	476.94	0.0199	0.8424	460.8	743.1	1203.9	0.6608	0.7934	1.4542	458.8	1118.2
600	486.21	0.0201	0.7698	471.6	731.6	1203.2	0.6720	0.7734	1.4454	469.4	1117.7
650	494.90	0.0203	0.7083	481.8	720.5	1202.3	0.6826	0.7548	1.4374	479.4	1117.1
700	503.10	0.0205	0.6554	491.5	709.7	1201.2	0.6925	0.7371	1.4296	488.8	1116.3
750	510.86	0.0207	0.6092	500.8	699.2	1200.0	0.7019	0.7204	1.4223	498.0	1115.4
800	518.23	0.0209	0.5687	509.7	688.9	1198.6	0.7108	0.7045	1.4153	506.6	1114.4
850	525.26	0.0210	0.5327	518.3	678.8	1197.1	0.7194	0.6891	1.4085	515.0	1113.3
900	531.98	0.0212	0.5006	526.6	668.8	1195.4	0.7275	0.6744	1.4020	523.1	1112.1
950	538.43	0.0214	0.4717	534.6	659.1	1193.7	0.7355	0.6602	1.3957	530.9	1110.8
1000	544.61	0.0216	0.4456	542.4	649.4	1191.8	0.7430	0.6467	1.3897	538.4	1109.4
1100	556.31	0.0220	0.4001	557.4	630.4	1187.8	0.7575	0.6205	1.3780	552.9	1106.4
1200	567.22	0.0223	0.3619	571.7	611.7	1183.4	0.7711	0.5956	1.3667	566.7	1103.0
1300	577.46	0.0227	0.3293	585.4	593.2	1178.6	0.7840	0.5719	1.3559	580.0	1099.4
1400	587.10	0.0231	0.3012	598.7	574.7	1173.4	0.7963	0.5491	1.3454	592.7	1095.4
1500	596.23	0.0235	0.2765	611.6	556.3	1167.9	0.8082	0.5269	1.3351	605.1	1091.2
2000	635.82	0.0257	0.1878	671.7	463.4	1135.1	0.8619	0.4230	1.2849	662.2	1065.6
2500	668.13	0.0287	0.1307	730.6	360.5	1091.1	0.9126	0.3197	1.2322	717.3	1030.6
3000	695.36	0.0346	0.0858	802.5	217.8	1020.3	0.9731	0.1885	1.1615	783.4	972.7
3206.2	705.40	0.0503	0.0503	902.7	0	902.7	1.0580	0	1.0580	872.9	872.9

* Abridged from *Thermodynamic Properties of Steam* by Joseph H. Keenan and Frederick G. Keyes. Copyright, 1937, by Joseph H. Keenan and Frederick G. Keyes. Published by John Wiley & Sons, New York.

TABLE A·3

PROPERTIES OF SUPERHEATED STEAM *

Abs Press., Lb Sq In. (Sat. Temp.)		200	300	400	500	600	700	800	900	1000	1100	1200	1400	1600
							Temperature—Degrees Fahrenheit							
1 (101.74)	v	392.6	452.3	512.0	571.6	631.2	690.8	750.4	809.9	869.5	929.1	988.7	1107.8	1227.0
	h	1150.4	1195.8	1241.7	1288.3	1335.7	1383.8	1432.8	1482.7	1533.5	1585.2	1637.7	1745.7	1857.5
	s	2.0612	2.1153	2.1720	2.2233	2.2702	2.3137	2.3542	2.3923	2.4283	2.4625	2.4952	2.5566	2.6137
5 (162.24)	v	78.16	90.25	102.26	114.22	126.16	138.10	150.03	161.95	173.87	185.79	197.71	221.6	245.4
	h	1148.8	1195.0	1241.2	1288.0	1335.4	1383.6	1432.7	1482.6	1633.4	1585.1	1637.7	1745.7	1857.4
	s	1.8718	1.9370	1.9942	2.0456	2.0927	2.1361	2.1767	2.2148	2.2509	2.2851	2.3178	2.3792	2.4363
10 (193.21)	v	38.85	45.00	51.04	57.05	63.03	69.01	74.98	80.95	86.92	92.88	98.84	110.77	122.69
	h	1146.6	1193.9	1240.6	1287.5	1335.1	1383.4	1432.5	1482.4	1533.2	1585.0	1637.6	1745.6	1857.3
	s	1.7927	1.8595	1.9172	1.9689	2.0160	2.0596	2.1002	2.1383	2.1744	2.2086	2.2413	2.3028	2.3598
14.696 (212.00)	v		30.53	34.68	38.78	42.86	46.94	51.00	55.07	59.13	63.19	67.25	75.37	83.48
	h		1192.8	1239.9	1287.1	1334.8	1383.2	1432.3	1482.3	1533.1	1584.8	1637.5	1745.5	1857.3
	s		1.8160	1.8743	1.9261	1.9734	2.0170	2.0576	2.0958	2.1319	2.1662	2.1989	2.2603	2.3174
20 (227.96)	v		22.36	25.43	28.46	31.47	34.47	37.46	40.45	43.44	46.42	49.41	55.37	61.34
	h		1191.6	1239.2	1286.6	1334.4	1382.9	1432.1	1482.1	1533.0	1584.7	1637.4	1745.4	1857.2
	s		1.7808	1.8396	1.8918	1.9392	1.9829	2.0235	2.0618	2.0978	2.1321	2.1648	2.2263	2.2834
40 (267.25)	v		11.040	12.628	14.168	15.688	17.198	18.702	20.20	21.70	23.20	24.69	27.68	30.66
	h		1186.8	1236.5	1284.8	1333.1	1381.9	1431.3	1481.4	1532.4	1584.3	1637.0	1745.1	1857.0
	s		1.6994	1.7608	1.8140	1.8619	1.9058	1.9467	1.9850	2.0212	2.0555	2.0883	2.1498	2.2069
60 (292.71)	v		7.259	8.357	9.403	10.427	11.441	12.449	13.452	14.454	15.453	16.451	18.446	20.44
	h		1181.6	1233.6	1283.0	1331.8	1380.9	1430.5	1480.8	1531.9	1583.8	1636.6	1744.8	1856.7
	s		1.6492	1.7135	1.7678	1.8162	1.8605	1.9015	1.9400	1.9762	2.0106	2.0434	2.1049	2.1621
80 (312.03)	v			6.220	7.020	7.797	8.562	9.322	10.077	10.830	11.582	12.332	13.830	15.325
	h			1230.7	1281.1	1330.5	1379.9	1429.7	1480.1	1531.3	1583.4	1636.2	1744.5	1856.5
	s			1.6791	1.7346	1.7836	1.8281	1.8694	1.9079	1.9442	1.9787	2.0115	2.0731	2.1303
100 (327.81)	v			4.937	5.589	6.218	6.835	7.446	8.052	8.656	9.259	9.860	11.060	12.258
	h			1227.6	1279.1	1329.1	1378.9	1428.9	1479.5	1530.8	1582.9	1635.7	1744.2	1856.2
	s			1.6518	1.7085	1.7581	1.8029	1.8443	1.8829	1.9193	1.9538	1.9867	2.0484	2.1056
120 (341.25)	v			4.081	4.636	5.165	5.683	6.195	6.702	7.207	7.710	8.212	9.214	10.213
	h			1224.4	1277.2	1327.7	1377.8	1428.1	1478.8	1530.2	1582.4	1635.3	1743.9	1856.0
	s			1.6287	1.6869	1.7370	1.7822	1.8237	1.8625	1.8990	1.9335	1.9664	2.0281	2.0854

Abs. Press. (Sat. Temp.)														
110 (353.02)	*v*	......	......	3.468	3.954	4.413	4.861	5.301	5.738	6.172	6.604	7.035	7.895	8.752
	h	......	......	1221.1	1275.2	1326.4	1376.8	1427.3	1478.2	1529.7	1581.9	1634.9	1743.5	1855.7
	s	......	......	1.6087	1.6683	1.7190	1.7645	1.8063	1.8451	1.8817	1.9163	1.9493	2.0110	2.0683
160 (363.53)	*v*	......	......	3.008	3.443	3.849	4.244	4.631	5.015	5.396	5.775	6.152	6.906	7.656
	h	......	......	1217.6	1273.1	1325.0	1375.7	1426.4	1477.5	1529.1	1581.4	1634.5	1743.2	1855.5
	s	......	......	1.5908	1.6519	1.7033	1.7491	1.7911	1.8301	1.8667	1.9014	1.9344	1.9962	2.0535
180 (373.06)	*v*	......	......	2.649	3.044	3.411	3.764	4.110	4.452	4.792	5.129	5.466	6.136	6.804
	h	......	......	1214.0	1271.0	1323.5	1374.7	1425.6	1476.8	1528.6	1581.0	1634.1	1742.9	1855.2
	s	......	......	1.5745	1.6373	1.6894	1.7355	1.7776	1.8167	1.8534	1.8882	1.9212	1.9831	2.0404
200 (381.79)	*v*	......	......	2.361	2.726	3.060	3.380	3.693	4.002	4.309	4.613	4.917	5.521	6.123
	h	......	......	1210.3	1268.9	1322.1	1373.6	1424.8	1476.2	1528.0	1580.5	1633.7	1742.6	1855.0
	s	......	......	1.5594	1.6240	1.6767	1.7232	1.7655	1.8048	1.8415	1.8763	1.9094	1.9713	2.0287
220 (389.86)	*v*	......	......	2.125	2.465	2.772	3.066	3.352	3.634	3.913	4.191	4.467	5.017	5.565
	h	......	......	1206.5	1266.7	1320.7	1372.6	1424.0	1475.5	1527.5	1580.0	1633.3	1742.3	1854.7
	s	......	......	1.5453	1.6117	1.6652	1.7120	1.7545	1.7939	1.8308	1.8656	1.8987	1.9607	2.0181
240 (397.37)	*v*	......	......	1.9276	2.247	2.533	2.804	3.068	3.327	3.584	3.839	4.003	4.597	5.100
	h	......	......	1202.5	1264.5	1319.2	1371.5	1423.2	1474.8	1526.9	1579.6	1632.9	1742.0	1854.5
	s	......	......	1.5319	1.6003	1.6546	1.7017	1.7444	1.7839	1.8209	1.8558	1.8889	1.9510	2.0084
260 (404.42)	*v*	......	......	......	2.063	2.330	2.582	2.827	3.067	3.305	3.541	3.776	4.242	4.707
	h	......	......	......	1262.3	1317.7	1370.4	1422.3	1474.2	1526.3	1579.1	1632.5	1741.7	1854.2
	s	......	......	......	1.5897	1.6447	1.6922	1.7352	1.7748	1.8118	1.8467	1.8799	1.9420	1.9995
280 (411.05)	*v*	......	......	......	1.9047	2.156	2.392	2.621	2.845	3.066	3.286	3.504	3.938	4.370
	h	......	......	......	1260.0	1316.2	1369.4	1421.5	1473.5	1525.8	1578.6	1632.1	1741.4	1854.0
	s	......	......	......	1.5796	1.6354	1.6834	1.7265	1.7662	1.8033	1.8383	1.8716	1.9337	1.9912
300 (417.33)	*v*	......	......	......	1.7675	2.005	2.227	2.442	2.652	2.859	3.065	3.269	3.674	4.078
	h	......	......	......	1257.6	1314.7	1368.3	1420.6	1472.8	1525.2	1578.1	1631.7	1741.0	1853.7
	s	......	......	......	1.5701	1.6268	1.6751	1.7184	1.7582	1.7954	1.8305	1.8638	1.9260	1.9835
350 (431.72)	*v*	......	......	......	1.4923	1.7036	1.8980	2.084	2.266	2.445	2.622	2.798	3.147	3.493
	h	......	......	......	1251.5	1310.9	1365.5	1418.5	1471.1	1523.8	1577.0	1630.7	1740.3	1853.1
	s	......	......	......	1.5481	1.6070	1.6563	1.7002	1.7403	1.7777	1.8130	1.8463	1.9086	1.9663
400 (444.59)	*v*	......	......	......	1.2851	1.4770	1.6508	1.8161	1.9767	2.134	2.290	2.445	2.751	3.055
	h	......	......	......	1245.1	1306.9	1362.7	1416.4	1469.4	1522.4	1575.8	1629.6	1739.5	1852.5
	s	......	......	......	1.5281	1.5894	1.6398	1.6842	1.7247	1.7623	1.7977	1.8311	1.8936	1.9513

* Abridged from *Thermodynamic Properties of Steam* by Joseph H. Keenan and Frederick G. Keyes. Copyright, 1937, by Joseph H. Keenan and Frederick G. Keyes. Published by John Wiley & Sons, New York.

TABLE A·3 (Continued)

PROPERTIES OF SUPERHEATED STEAM *

Abs Press. Lb Sq In. (Sat. Temp.)		500	550	600	620	640	660	680	700	800	900	1000	1200	1400	1600
450 (456.28)	v	1.1231	1.2155	1.3005	1.3332	1.3652	1.3967	1.4278	1.4584	1.6074	1.7516	1.8928	2.170	2.443	2.714
	h	1238.4	1272.0	1302.8	1314.6	1326.2	1337.5	1348.8	1359.9	1414.3	1467.7	1521.0	1628.6	1738.7	1851.9
	s	1.5095	1.5437	1.5735	1.5845	1.5951	1.6054	1.6153	1.6250	1.6699	1.7108	1.7486	1.8177	1.8803	1.9381
500 (467.01)	v	0.9927	1.0800	1.1591	1.1893	1.2188	1.2478	1.2763	1.3044	1.4405	1.5715	1.6996	1.9504	2.197	2.442
	h	1231.3	1266.8	1298.6	1310.7	1322.6	1334.2	1345.7	1357.0	1412.1	1466.0	1519.6	1627.6	1737.9	1851.3
	s	1.4919	1.5280	1.5588	1.5701	1.5810	1.5915	1.6016	1.6115	1.6571	1.6982	1.7363	1.8056	1.8683	1.9262
550 (476.94)	v	0.8852	0.9686	1.0431	1.0714	1.0989	1.1259	1.1523	1.1783	1.3038	1.4241	1.5414	1.7706	1.9957	2.219
	h	1223.7	1261.2	1294.3	1306.8	1318.9	1330.8	1342.5	1354.0	1409.9	1464.3	1518.2	1626.6	1737.1	1850.8
	s	1.4751	1.5131	1.5451	1.5568	1.5680	1.5787	1.5890	1.5991	1.6452	1.6868	1.7250	1.7946	1.8575	1.9155
600 (486.21)	v	0.7947	0.8753	0.9463	0.9729	0.9988	1.0241	1.0489	1.0732	1.1899	1.3013	1.4096	1.6208	1.8279	2.033
	h	1215.7	1255.5	1289.9	1302.7	1315.2	1327.4	1339.3	1351.1	1407.7	1462.5	1516.7	1625.5	1736.3	1850.0
	s	1.4586	1.4990	1.5323	1.5443	1.5558	1.5667	1.5773	1.5875	1.6343	1.6762	1.7147	1.7846	1.8476	1.9056
700 (503.10)	v		0.7277	0.7934	0.8177	0.8411	0.8639	0.8860	0.9077	1.0108	1.1082	1.2024	1.3853	1.5641	1.7405
	h		1243.2	1280.6	1294.3	1307.5	1320.3	1332.8	1345.0	1403.2	1459.0	1513.9	1623.5	1734.8	1848.8
	s		1.4722	1.5084	1.5212	1.5333	1.5449	1.5559	1.5665	1.6147	1.6573	1.6963	1.7666	1.8299	1.8881
800 (518.23)	v		0.6154	0.6779	0.7006	0.7223	0.7433	0.7635	0.7833	0.8763	0.9633	1.0470	1.2088	1.3662	1.5214
	h		1229.8	1270.7	1285.4	1299.4	1312.9	1325.9	1338.6	1398.6	1455.4	1511.0	1621.4	1733.2	1847.5
	s		1.4467	1.4863	1.5000	1.5129	1.5250	1.5366	1.5476	1.5972	1.6407	1.6801	1.7510	1.8146	1.8729
900 (531.98)	v		0.5264	0.5873	0.6089	0.6294	0.6491	0.6680	0.6863	0.7716	0.8506	0.9262	1.0714	1.2124	1.3509
	h		1215.0	1260.1	1275.9	1290.9	1305.1	1318.8	1332.1	1393.9	1451.8	1508.1	1619.3	1731.6	1846.3
	s		1.4216	1.4653	1.4800	1.4938	1.5066	1.5187	1.5303	1.5814	1.6257	1.6656	1.7371	1.8009	1.8595
1000 (544.61)	v		0.4533	0.5140	0.5350	0.5546	0.5733	0.5912	0.6084	0.6878	0.7604	0.8294	0.9615	1.0893	1.2146
	h		1198.3	1248.8	1265.9	1281.9	1297.0	1311.4	1325.3	1389.2	1448.2	1505.1	1617.3	1730.0	1845.0
	s		1.3961	1.4450	1.4610	1.4757	1.4893	1.5021	1.5141	1.5670	1.6121	1.6525	1.7245	1.7886	1.8474
1100 (556.31)	v			0.4532	0.4738	0.4929	0.5110	0.5281	0.5445	0.6191	0.6866	0.7503	0.8716	0.9885	1.1031
	h			1236.7	1255.3	1272.4	1288.5	1303.7	1318.3	1384.3	1444.5	1502.2	1615.2	1728.4	1843.8
	s			1.4251	1.4425	1.4583	1.4728	1.4862	1.4989	1.5535	1.5995	1.6405	1.7130	1.7775	1.8363
1200 (567.22)	v			0.4016	0.4222	0.4410	0.4586	0.4752	0.4909	0.5617	0.6250	0.6843	0.7967	0.9046	1.0101
	h			1223.5	1243.9	1262.4	1279.6	1295.7	1311.0	1379.3	1440.7	1499.2	1613.1	1726.9	1842.5
	s			1.4052	1.4243	1.4413	1.4568	1.4710	1.4843	1.5409	1.5879	1.6293	1.7025	1.7672	1.8263

Temperature—Degrees Fahrenheit

Abs. Press. Lb./Sq. In. (Sat. Temp.)												
1400 (587.10)	v	0.3174	0.3390	0.3580	0.3753	0.3912	0.4062	0.4714	0.5281	0.5805	0.6789	0.7727	0.8640
	h	1193.0	1218.4	1240.4	1260.3	1278.5	1295.5	1369.1	1433.1	1493.2	1608.9	1723.7	1840.0
	s	1.3639	1.3877	1.4079	1.4258	1.4419	1.4567	1.5177	1.5666	1.6093	1.6836	1.7489	1.8083
1600 (604.90)	v		0.2733	0.2936	0.3112	0.3271	0.3417	0.4034	0.4553	0.5027	0.5906	0.6738	0.7545
	h		1187.8	1215.2	1238.7	1259.6	1278.7	1358.4	1425.3	1487.0	1604.6	1720.5	1837.5
	s		1.3489	1.3741	1.3952	1.4137	1.4303	1.4964	1.5476	1.5914	1.6669	1.7328	1.7926
1800 (621.03)	v			0.2407	0.2597	0.2760	0.2907	0.3502	0.3986	0.4421	0.5218	0.5968	0.6693
	h			1185.1	1214.0	1238.5	1260.3	1347.2	1417.4	1480.8	1600.4	1717.3	1835.0
	s			1.3377	1.3638	1.3855	1.4044	1.4765	1.5301	1.5752	1.6520	1.7185	1.7786
2000 (635.82)	v			0.1936	0.2161	0.2337	0.2489	0.3074	0.3532	0.3935	0.4668	0.5352	0.6011
	h			1145.6	1184.9	1214.8	1240.0	1335.5	1409.2	1474.5	1596.1	1714.1	1832.5
	s			1.2945	1.3300	1.3564	1.3783	1.4576	1.5139	1.5603	1.6384	1.7055	1.7660
2500 (668.13)	v					0.1484	0.1686	0.2294	0.2710	0.3061	0.3678	0.4244	0.4784
	h					1132.3	1176.8	1303.6	1387.8	1458.4	1585.3	1706.1	1826.2
	s					1.2687	1.3073	1.4127	1.4772	1.5273	1.6088	1.6775	1.7389
3000 (695.36)	v						0.0084	0.1760	0.2159	0.2476	0.3018	0.3505	0.3966
	h						1060.7	1267.2	1365.0	1441.8	1574.3	1698.0	1819.9
	s						1.1966	1.3690	1.4439	1.4984	1.5837	1.6540	1.7163
3206.2 (705.40)	v							0.1583	0.1981	0.2288	0.2806	0.3267	0.3703
	h							1250.5	1355.2	1434.7	1569.8	1694.6	1817.2
	s							1.3508	1.4309	1.4874	1.5742	1.6452	1.7080
3500	v						0.0306	0.1364	0.1762	0.2058	0.2546	0.2977	0.3381
	h						780.5	1224.9	1340.7	1424.5	1563.3	1689.8	1813.6
	s						0.9515	1.3241	1.4127	1.4723	1.5615	1.6336	1.6968
4000	v						0.0287	0.1052	0.1462	0.1743	0.2192	0.2581	0.2943
	h						763.8	1174.8	1314.4	1406.8	1552.1	1681.7	1807.2
	s						0.9347	1.2757	1.3827	1.4482	1.5417	1.6154	1.6795
4500	v						0.0276	0.0798	0.1226	0.1500	0.1917	0.2273	0.2602
	h						753.5	1113.9	1286.5	1388.4	1540.8	1673.5	1800.9
	s						0.9235	1.2204	1.3529	1.4253	1.5235	1.5990	1.6640
5000	v						0.0268	0.0593	0.1036	0.1303	0.1696	0.2027	0.2329
	h						746.4	1047.1	1256.5	1369.5	1529.5	1665.3	1794.5
	s						0.9152	1.1622	1.3231	1.4034	1.5066	1.5839	1.6499
5500	v						0.0262	0.0463	0.0880	0.1143	0.1516	0.1825	0.2106
	h						741.3	985.0	1224.1	1349.3	1518.2	1657.0	1788.1
	s						0.9090	1.1093	1.2930	1.3821	1.4908	1.5699	1.6369

*Abridged from *Thermodynamic Properties of Steam* by Joseph H. Keenan and Frederick G. Keyes. Copyright, 1937, by Joseph H. Keenan and Frederick G. Keyes. Published by John Wiley & Sons, New York.

TABLE A·4

THERMODYNAMIC PROPERTIES OF AIR AT LOW PRESSURE

(For One Pound)

(The properties given here are condensed by permission from *Gas Tables*, by J. H. Keenan and J. Kaye, published by John Wiley and Sons, 1948.)

T, °F abs	t, °F	h, Btu/lb	p_r	u, Btu/lb	v_r	φ, Btu/lb °F	T, °F abs	t, °F	h, Btu/lb	p_r	u, Btu/lb	v_r	φ, Btu/lb °F
100	−360	23.7	.00384	16.9	9640	.1971	1200	740	291.3	24.0	209.0	18.51	.7963
120	−340	28.5	.00726	20.3	6120	.2408	1220	760	296.4	25.5	212.8	17.70	.8005
140	−320	33.3	.01244	23.7	4170	.2777	1240	780	301.5	27.1	216.5	16.93	.8047
160	−300	38.1	.01982	27.1	2990	.3096	1260	800	306.6	28.8	220.3	16.20	.8088
180	−280	42.9	.0299	30.6	2230	.3378	1280	820	311.8	30.6	224.0	15.52	.8128
200	−260	47.7	.0432	34.0	1715	.3630	1300	840	316.9	32.4	227.8	14.87	.8168
220	−240	52.5	.0603	37.4	1352	.3858	1320	860	322.1	34.3	231.6	14.25	.8208
240	−220	57.2	.0816	40.8	1089	.4067	1340	880	327.3	36.3	235.4	13.67	.8246
260	−200	62.0	.1080	44.2	892	.4258	1360	900	332.5	38.4	239.2	13.12	.8285
280	−180	66.8	.1399	47.6	742	.4436	1380	920	337.7	40.6	243.1	12.59	.8323
300	−160	71.6	.1780	51.0	624	.4601	1400	940	342.9	42.9	246.9	12.10	.8360
320	−140	76.4	.2229	54.5	532	.4755	1420	960	348.1	45.3	250.8	11.62	.8398
340	−120	81.2	.2754	57.9	457	.4900	1440	980	353.4	47.8	254.7	11.17	.8434
360	−100	86.0	.336	61.3	397	.5037	1460	1000	358.6	50.3	258.5	10.74	.8470
380	−80	90.8	.406	64.7	347	.5166	1480	1020	363.9	53.0	262.4	10.34	.8506
400	−60	95.5	.486	68.1	305	.5289	1500	1040	369.2	55.9	266.3	9.95	.8542
420	−40	100.3	.576	71.5	270	.5406	1520	1060	374.5	58.8	270.3	9.58	.8568
440	−20	105.1	.678	74.9	241	.5517	1540	1080	379.8	61.8	274.2	9.23	.8611
460	0	109.9	.791	78.4	215.3	.5624	1560	1100	385.1	65.0	278.1	8.89	.8646
480	20	114.7	.918	81.8	193.6	.5726	1580	1120	390.4	68.3	282.1	8.57	.8679
500	40	119.5	1.059	85.2	174.9	.5823	1600	1140	395.7	71.7	286.1	8.26	.8713
520	60	124.3	1.215	88.6	158.6	.5917	1620	1160	401.1	75.3	290.0	7.97	.8746
540	80	129.1	1.386	92.0	144.3	.6008	1640	1180	406.4	79.0	294.0	7.69	.8779
560	100	133.9	1.574	95.5	131.8	.6095	1660	1200	411.8	82.8	298.0	7.42	.8812
580	120	138.7	1.780	98.9	120.7	.6179	1680	1220	417.2	86.8	302.0	7.17	.8844
600	140	143.5	2.00	102.3	110.9	.6261	1700	1240	422.6	91.0	306.1	6.92	.8876
620	160	148.3	2.25	105.8	102.1	.6340	1720	1260	428.0	95.2	310.1	6.69	.8907
640	180	153.1	2.51	109.2	94.3	.6416	1740	1280	433.4	99.7	314.1	6.46	.8939
660	200	157.9	2.80	112.7	87.3	.6490	1760	1300	438.8	104.3	318.2	6.25	.8969
680	220	162.7	3.11	116.1	81.0	.6562	1780	1320	444.3	109.1	322.2	6.04	.9000
700	240	167.6	3.45	119.6	75.2	.6632	1800	1340	449.7	114.0	326.3	5.85	.9031
720	260	172.4	3.81	123.0	70.1	.6700	1820	1360	455.2	119.2	330.4	5.66	.9061
740	280	177.2	4.19	126.5	65.4	.6766	1840	1380	460.6	124.5	334.5	5.48	.9091
760	300	182.1	4.61	130.0	61.1	.6831	1860	1400	466.1	130.0	338.6	5.30	.9120
780	320	186.9	5.05	133.5	57.2	.6894	1880	1420	471.6	135.6	342.7	5.13	.9150
800	340	191.8	5.53	137.0	53.6	.6956	1900	1440	477.1	141.5	346.8	4.97	.9179
820	360	196.7	6.03	140.5	50.4	.7016	1920	1460	482.6	147.6	351.0	4.82	.9208
840	380	201.6	6.57	144.0	47.3	.7075	1940	1480	488.1	153.9	355.1	4.67	.9236
860	400	206.5	7.15	147.5	44.6	.7132	1960	1500	493.6	160.4	359.3	4.53	.9264
880	420	211.4	7.76	151.0	42.0	.7189	1980	1520	499.1	167.1	363.4	4.39	.9293
900	440	216.3	8.41	154.6	39.6	.7244	2000	1540	504.7	174.0	367.6	4.26	.9320
920	460	221.2	9.10	158.1	37.4	.7298	2020	1560	510.3	181.2	371.8	4.13	.9348
940	480	226.1	9.83	161.7	35.4	.7351	2040	1580	515.8	188.5	376.0	4.01	.9376
960	500	231.1	10.61	165.3	33.5	.7403	2060	1600	521.4	196.2	380.2	3.89	.9403
980	520	236.0	11.43	168.8	31.8	.7454	2080	1620	527.0	204.0	384.4	3.78	.9430
1000	540	241.0	12.30	172.4	30.1	.7504	2100	1640	532.6	212	388.6	3.67	.9456
1020	560	246.0	13.22	176.0	28.6	.7554	2120	1660	538.2	220	392.8	3.56	.9483
1040	580	251.0	14.18	179.7	27.2	.7602	2140	1680	543.7	229	397.0	3.46	.9509
1060	600	256.0	15.20	183.3	25.8	.7650	2160	1700	549.4	238	401.3	3.36	.9535
1080	620	261.0	16.28	186.9	24.6	.7696	2180	1720	555.0	247	405.5	3.27	.9561
1100	640	266.0	17.41	190.6	23.4	.7743	2200	1740	560.6	257	409.8	3.18	.9587
1120	660	271.0	18.60	194.2	22.3	.7788	2220	1760	566.2	266	414.0	3.09	.9612
1140	680	276.1	19.86	197.9	21.3	.7833	2240	1780	571.9	276	418.3	3.00	.9638
1160	700	281.1	21.2	201.6	20.29	.7877	2260	1800	577.5	287	422.6	2.92	.9663
1180	720	286.2	22.6	205.3	19.38	.7920	2280	1820	583.2	297	426.9	2.84	.9688